Acknowledgments

The College Board gratefully acknowledges the outstanding work of the classroom teachers and writers who have been integral to the development of this revised program. The end product is testimony to their expertise, understanding of student learning needs, and dedication to rigorous but accessible mathematics instruction.

Michael Allwood
Brunswick School
Greenwich, Connecticut

Floyd Bullard
North Carolina School of Science and Mathematics
Durham, North Carolina

Marcia Chumas
East Mecklenburg High School
Charlotte, North Carolina

Wendy DenBesten
Hoover High School
Fresno, California

Bonnie Fenwick
Atlantic High School
Port Orange, Florida

Kathy Fritz
Plano Independent School District
Plano, Texas

William B. Hubschmitt
Westview High School
San Diego, California

Marie Humphrey
David W. Butler High School
Charlotte, North Carolina

Brian Kotz
Montgomery College
Monrovia, Maryland

Chris Olsen
Prairie Lutheran School
Cedar Rapids, Iowa

Dr. Roxy Peck
California Polytechnic Institute
San Luis Obispo, California

Andrea Sukow
Mathematics Consultant
Nashville, Tennessee

SpringBoard Mathematics Product Development

Betty Barnett
Executive Director
Content Development

Kimberly Sadler, M.Ed.
Senior Math Product Manager

Allen M. D. von Pallandt
Senior Director
Mathematics Content Development

John Nelson
Mathematics Editor

Research and Planning Advisors

We also wish to thank the members of our SpringBoard Advisory Council and the many educators who gave generously of their time and their ideas as we conducted research for both the print and online programs. Your suggestions and reactions to ideas helped immeasurably as we planned the revisions. We gratefully acknowledge the teachers and administrators in the following districts.

ABC Unified
Cerritos, California

Albuquerque Public Schools
Albuquerque, New Mexico

Amarillo School District
Amarillo, Texas

Baltimore County Public Schools
Baltimore, Maryland

Bellevue School District 405
Bellevue, Washington

Charlotte Mecklenburg Schools
Charlotte, North Carolina

Clark County School District
Las Vegas, Nevada

Cypress Fairbanks ISD
Houston, Texas

District School Board of Collier County
Collier County, Florida

Denver Public Schools
Denver, Colorado

Frisco ISD
Frisco, Texas

Gilbert Unified School District
Gilbert, Arizona

Grand Prairie ISD
Grand Prairie, Texas

Hillsborough County Public Schools
Tampa, Florida

Houston Independent School District
Houston, Texas

Hobbs Municipal Schools
Hobbs, New Mexico

Irving Independent School District
Irving, Texas

Kenton County School District
Fort Wright, Kentucky

Lee County Public Schools
Fort Myers, Florida

Newton County Schools
Covington, Georgia

Noblesville Schools
Noblesville, Indiana

Oakland Unified School District
Oakland, California

Orange County Public Schools
Orlando, Florida

School District of Palm Beach County
Palm Beach, Florida

Peninsula School District
Gig Harbor, Washington

Polk County Public Schools
Bartow, Florida

Quakertown Community School District
Quakertown, Pennsylvania

Rio Rancho Public Schools
Rio Rancho, New Mexico

Ronan School District
Ronan, Montana

St. Vrain Valley School District
Longmont, Colorado

Scottsdale Public Schools
Phoenix, Arizona

Seminole County Public Schools
Sanford, Florida

Southwest ISD
San Antonio, Texas

Spokane Public Schools
Spokane, Washington

Volusia County Schools
DeLand, Florida

Contents

To the Student

Welcome to the SpringBoard program.

This program has been created with you in mind: the content you need to learn, the tools to help you learn, and the critical thinking skills that help you build confidence in your own knowledge of mathematics. The College Board publishes the SpringBoard program. It also publishes the PSAT/NMSQT, the SAT, and the Advanced Placement exams—all exams that you are likely to encounter in your student years. Preparing you to perform well on those exams and to develop the mathematics skills needed for high school success is the primary purpose of this program.

Standards-Based Mathematics Learning

The SpringBoard program is based on learning standards that identify the mathematics skills and knowledge that you should master to succeed in high school and in future college-level work. In this course, the standards follow these broad areas of mathematics knowledge:

- Mathematical practices
- Number and quantity
- Algebra
- Functions
- Modeling
- Statistics and probability

Mathematical practice standards guide your study of mathematics. They are actions you take to help you understand mathematical concepts rather than just mathematical procedures. For example, the mathematical practice standards state the following:

MP.1 Make sense of problems and persevere in solving them.

MP.2 Reason abstractly and quantitatively.

MP.3 Construct viable arguments and critique the reasoning of others.

MP.4 Model with mathematics.

MP.5 Use appropriate tools strategically.

MP.6 Attend to precision.

MP.7 Look for and make use of structure.

MP.8 Look for and express regularity in repeated reasoning.

As you continue your studies from middle school, you will examine expressions, equations, and functions, which will allow you to make comparisons between relations and functions. Expressions and equations connect with functions. Understanding the concept of functions is critical to future success in your study of algebra and the rest of the high school mathematics curriculum.

See pages xiii–xvi for a complete list of the College and Career Readiness Standards for Mathematics for this course.

Strategies for Learning Mathematics

Some tools to help you learn are built into every activity. At the beginning of each activity, you will see suggested learning strategies. Each of these strategies is explained in full in the Resources section of your book. As you learn to use each strategy, you'll have the opportunity to decide which strategies work best for you. Suggested learning strategies include:

- Reading strategies
- Writing strategies
- Problem-solving strategies
- Collaborative strategies

Building Mathematics Knowledge and Skills

The SpringBoard program is built around the following.

Problem Solving Many of the problems in this book require you to ***analyze*** the situation and the information in a problem, ***make decisions, determine the strategies*** you'll use to solve the problem, and ***justify*** your solution.

Reasoning and Justification You will be asked to explain the reasoning behind how you solved problems, the mathematics concepts involved, and why your approach was appropriate.

Communication Communicating about mathematics, orally and in writing, with your classmates and teachers helps you organize your learning and explain mathematics concepts.

Mathematics Connections As you develop your mathematics knowledge, you will see the many connections between mathematics concepts and between mathematics and your own life.

Representations In mathematics, representations can take many forms, such as numeric, verbal, graphic, or symbolic. In this course, you are encouraged to use representations to organize problem information, present possible solutions, and communicate your reasoning.

We hope you enjoy your study of mathematics using the SpringBoard program.

College and Career Readiness Standards

HSN-CN The Complex Number System

HSN-CN.A.3 (+) Find the conjugate of a complex number; use conjugates to find moduli and quotients of complex numbers.

HSN-CN.B.4 (+) Represent complex numbers on the complex plane in rectangular and polar form (including real and imaginary numbers), and explain why the rectangular and polar forms of a given complex number represent the same number.

HSN-CN.B.5 (+) Represent addition, subtraction, multiplication, and conjugation of complex numbers geometrically on the complex plane; use properties of this representation for computation. *For example,* $(-1 + \sqrt{3}i)^3 = 8$ *because* $(-1 + \sqrt{3}i)$ *has modulus 2 and argument 120°.*

HSN-CN.B.6 (+) Calculate the distance between numbers in the complex plane as the modulus of the difference, and the midpoint of a segment as the average of the numbers at its endpoints.

HSN-VM Vector and Matrix Quantities

HSN-VM.A.1 (+) Recognize vector quantities as having both magnitude and direction. Represent vector quantities by directed line segments, and use appropriate symbols for vectors and their magnitudes (e.g., $\boldsymbol{v}$, $|\boldsymbol{v}|$, $||\boldsymbol{v}||$, v).

HSN-VM.A.2 (+) Find the components of a vector by subtracting the coordinates of an initial point from the coordinates of a terminal point.

HSN-VM.A.3 (+) Solve problems involving velocity and other quantities that can be represented by vectors.

HSN-VM.B.4 (+) Add and subtract vectors.

HSN-VM.B.4a Add vectors end-to-end, component-wise, and by the parallelogram rule. Understand that the magnitude of a sum of two vectors is typically not the sum of the magnitudes.

HSN-VM.B.4b Given two vectors in magnitude and direction form, determine the magnitude and direction of their sum.

HSN-VM.B.4c Understand vector subtraction $\boldsymbol{v} - \boldsymbol{w}$ as $\boldsymbol{v} + (-\boldsymbol{w})$, where $-\boldsymbol{w}$ is the additive inverse of $\boldsymbol{w}$, with the same magnitude as $\boldsymbol{w}$ and pointing in the opposite direction. Represent vector subtraction graphically by connecting the tips in the appropriate order, and perform vector subtraction component-wise.

HSN-VM.B.5 (+) Multiply a vector by a scalar.

HSN-VM.B.5a Represent scalar multiplication graphically by scaling vectors and possibly reversing their direction; perform scalar multiplication component-wise, e.g., as $c(v_x, v_y) = (cv_x, cv_y)$.

HSN-VM.B.5b Compute the magnitude of a scalar multiple $c\boldsymbol{v}$ using $||c\boldsymbol{v}|| = |c|\boldsymbol{v}$. Compute the direction of $c\boldsymbol{v}$ knowing that when $|c|\boldsymbol{v} \neq 0$, the direction of $c\boldsymbol{v}$ is either along $\boldsymbol{v}$ (for $c > 0$) or against $\boldsymbol{v}$ (for $c < 0$).

HSN-VM.C.6 (+) Use matrices to represent and manipulate data, e.g., to represent payoffs or incidence relationships in a network.

HSN-VM.C.7 (+) Multiply matrices by scalars to produce new matrices, e.g., as when all of the payoffs in a game are doubled.

HSN-VM.C.8 (+) Add, subtract, and multiply matrices of appropriate dimensions.

HSN-VM.C.9 (+) Understand that, unlike multiplication of numbers, matrix multiplication for square matrices is not a commutative operation, but still satisfies the associative and distributive properties.

HSN-VM.C.10 (+) Understand that the zero and identity matrices play a role in matrix addition and multiplication similar to the role of 0 and 1 in the real numbers. The determinant of a square matrix is nonzero if and only if the matrix has a multiplicative inverse.

HSN-VM.C.11 (+) Multiply a vector (regarded as a matrix with one column) by a matrix of suitable dimensions to produce another vector. Work with matrices as transformations of vectors.

HSN-VM.C.12 (+) Work with 2×2 matrices as transformations of the plane, and interpret the absolute value of the determinant in terms of area.

HSA-REI Reasoning with Equations and Inequalities

HSA-REI.C.8 (+) Represent a system of linear equations as a single matrix equation in a vector variable.

HSA-REI.C.9 (+) Find the inverse of a matrix if it exists and use it to solve systems of linear equations (using technology for matrices of dimension 3×3 or greater).

HSF-IF Interpreting Functions

HSF-IF.C.7 Graph functions expressed symbolically and show key features of the graph, by hand in simple cases and using technology for more complicated cases.*

HSF-IF.C.7d (+) Graph rational functions, identifying zeros and asymptotes when suitable factorizations are available, and showing end behavior.

HSF-BF Building Functions

HSF-BF.A.1 Write a function that describes a relationship between two quantities.*

HSF-BF.A.1c (+) Compose functions. *For example, if $T(y)$ is the temperature in the atmosphere as a function of height, and $h(t)$ is the height of a weather balloon as a function of time, then $T(h(t))$ is the temperature at the location of the weather balloon as a function of time.*

HSF-BF.B.4 Find inverse functions.

HSF-BF.B.4b (+) Verify by composition that one function is the inverse of another.

HSF-BF.B.4c (+) Read values of an inverse function from a graph or a table, given that the function has an inverse.

HSF-BF.B.4d (+) Produce an invertible function from a non-invertible function by restricting the domain.

HSF-BF.B.5 (+) Understand the inverse relationship between exponents and logarithms and use this relationship to solve problems involving logarithms and exponents.

HSF-TF Trigonometric Functions

HSF-TF.A.3 (+) Use special triangles to determine geometrically the values of sine, cosine, tangent for $\frac{\pi}{3}$, $\frac{\pi}{4}$ and $\frac{\pi}{6}$, and use the unit circle to express the values of sine, cosine, and tangent for x, $\pi + x$, and $2\pi - x$ in terms of their values for x, where x is any real number.

HSF-TF.A.4 (+) Use the unit circle to explain symmetry (odd and even) and periodicity of trigonometric functions.

HSF-TF.B.6 (+) Understand that restricting a trigonometric function to a domain on which it is always increasing or always decreasing allows its inverse to be constructed.

HSF-TF.B.7 (+) Use inverse functions to solve trigonometric equations that arise in modeling contexts; evaluate the solutions using technology, and interpret them in terms of the context.*

HSF-TF.C.9 (+) Prove the addition and subtraction formulas for sine, cosine, and tangent and use them to solve problems.

HSG-GPE Expressing Geometric Properties with Equations

HSG-GPE.A.3 (+) Derive the equations of ellipses and hyperbolas given the foci, using the fact that the sum or difference of distances from the foci is constant.

HSG-GMD Geometric Measurement and Dimension

HSG-GMD.A.2 (+) Give an informal argument using Cavalieri's principle for the formulas for the volume of a sphere and other solid figures.

HSS-MD Using Probability to Make Decisions

HSS-MD.A.1 (+) Define a random variable for a quantity of interest by assigning a numerical value to each event in a sample space; graph the corresponding probability distribution using the same graphical displays as for data distributions.

HSS-MD.A.2 (+) Calculate the expected value of a random variable; interpret it as the mean of the probability distribution.

HSS-MD.A.3 (+) Develop a probability distribution for a random variable defined for a sample space in which theoretical probabilities can be calculated; find the expected value. *For example, find the theoretical probability distribution for the number of correct answers obtained by guessing on all five questions of a multiple-choice test where each question has four choices, and find the expected grade under various grading schemes.*

HSS-MD.A.4 (+) Develop a probability distribution for a random variable defined for a sample space in which probabilities are assigned empirically; find the expected value. *For example, find a current data distribution on the number of TV sets per household in the United States, and calculate the expected number of sets per household. How many TV sets would you expect to find in 100 randomly selected households?*

HSS-MD.B.5 (+) Weigh the possible outcomes of a decision by assigning probabilities to payoff values and finding expected values.

- **HSS-MD.B.5a** Find the expected payoff for a game of chance. *For example, find the expected winnings from a state lottery ticket or a game at a fast-food restaurant.*
- **HSS-MD.B.5b** Evaluate and compare strategies on the basis of expected values. *For example, compare a high-deductible versus a low-deductible automobile insurance policy using various, but reasonable, chances of having a minor or a major accident.*

Sequences, Series, Exponential and Logarithmic Functions

1

Unit Overview

In this unit you will study recursive and explicit representations of arithmetic and geometric sequences. You will also study exponential, logarithmic, and power functions and explore the key features of their graphs. In addition, you will look at transformations, compositions, and inverses of functions.

Key Terms

As you study this unit, add these and other terms to your math notebook. Include in your notes your prior knowledge of each word, as well as your experiences in using the word in different mathematical examples. If needed, ask for help in pronouncing new words and add information on pronunciation to your math notebook. It is important that you learn new terms and use them correctly in your class discussions and in your problem solutions.

Academic Vocabulary

- converge
- diverge
- depreciation
- conjecture

Math Terms

- sigma notation
- sequence of partial sums
- mathematical induction
- polar grid
- common ratio
- series
- *n*th partial sum
- infinite sequence
- infinite series
- iteration
- recursive sequence
- explicit form
- exponential function
- interest rate
- exponential growth factor
- exponential decay factor
- half-life
- logarithm
- common logarithm
- strictly monotonic
- parent function
- even function
- odd function
- composition
- inverse function

ESSENTIAL QUESTIONS

How are recursive relationships used to model and investigate long-term behavior involving sequential change?

How are exponential, logarithmic, and power functions used to model real-world problems?

EMBEDDED ASSESSMENTS

These assessments, following Activities 3, 5, and 8, will provide you opportunities to demonstrate your understanding of sequences, exponential and logarithmic functions, and transformations and compositions of functions.

Getting Ready

Write your answers on notebook paper. Show your work.

1. Solve the system of equations:

$$\begin{cases} 3x + 7y = 6 \\ 2x + 9y = 4 \end{cases}$$

2. Given the equation $2x + 3y = 6$:

a. Find the slope.

b. Graph the equation.

c. Find the slope of a line parallel to the line given by $2x + 3y = 6$.

d. Graph the line that passes through $(1, 3)$ and is parallel to the line given by $2x + 3y = 6$.

3. Simplify the following:

a. $\sqrt{3}(2 + \sqrt{3})$

b. $(3 + \sqrt{5})^2$

c. $\left(\frac{2}{\sqrt{3}}\right)^3$

4. High temperatures for the first 7 days of February in Miami are displayed in the table below.

Day	1	2	3	4	5	6	7
Temp. (°F)	66	63	71	73	75	75	76

a. Make a scatterplot of this data.

b. Estimate a line of best fit for the data.

5. Tell the next term in each of the following, and explain the pattern that generates the sequence.

a. 5, 7, 9, 11, . . .

b. $\frac{1}{2}, \frac{2}{3}, \frac{3}{4}, \frac{4}{5}, \ldots$

c. 8, 7, 5, 2, −2, . . .

6. Simplify $\left(\frac{6x^2}{y^3}\right)^2$.

7. Factor $x^2 - 6x + 5$. Then solve $x^2 - 6x + 5 = 0$.

8. Find the x- and y-intercepts of the graph of $y = -2(x - 3) + 4$.

9. A simple interest loan with a principal of \$5000 is paid back after $2\frac{1}{2}$ years. The total payment is \$5875. What is the annual rate of interest on the loan?

10. Draw the fourth stage of the figure below. Explain how you would create any figure in the pattern and find the number of squares.

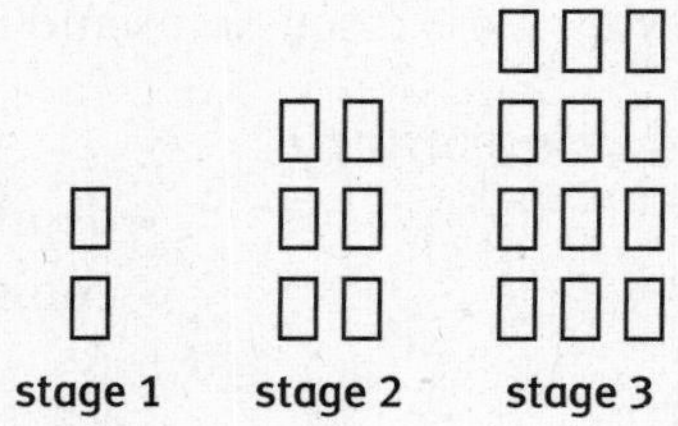

Arithmetic Sequences

DVD Promotions

Lesson 1-1 Sequences and Subscript Notation

My Notes

Learning Targets:

- Write an expression for a sequence.
- Use subscript notation.

SUGGESTED LEARNING STRATEGIES: Shared Reading, Summarizing, Paraphrasing, Close Reading, Interactive Word Wall, Quickwrite

Bopper's DVD Store has the latest in DVDs for rental or purchase. To attract more customers, Bopper's introduces the following promotion:

Bopper's DVD Store
Earn A Free DVD Rental!
Earn 3 DVD Points With Your 1st DVD Rental
Earn 2 DVD Points For Every Additional Rental
Redeem 24 DVD Points For 1 FREE DVD Rental!

1. Complete the following table to indicate the total number of DVD points after each indicated DVD rental.

Bopper's DVD Store						
DVD Rentals n	1	2	3	4	5	6
Total DVD Points B_n						

2. The table shows that the DVD points earned depend on the number of DVD rentals. Let B_n denote the total number of Bopper's DVD points earned after n rentals. What is the total number of DVD points for one, two, and three rentals?

$B_1 =$ $B_2 =$ $B_3 =$

The notation B_n is called ***subscript notation***. This notation can be used to describe a ***sequence***. In a sequence, B_n denotes the value of the nth term in the sequence, as well as the number of DVD points earned after n rentals. The values $B_1, B_2, B_3, B_4, B_5, \ldots$ form a sequence of values. This sequence of values can be denoted as $\{B_n\}$.

READING MATH

B_1 and B_n are read as "B sub 1" and "B sub n," where "sub" represents *subscript*. In B_n, n is the term number, or *index*.

3. Use $\{B_n\}$ to answer the following.

a. List the first eight terms of the sequence $\{B_n\}$.

b. Make use of structure. Explain the meaning of B_7.

c. Write an algebraic expression for the nth term, B_n, in terms of n, the number of DVD rentals at Bopper's DVD Store.

d. In the context of Bopper's DVD rentals, explain the meaning of n and the algebraic expression written in part c.

My Notes

4. On the coordinate grid below, the horizontal axis represents n, the number of DVD rentals, and the vertical axis represents B_n, the total number of DVD points earned from rentals at Bopper's.

a. Plot the sequence $\{B_n\}$ for $n = 1, 2, 3, \ldots 8$.

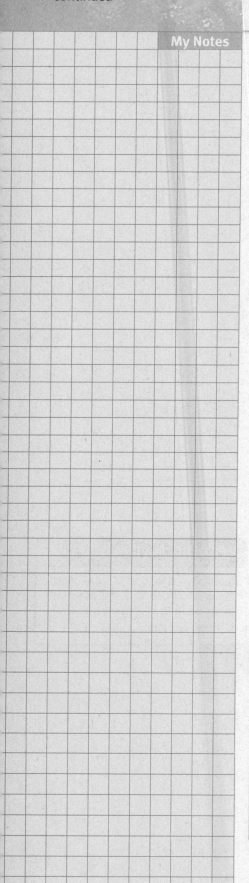

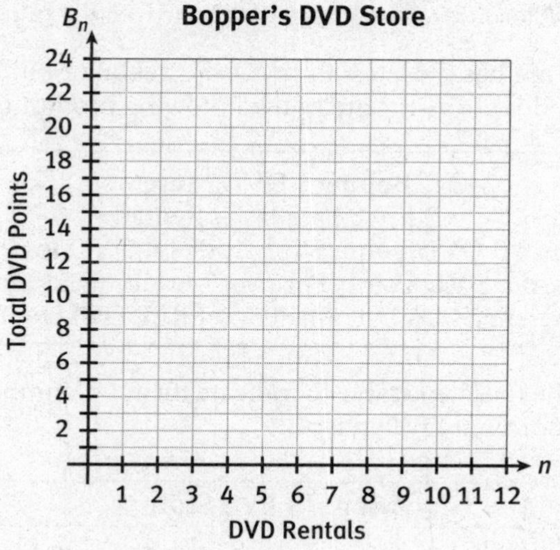

b. Using your graph, explain why $\{B_n\}$ is a function of n.

c. List as many properties of the graph of $\{B_n\}$ as possible.

5. How many rentals are needed to obtain a free DVD rental from Bopper's? Show the work that leads to your answer.

Check Your Understanding

6. Given the sequence 1, 8, 15, . . .:
a. Write an expression for a_n in terms of n, the term number.
b. Calculate a_{30}.
c. Given $a_n = 148$, solve for n.

7. Write an algebraic expression for the sequence {2, 5, 8, . . ., 20} in terms of n, the term number.

8. A sequence is defined by $a_1 = 5$, $a_{n+1} = 8 + a_n$. Write the first five terms in the sequence.

A new video rental business, Fantastik Flicks, opens near Bopper's. The new store offers its own DVD point program to attract customers.

Fantastik Flicks DVD Store
Earn more DVD Points with each rental at Flicks!
Earn a free DVD rental faster at Flicks!
Earn 3 DVD Points with the first rental.
Earn 5 DVD Points with the second rental.
Earn 7 DVD Points with the third rental, and so on.
Free DVD rental for every 100 Points earned at Flicks!

9. Complete the following table to indicate the number of DVD points earned with the nth rental and the total accumulated number of DVD points after each Fantastik Flicks DVD rental.

Fantastik Flicks DVD Store						
DVD Rentals, n	1	2	3	4	5	6
DVD Points Earned with n^{th} Rental, P_n	3	5	7	9	11	13
Total DVD Points After n Rentals, F_n						

10. Model with mathematics. The table in Item 9 indicates that there are two sequences associated with Fantastik Flicks DVD points, P_n and F_n.

a. At Fantastik Flicks, the number of points earned increases with each rental of a DVD. Write an algebraic expression for P_n, the number of points earned with the nth rental, in terms of n.

b. Explain how the values in the third row of the table in Item 9 are obtained from the values in the second row.

c. Find the value of the sum $P_1 + P_2 + P_3 + P_4 + P_5 + P_6 + P_7$.

d. What is the value of F_8? Show your work.

e. Write an equation that expresses F_{n+1} in terms of F_n and P_{n+1}.

My Notes

My Notes

11. On the coordinate grid below, the horizontal axis represents n, the number of DVD rentals at Fantastik Flicks, and the vertical axis represents P_n, the number of points earned per DVD rental. Use the grid to plot the sequence P_n for $n = 1, 2, \ldots, 8$.

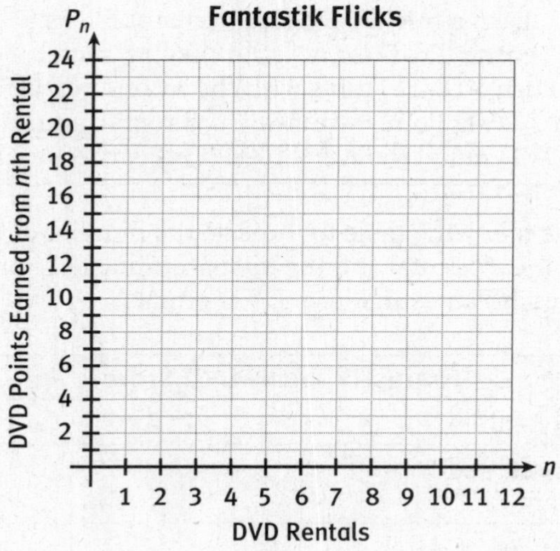

12. On the coordinate grid below, the vertical axis represents F_n, the total number of accumulated points earned after n rentals.

a. Plot the sequence F_n for $n = 1, 2, 3$, and 4.

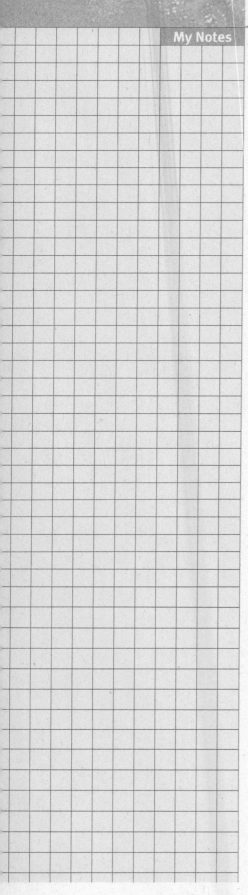

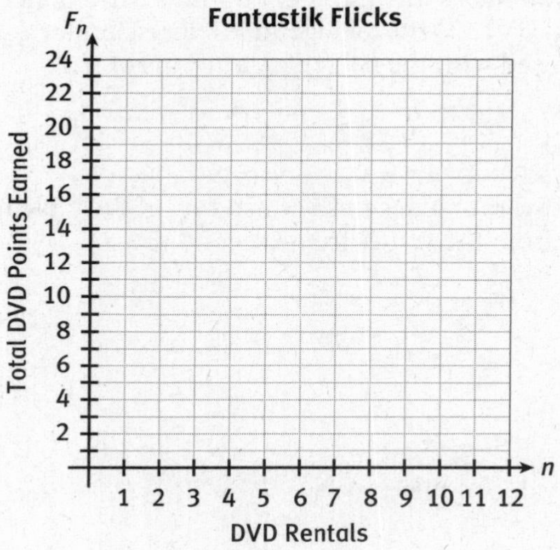

b. Construct viable arguments. Does the graph of F_n appear to be linear? Explain your answer.

My Notes

13. The graph shows the first four terms of the sequence $\{P_n\}$ as a shaded area.

a. Find the area of this shaded region. Explain how this area relates to the Fantastik Flicks DVD rental point promotion.

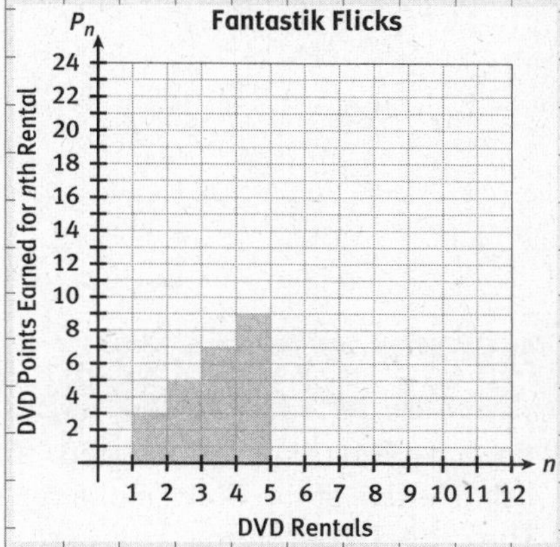

b. Extend the plot of the sequence $\{P_n\}$ to $n = 5, 6, 7$, and 8. Find the area of the region under each of these plotted values and the new total area for each.

c. Investigate the relationship of the area under the plotted points of P_n to the accumulated number of Fantastik Flicks DVD points earned after n rentals for $n = 5, 6, 7$, and 8. Does the pattern discovered in part a also hold for $n = 5, 6, 7$, and 8? Explain.

Check Your Understanding

14. Suppose $B_n = 3n + 1$. Let F_n represent the sequence made from the sum of the first n terms of B_n.

a. What does the term F_5 represent?

b. What is the value of F_8? Show your work.

c. Critique the reasoning of others. Mark thinks that the graph of F_n is linear because $F_2 - F_1 = 7$. Is Mark correct? Explain your answer without graphing the sequence.

LESSON 1-1 PRACTICE

15. $\{A_n\}$ is an arithmetic sequence with $a_1 = 7$ and $d = -2.5$.

a. Write the first five terms of this sequence.

b. Write an expression for A_n in terms of n, the term number.

c. Write an expression for A_{n+1} using the expression for A_n.

16. Make sense of problems. Gary rents three DVDs each week at Fantastik Flicks. Write an algebraic expression for W_n, the total number of points earned in the nth week.

17. Distinguish between the notation $\{A_n\}$ and A_n. Are they equivalent?

18. For the sequence $3, -2, -7, -12, \ldots$, determine the value of A_{12}.

My Notes

Learning Targets:

- Use sigma notation to represent a series.
- Write the algebraic form of an arithmetic sequence.
- Calculate the *n*th term or *n*th partial sum of an arithmetic series.

SUGGESTED LEARNING STRATEGIES: Close Reading, Interactive Word Wall, Activating Prior Knowledge, Think-Pair-Share, Debriefing, Self Revision/Peer Revision, Group Presentation

READING MATH

Several math terms are denoted using letters of the Greek alphabet. The capital letter sigma, $\sum$, is used for summation. The lowercase sigma, σ, is used for standard deviation. $\sum_{j=1}^{n} P_j$ is read "The summation of *P* sub *j* for $j = 1$ to n."

Fantastik Flicks DVD points accumulate according to the sum $P_1 + P_2 + \ldots + P_{n-1} + P_n$ for the first n DVD rentals. ***Sigma notation*** can be used to streamline the writing of such sums. Using sigma notation, the sum $P_1 + P_2 + \ldots + P_{n-1} + P_n$ is written as $\sum_{j=1}^{n} P_j = P_1 + P_2 + P_3 + \ldots + P_{n-1} + P_n$.

The notation $\sum_{j=1}^{n} P_j$ means the sum of the terms P_j, where j takes on the consecutive integer values starting with 1 and ending with n.

1. Let P_j denote the number of DVD points earned with the jth rental at Fantastik Flicks. For each part, write the sum indicated by the sigma notation, and then determine the value of the sum.

a. $\sum_{j=1}^{5} P_j =$

b. $\sum_{j=3}^{5} P_j =$

Example A

Evaluate $\sum_{j=2}^{7} (2j+3)$.

Step 1: The values of j are 2, 3, 4, 5, 6, and 7. Write a sum with six addends, and substitute each value of the variable.

$$\sum_{j=2}^{7} (2j+3) = [2(2)+3] + [2(3)+3] + [2(4)+3] + [2(5)+3] + [2(6)+3] + [2(7)+3]$$

Step 2: Evaluate each expression. Then simplify.

$7 + 9 + 11 + 13 + 15 + 17 = 72$

Solution: $\sum_{j=2}^{7} (2j+3) = 72$

My Notes

Try These A

a. Evaluate $\sum_{j=1}^{4}(5j-1)$.

b. Evaluate $\sum_{j=1}^{4}5j-1$.

c. Evaluate $\sum_{k=0}^{3}k^2$.

Check Your Understanding

2. Rewrite the following sum using sigma notation:

$1+5+9+13+17+21+25$

3. Trip is the head cheerleader. Each time his team scores, he does push-ups, one push-up for each point his team has on the scoreboard. At the Homecoming game, Trip's team scored a field goal, so he did three push-ups. Trip's team then scored seven points, so he did 10 push-ups. That day, Trip's team went on to score seven points five more times, and his team won, 45–17. How many push-ups did Trip do at the Homecoming game?

4. In Item 13 of the previous lesson, the number of Fantastik Flicks DVD points that accumulate with successive rentals can be modeled by the area that accumulates under the graph of the successive terms of P_n. Use the figures shown below to answer the following.

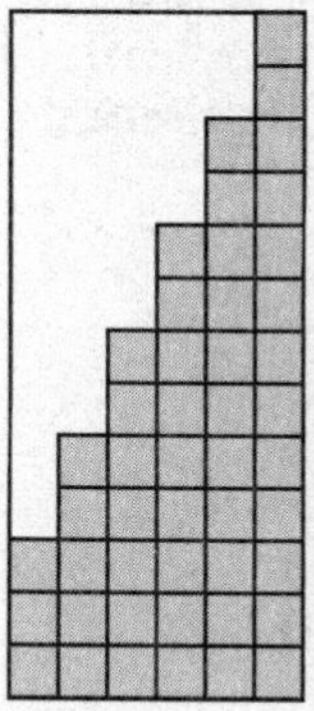

Figure 1

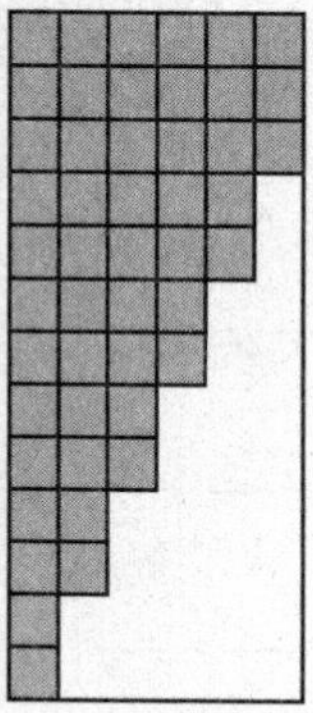

Figure 2

a. If Figure 1 represents a given number of DVDs rented from Fantastik Flicks and the total number of DVD points from these rentals, how many rentals are represented by this figure, and how many DVD points have been accumulated from these rentals?

Number of rentals: _______ Number of accumulated points: _______

My Notes

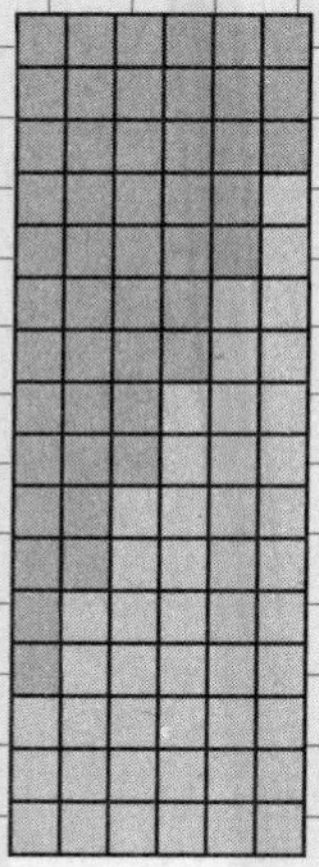

Figure 3

b. How does Figure 2 relate to Figure 1? Explain.

c. Figure 3 has a width that is equal to a given number of DVD rentals from Fantastik Flicks. How is the height of Figure 3 related to the first and last terms of the sum $\sum_{j=1}^{6} P_j$?

d. Find the area of the rectangle in terms of 6, P_1, and P_6.

e. Find the area of each of the two regions in Figure 3 in terms of 6, P_1, and P_6.

5. Use the results in Item 4 to answer the following.

a. Write an expression for the sum $\sum_{j=1}^{6} P_j$ in terms of 6, P_1, and P_6.

b. Reason abstractly. Express the sum $\sum_{j=1}^{n} P_j$ as a formula in terms of n, P_1, and P_n.

c. Complete the following table to verify that the formula in part b is true for other values of n besides $n = 6$.

DVD Rentals, n	Points Earned with n^{th} Rental, P_n	Total Points after n Rentals, F_n	Formula from Part b
1			
2			
3			
4			
5			
6			

My Notes

6. a. How many Fantastik Flicks DVD rentals are needed to obtain a free DVD rental? Show your work.

b. Fantastik Flicks has created a display for 260 DVDs. There are 8 DVDs in the top row of the display and the number of DVDs in each successive row will increase by a constant amount. If there are 10 rows in the display, how many DVDs will be in the 10th row?

Check Your Understanding

7. Bopper's is designing a new DVD display. Fifteen DVDs will be placed on the top row of the display, and the number of DVDs in each successive row will increase by four from the top row to the bottom row of the display.

a. Let r_n denote the number of DVDs in the nth row of the display. Write an expression for r_n in terms of n, the term number.

b. Let T_n denote the total number of DVDs in the display for n rows. Write a formula for T_n in terms of n.

c. Bopper's currently has 232 DVDs. How many rows will be in the display?

d. If Bopper's new DVD display will hold 135 DVDs in six rows, how many DVDs will be in the sixth row?

The Fantastik Flicks DVD point program provides an example of an arithmetic sequence $\{P_n\}$. An ***arithmetic sequence*** has the general algebraic form $a_n = a_1 + (n - 1)d$, where a_1 is the first term and d is the constant difference between consecutive terms.

READING MATH

When used as an adjective in "arithmetic sequence," the word *arithmetic* is pronounced with the accent on *-met-*, not on *-rith-*.

8. Use the table in Item 9 of Lesson 1-1 and examine the values for P_n and F_n.

a. Construct viable arguments. Explain why $\{P_n\}$ is an arithmetic sequence.

b. Explain why $\{F_n\}$ is a sequence but not an arithmetic sequence.

My Notes

The sum of all the terms of an arithmetic sequence forms an ***arithmetic series***. The sequence $\{F_n\}$ is called a ***sequence of partial sums*** of an arithmetic series, because each term of the sequence $\{F_n\}$ is a sum of the first n terms of an arithmetic sequence.

The following illustration shows the connection between an arithmetic sequence, an arithmetic series, and the partial sums.

Arithmetic Sequence	Arithmetic Series	Sequence of Partial Sums
1, 2, 3, 4, . . .	1 + 2 + 3 + 4 + . . .	$S_1 = 1$
		$S_2 = 1 + 2$
		$S_3 = 1 + 2 + 3$
		$S_4 = 1 + 2 + 3 + 4 \ldots$

Check Your Understanding

9. Write the sequence of the first five partial sums of the sequence $\{20 - 4n\}$, where $n = 1, 2, 3, \ldots$.

10. Write the sequence of the first five partial sums of the sequence $\{30 - 4n\}$, where $n = 1, 2, 3, \ldots$.

LESSON 1-2 PRACTICE

For Items 11–13, an arithmetic sequence has $a_1 = 4$ and $d = \frac{1}{2}$.

11. Write the general term for the sequence.

12. Write the associated arithmetic series using the first six terms, and express that sum using sigma notation.

13. Write the sequence of the first six partial sums of the sequence.

14. Model with mathematics. Consider a job offer with a starting salary of \$35,600 and a guaranteed raise of \$1200 per year for the next 5 years. What is the total amount of compensation at the end of the sixth year?

15. Is $\sum_{k=1}^{6}(3n+1) = \sum_{k=1}^{3}(3n+1) + \sum_{k=4}^{6}(3n+1)$? Verify your answer.

16. Evaluate $\sum_{k=1}^{6}(k^2 - 3)$.

17. Rewrite the following series using sigma notation:

$$\left(-\frac{5}{2}\right) + \left(-\frac{3}{2}\right) + \left(-\frac{1}{2}\right) + \frac{1}{2} + \frac{3}{2}$$

18. How many terms of the arithmetic sequence $-12, -3, 6, \ldots$ must be added to arrive at a sum of 363?

19. The sum of the first 24 terms of an arithmetic sequence is 300. If $P_1 = 47$, what is the value of P_{24}?

My Notes

Learning Targets:

- Understand the method of mathematical induction.
- Use mathematical induction to prove statements.

SUGGESTED LEARNING STRATEGIES: Look for a Pattern, Think-Pair-Share, Debriefing, Self Revision/Peer Revision

Graphical representations of P_n and the area under the graph of the terms of P_n were used to develop the formula $F_n = \frac{1}{2}n(P_1 + P_n)$. The fact that this formula holds true for values of n greater than 6 could be verified by extending the table created in Item 18c for larger values of n. However, extending the table would not prove that the formula is true for all positive integers n unless the table went on forever.

1. Use the formula $p(n) = n^2 - n + 41$.

a. Generate p_1, p_2, p_3, p_4, and p_5. Are all of these prime numbers?

b. Attend to precision. Try other values of $n > 5$. Is p a prime number for your choices of n?

c. Construct viable arguments. Based upon your work in parts a and b, do you think that p is a prime number for all positive integers n? Explain why or why not.

d. There are positive integers n for which $p(n)$ is not a prime number. Try to find one of these integer values.

To prove that a property or algebraic rule is true for all positive integers, mathematicians have developed a method called ***mathematical induction***. The method is described below.

To prove that a property P_n is true for all positive integers n, two important steps are required.

Step 1: Verify that the property is true for the initial value P_1.
Step 2: Prove the inductive step: If P_n is true for $n = k$, then P_n must be true for the next value of n, $n = k + 1$.

MATH TIP

Mathematical induction is sometimes incorrectly referred to as *inductive reasoning*, which is arguing logically from the specific to the general.

My Notes

Imagine dominoes lined up in a row so that when one domino is tipped, that domino will tip the next domino in the line. That domino will tip the next domino, which, in turn, will tip the next one. This process will continue as long as the dominoes are properly lined up.

The method of mathematical induction can be compared to dominoes properly lined up in a row.

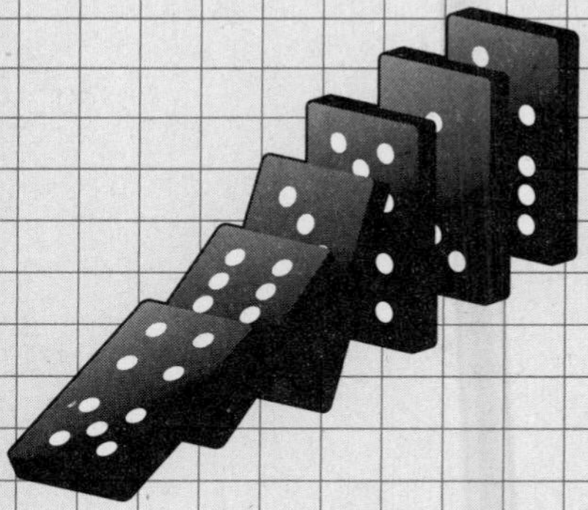

2. **Make sense of problems.** Suppose dominoes are properly lined up in a row.
   a. Do the dominoes tip one another if the first domino is never tipped? How is this like Step 1 of the mathematical induction method described above?

   Dominoes properly lined up in a row are spaced close enough to each other so that when one domino in the row, for example, the domino in the kth position, is tipped, it will tip the next domino in the $(k + 1)^{\text{st}}$ position.

   b. How is the condition of "dominoes properly lined up" like Step 2 of the mathematical induction method?

If a property expressed in terms of the positive integers n is true, mathematical induction proves this by showing that there is a starting point at which the property is true (like the first tipped domino).

If the property is true for $n = k$, this implies the truth of the property for $n = k + 1$ (like dominoes properly lined up).

By mathematical induction, the truth of the property progresses through the positive integers, starting with the first occurrence where the property is true and continuing on through all successive integers.

My Notes

3. Make use of structure. The formula for the sum of the first n positive integers is $1 + 2 + 3 + \ldots + (n - 1) + n = \sum_{j=1}^{n} j = \frac{n(n+1)}{2}$. The parts below illustrate the two steps of mathematical induction, a proof that this formula is correct for all positive integers n.

a. Evaluate $\frac{n(n+1)}{2}$ for $n = 1$.

Does the formula give the value of the sum $\sum_{j=1}^{n} j$ for $n = 1$?

b. Suppose $\sum_{j=1}^{k} j = \frac{k(k+1)}{2}$. Will it be true for $k + 1$? Adding $k + 1$, the value of the $(k + 1)^{st}$ term, to both sides of $\sum_{j=1}^{k} j = \frac{k(k+1)}{2}$ gives $k+1+\sum_{j=1}^{k} j = (k+1) + \frac{k(k+1)}{2}$. Verify algebraically that $(k+1) + \frac{k(k+1)}{2} = \frac{(k+1)(k+2)}{2}$.

c. Does $\frac{(k+1)(k+2)}{2}$ represent $\sum_{j=1}^{n} j = \frac{n(n+1)}{2}$ when n is replaced by $k + 1$? Explain.

My Notes

d. Review your work in parts a–c and explain how this work proves that $\sum_{j=1}^{n} j = \frac{n(n+1)}{2}$ is true for all positive integers $n \geq 1$.

Check Your Understanding

The sum of the first n positive odd integers can be represented as

$1 + 3 + 5 + 7 + 9 + \ldots = \sum_{j=1}^{n} (2j - 1)$.

Complete Items 4 and 5 to prove $\sum_{j=1}^{n} (2j - 1) = n^2$ for all positive integers $n \geq 1$.

4. Carry out Step 1 of the mathematical induction method. Show your work.

5. Carry out Step 2 of the mathematical induction method. Show your induction assumption (let $n = k$) and the algebraic proof to establish that the formula is valid for $n = k + 1$.

6. Use mathematical induction to prove $\sum_{j=1}^{n} j^2 = \frac{n(n+1)(2n+1)}{6}$ is true for all positive integers $n \geq 1$.

LESSON 1-3 PRACTICE

Verify the following formulas using mathematical induction.

7. $\sum_{k=1}^{n} \frac{1}{k(k+1)} = \frac{n}{n+1}$

8. $\sum_{k=1}^{n} 2k = n(n+1)$

9. Construct viable arguments. Must the value of n in the initial step of a mathematical induction proof always be 1? Justify your answer.

ACTIVITY 1 PRACTICE

Write your answers on notebook paper. Show your work.

Lesson 1-1

1. Which of the following sequences are arithmetic? For those sequences that are arithmetic, identify d and write an expression for a_n in terms of n, the term number.
   I. 100, 98, 96, 94, . . .
   II. 64, 32, 16, 8, . . .
   III. $2^1 + 1, 2^2 + 1, 2^3 + 1, 2^4 + 1, \ldots$
   IV. $\frac{3}{4}, \frac{13}{12}, \frac{17}{12}, \frac{7}{4}, \ldots$

2. A marathon is 26.2 miles. A runner begins training by running 3 miles on the first day. He increases his distance by 0.8 mile each day thereafter. How many days does it take for him to run the distance of a marathon?

3. An essay-writing contest ranks the essays from 1 to 20. The prizes are \$100, \$97, \$94, and so on. How much does the person writing the 13th essay receive?

4. The arithmetic sequence with $a_1 = 3$ and $d = 2.4$ contains each term below except:
   A. 12.6
   B. 19.6
   C. 27
   D. 29.4
   E. 34.2

5. Find x such that $x + 4$, $3x - 9$, and $2x + 8$ are consecutive terms of an arithmetic sequence.

6. Two sequences have the same common difference. How many terms could the sequences have in common? Justify your answer.

7. If a_1, a_2, a_3, a_4, a_5, and a_6 are the first six terms of an arithmetic sequence, is $3a_1, 3a_2, 3a_3, 3a_4, 3a_5, 3a_6, \ldots$ also an arithmetic sequence? Give an example or a counterexample to support your answer.

8. In an arithmetic sequence, a_3 is 27 and a_{12} is 90. Find a_{18}.

Lesson 1-2

9. Rewrite the following series using sigma notation: $27 + 22 + 17 + 12 + 7 + 2$.

10. Find the sum of the first 20 terms of the arithmetic sequence 27, 22, 17, ...

11. Evaluate $\sum_{j=1}^{5}(3j + 4)$.

12. Evaluate $\sum_{k=0}^{5}\left(\frac{1}{2}\right)^k$.

13. Find the sum of the first 20 terms of an arithmetic sequence with an 18th term of 8.1 and a common difference of 0.25.

14. Write the sequence of the first six partial sums of the sequence $\{3n - 4\}$, where $n = 1, 2, 3, \ldots$.

15. Will has \$210 in his bank account. Each Saturday, he deposits \$40. Describe what the partial sums of the sequence for this situation represent in terms of the context.

16. If $\sum_{i=1}^{K}(2 - i) = -2$, what is the value of K?

17. Claire and Jeremy are reading the same 240-page book. Claire has read 72 pages, and Jeremy has read 90 pages. On Monday, Claire begins to read 12 pages per day, and Jeremy continues to read 10 pages per day.

a. Write equations for the sequences C_n and J_n to represent how many total pages Claire and Jeremy have read n days after Sunday.
b. In this context, what should be the value of the last term of each sequence?
c. How many terms does each sequence have? How does this relate to who finished reading the book first?

18. The number of seats in the first three rows of the MIU theater is given in the table below.

Row Number	No. of Seats
1	18
2	20
3	22

The theater has 26 rows of seats, and the pattern in the table continues for all of the rows. Write an expression for the total number of seats in the first n rows and use this expression to calculate the seating capacity of the theater.

19. Write the sequence of the first five partial sums of the sequence $\{16 - 3n\}$, where $n = 1, 2, 3, \ldots$.

20. a. Find the value of n for which the following equation is true:

$$\sum_{k=1}^{n}(2k-1) = 100$$

b. Describe a characteristic of each term in the sequence.

21. Find the sum of $1 + 6 + 11 + \ldots + 96$.
A. 960
B. 970
C. 1,440
D. 1,940

Lesson 1-3

22. Verify the following formula using mathematical induction.

$$1+4+7+\ldots+(3n-2)=\frac{n(3n-1)}{2}$$

23. Verify the following formula using mathematical induction.

$$1+5+9+\ldots+(4n-3)=n(2n-1)$$

24. Consider the following equation:

$$1 + 4 + 9 + \ldots + 3n - 2 = 4n - 3$$

a. Is the equation true for $n = 1$?
b. Is the equation true for $n = 2$?
c. Is the equation true for all natural numbers?

25. Suzanne's teacher writes the following statement on the board:

For all integers $n \geq 5$, $n^3 \geq n^2 + 100$.

a. Show that the statement is true for $n = 5$.
b. Show that the mathematical induction step can be written $n^3 + 3n^2 + n \geq n^2 + 100$.
c. Explain in your own words why the inequality in part b is a true statement.

MATHEMATICAL PRACTICES
Look For and Make Use of Structure

26. For what types of problems is it useful to find an expression for a_n?

Geometric Sequences
She Sells Sea Shells
Lesson 2-1 Identifying Geometric Sequences

My Notes

Learning Targets:
- Identify a geometric sequence.
- Determine the common ratio of a geometric sequence.

SUGGESTED LEARNING STRATEGIES: Shared Reading, Marking the Text, Activating Prior Knowledge, Think-Pair-Share

Shy Shelly Sellers sells seashells in her *Fourth North Shore Store.* She is planning a sign for the storefront. She wants a large neon spiral reminiscent of the cross section of a shell. Each triangle in the design is a 30°–60°–90° triangle, and the length of the longest segment in the figure is 8 feet.

1. Recreate Shelly's design on the ***polar grid*** below. The first triangle is already drawn with the longest hypotenuse from the origin along the positive x-axis. Each successive hypotenuse is angled 30° counterclockwise from the previous one. As you calculate each hypotenuse length, record it in the table below the graph.

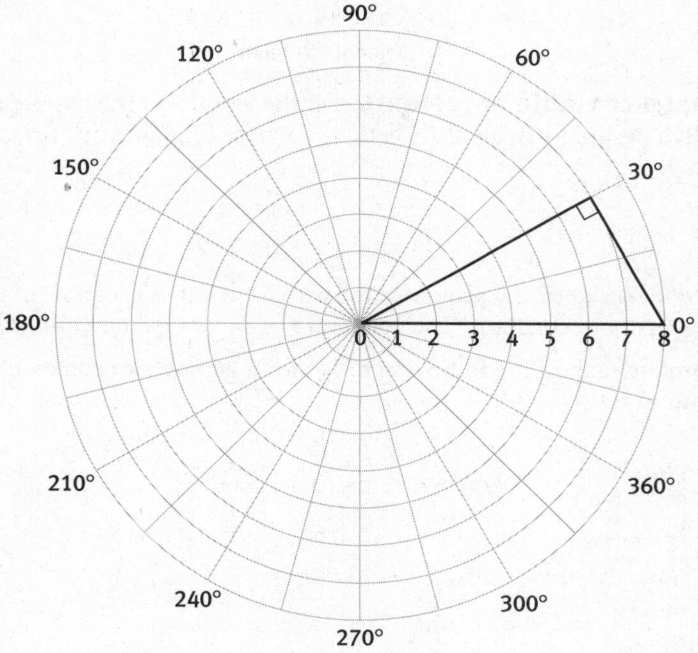

Triangle number	1	2	3	4	5	6	7	8	9
Exact hypotenuse length (ft)	8								
Decimal approximation to nearest hundredth									

MATH TIP

The length of the hypotenuse in a 30°–60°–90° triangle is twice the length of the shorter leg and the length of the longer leg is $\sqrt{3}$ times the length of the shorter leg.

MATH TERMS

A **polar grid** is made up of concentric circles, the center of which is the **pole**. Coordinates for points on this grid are given in the form (r, θ), where r represents the distance from the pole and θ represents an angle measured from the positive x-axis, as shown.

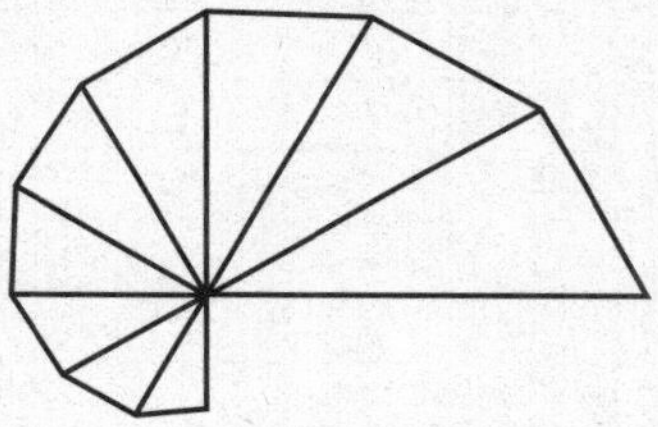

My Notes

2. a. List the exact values of the hypotenuse lengths from the table in Item 1 as a sequence with $a_1 = 8$.

b. Plot the approximations on the grid.

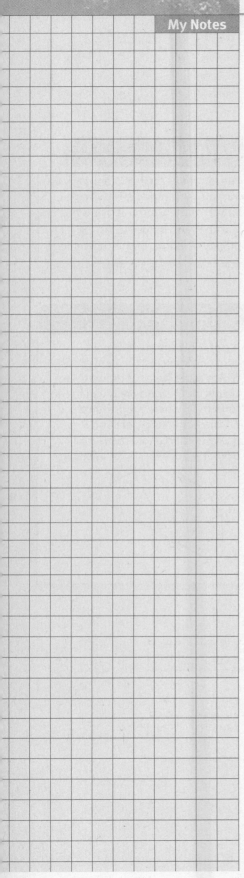

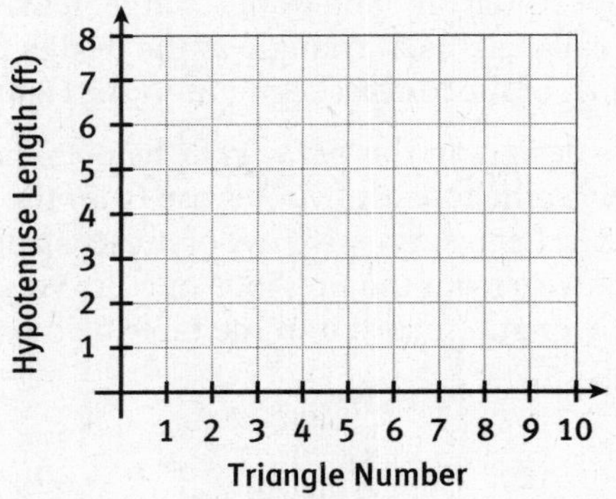

3. Construct viable arguments. Do the lengths of the hypotenuses in Shelly's design form an arithmetic sequence? Explain your reasoning.

A ***geometric sequence*** is a sequence for which the ratio, r, of a term to its preceding term is a constant. The constant r is known as the ***common ratio***.

4. Complete each of the following ratios for a geometric sequence with common ratio r.

$r = \frac{a_2}{\square}$ $\qquad r = \frac{\square}{a_5}$ $\qquad r = \frac{a_n}{\square}$

My Notes

5. Explain why the sequence in Item 2 is a geometric sequence.

6. Each term in a geometric sequence can be written as a product of the first term and powers of the common ratio.

a. Complete the table for the terms in the sequence in Item 2.

n	a_n	a_n Written as a Product of a_1 and a Power of the Ratio
1	8	$8\left(\frac{\sqrt{3}}{2}\right)^0$
2		
3		
4		
5		
6		

b. Write an equation that gives a_n in terms of n.

My Notes

c. Use your equation from Item 6b to calculate a_{11} directly. Does the pattern in the table from Item 6a help to confirm your answer?

Check Your Understanding

7. How does a geometric sequence differ from an arithmetic sequence?

8. Identify the missing terms in the geometric sequence ______, ______, 22.5, 67.5, ______, 607.5.

9. Identify which of the sequences below are geometric. If the sequence is a geometric sequence, identify a_1 and r, write an expression for a_n, and calculate a_{15}.

I. −5, −15, −45, −135, −405

II. −5, −1, 3, 7, 11

III. 1, 4, 9, 16, 25

IV. 6, −9, 13.5, −20.25, 30.375

LESSON 2-1 PRACTICE

10. Find x such that $x - 4$, x, and $3x - 8$ are three consecutive terms in a geometric sequence.

11. Determine the first term of a geometric sequence with $r = 1.4$ and $a_5 = 76.832$.

12. Calculate n for a geometric sequence with $a_1 = \frac{1}{32}$, $r = 2$, and $a_n = 4$.

13. **Attend to precision.** A new scooter costs $2,500. The depreciation rate is 30% per year. What is the value of this scooter after 5 years? Round to the nearest dollar.

14. Do the lengths of the short legs in the right triangles in Shelly's design form a geometric sequence? Make a prediction, calculate the actual lengths, and confirm or change your response.

My Notes

Learning Targets:

- Write the algebraic form of a geometric sequence.
- Calculate the sum of a finite geometric series.

SUGGESTED LEARNING STRATEGIES: Think-Pair-Share, Group Presentation, Debriefing, Self Revision/Peer Revision

1. A function of the form $f(x) = ab^x$ is an *exponential function*. Show why the expression that you wrote in Item 6 in Lesson 2-1 for a_n is an exponential function by identifying a and b.

2. Use the expression for a_n in Item 6 to verify the length of the ninth hypotenuse that you found in Item 1. (Do not use a_8.)

3. Suppose the spiral in Shelly's design is continued beyond the ninth triangle. Use the expression for a_n in Item 6 to calculate a_{115}.

My Notes

4. Given another geometric sequence with $a_1 = \frac{1}{2}$ and $a_2 = \frac{-3}{2}$, calculate r and a_{10}.

5. Write an expression for a_n in terms of a_1, r, and n that can be used for any geometric sequence.

MATH TERMS

The sum of the terms of a sequence is often used in applications. These sums are known as a **series**. The sum of the first n terms of a sequence is called the ***n*****th partial sum**.

6. a. Attend to precision. For each ***partial sum*** in the table, write an expression for $\frac{\sqrt{3}}{2}S_n$ in expanded form. Use exact values.

n	S_n	$\frac{\sqrt{3}}{2}S_n$
1	8	
2	$8+4\sqrt{3}$	
3	$8+4\sqrt{3}+6$	
4	$8+4\sqrt{3}+6+3\sqrt{3}$	
5	$8+4\sqrt{3}+6+3\sqrt{3}+\frac{9}{2}$	

My Notes

b. Use your table from Part a to complete the table below.
- Complete the second column by writing an expression for $S_n - \frac{\sqrt{3}}{2}S_n$ as the difference of two terms.
- Complete the third column by factoring a_1 from each term in the second column.
- Complete the fourth column by expressing q in the third column as a power of r.

n	$S_n - \frac{\sqrt{3}}{2}S_n$	$a_1(1 - q)$	$a_1(1 - r^n)$
1	$8 - 4\sqrt{3}$	$8\left(1 - \frac{\sqrt{3}}{2}\right)$	$8\left(1 - \left(\frac{\sqrt{3}}{2}\right)^1\right)$
2			
3			
4			
5			

7. Use the results of the table in Item 6 to complete the following equation in terms of a_1, r, and n: $S_n - rS_n =$

My Notes

MATH TERMS

Recall that a *series* is the sum of the terms in a sequence. A **geometric series** is the sum of the terms in a geometric sequence.

8. **Use appropriate tools strategically.** Use factoring to solve the equation in Item 7 for S_n, and write the formula for the sum of a finite ***geometric series***.

9. Use the equation that you wrote in Item 8 to calculate the sum of the first 9 hypotenuses in Shelly's design.

Check Your Understanding

10. Find the sum of the first 5 terms of the geometric sequence if $a_2 = 8$ and $a_3 = 10$. Show your work.

11. Find the sum of the areas of the first 10 right triangles in Shelly's design. Show your work.

12. Shelly sends an email to three customers to invite them to a sale. The customers each forward the email to three of their friends. If this pattern continues, find the total number of emails sent after an email was forwarded six times.

LESSON 2-2 PRACTICE

13. **Make use of structure.** For the geometric sequence $a_n = \left(\frac{1}{2}\right)^n$, $S_2 = \frac{3}{4}$, $S_3 = \frac{7}{8}$, and $S_4 = \frac{15}{16}$, predict S_5 and S_6.

14. Write a general term, S_n, for the geometric sequence above.

15. Find the sum of the first eight terms of the geometric sequence whose first term is -2.5 and ratio is 2.

16. **Attend to precision.** Evaluate $\sum_{k=0}^{9} 6(1.5)^k$. Round to the nearest hundredth.

17. Express the sum in Item 15 using sigma notation.

My Notes

Learning Targets:

- Determine if a sequence converges or diverges.
- Find the sum of an infinite geometric series.

SUGGESTED LEARNING STRATEGIES: Quickwrite, Think-Pair-Share, Summarizing, Paraphrasing, Interactive Word Wall, Debriefing, Self Revision/Peer Revision

1. As n increases, what is happening to the length of each successive hypotenuse in the triangles in Shelly's design?

If the terms of an infinite sequence approach some number L as n increases without bound, the sequence is said to ***converge***. If the sequence does not converge, it ***diverges***.

2. Does the sequence whose terms are the lengths of the hypotenuses in Shelly's design converge or diverge? If the sequence converges, what is the value that the terms appear to approach as n increases?

ACADEMIC VOCABULARY

Diverge can mean to move away from a location, and ***converge*** can mean to approach it. Think of a series that diverges as moving away from a specific value.

3. For each infinite geometric sequence below, answer the following questions.

a. Determine the common ratio for each sequence.

b. Which of the sequences converge and which diverge? For each sequence that converges, determine, if possible, the value to which the terms are approaching.

I. 0.025, 0.25, 2.5, 25, 250, . . .

II. 100, 50, 25, 12.5, 6.25, . . .

III. $-4.2, 4.2\ -4.2, 4.2, -4.2, \ldots$

IV. $\frac{1}{9}, -\frac{1}{3}, 1, -3, 9, \ldots$

V. $25, \frac{25}{\sqrt{5}}, \frac{25}{5}, \frac{25}{5\sqrt{5}}, \frac{25}{25}, \ldots$

VI. 32,000, 320, 3.2, 0.032, 0.00032, . . .

VII. $1, \sqrt{2}, 2, 2\sqrt{2}, 4, \ldots$

CONNECT TO AP

The value to which a sequence converges is called the limit of the sequence. Later in this course and in AP Calculus, you will learn about and use limits in a variety of ways.

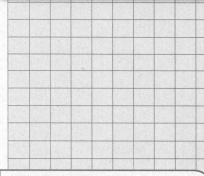

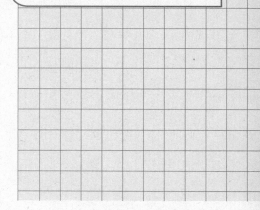

My Notes

4. Create two infinite geometric sequences of your own, one that converges and one that diverges.

DISCUSSION GROUP TIPS

In your discussion groups, read the text carefully to clarify meaning. Reread definitions of terms as needed to help you comprehend the meanings of words, or ask your teacher to clarify vocabulary terms.

5. Reason quantitatively. How can the ratio of a geometric sequence be used to determine whether a sequence converges or diverges? If the sequence converges, what can be said about the value to which the terms are drawing near?

6. Calculate the first five partial sums for sequences I, II, and III in Item 3 and the sequences you created in Item 4. Which sequences of partial sums appear to converge and which appear to diverge?

7. If you calculated the 100th partial sum for each of the sequences in Item 6, would any of your responses change? Explain your reasoning.

8. Suppose the spiral in Shelly's shell design continues and is allowed to overlap itself. As n increases, is there a length to which the hypotenuses are drawing near? Is there a value to which the sum of the lengths of the hypotenuses is drawing near?

9. Express regularity in repeated reasoning. What must be true for r, the common ratio of a geometric sequence, in order to have the sequence of the partial sums converge?

My Notes

An ***infinite sequence*** is a sequence with an infinite number of terms.
An ***infinite series*** is the sum of the terms of an infinite sequence.

10. For some series, an infinite number of terms can be added to get a finite sum. Recall the formula for the sum of the first n terms in a geometric sequence: $S_n = \frac{a_1(1-r^n)}{(1-r)}$. Let $|r| < 1$. As n increases and gets very large, what happens to each of the following expressions?

a. r^n

b. $1 - r^n$

c. $\frac{a_1(1-r^n)}{(1-r)}$

11. Shelly wants to know the total length of material she will need for the display. Find the sum of the lengths of the hypotenuses in the triangles in her design if $a_1 = 8$ and the number of triangles in her design increases without bound.

Example A

An ant located at the origin crawls 1 unit right, then $\frac{1}{2}$ unit up, then $\frac{1}{4}$ unit right, then $\frac{1}{8}$ unit up, and continues following this pattern indefinitely. What point is the ant approaching?

Step 1: Find the horizontal distance traveled.
The horizontal distances are $1, \frac{1}{4}, \frac{1}{16}, \ldots$. This is an infinite geometric sequence with $a_1 = 1$ and $r = \frac{1}{4}$. Therefore, the horizontal distance approaches $\frac{1}{1-\frac{1}{4}} = \frac{4}{3}$.

Step 2: Find the vertical distance traveled.
The vertical distances are $\frac{1}{2}, \frac{1}{8}, \frac{1}{32}, \ldots$. This is an infinite geometric sequence with $a_1 = \frac{1}{2}$ and $r = \frac{1}{4}$. Therefore, the vertical distance approaches $\frac{\frac{1}{2}}{1-\frac{1}{4}} = \frac{2}{3}$.

Solution: The ant is approaching the point $\left(\frac{4}{3}, \frac{2}{3}\right)$.

CONNECT TO AP

If a sequence diverges, then the corresponding series also diverges. However, if a sequence converges, the corresponding series may or may not converge. Determining whether or not an infinite series converges or diverges is a topic you will study in AP Calculus.

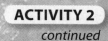

My Notes

Try These A

a. For each infinite sequence in Item 34 that converges, find the sum of its corresponding series.

b. The repeating decimal 0.363636 . . . can be written as an infinite geometric series: $0.36(.01)^0 + 0.36(.01)^1 + 0.36(.01)^2 + \ldots$. Express the repeating decimal in sigma notation and as a fraction by finding the sum of the corresponding infinite series.

c. Evaluate $\sum_{k=1}^{\infty} 10(0.8)^k$.

Check Your Understanding

12. Find the value of $-3 + 2 - \frac{4}{3} + \frac{8}{9} - \ldots$.

13. **Critique the reasoning of others.** Amy says, "Each term of an infinite geometric series must be less than the previous term for the series to converge." Roger points out that if r is negative, this is not true. Rewrite Amy's statement so that it is true.

14. Give an example of an infinite geometric series that diverges.

LESSON 2-3 PRACTICE

15. Write the sum $8 + 2.4 + 0.72 + 0.216 + \ldots$ using summation notation.

16. **Make use of structure.** Express the repeating decimal 0.4444 . . . as a fraction.

17. Solve for r: $\sum_{n=1}^{\infty} 5r^n = 2.5$.

18. An infinite series converges to 10 with a common ratio of 0.6. What is a_1?

19. **Model with mathematics.** Suppose the ant in Example 1 crawled to (0, 1), and then turned to its right before crawling each additional distance. Describe how you would approach this problem.

ACTIVITY 2 PRACTICE

Write your answers on notebook paper. Show your work.

Lesson 2-1

1. Determine which of the sequences below are geometric. For each geometric sequence, calculate r, find an expression for a_n, and calculate a_{12}.

I. 100, 98, 96, 94, . . .

II. $2^0, 2^1, 2^2, 2^3, \ldots$

III. $3, 3\sqrt{6}, 18, 18\sqrt{6}, \ldots$

IV. $2^0 + 1, 2^1 + 2, 2^2 + 3, 2^3 + 4, \ldots$

2. Find a_1 for a geometric sequence if $r = 5$ and $a_6 = 1000$.

3. Each month, the balance in Freda's bank account is 1.003 times as large as the previous month's due to interest. If Freda does not deposit or withdraw any money from this account and she begins with $2500, find the balance in this account at the beginning of the 36th month.

4. Complete the following analogy and explain your response. Arithmetic sequences are to linear functions as geometric sequences are to ______________.

5. Find the first term of the geometric sequence with a common ratio of 0.4 and $a_7 = 32$.

6. Find the common ratio of the geometric sequence with $a_1 = \frac{3}{5}$ and $a_6 = \frac{1875}{1024}$.

7. Write the first five terms of the geometric sequence with $a_3 = -135$ and $a_4 = 405$.

8. Find the eighth term of a geometric sequence with $a_1 = 6$ and $r = 1.2$.

9. Explain why $a_{n+1} = ra_n$ in any geometric sequence.

Lesson 2-2

10. Find the sum of the first 10 terms in each of the geometric sequences in Item 1.

11. Find a_n when $S_3 = \frac{122}{25}$ and $r = \frac{4}{5}$.

12. As a reward for inventing chess, Ja'qubi asked the Shah of Persia for 1 grain of wheat for the first of the 64 chessboard squares, 2 grains for the second, 4 grains for the third, 8 grains for the fourth, and so on, for all 64 squares. Calculate the number of wagons needed to transport the wheat if there are 20 million grains of wheat per ton and each wagon can carry 5 tons of grain.

13. A geometric sequence has $a_1 = 0.56$ and $r = 10$. Write the series representing the sum of the first six terms of the sequence, and express this sum using sigma notation.

14. Evaluate each sum.

a. $\sum_{k=0}^{4} 9\left(\frac{-1}{3}\right)^k$

b. $\sum_{k=1}^{6} 3(0.4)^k$

c. $\sum_{k=0}^{5} \left(\frac{1}{2}\right)^k$

15. Find the sum of $2 + 1 + \frac{1}{2} + \ldots + \frac{1}{256}$.

A. 3.976
B. 3.992
C. 4.500
D. 4.992

16. Which provides a greater annual amount: 8.5% interest compounded annually or 8% compounded quarterly?

17. Suppose you and your spouse have four children and suppose that each child has two children, and this pattern continues for 14 generations. How many people, starting with you and your spouse, are in your family tree?

18. Express this sum of the following series using sigma notation. Then, find the sum.

$4 + 4(2) + 4(2)^2 + 4(2)^3 + 4(2)^4 + 4(2)^5$

19. Find n such that $\sum_{k=1}^{n} (3)^k = 363$.

Lessons 2-3 and 2-4

20. Calculate the sum for each of the following infinite geometric series that converge.

I. $4 + 2 + 1 + \frac{1}{2} + \ldots$

II. $4^2 + 2^2 + 1^2 + \left(\frac{1}{2}\right)^2 + \ldots$

III. $\frac{-16}{81} + \frac{-8}{27} + \frac{-4}{9} + \frac{-2}{3} + \cdots$

IV. $\frac{\sqrt{10}}{4} + \frac{10}{16} + \frac{10\sqrt{10}}{64} + \frac{100}{256} + \cdots$

V. $1 + 1.1 + 1.21 + 1.331 + \ldots$

21. Express the repeating decimal 0.757575 . . . as an infinite series and write it as a fraction.

22. Not all infinite geometric series can be calculated. What must be true about an infinite geometric series if that series can be calculated?

23. Do the even-numbered terms of an infinite geometric sequence form another infinite geometric sequence? Justify your answer.

24. Find the common ratio, r, for an infinite series with an initial term of 4 that converges to a sum of $\frac{16}{3}$.

25. Consider the infinite geometric series

$\frac{8}{25} + \frac{4\sqrt{5}}{25} + \frac{2}{5} + \frac{\sqrt{5}}{5} + \ldots .$

a. What is the exact value of the common ratio of the series?

b. Does the series converge? Justify your answer without making calculations.

26. Find the sum of $1 + (0.2) + (0.2)^2 + (0.2)^3 + \ldots .$

A. 1.2

B. 1.22

C. 1.25

D. 2

27. Helena makes a perspective drawing as shown below. Each rectangle is 75% as wide and as tall as the rectangle below it.

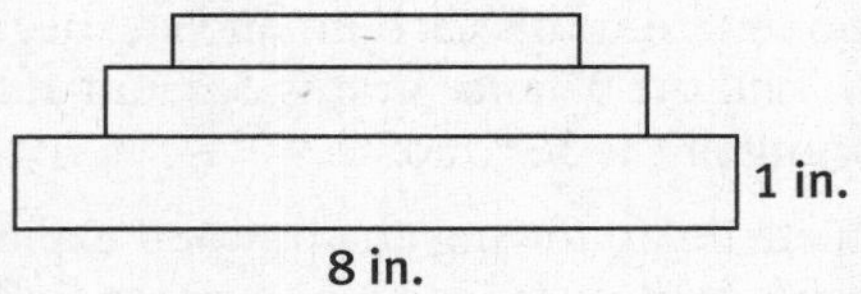

If the pattern continues indefinitely, what will be the total area of the figure?

MATHEMATICAL PRACTICES
Look For and Make Use of Structure

28. Compare and contrast arithmetic and geometric sequences and series as to structure, notation, and patterns.

Modeling Recursive Relationships

ACTIVITY 3

Money Market Accounts

Lesson 3-1 Exploring a Recursive Relationship

My Notes

Learning Targets:

- Represent arithmetic and geometric sequences recursively.
- Determine the explicit form of a recursive sequence.

SUGGESTED LEARNING STRATEGIES: Chunking the Activity, Summarizing, Paraphrasing, Predict and Confirm, Think-Pair-Share, Activating Prior Knowledge

As you read, mark the text to identify key information and parts of sentences that help you make meaning from the text.

Maurice and Lester are twins who have just graduated from college. They have both been offered jobs where their take-home pay would be $2500 per month. Their parents have given Maurice and Lester two options for a graduation gift.

Option 1: If they choose to pursue a graduate degree, their parents will give each of them a gift of $35,000. However, they must pay for their tuition and living expenses out of the gift.

Option 2: If they choose to go directly into the workforce, their parents will give each of them a gift of $5000.

Maurice decides to go to graduate school for 2 years. He locks in a tuition rate by paying $11,500 for the 2 years in advance, and he figures that his monthly expenses will be $1000.

Lester decides to go straight into the workforce. Lester finds that after paying his rent, utilities, and other living expenses, he will be able to save $200 per month.

Their parents deposit the appropriate amount of money in a money market account for each twin. The money market accounts are currently paying a nominal interest rate of 3 percent, compounded monthly.

1. Before doing any calculations, predict which twin will have the greater balance in his money market account after 2 years. Will that twin always have more money in the account?

2. After Maurice withdraws $11,500 for tuition, how much money is left in his money market account?

DISCUSSION GROUP TIPS

If you do not understand something in group discussions, ask for help or raise your hand for help. Describe your questions as clearly as possible, using synonyms or other words when you do not know the precise words to use.

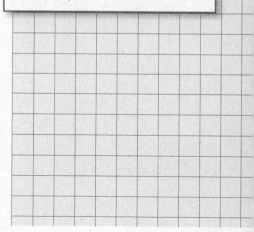

My Notes

MATH TIP

To compute the monthly interest rate when a yearly rate is given and the interest is compounded monthly, divide the interest rate by 12. For example, to calculate the balance in an account that pays 3 percent interest, compounded monthly, after one month, multiply the beginning balance by $\left(1+\frac{0.03}{12}\right)$, or 1.0025.

TECHNOLOGY TIP

Many calculators will perform recursive operations on the home screen by establishing the pattern and then pressing the ENTER key successively. A spreadsheet may also be used; a copied formula filled down a column can generate sequences quickly.

3. At the end of the first month, Maurice has earned a little interest from his money market account and pays his monthly bills out of this account. Find Maurice's current balance and show the work that supports your answer.

4. Complete the table below to record Maurice's monthly money market account balance after he collects interest and pays his bills.

Month	Computation	Account Balance
0		
1		
2		
3		
4		
5		

5. If Maurice's initial balance is $u_0 = 23{,}500$, u_n is the current month's balance, and u_{n-1} is last month's balance, write an expression for u_n in terms of u_{n-1}.

6. Maurice decides to use a spreadsheet to determine the balance of his money market account when he graduates.

	A	B
1	**Month**	**Maurice's Account Balance**
2	0	$23,500
3	1	$22,558.75
4	2	$21,615.15
5	3	$20,669.19
6	4	$19,720.86
7	5	$18,770.16
8	6	
9	7	
10	8	
11	9	
12	10	
13	11	
14	12	
15	13	
16	14	
17	15	
18	16	
19	17	
20	18	
21	19	
22	20	
23	21	
24	22	
25	23	
26	Graduation	

a. If month 0 is identified as A2 and u_0 as B2 on the spreadsheet, how would Month 1 and $22,558.75 be identified?

b. Using the expression from Item 5, determine the relationship on the spreadsheet between B3 and B2.

c. Determine the relationship on the spreadsheet between B4 and B3.

My Notes

MATH TERMS

The process of **iteration** is a repetitive application of the same rule.

My Notes

d. Determine a relationship between B8 and B7, and find the account balance at 6 months.

e. Use appropriate tools strategically. Use a spreadsheet program or graphing calculator to complete the spreadsheet above. How much money is in Maurice's account upon graduation?

7. On the grid below, plot the balance for Maurice's money market account for each month of the 2 years he will attend graduate school. Label the axes.

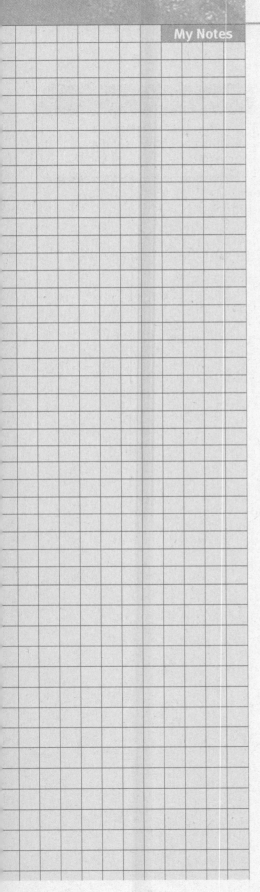

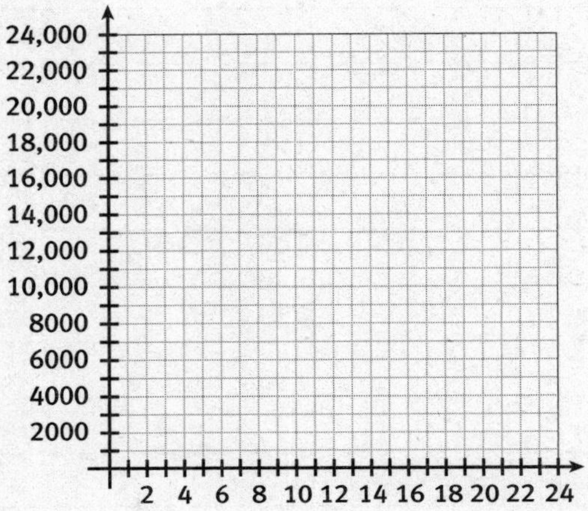

8. As the number of months that Maurice attends graduate school increases, what is happening to his money market account balance?

9. Reason quantitatively. Consider the sequence of Maurice's monthly money market account balances. Is this an arithmetic sequence, a geometric sequence, or neither? Explain.

My Notes

Lester works during the time that Maurice attends graduate school. Each month, Lester saves $200 and deposits this amount into the $5000 money market account that his parents set up for him when he graduated.

10. Complete the table below to record Lester's money market account balance each month for the first 5 months that he works. Recall that Lester's money market account earns him 3 percent interest, compounded monthly.

Month	Account Balance
0	
1	
2	
3	
4	
5	

11. If Lester's initial balance is $u_0 = 5000$, u_n is the current month's balance, and u_{n-1} is last month's balance, write an expression for u_n in terms of u_{n-1}.

12. How much money does Lester have in his money market account after 1 year? How does his account balance compare to Maurice's account balance after 1 year?

13. Add a column C on the spreadsheet for Lester's money market account, for the 2 years he has been working. Enter 5000 for the value of C2. Plot the balance for Lester's money market account for each month of the first 2 years he will work on the grid of Item 7.

a. Write an equation that gives C3 in terms of C2.

b. Model with mathematics. When do the twins have approximately the same amount of money in their accounts? Explain your reasoning.

c. At the end of 2 years, which twin has the larger money market account balance, and how much more money does this twin have?

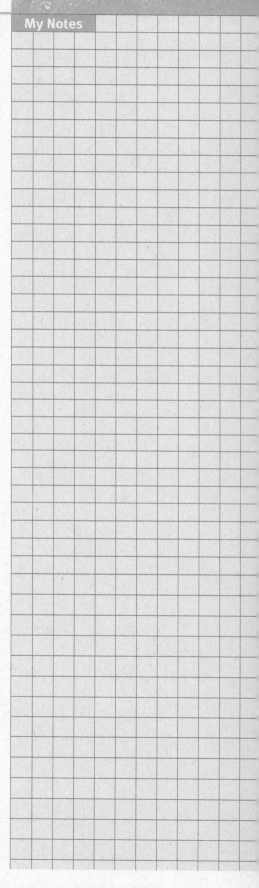

My Notes

Check Your Understanding

14. At the end of 2 years, Lester receives a raise and decides to save \$250 each month. Maurice receives a \$5000 graduation gift from his parents and deposits this amount into his money market account. Maurice goes to work and saves \$500 each month.

Complete the equations below for the money market account balance for each twin. Let the initial balance u_0 be the account balance at the end of 2 years. Write an expression for this month's account balance u_n in terms of u_{n-1}. Recall that the interest rate for the account is 3 percent, compounded monthly.

Maurice: $u_0 = \$5248.47$, $u_n =$ ______
Lester: $u_0 =$ ______, $u_n =$ ______

15. Construct viable arguments. Suppose Maurice has \$6953.11 in his account at the end of a certain month. How could you determine how much was in the account at the end of the previous month? Explain your method.

LESSON 3-1 PRACTICE

16. Model with mathematics. The number of bacteria in a Petri dish grows by 10 percent every hour. After the growth, about 100 bacteria die.

a. Suppose initially there are 500 bacteria. How many bacteria are alive after 1 hour?
b. How many bacteria are alive after 2 hours?
c. Write expressions for u_0 and u_n for this situation.
d. What is happening to the bacteria population?

17. For the sequence 3, 4, 6, 9, 13, ..., write expressions for u_0 and u_n.

18. An arithmetic sequence has a first term of 40 and a constant difference of −4. Write expressions for u_0 and u_n to represent this sequence.

19. Use appropriate tools strategically. Use a spreadsheet or calculator to determine how long it will take for the bacteria from Item 16 to die off completely.

My Notes

Learning Targets:

- Represent arithmetic and geometric sequences recursively.
- Determine the explicit form of a recursive sequence.

SUGGESTED LEARNING STRATEGIES: Chunking the Activity, Summarizing, Paraphrasing, Predict and Confirm, Think-Pair-Share, Activating Prior Knowledge

A ***recursive sequence*** of the form $\begin{cases} u_0 = \text{Initial amount} \\ u_n = r \cdot u_{n-1} + d \end{cases}$ has an ***explicit form*** $u_n = a + b \cdot r^n$, where a and b are constants, r is the same growth factor used in the recursive form, and n is the time in months.

1. Refer to the recursive sequence for Maurice's money market account that you wrote in Item 5 of Lesson 3-1. When Maurice's value for u_0 is substituted into the explicit form $u_n = a + b \cdot r^n$, what is the resulting equation?

2. When Maurice's value for u_1 is substituted into the explicit form $u_n = a + b \cdot r^n$, what is the resulting equation?

3. Find the solution to the system of equations you developed in Items 1 and 2. Show the work that supports your solution.

MATH TIP

You can solve a two-variable system of equations by multiplying one or both of the equations by a constant. The sum of the two equations will eliminate one of the variables, resulting in one equation with one variable.

4. Using the values of a and b from Item 3, state the explicit form of the sequence for Maurice's money market account balance while he attended graduate school.

My Notes

5. Use the explicit form of the sequence for Maurice's money market account balance while he attended graduate school to determine the balance at the end of 1 year and 2 years. Do these answers agree with the values found in the spreadsheet for Item 6 of Lesson 3-1?

6. How does the graph of the explicit form of the sequence for Maurice's money market account balance while he attended graduate school compare to the graph of the recursive form?

7. What is the sum of a and b in the explicit form of the sequence for Maurice's money market account balance? What does this sum represent?

My Notes

8. Recall that while Maurice was attending graduate school, Lester was working. The beginning balance for Lester's money market account was $5000, earning 3 percent interest, compounded monthly. Lester also deposited $200 into this account each month.

a. Find the explicit form of the sequence for Lester's money market account balance while Maurice was attending graduate school. Show the work that supports your answer.

b. Use the explicit form of the sequence for Lester's money market account balance to determine the balance at the end of 1 year and 2 years. Do these answers agree with the values found in Item 12 and the graph for Item 13 in Lesson 3-1?

c. What is the sum of a and b in the explicit form of the sequence for Lester's money market account balance, and what does this sum represent?

9. Use the explicit form of each twin's sequence to determine when Maurice and Lester have approximately the same amount of money in their accounts. Show the work that supports your answer.

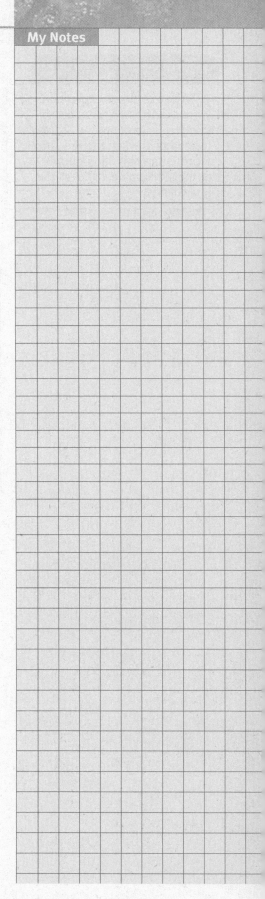

My Notes

MATH TIP

To write a recursive expression, write a_1 and a rule for a_n based upon a_{n-1}. Sometimes a_0 is used instead of a_1 when the sequence represents a real situation, with a_0 as the initial value and a_1 as the first change.

10. Given the geometric sequence 3, 6, 12, 24, ...

a. Write an expression for a_n two ways: recursively and explicitly.

b. Explain why geometric sequences are a subset of the sequences in this activity where $u_n = ru_{n-1} + d$.

11. Given the arithmetic sequence 25, 22, 19, 16, ... Write an expression for a_n two ways: recursively and explicitly.

Check Your Understanding

12. Refer to Item 14 of Lesson 3-1. Find the explicit form of the sequence for Maurice and Lester's money market account balances after Maurice graduated from graduate school. Show your work.

13. Use the explicit form of the sequences found in Item 12, after Maurice finished graduate school, to confirm when the twins had approximately the same amount of money in their accounts. Show the work that supports your answer.

14. Write a recursive expression and an explicit expression for a_n for the sequence \$400, \$480, \$576, ...

15. Write a recursive expression and an explicit expression for a_n for the sequence \$400, \$400(1.003) + \$10, \$411.20(1.003) + \$10, ...

LESSON 3-2 PRACTICE

Catarina opens a savings account with \$50 and deposits \$20 each month. Her bank pays 3.6 percent interest, compounded monthly.

16. Write a recursive expression for a_n.

17. If $a_{15} = 358.68$, find a_{16}.

18. Write an explicit expression for a_n.

19. Use the explicit form for a_n to find a_{16}.

20. **Construct viable arguments.** Explain why it would be preferable to use an explicit formula rather than a recursive formula to find a_{20}.

ACTIVITY 3 PRACTICE

Write your answers on notebook paper. Show your work.

Lesson 3-1

1. For each of the sequences below, write a recursive expression for a_n.
   a. \$400, \$200, \$100, . . .
   b. \$400, \$400(1.003) + \$10, \$411.20(1.003) + \$10, . . .
   c. \$400, \$480, \$576, . . .
   d. \$400, \$418, \$436, . . .

2. For each of the following geometric sequences, write an expression for a_n recursively.
   a. 48, 24, 12, . . .
   b. 100, −150, 225, . . .
   c. \$600, \$602.40, \$604.81, . . .

3. For each of the following sequences, write an expression for a_n recursively.
   a. 2, 7, 12, . . .
   b. $\frac{\sqrt{3}}{2}, \frac{3\sqrt{3}}{2}, \frac{5\sqrt{3}}{2}, \ldots$
   c. $(x + y), (x + y)^2, (x + y)^3, \ldots$

4. The first eight terms of the Fibonacci sequence are 1, 1, 2, 3, 5, 8, 13, 21. Write a recursive formula to find a_n for any term in the sequence.

5. If $a_n = 3a_{n-1}$ and $a_1 = \frac{4}{27}$, which statement is NOT correct?
   A. $a_2 = \frac{4}{9}$
   B. $a_4 = 4$
   C. $a_6 = 36$
   D. $a_8 = 108$

6. Write the first five terms of $a_n = -2a_{n-1}$ if $a_1 = 5$.

7. Write the recursive function that gives the values $f(1), f(2), f(3), \ldots$, where $f(x)$ is graphed below.

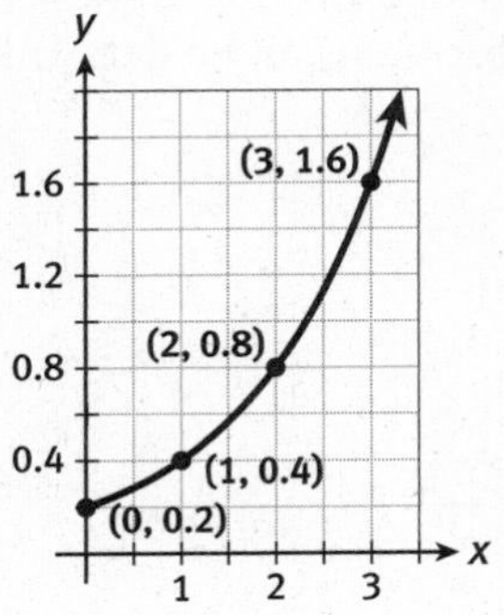

8. Write $n!$ as a recursive expression.

9. Supply the formula entries for the calculations of B4, B5, B6, and B7 in the spreadsheet.

	A	B
1	Open account	\$525
2	Monthly interest rate	0.5%
3	January	\$525
4	February	\$527.63
5	March	\$530.26
6	April	\$532.92
7	May	\$535. 58

10. Write a recursive expression for the set of ordered pairs (n, a_n).

x	y
0	3
1	9
2	15
3	21

11. A recursive expression is given as $a_n = a_{n-1} + 2n - 1$, where $a_1 = 1$.
   a. Find a_2, a_3, and a_4.
   b. What sequence of numbers is defined by this recursive expression?
   c. Does the structure of the recursive expression look familiar? Explain.

Lesson 3-2

12. Identify the explicit formula equivalent to the recursive formula $a_n = 5a_{n-1}$, with $a_4 = 12.5$.
A. $a_n = 10(5)^{n-1}$
B. $a_n = 10(0.5)^{n-1}$
C. $a_n = 0.1(5)^{n-1}$
D. $a_n = 0.1(0.5)^{n-1}$

13. For each of the following geometric sequences, write an expression for a_n explicitly.
I. 48, 24, 12, . . .
II. 100, −150, 225, . . .
III. \$600, \$602.40, \$604.81, . . .

14. For each of the following arithmetic sequences, write an expression for a_n explicitly.
I. −10, −4, 2, . . .
II. $\frac{\sqrt{3}}{2}, \frac{3\sqrt{3}}{2}, \frac{5\sqrt{3}}{2}, \ldots$
III. \$900, \$850, \$800, . . .

15. Pete starts with \$500 in a savings account that pays 3.6 percent interest, compounded monthly, and he deposits \$150 each month. Pete's sister, Rose, opens a savings account with \$800 that pays 3 percent interest, compounded monthly, and she deposits \$120 each month. How long will it take for Pete's account balance to catch up to Rose's account balance?

16. Eddie opens a money market account with \$4500. The account pays 3 percent interest, compounded monthly. Each month, Eddie takes out \$248 for a car payment.
a. Write a recursive expression for a_n.
b. Write an explicit expression for a_n.
c. Calculate a_{12}.
d. Explain the meaning of a_{12} in this problem.
e. Eddie does not want the balance in his account to go below \$500. How many months can Eddie go before he needs to add money to his account?

17. A recursive expression is defined as $a_{n+1} = 1.07a_n$.
a. Find r, the common ratio.
b. If $a_5 = 3.93$, find a_1.
c. Write the explicit expression for a_n.

18. The picture below represents the first five triangular numbers.

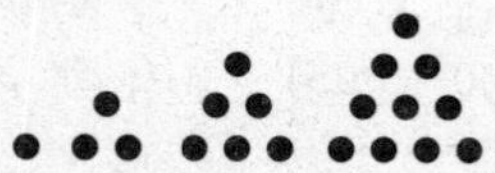

a. Use manipulatives to model and write the next three triangular numbers.
b. Write a recursive expression for a_n.
c. Is the sequence arithmetic, geometric, or neither?

19. The first four terms in a sequence are 200, 190, 180.5, and 171.475. Which of the following expressions defines this sequence?
A. $a_n = 210 - 10n$
B. $a_n = 200(0.95)^{n-1}$
C. $a_n = a_{n-1} - 10$
D. $a_n = 200a_{n-1}$

20. a. Define the set of odd natural numbers by means of an explicit formula.
b. Define the set of odd natural numbers by means of a recursive formula.
c. Define the set of even natural numbers by means of an explicit formula.
d. Define the set of even natural numbers by means of a recursive formula.
e. What is the difference between the recursive formulas for the odd and the even integers?

MATHEMATICAL PRACTICES
Look For and Make Use of Structure

21. A sequence a_n can often be written recursively or explicitly. Describe ways to identify, given the first several terms of a sequence, if a recursive or explicit formula can be determined.

A design was created for the Pacesetter Museum's advertising campaign. This design included a square divided into smaller regions. In each phase, the innermost quadrilateral is a square, and the triangles are isosceles right triangles. The design was created in phases, as shown.

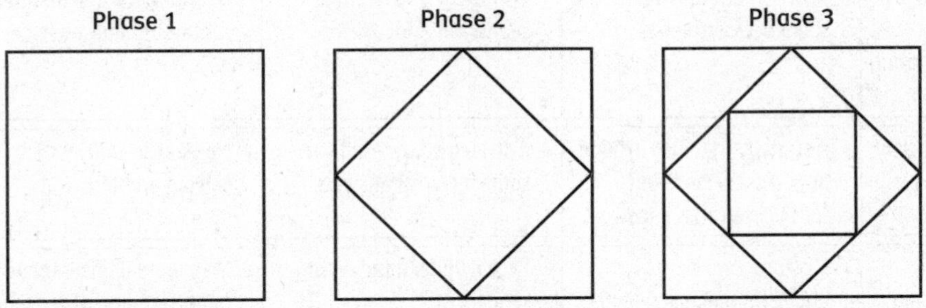

1. In each phase, the number of nonoverlapping squares and triangles is determined. The list of these numbers forms a sequence.
   - **a.** List the first five terms of this sequence.
   - **b.** Is this sequence arithmetic, geometric, or neither? Explain how you know.
   - **c.** Express the terms of this sequence two ways: recursively and explicitly.
   - **d.** Suppose this pattern were continued. How many nonoverlapping regions would occur in Phase 10?
   - **e.** Express the sum of the first 20 terms of this sequence using sigma notation, and calculate this sum.

2. In each phase, the length of the side of the smallest square drawn is determined. The list of these lengths forms a sequence. Let the length of the side of the square in Phase 1 be 20 cm. Use exact values in your responses. Add units to your answers.
   - **a.** List the lengths represented by the first five terms of this sequence.
   - **b.** Is this sequence arithmetic, geometric, or neither? Explain how you know.
   - **c.** Express the terms of this sequence two ways: recursively and explicitly.

3. In each phase, the area of the smallest square is calculated. The list of these areas is a sequence.
   - **a.** List the areas represented by the first five terms of this sequence, beginning with Phase 1.
   - **b.** Suppose this pattern were continued. Determine the area of the innermost square in Phase 10.
   - **c.** Express the sum of the first 10 terms of this sequence using sigma notation, and calculate this sum. What does this represent in terms of the situation?
   - **d.** Suppose this pattern were continued without end. Find the sum of this infinite series, if possible, and its meaning in terms of the situation.
   - **e.** Suppose the pattern developed in reverse, from a small square outward. Would the resulting infinite geometric series have a sum? Explain why or why not.

Scoring Guide	Exemplary	Proficient	Emerging	Incomplete
	The solution demonstrates these characteristics:			
Mathematics Knowledge and Thinking (Items 1, 2, 3)	• Clear and accurate understanding of arithmetic and geometric sequences and series, including writing series in sigma notation	• A functional understanding of arithmetic and geometric sequences and series	• Partial understanding of arithmetic and geometric sequences and series	• Little or no understanding of arithmetic and geometric sequences and series
Problem Solving (Items 1, 2, 3)	• An appropriate and efficient strategy that results in a correct answer	• A strategy that may include unnecessary steps but results in a correct answer	• A strategy that results in some incorrect answers	• No clear strategy when solving problems
Mathematical Modeling / Representations (Items 1c, 2c, 3d, 3e)	• Clear and accurate understanding of creating arithmetic and geometric sequences, including using sigma notation • Clear and accurate understanding of representations of geometric series, including infinite geometric series and when they converge	• Mostly accurate understanding of creating arithmetic and geometric sequences • A functional understanding of geometric series	• Partial understanding of sequences • Partial understanding of geometric series	• Inaccurate or incomplete understanding of sequences • Little or no understanding of geometric series
Reasoning and Communication (Items 1b, 1c, 2b, 2c, 3e)	• Precise use of appropriate math terms and language to evaluate sequences and series, including the representation of recursive sequences	• Correct characterization of sequences and series	• Misleading or confusing characterization of sequences and series	• Incomplete or inaccurate characterization of sequences and series

Exponential Functions

Pennsylvania Lottery

Lesson 4-1 Writing an Exponential Function

My Notes

Learning Targets:

- Write, graph, analyze, and model with exponential functions.
- Solve exponential equations.

SUGGESTED LEARNING STRATEGIES: Shared Reading, Summarizing, Paraphrasing, Create Representations, Look for a Pattern, Quickwrite, Note Taking

Suppose your neighbor, Margaret Anderson, has just won the state lottery, and her first payment will be $50,000. Margaret is interested in options that involve spending part of her winnings and saving the balance so that she can accumulate a nest egg at the end of the 20-year period. The tasks that follow will help you analyze Margaret's situation.

CONNECT TO HISTORY

Harry Casey was the first winner of the Pennsylvania lottery in 1972. He won $1 million, which was paid in 20 annual installments of $50,000. Harry retired immediately, spent $50,000 each year, received his last check in 1991, and was broke by the spring of 1992.

1. **Model with mathematics.** If Margaret saves only her first lottery payment of $50,000 and deposits it in a savings account paying 5% interest, compounded annually, determine how much money she will have in her account at the end of the each year given in the table below.

Year	Years Since 2004	Account Balance
2004	0	$50,000
2005	1	$52,500
2006	2	$55,125
2007		
2008		
2009		
2014		

2. What patterns do you notice in the table?

Exponential functions are multiplicative. That is, when a change in the input is constant, there is a constant multiplicative change in the output. The general form of an ***exponential function*** can be expressed as $f(x) = a(b)^x$, where a is a nonzero constant and b is a positive constant, $b \neq 1$.

3. Why is an exponential function appropriate for representing the data in the table?

4. What is the constant multiplier for the exponential function representing the data in the table? Explain how to find the constant multiplier for a set of data.

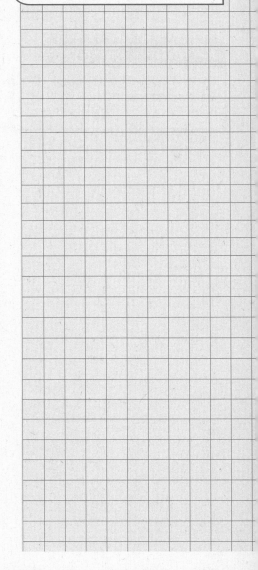

My Notes

5. Complete the table below.

Years Since 2004	Change in Account Value from Previous Year	Annual Growth Factor
1	$2500.00	1.05
2		
3		
4		
5		

6. As described in Item 1, the amount of money in Margaret's account, her account balance $A(t)$, is a function of the number of years t that have elapsed since 2004. Write an equation that defines $A(t)$.

MATH TIP

The end behavior of the graph of $A(t)$ continues to increase without bound. As $t \to \infty$, $A(t) \to \infty$.

7. Use appropriate tools strategically. Using a graphing calculator, graph $A(t)$ in an appropriate viewing window. Sketch the function on the grid below and estimate the following values.

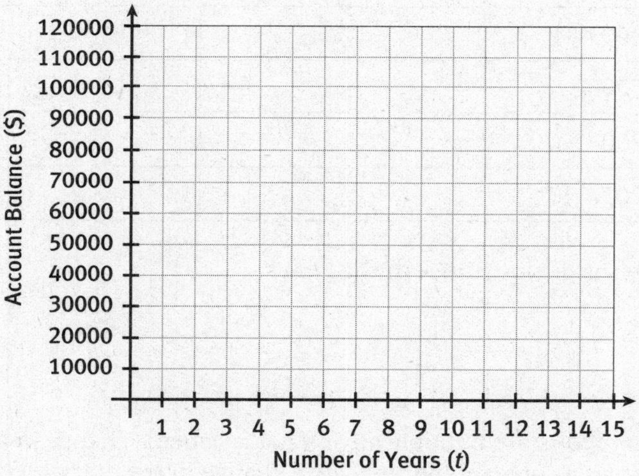

a. the money in Margaret's account after 10 years

b. the years needed to double her initial investment

c. Attend to precision. Use your equation from Item 6 to find precise answers for parts a and b.

The parameters of the function A represent particular features of the situation. The \$50,000 value represents the amount of money that was deposited to open Margaret's savings account. This value is known as the initial amount, or the ***principal***, P. For a 5% interest rate, the value $1 + 0.05$, or 1.05, represents the amount by which the current balance is multiplied to get the following year's balance. For any ***interest rate*** r, $1 + r$ is the annual ***growth factor***.

8. Using parameters P and r, define a general function $A(t)$, where t is the number of years since the principal was deposited in Margaret's savings account.

9. Write a function for Margaret's account balance at the same annual interest rate of 5%, but with a principal of \$30,000.

10. Margaret wants to compare how her investment grows over time when the principal changes.

a. Write the equation to find the time it will take to double the \$30,000 initial investment.

b. How long would it take for Margaret to double her investment if she deposited \$30,000 instead of \$50,000? Explain how you arrived at this conclusion.

c. From the results of Items 7c and 10b, and any other principal amounts you choose to investigate, what conclusion can you make regarding the doubling time for any principal amount P at an annual interest rate of 5%?

My Notes

MATH TERMS

In an exponential function, the constant multiplier, or scale factor, is known as an **exponential growth factor** when the constant is greater than 1. The constant multiplier is known as an **exponential decay factor** when the constant is between 0 and 1.

Check Your Understanding

11. Write a function for Margaret's account balance at the annual interest rate of 4% with a principal of \$50,000.

12. How long would it take to double Margaret's initial investment of \$50,000 if the annual interest rate were 4%?

13. Explain why $A(t) = P(1.05)^t$ forms a geometric sequence for $t = 1, 2, 3, \ldots$.

My Notes

Margaret will invest in an account that offers a 5% annual interest rate, compounded annually. However, she may not invest all of the $50,000.

14. Write functions $A(t)$, $B(t)$, and $C(t)$ for the amount of money Margaret would have in her account if she makes initial investments of $10,000, $25,000, and $50,000.

15. For each function, find the amount of money Margaret would have in her account after 10 years and after 20 years.

MATH TIP

Determine an appropriate viewing window on which to view the graphs. Use your input and output values from Item 16.

16. Use appropriate tools strategically. Use a graphing calculator. Graph each function for the first 20 years of the investment on one graph.

a. What is the relationship between the y-intercepts of the graphs and the investments?

b. Describe the end behavior of each graph as t increases.

Margaret makes another small investment with some of her money. The investment has an annual interest rate that is compounded annually. A graph of her account balance over time in years passes through the points (1, 3240) and (2, 3499.20).

17. Reason quantitatively. What interest rate does the account earn? How did you determine this?

18. What was Margaret's principal for the account? Explain your reasoning.

My Notes

19. Graph the functions $f(x) = a(b)^x$ and $g(x) = a(b)^{-x}$ on a graphing calculator. Choose various positive values for a and b, where $b \neq 1$. Then determine if the descriptions below are true for the functions by writing $f(x)$, $g(x)$, *both*, or *neither* next to each.
  a. increasing on the interval $(-\infty, \infty)$
  b. decreasing on the interval $(-\infty, \infty)$
  c. x-intercept: $(a, 0)$
  d. y-intercept: $(0, a)$
  e. horizontal asymptote: $y = 0$
  f. domain: all real numbers
  g. range: $y > 0$
  h. range: $y < 0$

20. Make use of structure. Consider the functions $f(x)$ and $g(x)$ from Item 19. How is the graph of $f(x)$ related to the graph of $g(x)$? Explain by writing an equation that defines $f(x)$ in terms of $g(x)$.

Check Your Understanding

21. Chad invests \$12,000 at a 5% annual interest rate, compounded annually. Write a function $A(t)$ that finds the amount Chad has in his account after t years. Explain what the y-intercept represents. Describe the end behavior of the graph of $A(t)$ as t increases.

22. Reason quantitatively. After t years, Chad has \$16,081.15. How many years did it take for the account to reach this balance? Explain how to find the number of years it took to reach the balance.

LESSON 4-1 PRACTICE

23. Michael opened a savings account at an annual interest rate of 5%. At the end of 3 years, the account balance is \$4630.50. If Michael did not add any other amounts to this account, how much was his initial deposit?

24. Find the annual interest rate when the amount of \$25,000 grows to \$26,625 in the first year and \$28,355.63 in the second year.

25. Write and solve an equation to determine the balance after 25 years in an account that had an initial investment of \$18,000 at 5% interest, compounded annually.

26. Any principal amount invested at 5% annual interest takes 15 years to double. How many years does it take for the principal amount to triple?

27. Express regularity in repeated reasoning. Repeat Item 19 assuming a negative value of a.

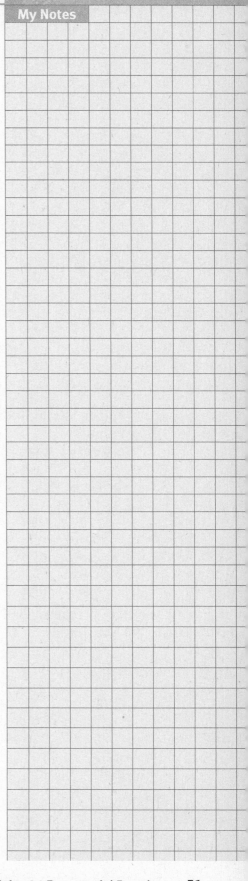

My Notes

Learning Targets:

- Write, graph, analyze, and model with exponential functions.
- Calculate compound interest.
- Solve exponential equations.

SUGGESTED LEARNING STRATEGIES: Think-Pair-Share, Create Representations, Quickwrite, Group Presentation, Debrief

1. **Model with mathematics.** Consider two investments made at the same time. In the first investment, \$50,000 is deposited in an account that offers an annual interest rate of 5% compounded annually. In the second investment, \$30,000 is deposited in an account that offers an annual interest rate of 8.5% compounded annually.
   a. Use a graphing calculator. Graph the balance in each account for the first 20 years of the investments. Write a function for each investment.

   b. Over the first 20 years, for which years is the amount of money greater in the account that began with an investment of \$50,000? For which years is the amount of money greater in the account that began with an investment of \$30,000?

2. Over a long period of time, which parameter, principal or interest, has a greater effect on the amount of money in an account that has interest compounded annually? Explain your reasoning.

Most savings institutions offer compounding intervals other than annual compounding. For example, a bank that offers *quarterly compounding* computes interest on an account every quarter, that is, every 3 months. Instead of computing the interest once each year, interest is computed four times each year. If a bank advertises that it is offering 8% annual interest, compounded quarterly, 8% is not the growth factor. Instead, the bank will use $\frac{8\%}{4} = 2\%$ to determine the quarterly growth factor. In this example, 8% is the *nominal interest rate*, and 2% is the *quarterly interest rate*.

3. What is the quarterly interest rate for an account with a nominal rate of 5%, compounded quarterly?

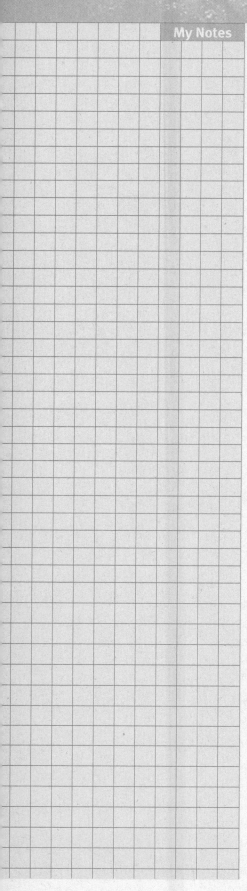

My Notes

4. Suppose that Margaret invested $50,000 at 5% interest, compounded quarterly.

a. In the table below, determine Margaret's account balance after the specified periods of time since her initial investment.

Time Since Initial Investment	Account Balance
3 months	
6 months	
9 months	
1 year	
4 years	
t years	

b. Write the amount A in the account as a function of t, the number of years since the investment was made.

5. How long will it take for Margaret's investment, as described in Item 4, to double?

6. Make sense of problems. How much less time is required for Margaret's initial amount of money to double at the rate of 5% compounded quarterly, than at the rate of 5% compounded annually?

7. For the compounding periods given below, determine the amount of money that Margaret would have in an account after 20 years if the principal is $50,000 and the nominal rate is 5%.

a. yearly
b. quarterly
c. monthly
d. daily (assume that there are 365 days in a year)

8. What is the effect of the compounding period on the amount of money after 20 years as the number of times the interest is compounded each year increases?

My Notes

9. **Attend to precision.** Consider an initial investment of $1 and an interest rate of 100%. Find the amount of money in this account after one year with the following number of compounding periods per year. Record your answers to four decimal places in the table.

Compounding Periods per Year	Account Balance
1	
10	
100	
1,000	
10,000	
100,000	
1,000,000	

10. As the number of times the account in Item 9 is compounded per year increases, what appears to be happening to the amount of money in the account after 1 year?

Check Your Understanding

11. A bank offers a certificate of deposit, or CD, with a monthly interest rate of 2.5%. What is the nominal interest rate for the CD?
12. Which yields more interest after 5 years: $4000 invested at an annual interest rate of 5% compounded monthly, or $4000 invested at an annual interest rate of 4% compounded daily?

LESSON 4-2 PRACTICE

13. Write and solve an equation to determine the balance after 10 years in an account that had an initial investment of $25,000 at 3.5% interest, compounded quarterly.
14. **Make sense of problems.** How much additional interest could $2500 earn in 10 years, compounded quarterly, if the annual interest rate were $3\frac{1}{4}\%$ as opposed to 3%?
15. How much money needs to be deposited into an account that earns 4% annual interest, compounded monthly, to have a balance of $5000 after 5 years?

My Notes

Learning Targets:

- Write, graph, analyze, and model with exponential functions.
- Calculate compound interest.
- Solve exponential equations.

SUGGESTED LEARNING STRATEGIES: Note Taking, Interactive Word Wall, Create Representations, RAFT

The exponential function $A(t) = Pe^{rt}$, where P is the principal, r is the interest rate, t is time, and e is a constant with a value of 2.718281828459…, is used to calculate a quantity (most frequently money) that is *compounded continuously* (that is, the number of compounding periods approaches infinity).

1. Find the amount of money in an account after 20 years if the principal is $50,000 and the nominal rate is 5% compounded continuously. Compare this answer to your answers in Item 7 of Lesson 4-2.

2. Margaret would like information on a few different investment options. She wants to invest either all or half the amount of her first $50,000 lottery check. Write a proposal to Margaret giving her advice on where to invest her money. Include an explanation of why you are making these recommendations. Include options for both a $50,000 and a $25,000 initial investment. Use the following account information to help make your recommendations.

Big Bucks Bank:	Annual rate of 4% on amounts greater than or equal to $30,000
	Annual rate of 3.7% on amounts less than $30,000
Serious Savings:	Nominal rate of 3.67% compounded weekly
Infinite Investments:	Nominal rate of 3.5% compounded continuously

CONNECT TO STATISTICS

In 1683, Jacob Bernoulli looked at the problem of continuously compounded interest and tried to find the limit of $\left(1+\frac{1}{n}\right)^n$ as $n \to \infty$. Bernoulli used the *Binomial Theorem* to show that this limit had to lie between 2 and 3. In 1731, Leonhard Euler first used the notation e to represent this limit; he gave an approximation of the irrational number e to 18 decimal places.

The number e is believed to be the first number to be defined using a limit and has since been calculated to thousands of decimal places. This number is very important in advanced mathematics and frequently appears in statistics, science, and business formulas.

My Notes

CONNECT TO FINANCE

Depreciation is the reduction in the value of an asset due to usage, passage of time, wear and tear, technological outdating or obsolescence, depletion, or other such factors.

3. Margaret plans to purchase a boat that will cost her \$10,000. The boat continuously ***depreciates*** at an annual rate of 17%.

a. Write an exponential function for the value. How much will the boat be worth in 15 years?

b. Model with mathematics. How long will it take for the boat to be worth half of its original value?

4. Use a graphing calculator to graph a function with 17% growth and a function with 17% depreciation. Compare and contrast the graph of the exponential growth function with that of the exponential decay function.

Check Your Understanding

5. Explain why investing \$1000 at 4% interest, compounded continuously, for 2 years is equivalent to investing \$1000 at 8% interest for 1 year.

6. Make use of structure. Recall that the constant multiplier of an exponential function is known as an *exponential decay factor* when the constant is between 0 and 1. Rewrite the function $f(x) = 100e^{-x}$ with a constant multiplier between 0 and 1.

7. Critique the reasoning of others. Edgar says that the function $f(x) = -50e^{-x}$ is a decreasing function because the negative sign on the exponent always represents exponential decay. Explain Edgar's mistake.

LESSON 4-3 PRACTICE

8. An account that was invested at 5% with continuous compounding for 10 years now contains \$5900. What was the initial investment?

9. A new car is purchased for \$25,000. It depreciates continuously at a rate of 12%. Write an exponential function that represents the value of the car after t years of ownership. When will the car have a value of \$0. Explain.

10. The ***half-life*** of the radioactive substance C-14 is about 5730 years. This means after every 5730 years, the amount present is half as much as before. Solve the equation $0.5 = e^{-5730r}$ to find the decay rate r. Round your answer to five decimal places.

MATH TERMS

The **half-life** of an exponentially decaying quantity is the time required for the quantity to be reduced by a factor of one-half.

ACTIVITY 4 PRACTICE

Write your answers on notebook paper.
Show your work.

Lesson 4-1

1. Write and solve an equation to determine the balance after 25 years in an account that had an initial investment of $18,000 at 3% interest, compounded annually.
2. Determine the balance after 10 years in an account that had an initial investment of $25,000 at 5% interest, compounded annually.
3. On a graphic calculator, enter $y_1 = 2000(1.04)^t$ and $y_2 = 1000(1.08)^t$. Open the table function. Record the value of each at $t = 1$. Which function has the greater value?
4. In Item 3, between which two values of t are the two functions approximately equal?
5. What will a $150,000 house be worth in 10 years if the inflation rate remains constant at 3%?
6. Katie has $15,000 to invest in an account earning 4.75% interest, compounded monthly. How much interest has Katie earned after 5 years?
7. If Katie withdraws $10,000 at the end of the second year, how much interest will she lose?
8. How much interest is earned on an investment of $5200 earning 7.5% interest, compounded annually, over a period of 3 years?
   A. $22.50
   B. $1259.94
   C. $2250
   D. $459.95
9. Find the annual interest rate when the amount of $15,000 grows to $15,525 in the first year and $16,068.38 in the second year.
10. Which piece of information is missing to determine the balance with $5000 at 5%?
    A. principal
    B. amount
    C. rate
    D. time
11. A company that makes mobile apps has profits of $7000 in its first year. The CEO says that this will triple each year over the next 5 years.
    a. Write an exponential function that represents this situation.
    b. In the fifth year after the CEO's statement, the company had a profit of 1.5 million dollars. Was the CEO's goal realized that year?

Lesson 4-2

12. Determine the interest earned after 5 years in an account that had an initial investment of $25,000 at 3.5% interest, compounded daily.
13. Determine the balance after 10 years in an account that had an initial investment of $25,000 at 3.5% interest, compounded quarterly.
14. Determine the amount of money that needs to be invested at 6% compounded monthly, to have $20,000 in 15 years.
15. Complete the table by finding each balance.

$10,000	5% annually	5% quarterly	5% monthly	5% weekly
in 5 years				
in 10 years				

16. Harry has $3100 to invest. In 2 years, he needs $3500. Which investment will allow Harry to meet his goal?
    A. 4% compounded weekly
    B. 5% compounded monthly
    C. 6% compounded quarterly
    D. 8% compounded annually

17. How much additional interest could \$15,000 earn in 20 years, compounded monthly, if the annual interest rate were $5\frac{1}{4}\%$ as opposed to 5%?

18. If a balance of \$20,000 grew to \$29,816.66 in 10 years, determine the rate of interest.
A. 4% compounded weekly
B. 5% compounded weekly
C. 4% compounded monthly
D. 5% compounded monthly

19. The graph shows the value of an account after *t* months.

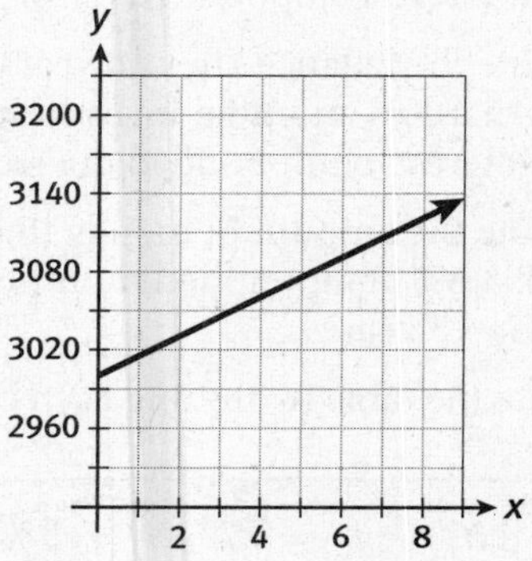

a. What is the initial deposit of the account?
b. What is the balance at 7 months?
c. Estimate the rate of interest.

Lesson 4-3

20. Determine the balance after 20 years in an account that had an initial investment of \$25,000 at 5% interest, compounded continuously.

21. Graph the ordered pairs (1, 2400), (2, 2308), and (3, 2219). Find the rate of change and the initial amount from the graph.

22. Find the interest rate when an investment of \$200, compounded continuously for 5 years, 3 months, is valued at \$253.30.

23. The population of deer on an island is growing exponentially. The first year the population was measured, there were 500 deer. Five years later, there were 552.
a. Write an exponential function that represents the number of deer on the island given the years since the initial population count.
b. How long will it take for the number of deer in Item 23a to double?

24. Write and solve an equation to determine the balance after 15 years in an account that had an initial investment of \$25,000 at 3.5% interest, compounded continuously.

25. The Tamerix tree was introduced to a region in 2006 and has been spreading exponentially. The initial population was 20 trees, and the population is increasing at an annual rate of 15%.
a. Create a continuous exponential function that represents the number of Tamerix trees in the region in a given year since the first population was measured.
b. In what year will the population reach 300?

26. A new car was purchased in 2005 for \$20,000. It depreciates at a rate of 9%.
a. Write a continuous exponential function that represents the value of the car after *t* years of ownership.
b. When will the car have a value of \$10,000?

27. Complete the table below for each interest rate for \$1000, compounded continuously.

	4%	5%	6%	8%
\$1000	1040.81	1051.27	1061.83	1083.29
2 yr	1083.29			
5 yr	1221.40			

MATHEMATICAL PRACTICES
Look For and Make Use of Structure

28. How do exponential functions relate to geometric sequences?

Logarithms

Power Trip

Lesson 5-1 Common and Natural Logarithms

My Notes

Learning Targets:

- Explore the inverse relationship between exponents and logarithms.
- Graph logarithmic functions and analyze key features of the graphs.

SUGGESTED LEARNING STRATEGIES: Look for a Pattern, Discussion Groups, Interactive Word Wall, Note Taking, Create Representations

As you work in groups, read the problem scenario carefully and explore together the information provided. Discuss your understanding of the problem and ask peers or your teacher to clarify any areas that are not clear.

The concentration of hydrogen ions (H^+) in a solution determines how acidic or basic the solution is. Pure water is neither acidic nor basic. A solution with a higher concentration of H^+ than pure water is acidic. A solution with a lower concentration of H^+ than pure water is basic.

For a strong acid, the concentration of H^+ may be 1 mole/liter. For a strong base, the concentration of H^+ may be 0.00000000000001 mole/liter. So the H^+ concentration of a strong acid may be 100,000,000,000,000 times greater than the H^+ concentration of a strong base.

To deal with such wide variations in concentration, scientists have developed a shorthand way of representing how acidic or basic a solution is. This method is based on *logarithms*. Logarithms can be used to simplify computations involving very large or very small numbers. You will begin to explore logarithms in this activity.

CONNECT TO CHEMISTRY

An *ion* is an atom or group of atoms with a net electric charge. A hydrogen ion is a hydrogen atom with a net charge of +1.

A *mole* is a quantity that is equal to about 6.022×10^{23} units of a substance. A mole of hydrogen ions is equal to about 6.022×10^{23} hydrogen ions.

1. What type of sequence is represented by each pattern shown below? Explain how you know.

A	0	1	2	3	4	5	6	7	8	9	. . .
B	1	10	100	1000	10,000	100,000	1,000,000	10,000,000	100,000,000	1,000,000,000	. . .
C	1	2	4	8	16	32	64	128	256	512	. . .

2. Use patterns A and B to answer the following.

a. Circle two columns in the table so that the sum in row A is 9 or less. Find the product of the two numbers you circled in pattern B and circle the column that contains that product.

b. Explain how the circled numbers in pattern A are related.

c. Explain how the answer to Part b is related to the product from pattern B.

d. If the numbers 2 and 9 are selected from pattern A, how can they be used to find the product of 100 and 1,000,000,000?

3. Use patterns A and C to answer the following.

a. Find the product of the two numbers you circled in pattern C and circle the column that contains that product.

b. Look at the circled numbers from pattern A. How are these numbers related to the circled numbers from pattern C and their product?

c. If the numbers 2 and 9 are selected from pattern A, how can they be used to find the product of 4 and 512?

The process you went through in Items 1–3 is the basis for the concept of logarithms. If b and x are positive real numbers with $b \neq 1$, then the ***logarithm*** of x ***base*** b is written as $\log_b x$ and is defined as:

$$\log_b x = y \text{ if and only if } b^y = x.$$

In Item 1, the numbers in pattern A are the logarithms to base 10 of the corresponding numbers in pattern B. The numbers in pattern A are also the logarithms to base 2 of the corresponding numbers in pattern C.

Although any number may be used as the base of a logarithm, the two most frequently used bases are the numbers 10 and e.

4. Use your graphing calculator to graph the functions $y = 10^x$ and $y = \log x$.

a. Sketch a graph of each function.

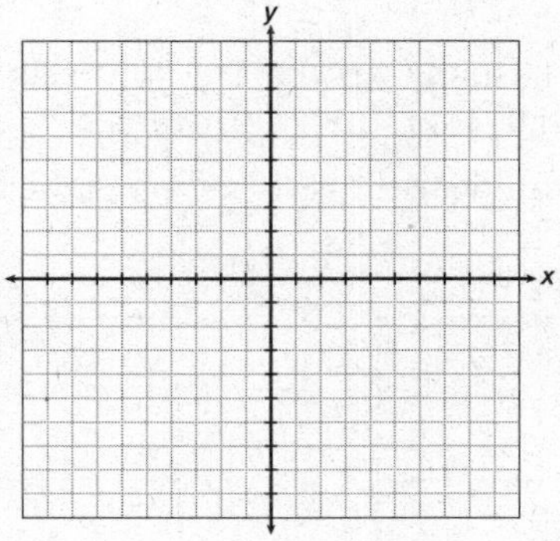

b. The functions $y = \log x$ and $y = 10^x$ are *inverses*. How does the graph support this statement?

c. The point (2, 100) lies on the graph of $y = 10^x$ because $10^2 = 100$. Explain how you can use this point and the properties of inverse functions to determine the value of log 100.

5. a. What are the domain and range of $y = \log x$?

b. What are the domain and range of $y = 10^x$?

c. What is the relationship between the domains and the ranges of the two functions?

My Notes

MATH TERMS

A **logarithm** is the power to which a **base** is raised: $\log_b x = y$ if and only if $b^y = x$, where $b > 0$, $b \neq 1$, and $x > 0$.

The logarithm to base 10 is called the **common logarithm**.
$\log_{10} x = y$ means $10^y = x$.
$\log_{10} x$ is usually written as just $\log x$.

CONNECT TO HISTORY

John Napier of Scotland (1550–1617) is credited with the invention of logarithms.

My Notes

MATH TERMS

Functions that either increase or decrease over their entire domain are called **strictly monotonic**.

MATH TERMS

The **natural logarithm** is the logarithm to base *e*.

6. Use the concept of exponents to explain why the function $y = \log_b x$ has a vertical asymptote at $x = 0$.

7. Is $y = \log x$ increasing or decreasing over its entire domain or is there a turning point?

8. a. What happens to the value of $y = \log x$ as x approaches infinity?

b. What happens to the value of $y = \log x$ as x approaches 0 for $x > 0$?

The function $y = \log_e x$, usually written as $y = \ln x$, is called the ***natural logarithm***. In exponential form, $\ln x = y$ means $e^y = x$.

9. Use the definition of logarithms to complete the following tables.

$y = \log x$

x	y
1	
10	
10^2	
10^5	

$y = \ln x$

x	y
1	
e	
e^2	
e^5	

10. Express regularity in repeated reasoning. Use the information you found in the table above to complete the properties of logarithms and rewrite each property in exponential form.

Properties of Logarithms	Exponential Form
$\log_b 1 =$	$b^0 =$
$\log_b b =$	$b^1 =$
$\log_b b^x =$	$b^x =$
$\ln 1 =$	$e^0 =$
$\ln e =$	$e^1 =$
$\ln e^x =$	$e^x =$

11. Use properties of logarithms to evaluate.

a. $\log_3 27$ **b.** $\log_4 2$ **c.** $\log_{10}\left(\frac{1}{100}\right)$

My Notes

12. The pH scale is a logarithmic scale from 0 to 14 used to determine how acidic a solution is. The pH of a solution is determined by using the formula $\text{pH} = -\log[\text{H}^+]$, where $[\text{H}^+]$ is the hydrogen ion concentration of the solution in moles/liter.

a. What is the pH of a solution with a hydrogen ion concentration of 0.001 mole/liter? Explain how you know. (Try graphing $y = -\log x$, and look for the value of y when $x = 0.001$.)

b. What is the hydrogen ion concentration of a solution with a pH of 7? Explain how you know.

c. The hydrogen ion concentration of a solution with a pH of 4 is how many times the hydrogen ion concentration of a solution with a pH of 5? Explain.

MATH TIP

$[\text{H}^+]$ can be written as bx where b and x are any real numbers. Graph the pH formula $y = -\log bx$ for different values of b. Notice the end behavior of the graph: as $x \to \infty, y \to \infty$ and as $x \to 0$, $y \to -\infty$.

MATH TIP

You can also graph $Y1 = -\log x$ and $Y2 = 7$, and determine where they intersect.

13. Let $f(x) = \ln x$ and $g(x) = e^x$.

a. Find $f(g(x))$ and $g(f(x))$.

b. What do your results from Part a indicate about the relationship between $f(x) = \ln x$ and $g(x) = e^x$?

MATH TIP

Recall that two functions are inverses when

$f(f^{-1}(x)) = f^{-1}(f(x)) = x$.

14. Verify that $f(x) = \frac{1}{2} + \ln x$ and $g(x) = e^{x-\frac{1}{2}}$ are inverses.

My Notes

15. Given the function $f(x) = \log x$, find the following.
a. Find x when $f(x) = 7$.
b. Find $f(x)$ for $x = 158$.

Check Your Understanding

Write each logarithmic equation as an exponential equation.

16. $\log 1000 = 3$

17. $\log_2 32 = 5$

18. Critique the reasoning of others. A student claims that the expression $\log_3 9$ represents the exponent to which the base 9 must be raised to equal 3. Is the student's claim correct? Explain.

19. An exponential function of the form $y = b^x$, where $b > 0$ and $b \neq 1$, has a y-intercept of 1. Based on this information, what can you conclude about the x-intercept of a logarithmic function of the form $y = \log_b x$? Justify your conclusion.

20. Explain how you could use the graph of $y = 4^x$ to graph the function $y = \log_4 x$.

21. Explain how scientists use logarithms to make it easier to describe and compare the acidity of solutions.

LESSON 5-1 PRACTICE

Evaluate each logarithm.

22. $\log_3\left(\frac{1}{9}\right)$

23. $\log_4 64$

24. a. Complete the table for the function $y = \log_2 x$, a real-world model.

x	$\frac{1}{8}$	$\frac{1}{4}$	$\frac{1}{2}$	1	2	4	8
y							

b. Graph the function.

c. Describe key features of the function, including the domain, range, x-intercept, asymptote, and end behavior.

25. If a solution has a pH less than 7, then the solution is acidic. If the pH is greater than 7, then the solution is basic. Honey has a hydrogen ion concentration of 0.0001 mole/liter. Is honey acidic or basic? Use a logarithmic function and its graph to support your answer.

26. Construct viable arguments. Explain how you could use multiple representations to convince someone that $y = e^x$ and $y = \ln x$ are inverse functions.

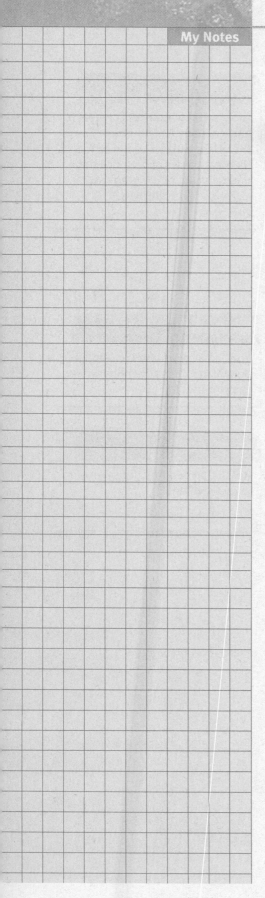

My Notes

Learning Targets:

- Apply the Change of Base Formula.
- Use properties of logarithms to evaluate and transform expressions.

SUGGESTED LEARNING STRATEGIES: Note Taking, Look for a Pattern, Think-Pair-Share, Think Aloud, Construct an Argument

Common logarithm and natural logarithm functions are typically built into calculator systems. However, it is possible to use a calculator to evaluate logarithms in other bases by using the Change of Base Formula.

Change of Base Formula
Let a, b, and x be positive real numbers such that $a \neq 1$ and $b \neq 1$. Then $\log_b x = \dfrac{\log_a x}{\log_a b}$.

Example A

Use a calculator and the Change of Base Formula to find an approximation of $\log_5 28$.

$$\log_5 28 = \frac{\log 28}{\log 5} \approx 2.070$$

Try These A

Use the Change of Base Formula to rewrite. For Items a and b, use a calculator to find an approximation.

a. $\log_5 8$ with a base of 10

b. $\log_2 12$ with a base of e

c. $\log_b x$ with a base of 10

d. $\log_b x$ with a base of e

CONNECT TO BIOLOGY

The doubling time of a population is the length of time it takes a population to double. The smaller the doubling time, the faster the population is growing.

1. Reason quantitatively. A biologist is studying a colony of bacteria with a doubling time of 1 hour. The colony initially contains 20 bacteria.

a. Write the equation of an exponential function $n(t)$ that can be used to determine the number of bacteria n in the colony after t hours.

b. Use your function to write an equation that can be used to determine how many hours must pass before the population of the colony is 10,000 bacteria.

My Notes

c. Rewrite your equation from Part b so that 2^t is isolated on one side.

d. Write your equation from Part c as an equivalent logarithmic equation.

e. Use the Change of Base Formula to solve the equation from Part d for *t*. Interpret the solution in the context of the problem.

CONNECT TO AP

You can prove the Change of Base Formula $b^{\log_b x} = x$ because exponents and logarithms are inverses. Take the log base *a* of both sides: $\log_a b^{\log_b x} = \log_a x$. By the Power Property of Logarithms, $(\log_b x)\log_a b = \log_a x$. Dividing both sides by $\log_a b$ gives $\log_b x = \dfrac{\log_a x}{\log_a b}$.

Each property of exponents has a corresponding property for logarithms.

Properties	Properties of Exponents	Properties of Logarithms
Product of a Power	$b^m b^n = b^{m+n}$	$\log_b (mn) = \log_b m + \log_b n$
Quotient of Power	$\dfrac{b^m}{b^n} = b^{m-n}$	$\log_b \left(\dfrac{m}{n}\right) = \log_b m - \log_b n$
Power of a Power	$(b^m)^n = b^{mn}$	$\log_b m^n = n \log_b m$
One to One	if $b^m = b^n$, then $m = n$	if $\log_b m = \log_b n$, then $m = n$

2. Use your graphing calculator to graph $y = \log 3x$ and $y = \log 3 + \log x$. How do the graphs compare?

3. Write each property for the natural logarithm that corresponds to the property for common logarithms in the table below.

Properties of Logarithms	Properties of Natural Logarithms
$\log_b (mn) = \log_b m + \log_b n$	
$\log_b \left(\dfrac{m}{n}\right) = \log_b m - \log_b n$	
$\log_b m^n = n \log_b m$	
if $\log_b m = \log_b n$, then $m = n$	

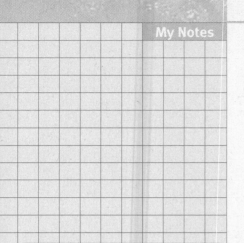

My Notes

Example B

Use the properties of logarithms to expand $\ln\left(\frac{3xy}{z}\right)$.

$$\ln\left(\frac{3xy}{z}\right) = \ln 3xy - \ln z$$
$$= \ln 3 + \ln x + \ln y - \ln z$$

Try These B

Use the properties of logarithms to expand each expression.

a. $\log(5xy^3)$

b. $\ln\left(\frac{xy}{z^4}\right)$

c. $\ln\left(\frac{x}{\sqrt{x^2+1}}\right)$

d. $\log_2 \sqrt{2x(x^2+2)}$

MATH TIP

Logarithms of sums and differences, $\log_a(m \pm n)$, *cannot* be rewritten using general properties of logarithms.

Example C

Use the properties of logarithms to write $\frac{1}{2}(3\log x + \log(x+1) - \log x)$ as a single logarithm.

$\frac{1}{2}(3\log x + \log(x+1) - \log x)$	
$\frac{1}{2}(\log x^3 + \log(x+1) - \log x)$	Power Property of Logarithms
$\frac{1}{2}\left(\log\left(\frac{x^3(x+1)}{x}\right)\right)$	Product and Quotient Properties
$\frac{1}{2}\log(x^3 + x^2)$	Divide.
$\log(x^3 + x^2)^{\frac{1}{2}}$	Power Property of Logarithms
$\log\sqrt{x^3 + x^2}$	Write as a radical expression.

Try These C

Write each expression as a single logarithm.

a. $3\ln(x-1) - \ln x$

b. $\log x - 4[\log(x-2) + \log(x+2)]$

c. $\frac{1}{2}[\ln(x+2) - \ln(x^2-4)]$

d. **Make use of structure.** Explain why you cannot write the expression $\log_2(x+5) + \log_5(x+2)$ as a single logarithm.

My Notes

Check Your Understanding

Use properties of logarithms to find the value of each expression without using a calculator. List a property or give an explanation for each step in your work.

4. $\log_3\left(\frac{1}{9}\right)^4$

5. $\log 25 + 2\log 2$

6. Explain how you could use the Change of Base Formula to help you graph the function $y = \log_4 x + 3$ on a graphing calculator.

7. Use properties of logarithms to explain why the functions $f(x) = \log(2x^2)$ and $g(x) = 2\log x + \log 2$ have the same graph.

8. A student expanded the expression $\log(3x^2)$ as follows. Identify the error that the student made. Fix the error and expand the expression correctly.

$\log(3x^2) = 2\log(3x)$	Power Property of Logarithms
$= 2(\log 3 + \log x)$	Product Property of Logarithms
$= 2\log 3 + 2\log x$	Distributive Property

LESSON 5-2 PRACTICE

Use a calculator and the Change of Base Formula to find an approximation.

9. $\log_7 4$

10. $\log_3 30$

Use the properties of logarithms to expand each expression.

11. $\ln xyz$

12. $\ln\sqrt{x-1}$

Write each expression as a single logarithm.

13. $\ln x - 3\ln(x+1)$

14. $2\log 6 + \log x$

15. Present a numerical example that illustrates the Quotient Property of Logarithms.

16. **Make sense of problems.** The number of visitors to a website is tripling each month. This month, the website had 1500 visitors. Explain how you can use a logarithm and the Change of Base Formula to predict how many months it will take for the number of visitors to the website to reach 300,000.

My Notes

Learning Targets:

- Solve exponential equations by taking the logarithm of both sides.
- Use properties of exponents and logarithms to solve logarithmic equations.

SUGGESTED LEARNING STRATEGIES: Close Reading, Levels of Questions, Note Taking, Think-Pair-Share, Identify a Subtask

In a previous activity, you solved exponential equations with the aid of a graphing calculator. You can use the properties of logarithms and exponents to solve these same equations algebraically.

Example A

Jose invested \$100,000 in a retirement account that averages 6.5% interest compounded continuously. How long will it take for him to double his money?

$200{,}000 = 100{,}000e^{0.065t}$

$2 = e^{0.065t}$	Divide both sides by 100,000.
$\ln 2 = \ln e^{0.065t}$	Take the ln of both sides.
$\ln 2 = 0.065t \ln e$	Power Property of Logarithms
$\ln 2 = 0.065t$	Inverse Property of Exponents and Logarithms: $\ln e = 1$
$\frac{\ln 2}{0.065} = t$	Solve for t.
$t \approx 10.664$	

Jose will double his money in about 10.664 years.

Try These A

Use the information from the example to determine how long it will it take for Jose to have the following amounts of money in his account.

a. \$120,000 **b.** \$250,000 **c.** \$1,000,000

My Notes

Example B

Solve $4(2^{2x-1}) + 5 = 29$.

$4(2^{2x-1}) + 5 = 29$	
$4(2^{2x-1}) = 24$	Isolate the exponential term.
$2^{2x-1} = 6$	
$\log_2 2^{2x-1} = \log_2 6$	Take the logarithm of both sides.
$(2x-1)\log_2 2 = \log_2 6$	Power Property of Logarithms
$2x - 1 = \log_2 6$	Inverse Property of Exponents and Logarithms: $\log_2 2 = \log_2 2^1 = 1$
$x = \dfrac{\log_2 6 + 1}{2}$	Solve for x.
$x = \dfrac{\frac{\ln 6}{\ln 2} + 1}{2}$	Change the base to 10 or e.
$x \approx 1.792$	

Try These B

Solve.

a. $10^{x-1} = 270$ **b.** $5e^{x+1} - 3 = 12$ **c.** $3(4^{2x}) = 7$

d. Make use of structure. $e^{2x} - 4e^{x} - 5 = 0$ (*Hint:* Factor.)

TECHNOLOGY TIP

Logarithms on the graphing calculator may appear with an opening parenthesis.

log(

ln(

To assure correct order of operations, close the parentheses when performing additional operations, for example: ln(6)/ln(2).

Example C

Solve $3 \log_2 3x = 9$.

$3 \log_2 3x = 9$	
$\log_2 3x = 3$	Isolate the logarithm.
$2^{\log_2 3x} = 2^3$	Take the base 2 to both sides.
$3x = 8$	Inverse Property of Exponents and Logarithms: $2^{\log_2 3x} = 3x$
$x = \dfrac{8}{3}$	

Try These C

Simplify and solve.

a. $2 \ln 3x = 12$ **b.** $\log x^2 = 10$

c. $3 \log (x - 4) = 13$ **d.** $\ln \sqrt{x+2} = 7$

My Notes

1. Sound pressure level L in decibels is given by $L = 20 \log \frac{p}{p_0}$, where p is the sound pressure and p_0 is a reference pressure. The sound pressure level of a jet engine is 145 decibels, when p_0 is the sound pressure at the threshold of hearing, 2×10^{-5} pascal.

a. Write and solve an equation to find the sound pressure p of the jet engine to the nearest pascal.

b. How many times the sound pressure at the threshold of hearing is the sound pressure of the jet engine?

CONNECT TO PHYSICS

A pascal is a unit of pressure equal to a force of 1 newton per square meter.

The properties of logarithms can also be used to solve equations. You must check to see that solutions are not *extraneous*, however.

MATH TIP

An extraneous solution is a root of a transformed equation that is *not* a root of the original equation because it was not in the domain of the original equation.

Example D

Solve $\ln(2x - 3) + \ln(x + 2) = 2 \ln x$ for x.

$\ln(2x - 3) + \ln(x + 2) = 2 \ln x$

$\ln((2x - 3)(x + 2)) = \ln x^2$ — Use properties of logarithms to simplify.

$\ln(2x^2 + x - 6) = \ln x^2$ — Multiply.

$2x^2 + x - 6 = x^2$ — One to One Property

$x^2 + x - 6 = 0$

$(x + 3)(x - 2) = 0$ — $x = -3$ and $x = 2$

Substitute the values in the original equation to see if they are solutions.

For $x = -3$, $\ln(2(-3) - 3)) + \ln((-3) + 2)) = 2 \ln(-3)$.

Note that $2 \ln(-3)$ is undefined. Because negative numbers are not in the domain of the natural log function, -3 is *not* a solution.

Check $x = 2$ in the same way to verify that is the only solution.

Try These D

Solve each equation for x. Check your solutions in the original equation.

a. $\log_2 x - \log_2 (x - 1) = 1$

b. $\ln x + \ln(x^2 - 8) = \ln 8x$

c. $\log(x + 5) = \log(x - 1) - \log(x + 1)$

My Notes

Check Your Understanding

2. You can solve the equation $3^{x+2} = 50$ by taking the logarithm of both sides. Does it matter which base you use for the logarithms?

3. Explain how the Inverse Property of Exponents and Logarithms can help you solve the equation $\log_4 (x - 3) = 2$.

4. Explain why the equation $\log (x + 3) + \log (x - 3) = \log (9 - 3x)$ has no solution.

5. **Attend to precision.** Write a set of step-by-step instructions for a student who is absent from class explaining how to solve the equation $\ln x - \ln 2 = \ln (x - 6)$.

LESSON 5-3 PRACTICE

Solve.

6. $8^{-x-2} = 237$

7. $e^{2x} - 5e^x + 6 = 0$

8. $4 \ln 3x = 16$

9. $\log (x - 2) = 4$

10. $\ln (x + 2) - \ln x = \ln (x + 5)$

11. **Reason quantitatively.** A biologist is studying a colony of bacteria with a doubling time of 20 minutes. The colony initially contains 16 bacteria.

a. Write an equation that can be used to determine t, the number of hours it will take for the population of the bacteria colony to reach 10,000.

b. Solve the equation and interpret the solution.

c. Explain how you know that your answer to part b is reasonable.

12. Laura invested \$3000 in an account that earns continuously compounded interest. After three years, she had \$3332.13 in the account. Write and solve an equation to find the annual interest rate to the nearest tenth of a percent.

ACTIVITY 5 PRACTICE

Write your answers on notebook paper.
Show your work.

Lesson 5-1

Write each logarithmic equation as an exponential equation.

1. $\log 0.01 = -2$
2. $\log_2 8 = 3$
3. $\log_4 x = 0$

Write each exponential equation as a logarithmic equation.

4. $10^5 = 100{,}000$
5. $2^{-1} = \frac{1}{2}$
6. $4^x = 64$

Use the logarithmic function $f(x) = -\log_3 x$ for Items 7–13.

7. Make a table of values for the function, using the x-values $\frac{1}{9}$, $\frac{1}{3}$, 1, 3, 9, and 27.
8. Graph the function on a coordinate plane.
9. What are the domain and range of the function?
10. What are the intercepts of the function, if any?
11. Identify the asymptote of the function.
12. a. What happens to the value of $f(x)$ as x approaches infinity?
    b. What happens to the value of $f(x)$ as x approaches 0 for $x > 0$?
13. a. Let g be the inverse function of f. What is the equation of g?
    b. Show both graphically and algebraically that f and g are inverse functions.
14. Explain why $\ln 1 = 0$.

Evaluate each expression without using a calculator.

15. $\log_3 81$
16. $\log 0.001$
17. $\log_{16}\left(\frac{1}{4}\right)$
18. $\log_5 125$
19. Sound pressure level L in decibels is given by $L = 20 \log \frac{p}{p_0}$, where p is the sound pressure and p_0 is a reference pressure. The sound pressure of a vacuum cleaner is 10,000 times the reference pressure. Write and solve an equation to find the sound pressure level of the vacuum cleaner in decibels. Alternatively, graph the function L.

Lesson 5-2

Use a calculator and the Change of Base Formula to find an approximation to the nearest thousandth.

20. $\log_2 24$
21. $\log_5 36$
22. $\log_3 400$
23. $\log_8 0.03$
24. Which of the following can be used to find $\log_3 8$?
    A. $\frac{\ln 8}{\ln 3}$
    B. $\frac{\log_8 3}{\log 8}$
    C. $\frac{\ln 3}{\ln 8}$
    D. $\frac{\ln 3}{8}$

Use the properties of logarithms to expand each expression.

25. $\log (3x^2)$
26. $\log \frac{4x}{y^2}$
27. $\ln \frac{x}{yz}$
28. $\ln \sqrt{\frac{x^2}{y^2}}$
29. Explain how to graph the function $y = 3 \log_3 (x + 2)$ on a graphing calculator.

Write each expression as a single logarithm.

30. $2 \log x + \log (x + 3)$

31. $2[\log (x - 8) - \log 8]$

32. $\ln (x - 2) - \ln (x + 2) + \ln x$

33. Which expression is equivalent to $\ln (3x^2)$?
A. $(\ln 3)(\ln x^2)$
B. $2 \ln x + \ln 3$
C. $3(\ln x + \ln x)$
D. $2(\ln 3 + \ln x)$

34. The population of a city is growing at a rate of 3 percent per year. The city's current population is 520,000.
a. Write an exponential equation that can be used to determine how many years it will take before the city's population reaches 1,000,000.
b. Write the equation as an equivalent logarithmic equation.
c. Use the Change of Base Formula to solve the equation. Interpret the solution in the context of the problem.

Lesson 5-3

Solve.

35. $200 + 10^{x+3} = 1600$

36. $30(3^{-2x}) = 20$

37. $100e^{-2x} = 25$

38. $\dfrac{500}{1+e^{-x}} = 275$

39. $\log x^2 = 6$

40. $5 \ln 2x = 25$

41. $18 - \log_2 (x - 4) = 7$

42. $6 \ln (x + 8) = 24$

Solve. Check your solutions.

43. $\log x + \log (x + 3) = 1$

44. $\ln (x + 2) + \ln (x - 8) = \ln (-5x - 4)$

45. $\log (x^2 - 2x) - \log (-x) = 2 \log x$

46. The equation $T = T_a + (T_0 - T_a)e^{-kt}$ can be used to determine the temperature T of an object after t minutes, where T_0 is the initial temperature of the object, T_a is the ambient or room temperature, and k is a constant. How many minutes will it take a cup of hot tea with an initial temperature of 212°F to cool to 150°F? The room temperature is 72°F, and the value of the constant k is 0.0576 per minute.

47. The pH of a solution is given by $\text{pH} = -\log[H^+]$, where $[H^+]$ is the hydrogen ion concentration of the solution in moles/liter. A chemist mixes a solution that has a pH of 5.5. Next, the chemist mixes a solution with a hydrogen ion concentration that is twice that of the first solution. What is the pH of the second solution?

48. The half-life of a medication is the amount of time it takes for half of the original amount to be eliminated from the patient's bloodstream. A patient is given a dose of 400 mg of a medication. After four hours, the patient's blood is tested, showing that about 85 mg of the medication remains in the patient's bloodstream. Write and solve an equation to find the half-life of the medication to the nearest minute.

MATHEMATICAL PRACTICES
Look For and Make Use of Structure

49. Find the value of each expression without using a calculator. List a property or give an explanation for each step in your work.
a. $2 \log 2 - \log 40$
b. $2(\log_6 2 + \log_6 3)$
c. $3 \log_3 2 - \log_3 8$
d. $\log_2 36 - \log_2 9$

POPULATION EXPLOSION

According to 2010 census data, Houston, Texas, is the fourth-largest city in the United States. In 2011, its population was 2,145,000, an increase of 2.2% compared to the previous year.

1. Assuming that Houston's population continues to grow at a rate of 2.2% per year, write the equation of a function $f(x)$ that can be used to model Houston's population in millions, where x is the number of years since 2011.

2. Graph the function on the coordinate grid.

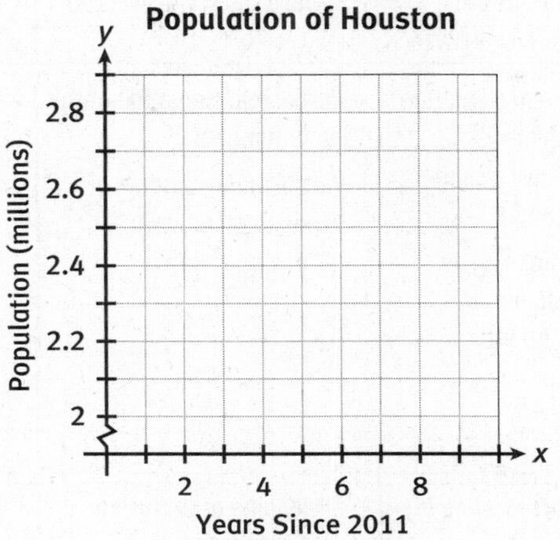

3. What is the y-intercept of the function? What does the y-intercept represent in this situation?

4. Based on the model, what will the population of Houston be in 2023? Explain how you determined your answer.

5. a. Write an equation that can be used to predict when the population of Houston will reach 3 million.

b. Solve your equation. For each step, list a property or give an explanation. Then interpret the solution.

c. Describe how the inverse relationship between exponents and logarithms helped you solve the equation.

6. According to the 2010 census, Chicago is the third-largest city in the United States. In 2011, its population was 2,707,000, an increase of 0.4% compared to the previous year.

a. Assuming that the populations of Chicago and Houston are growing exponentially, write an equation that can be used to predict when the population of Houston will equal that of Chicago.

b. Solve your equation. For each step, list a property or give an explanation. Then interpret the solution.

7. The function $g(x) = 112 \ln (0.121x) + 2011$ models the year in which the population of New York City will equal x million people. Write and solve an equation to estimate the population of New York City in 2020. For each step, list a property or give an explanation.

Scoring Guide	Exemplary	Proficient	Emerging	Incomplete
	The solution demonstrates these characteristics:			
Mathematics Knowledge and Thinking (Items 1, 6)	• Clear and accurate understanding of exponential growth (annual rate model)	• A functional understanding of exponential growth (possible use of alternate exponential model)	• Partial understanding of exponential growth model	• Little or no understanding of exponential growth
Problem Solving (Items 1, 2, 4, 5, 6)	• An appropriate and efficient strategy that results in a correct answer	• A strategy that may include unnecessary steps but results in a correct answer	• A strategy that results in some incorrect answers	• No clear strategy when solving problems
Mathematical Modeling / Representations (Items 1, 2, 3, 6)	• Clear and accurate representation of the exponential model graphically (nearly linear looking, yet exponential, with an initial slope of $0.0467 \approx 0.05$) • Clear and accurate understanding of exponential growth	• A functional representation of the growth model (maybe with just a single other point used.) • Mostly accurate understanding of exponential growth	• Partial representation of the growth model • Partial understanding of exponential growth	• Little or no understanding of the growth model • Inaccurate or incomplete understanding of exponential growth
Reasoning and Communication (Items 4, 5, 6, 7)	• Precise use of appropriate math terms and language to solve exponential equations logarithmically	• Correct characterization of solving exponential equations	• Misleading or confusing characterization of solving exponential equations	• Incomplete or inaccurate characterization of solving exponential equations

Transformations of Functions

I Doubt It

Lesson 6-1 Transforming Functions

My Notes

Learning Targets:

- Graph transformations of functions and write the equations of the transformed functions.
- Describe the symmetry of the graphs of even and odd functions.

SUGGESTED LEARNING STRATEGIES: Close Reading, Create Representations, Look for a Pattern, Group Presentation, Self Revision/ Peer Revision

Functions can be organized into families, with the most basic function of each family known as the ***parent function***.

MATH TERMS

A **parent function** is the most basic function of a particular type.

1. Sketch a graph of each parent function and label some key points.

a. Absolute value $f(x) = |x|$ **b.** Quadratic $f(x) = x^2$
c. Cubic $f(x) = x^3$ **d.** Quartic $f(x) = x^4$
e. Natural logarithm $f(x) = \ln x$ **f.** Linear $f(x) = x$
g. Exponential $f(x) = e^x$ **h.** Rational $f(x) = \frac{1}{x}$
i. Square root $f(x) = \sqrt{x}$

Recall that transformations of functions can be horizontal or vertical translations, horizontal or vertical stretches or compressions, reflections, or a combination of transformations.

2. Express regularity in repeated reasoning. Match each function with the corresponding transformation.

a. $y = a(f(x))$, $|a| > 1$ ______ **A** Horizontal compression

b. $y = a(f(x))$, $|a| < 1$ ______ **B** Reflection over the x-axis

c. $y = f(bx)$, $|b| > 1$ ______ **C** Vertical translation

d. $y = f(bx)$, $|b| < 1$ ______ **D** Vertical stretch

e. $y = f(x - c)$ ______ **E** Vertical compression

f. $y = f(x) + d$ ______ **F** Horizontal stretch

g. $y = -f(x)$ ______ **G** Reflection over the y-axis

h. $y = f(-x)$ ______ **H** Horizontal translation

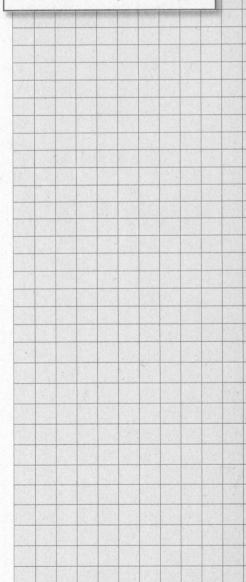

My Notes

I Doubt It!

Shuffle the 16 Category cards and place them in the center.

Vertical translation

Shuffle the 90 Transformation cards and deal them to the players until no cards remain.

$f(x) = |2x| - 1$

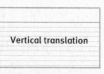

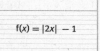

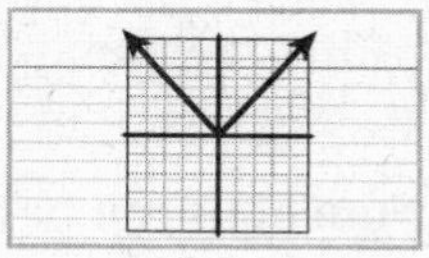

Some players may have more cards than others. The object of the game is to be the first player to discard all of the cards in your hand.

The youngest player goes first, and play proceeds clockwise.

The discard pile will be in the center and starts empty. To begin a turn, the player flips over a Category card. Then, one at a time, each player must discard one or more Transformation cards facedown on the discard pile, calling out the number of cards they discard. Because the transformation cards are discarded facedown, players may discard ones that match the Category card or ones that do not match.

After any person discards Transformation cards, any player who suspects that the card(s) played do not match the current Category card may challenge the play by calling "I doubt it!" The cards played by the challenged player during that turn are flipped over, and one of two things happens.

1. If *all* of the challenged player's discards match the current Category card, the challenger must pick up the entire discard pile, including cards previously played by others.
2. If *any* of the challenged player's discards differ from the current Category card, the person who played the cards must pick up the entire discard pile, including cards previously played by others.

After the challenge is resolved, or if there is no challenge, play continues clockwise. A new Category card is turned over by the next player, and play continues.

The first player to get rid of all of his or her cards and survive any final challenge wins the game. Play "I Doubt It!"

My Notes

When you played "I Doubt It," you examined transformations graphically and algebraically. You can also look at functions numerically to see the effects of transformations.

3. Create a table of values for each transformation of $f(x)$.

x	$f(x)$
−8	512
−6	216
−4	64
−2	8
1	1
3	27
5	125
7	343

a.

x	$f(x) + 3$
−8	
−6	
−4	
−2	
1	
3	
5	
7	

b.

x	$3f(x)$

4. Create a table of values for each transformation of $g(x)$.

x	$g(x)$
−7	−100
−5	−76
−3	−52
−2	−40
3	−20
4	−32
6	−56
9	−92

a.

x	$g(2x)$

b.

x	$g(x + 2)$

5. Create a table of values for each transformation of $h(x)$.

x	$h(x)$
−4	−4
−2	−7
0	−8
2	−7
6	1
8	8
12	−3
16	56

a.

x	$-h(x)$

b.

x	$h(-x)$

6. How does the transformation $h(-x)$ differ from $-h(x)$?

My Notes

You can use what you know about transformations to help you write the equations of functions and to graph the equations.

Example A

A card game can have between two and six players. The number of cards a player receives at the beginning of the game is given by the function $g(x)$, where x is the number of players. The graph of $g(x)$ is a vertical stretch of the graph of $f(x)=\frac{1}{x}$ by a factor of 60. Write the equation of $g(x)$, and then graph $g(x)$.

$g(x) = 60\,f(x)$ — $g(x)$ is a vertical stretch of $f(x)$ by a factor of 60.

$g(x) = 60\left(\frac{1}{x}\right)$ — Substitute $\frac{1}{x}$ for $f(x)$.

$g(x) = \frac{60}{x}$ — Simplify.

To graph $g(x)$, start by making a table of values. Use values of $f(x)$ to find values of $g(x)$.

x	$f(x)$	$g(x) = 60f(x)$
2	$\frac{1}{2}$	30
3	$\frac{1}{3}$	20
4	$\frac{1}{4}$	15
5	$\frac{1}{5}$	12
6	$\frac{1}{6}$	10

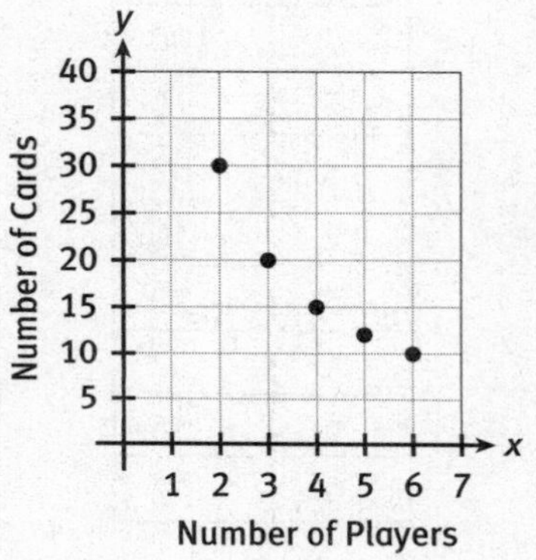

MATH TIP

Because the number of players x must be between 2 and 6, the domain of $g(x)$ is set of whole numbers 2, 3, 4, 5, and 6.

Try These A

Use the given information to write the equation of $g(x)$, and then graph $g(x)$.

a. The graph of $g(x)$ is a translation 4 units to the left and 3 units up of the graph of $f(x) = x^3$.

b. The graph of $g(x)$ is a reflection of the graph of $f(x) = \log_2 x$ over the y-axis.

c. A strategy game is played on a square grid. The function $g(x)$ gives the average length of the game in minutes when the side length of the grid is x squares, where $x \geq 2$. The graph of $g(x)$ is a horizontal stretch of the graph of $f(x) = e^x$ by a factor of 2.

My Notes

A function whose graph is symmetric with respect to the y-axis is called an ***even function***. A function whose graph is symmetric with respect to the origin is called an ***odd function***.

MATH TERMS

A function f is **even** if and only if for each x in the domain of f, $f(-x) = f(x)$.

A function f is **odd** if and only if for each x in the domain of f, $f(-x) = -f(x)$.

7. Model with mathematics. Sketch each function shown below to help classify it as even, odd, or neither. Then describe the symmetry of the graph, if any. Use the definitions of even and odd functions to verify your answer algebraically.

a. $f(x) = x^3 + 1$

b. $f(x) = x^2 - 3$

c. $f(x) = x^5 + x$

d. $f(x) = |x|$

e. $f(x) = x^2 - 2x - 8$

f. $f(x) = -\dfrac{1}{x^2}$

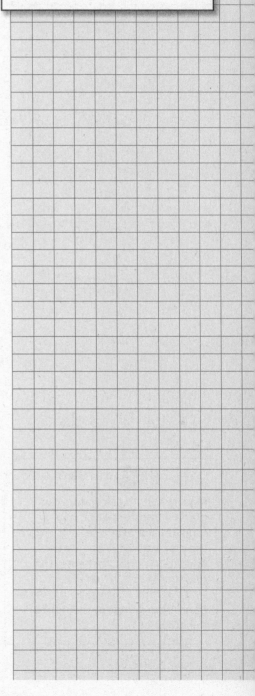

My Notes

8. Table 1 shows some values for an even function $f(x)$. Use the definition of an even function to find four more ordered pairs $(x, f(x))$.

Table 1

x	$f(x)$
−2	11
1	2
5	578
9	6402

9. Table 2 shows some values for an odd function $g(x)$. Use the definition of an odd function to find four more ordered pairs $(x, g(x))$.

Table 2

x	$g(x)$
−4	−60
−2	−6
3	24
10	990

10. Reason abstractly. If a function is even, which transformations will always maintain the symmetry of the graph? Explain.

11. If a function is odd, which transformations will always maintain the symmetry of the graph? Explain.

CONNECT TO TECHNOLOGY

Most graphing calculators can graph a transformation of a function. For example, to translate the graph of $f(x) = x^2 + 4x$ by 3 units to the right, first enter the rule for $f(x)$ as Y_1. Then enter $Y_1(X-3)$ for Y_2. The graph of Y_2 is a translation 3 units to the right of the graph of Y_1.

12. You can use a graphing calculator to determine whether a function $f(x)$ is even. First, enter the function rule for $f(x)$ as Y_1. Then enter $Y_1(-X)$ for Y_2. The rule for Y_2 represents $f(-x)$. View the graphs of the two functions on the same screen. What should you expect to see on the screen if $f(x)$ is even?

My Notes

13. **Use appropriate tools strategically.** Describe how you could use a graphing calculator to determine whether a function $f(x)$ is odd.

14. Use a graphing calculator to classify each function as even, odd, or neither.
   a. $f(x)=\frac{2}{x}$
   b. $f(x) = 2 \log x$
   c. $f(x) = 0.25x^3$
   d. $f(x) = -|x| + 2$

Check Your Understanding

Describe each real-world function as a transformation of its parent function. Remember to use complete sentences and words such as *and, or, since, because* to make connections between your thoughts.

15. $g(x) = (2x)^3$

16. $g(x) = |x| - 4$

17. The table represents a function. For each transformation of the function, describe how you would need to change each x-coordinate and each y-coordinate, if at all.

x	−2	−1	0	1	2	3
y	6	3	2	3	2	6

   a. a translation 3 units to the right
   b. a vertical stretch by a factor of 3
   c. a reflection over the x-axis

18. The function $f(x)$ has a y-intercept of -3. The graph of $g(x)$ is a vertical compression of the graph of $f(x)$ by a factor of $\frac{1}{3}$. What is the y-intercept of $g(x)$? Explain how you know.

19. There is only one function that is both odd and even. What is the equation of this function? ***Justify*** your answer.

ACADEMIC VOCABULARY

When you ***justify*** a statement, you show that it is correct.

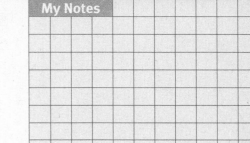

My Notes

LESSON 6-1 PRACTICE

Use the given information to write the equation of $g(x)$, and then graph $g(x)$.

20. The graph of g(x) is a reflection of the graph of $f(x) = \log_2 x$ over the x-axis.

21. The graph of g(x) is a vertical compression of the graph of $f(x) = x^2 + 2x$ by a factor of $\frac{1}{2}$.

22. The graph of g(x) is a reflection of the graph of $f(x) = 2^x$ over the y-axis followed by a translation 2 units up.

Determine if the following functions are odd, even, or neither. Then describe the symmetry of the graph of the function, if any.

23. $f(x) = x^4 - 3x^2 + x + 1$

24. $f(x) = x^3 - 3x$

25. $f(x) = x^6 - 4x^4 + 2$

26. $f(x) = \frac{1}{2x}$

27. Make sense of problems. Landon kicks a football from a height of 3 ft with an initial vertical velocity of 20 ft/s. The function $f(t) = -16t^2 + 20t + 3$ models the height in feet of the ball t seconds after it is kicked. Next, Mitch kicks a football. The function $g(t)$ models the height in feet of Mitch's football t seconds after it is kicked. The graph of $g(t)$ is a translation 3 units down of the graph of $f(t)$.

a. Write the equation of $g(t)$.

b. From what height does Mitch kick the football? What is its initial vertical velocity? Explain how you know.

CONNECT TO PHYSICS

The height h in feet of a kicked or thrown object after t seconds can be modeled by the equation $h = -16t^2 + v_0t + h_0$, where v_0 is the initial vertical velocity in feet per second and h_0 is the initial height in feet.

My Notes

Learning Targets:

- Add, subtract, multiply, and divide functions.
- Transform and perform operations with piecewise-defined functions.

SUGGESTED LEARNING STRATEGIES: Note Taking, Create Representations, Summarizing, Discussion Groups, Critique Reasoning

Let f and g be any two functions. The sum, difference, product, and quotient of f and g are functions whose domains are the set of all numbers common to the domains of f and g, and are defined as follows:

$$(f+g)(x) = f(x) + g(x)$$
$$(f-g)(x) = f(x) - g(x)$$
$$(fg)(x) = f(x)g(x)$$
$$\left(\frac{f}{g}\right)(x) = \frac{f(x)}{g(x)}, \text{ where } g(x) \neq 0$$

Example A

Let $f(x) = 2x + 3$ and $g(x) = 2x^2 + 5x - 12$. Find $f + g$ and $\frac{f}{g}$. State the domain.

$$\begin{aligned}(f+g)(x) &= f(x) + g(x)\\ &= 2x + 3 + 2x^2 + 5x - 12\\ &= 2x^2 + 7x - 9\end{aligned}$$

The domain of f is all real numbers, and the domain of g is all real numbers; therefore, the domain of $f + g$ is $\mathbb{R}$. ← $(-\infty, \infty)$

For $\frac{f}{g}$, the denominator cannot be zero, so its domain is restricted.

$g(x) = 2x^2 + 5x - 12$, or $g(x) = (2x - 3)(x + 4)$, so $x \neq \frac{3}{2}, x \neq -4$

$$\left(\frac{f}{g}\right)(x) = \frac{f(x)}{g(x)} = \frac{2x+3}{2x^2+5x-12}; \text{domain: } \left\{x \mid x \neq \frac{3}{2}, x \neq -4\right\}$$

"the set of"

$2x^2+5x-12$
$(2x-3)(x+4)$
$2x-3=0$ $x+4=0$
$x=\frac{3}{2}$ $x=-4$
$(-\infty,-4) \cup (-4,\frac{3}{2}) \cup (\frac{3}{2},\infty)$

Try These A

Find the sum, difference, product, and quotient for the following functions. State the domain of each resulting function.

a. $f(x) = 3x - 4, g(x) = 4 - x$

b. $f(x) = x^2 + 6, g(x) = \sqrt{1 - x}$

c. $f(x) = \sqrt{x^2 - 9}, g(x) = \frac{x^2}{x^2 + 2}$

$(f+g)(x) = f(x) + g(x)$
$= 3x - 4 + 4 - x$
$= 2x$ domain: $\mathbb{R}$

$(f-g)(x) = f(x) - g(x)$
$= 3x - 4 - 4 - x$ ← domain: $\mathbb{R}$
$= 2x - 8$

$\left(\frac{f}{g}\right)(x) = \frac{3x-4}{4-x}$ ← $4 - x = 0$, $-x = -4$, $x = 4$
domain: $\{x \mid x \neq 4\}$

$(fg)(x) = (3x-4)(4-x)$
$= 12x - 3x^2 - 16 + 4x$ ← domain: $\mathbb{R}$
$= -3x^2 + 16x - 16$

My Notes

MATH TIP

A piecewise-defined function is called a step function if each rule that defines the function is a constant. For example, the function $f(x)=\begin{cases}-1 & \text{if } x<0\\ 1 & \text{if } x\geq 0\end{cases}$ is a step function. The graph looks like steps, and would show a domain of all real numbers and a range of $\{-1, 1\}$.

A piecewise-defined function is a function that is defined by two or more rules. Each rule applies to a different part of the domain of the function.

For example, $f(x)=\begin{cases}x+2 & \text{if } x<0\\ x^2 & \text{if } x\geq 0\end{cases}$ is a piecewise-defined function. The rule $x+2$ describes the function for the interval $x<0$, and the rule x^2 describes the function for the interval $x\geq 0$.

When you transform a piecewise-defined function, you must perform the transformation on each rule that defines the function. Similarly, when you perform a function operation involving a piecewise-defined function, you must perform the operation on each rule that defines the function.

Example B

The function $f(x)=\begin{cases}20x & \text{if } x\leq 4\\ 10x+40 & \text{if } x>4\end{cases}$ gives the total cost in dollars of x tickets to a board game convention.

a. Graph the function. Determine and analyze any key features.

Apply the rule $20x$ for values of x less than or equal to 4 and the rule $10x+40$ for values of x greater than 4.

x	$20x$
1	20
2	40
3	60
4	80

x	$10x + 40$
5	90
6	100
7	110
8	120

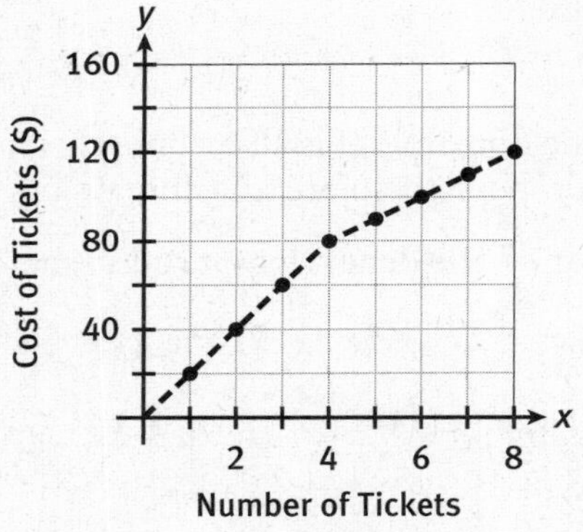

Key features include the following:

- The domain of $f(x)$ is all the real numbers.
- The range of $f(x)$ is all the real numbers.
- $f(x)$ has a relative maximum at (4, 80).

b. The function $g(x) = 10x$ gives the total cost in dollars for x people to buy a board game at the convention. Find $f + g$, and tell what it represents in this situation.

$$(f+g)(x) = \begin{cases} 20x + 10x & \text{if } x \le 4 \\ 10x + 40 + 10x & \text{if } x > 4 \end{cases}$$ Add the rule for $g(x)$ to each rule that defines $f(x)$.

$$= \begin{cases} 30x & \text{if } x \le 4 \\ 20x + 40 & \text{if } x > 4 \end{cases}$$ Then simplify.

$f + g$ represents the cost in dollars for a group of x people to buy one ticket each for the convention, plus a board game.

c. The graph of $h(x)$ is a vertical stretch of the graph of $f(x)$ by a factor of 1.25. Write the equation of $h(x)$. Then tell what $h(x)$ represents in this situation.

$$h(x) = 1.25f(x)$$ To represent the vertical stretch, multiply $f(x)$ by 1.25.

$$= \begin{cases} 1.25(20x) & \text{if } x \le 4 \\ 1.25(10x + 40) & \text{if } x > 4 \end{cases}$$ To find $1.25f(x)$, multiply each rule that defines $f(x)$ by 1.25.

$$= \begin{cases} 25x & \text{if } x \le 4 \\ 12.5x + 50) & \text{if } x > 4 \end{cases}$$ Then simplify.

$h(x)$ represents the total cost in dollars of x tickets to the convention after an increase in ticket prices of 25 percent.

Try These B

a. Reason abstractly. Refer back to the function $f(x)$ in Example B. The graph of $j(x)$ is a translation 2 units up of the graph of $f(x)$. Write the equation of $j(x)$. Then tell what $j(x)$ could represent in this situation.

Consider the functions $p(x) = \begin{cases} x + 2 & \text{if } x < 0 \\ x^2 & \text{if } x \ge 0 \end{cases}$ and $q(x) = x + 3$.

b. Graph $p(x)$ on a coordinate plane. Determine and analyze any key features such as domain, range, relative extrema, and zeros.

c. Find the sum, difference, product, and quotient of the functions. State the domain of each.

d. The graph of $r(x)$ is a translation 3 units to the left of the graph of $p(x)$. Write the equation of $r(x)$.

My Notes

MATH TIP

Some transformations of piecewise-defined functions affect not only the rules that define the function but also the interval for each rule. Transformations that affect the intervals include horizontal translations, horizontal stretches, horizontal compressions, and reflections across the y-axis.

My Notes

2x² − 3x + 5 = 0

Check Your Understanding

1. **Express regularity in repeated reasoning.** Is addition of functions commutative? Give an example to support your answer.
2. Explain how to determine the domain of the quotient of two functions $f(x)$ and $g(x)$.
3. Explain why $y = \begin{cases} 3 & \text{if } x \le 5 \\ 6 & \text{if } x \ge 5 \end{cases}$ is *not* a piecewise-defined function.
4. **Critique the reasoning of others.** A student claims that the graph of $g(x) = \begin{cases} x+2 & \text{if } x < 0 \\ (x-2)^3 & \text{if } x \ge 0 \end{cases}$ is a translation 2 units to the right of the graph of $f(x) = \begin{cases} x+4 & \text{if } x < 0 \\ x^3 & \text{if } x \ge 0 \end{cases}$. Is the student correct? Explain.

LESSON 6-2 PRACTICE

Find the sum, difference, product, and quotient of these functions. State the domain.

5. $f(x) = x^2 + 1,\ g(x) = 2x^2 - 3x + 5$
6. $f(x) = 2^x,\ g(x) = 2^{x-1}$
7. $f(x) = \begin{cases} 2x+1 & \text{if } x \le 2 \\ 4x-3 & \text{if } x > 2 \end{cases},\ g(x) = 2x + 1$

Use the function $f(x) = \begin{cases} x^2 - 1 & \text{if } x < 1 \\ -2x & \text{if } x \ge 1 \end{cases}$ and the given information to write the equation of $g(x)$, and then graph $g(x)$.

8. The graph of $g(x)$ is a reflection of the graph of $f(x)$ over the x-axis.
9. The graph of $g(x)$ is a reflection of the graph of $f(x)$ over the y-axis.
10. **Model with mathematics.** The charges at an airport parking garage are \$4 per hour for the first 5 hours and a maximum of \$20 per day.
    - **a.** Write the equation of a piecewise-defined function $f(x)$ that represents the cost in dollars of parking in the garage for x hours in a single day.
    - **b.** The airport plans to add a security charge of \$1 per day regardless of the number of hours parked in the garage. Write the equation of a function $g(x)$ that represents the new cost in dollars of parking in the garage. Describe the graph of $g(x)$ as a transformation of the graph of $f(x)$.

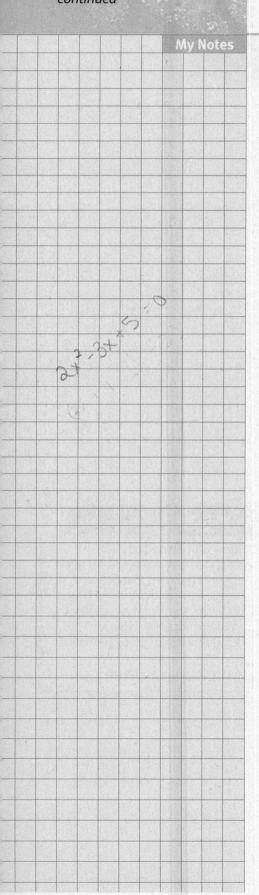

Modeling with Power Functions

ACTIVITY 7

Highway Safety

Lesson 7-1 Finding a Regression Line

My Notes

Learning Targets:

- Write an equation that models a data set.
- Transform data to determine whether a power function is a good model for a data set.

SUGGESTED LEARNING STRATEGIES: Create Representations, Look for a Pattern, Discussion Groups, Quickwrite, Group Presentation

The braking distance of a car is the distance the car travels between the time the driver hits the brakes and the time the car stops. The braking distance is dependent on the car's speed.

The Federal Highway Administration is one agency interested in determining safe stopping distances under various conditions. Below is a table of data collected by the agency under test conditions in which the road was dry and the driver traveling at a constant speed was confronted with a situation requiring a sudden stop.

DISCUSSION GROUP TIPS

As you listen to the group discussion, take notes to aid comprehension and to help you describe your own ideas to others in your group. Ask questions to clarify ideas and to gain further understanding of key concepts.

Observed Braking Distances

Speed (mi/h)	Average Braking Distance (ft)
20	20
25	28
30	40.5
35	52.5
40	72
45	92.5
50	118
55	148.5
60	182
65	220.5

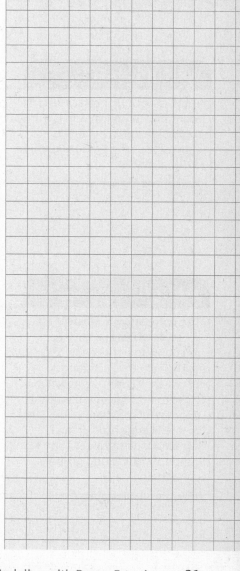

My Notes

1. Make a scatter plot showing the relationship between a car's speed and the average braking distance.

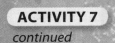

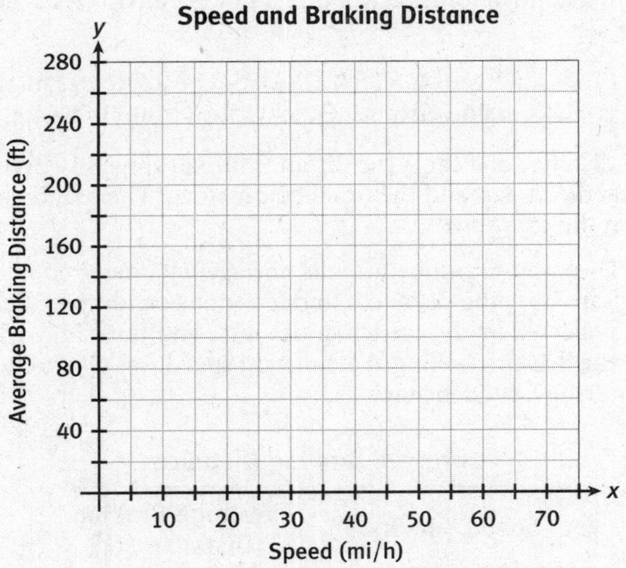

2. Perform a linear regression using the speed data and the braking distance data.

a. Give the equation of the regression line and graph the line on the scatter plot. Round numerical values to three decimal places.

b. Give the meaning of the slope and *y*-intercept of the model in terms of the context of the situation.

c. What is the correlation coefficient for the data? Interpret the meaning of this value.

d. Do you think a linear model is necessarily the best model for the data in the scatter plot? Explain your answer.

WRITING MATH

There is not a universal rule for rounding numerical values from a regression equation. In this activity, round the values to three decimal places.

MATH TIP

The correlation coefficient r is a measure of how linear the relationship between two variables is. The value of r can range between -1 and 1, with values close to -1 indicating a strong negative correlation, values close to 0 indicating little or no correlation, and values close to 1 indicating a strong positive correlation.

My Notes

3. Transform the x-values and y-values of the original scatter plot.
   a. Take the common logarithm of the speeds and the common logarithm of the stopping distances to complete the table. Round values to the nearest thousandth.

Speed (mi/h)	Average Braking Distance (ft)
20	20
25	28
30	40.5
35	52.5
40	72
45	92.5
50	118
55	148.5
60	182
65	220.5

Log of Speed	Log of Braking Distance

MATH TIP

When you transform a data set, you perform the same operation or set of operations on each value in the data set.

   b. Make a new scatter plot showing the relationship between the common logarithm of the speed and the common logarithm of the average stopping distance.

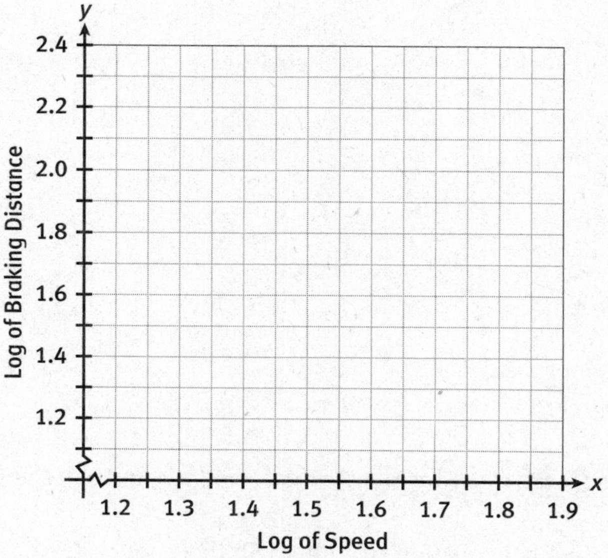

   c. What pattern do you notice in the new scatter plot?

My Notes

4. Perform a linear regression using the transformed data.
   a. Give the equation of the regression line and graph the line on the scatter plot.
   b. What is the correlation coefficient for the transformed data? What does the value indicate about the transformed data?
   c. Is a linear model a better fit for the original data or the transformed data? Use the correlation coefficient to explain how you know.

You can use the equation of the regression line of the log-log transformed data to write the equation of a function that models the original data set.

MATH TIP

When a data set is transformed by taking the logarithm of both the x-values and the y-values, the transformation is called a log-log transformation.

5. To do so, start with the equation for the regression line of the transformed data.
   a. Substitute $\log x$ for x and $\log y$ for y in the equation.
   b. Use the properties of logarithms to solve the equation from Part a for y. List a property or give an explanation for each step in your work.

MATH TIP

In Item 5b, start by rewriting the equation so that it has a single logarithm on one side of the equation and a constant on the other side. Then write the equation in exponential form. Finally, solve for y.

A ***power function*** has the form $f(x) = ax^b$, where a and b are nonzero real numbers.

6. Look at the final equation from Item 5b that models the braking distance of a car. Is this equation a power function? Explain.

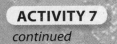

7. Use appropriate tools strategically. Use a graphing calculator to perform a power regression using the speed and braking distance data.

a. Give the equation of the regression.

b. How does the regression confirm that a power function is an appropriate model for the speed and braking distance data?

c. How does the regression equation confirm that you solved the equation in Item 5b correctly?

8. A car is traveling on a highway at a speed of 70 mi/h. The driver sees a tree ahead that has fallen across the road.

a. Use your braking distance model to determine how far the car will travel from the time the driver hits the brakes to the time the car comes to a stop, assuming it does not hit the tree first. Consider the precision of the original data set when rounding your answer.

b. Attend to precision. Explain how you used the precision of the original data set to decide how to round your answer.

My Notes

CONNECT TO TECHNOLOGY

After you enter the speed and braking distance data into a graphing calculator, you can perform a power regression by pressing STAT. Move the cursor to the right to highlight the CALC menu. Then scroll down and select A:PwrReg.

Check Your Understanding

9. Construct viable arguments. Use properties of logarithms to show that if $\log y = \log a + b \log x$ where a and b are nonzero real numbers, then $y = ax^b$.

10. The graph of the equation $\log y = \log 4 + 3 \log x$ is linear. Explain how you can write a power function that models the relationship between x and y.

11. Explain how you can transform a data set to determine whether a power function is a good model for the data.

12. Is a power function a type of exponential function? Explain.

13. The correlation coefficient for a power regression for a data set is 0.542. Based on this information, is a power function a good model for the data set? Explain.

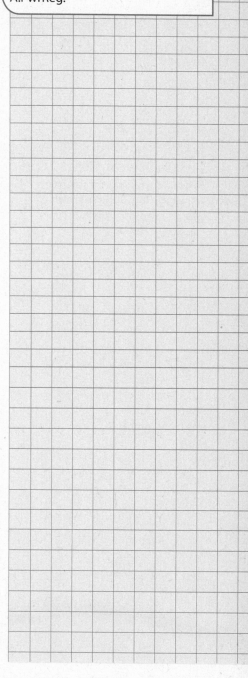

My Notes

LESSON 7-1 PRACTICE

The table shows the relationship between the body mass and heart rate of several mammals.

Mass and Heart Rate of Mammals

Animal	Mass (kg)	Heart Rate (beats/min)
Mouse	0.027	723
Hamster	0.09	400
Rat	0.26	250
Japanese monkey	6.6	147
Roe deer	20	104
Human	66	80
Horse	494	40

14. **Attend to precision.** Make a scatter plot of the data.

15. Do you think a linear model is necessarily the best model for the data in the scatter plot? Support your answer.

16. What transformation can you perform on the data to check whether a power function is a good model for the data?

17. Transform the data using the transformation you chose.
a. Find a linear regression equation for the transformed data.
b. Find the correlation coefficient. What does this indicate about the transformed data?

18. **Model with mathematics.** What power function models the original data set?

19. Use your model to predict the heart rate of an elephant with a mass of 3400 kg.

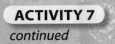

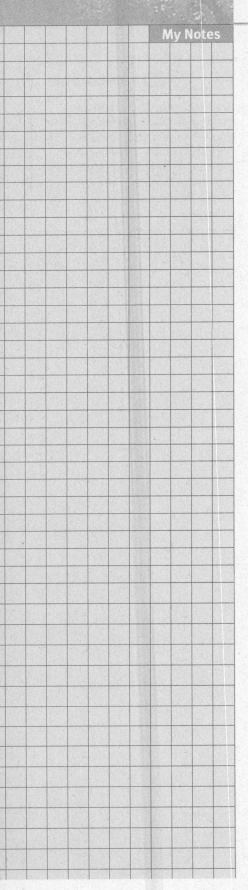

My Notes

Learning Targets:

- Graph power functions.
- Identify and analyze key features of the graphs of power functions.

SUGGESTED LEARNING STRATEGIES: Create Representations, Look for a Pattern, Think-Pair-Share, Self-Revision/Peer Revision, Graphic Organizer

1. The scatter plot below shows the braking distance and speed data from the previous lesson.

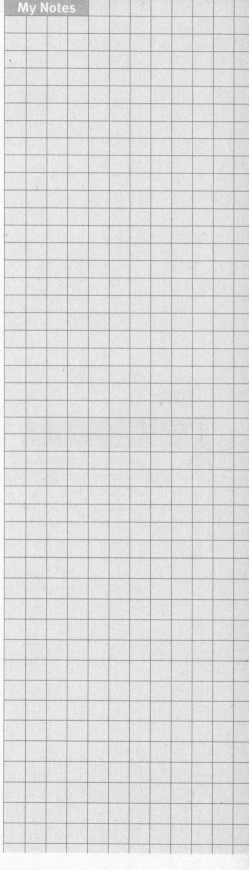

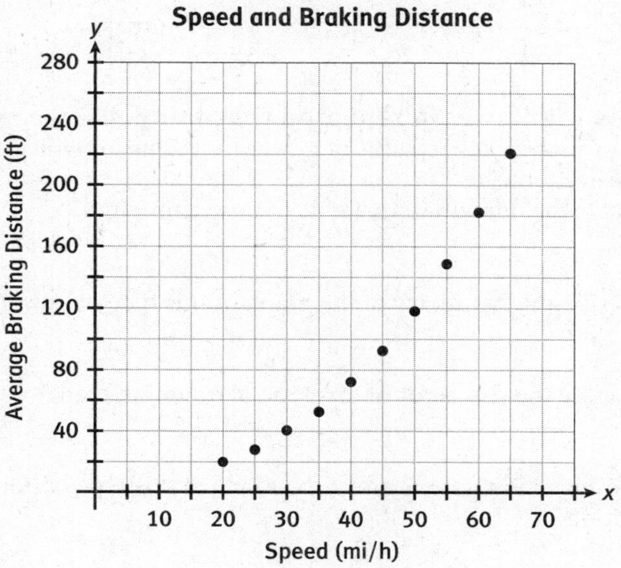

a. Graph the power function from Item 7a in Lesson 7-1 on the scatter plot.

b. Explain how the graph confirms that a power function is a good model for the data set.

2. Analyze the key features of the graph of the power function.

a. What are the domain and range of the function?

b. What is the minimum value of the function? Why does it make sense in the context of the problem situation that the function has this minimum value?

c. Does the value of the function increase or decrease over its domain? Why does it make sense in the context of the problem situation that the function behaves in this way?

My Notes

3. Graph the power functions $y = x^2$ and $y = x^4$ on the coordinate plane on the left and the power functions $y = -x^2$ and $y = -x^4$ on the coordinate plane on the right.

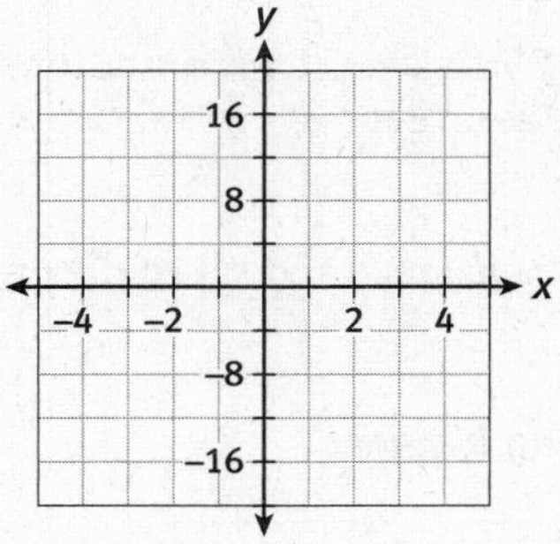

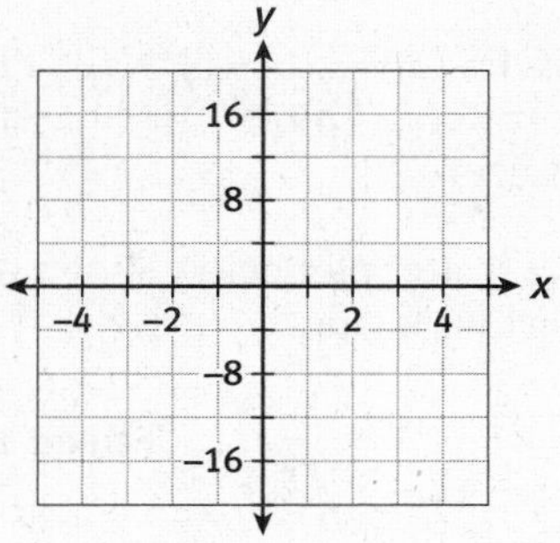

4. **Express regularity in repeated reasoning.** Use the graphs from Item 3 to analyze key features of power functions for which b is a positive even integer.

   a. What is the domain of this type of power function?

   b. Describe the symmetry of the graph of this type of power function.

   c. What are the real zeros of this type of function, if any?

   d. How does the sign of a affect the range of this type of power function?

   e. How does the sign of a affect the end behavior of the function's graph?

   f. How does the sign of a affect the intervals over which the function is increasing and decreasing?

MATH TIP

The end behavior of a graph is a description of what happens to the value of the function as x approaches negative infinity and as x approaches positive infinity.

5. Graph the power functions $y = x^3$ and $y = x^5$ on the coordinate plane on the left and the power functions $y = -x^3$ and $y = -x^5$ on the coordinate plane on the right.

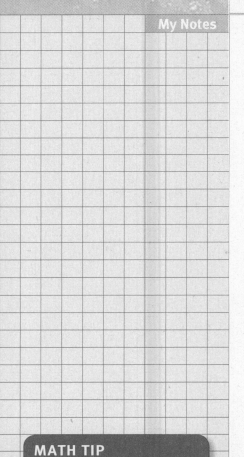

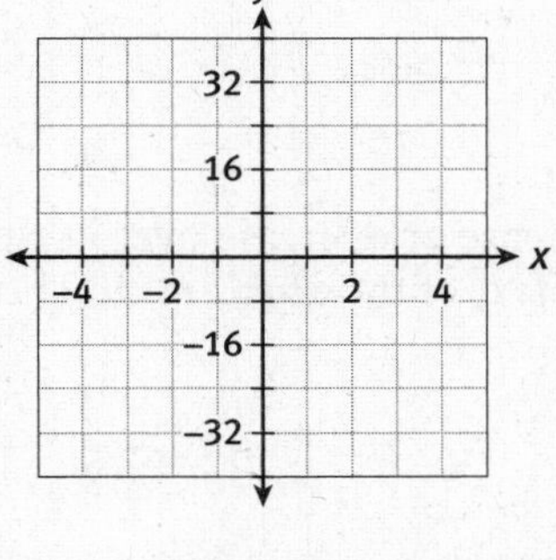

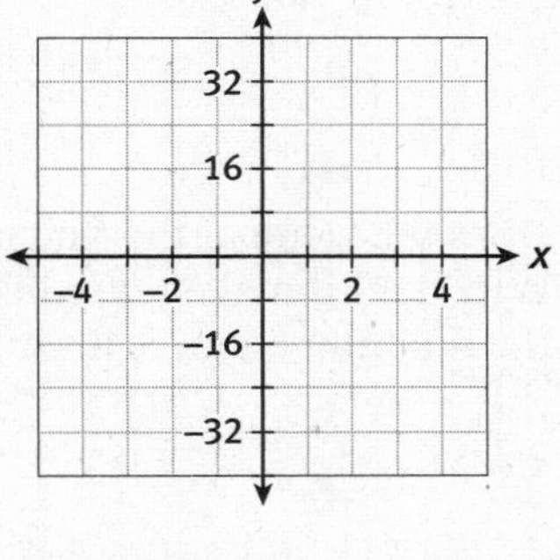

My Notes

6. **Express regularity in repeated reasoning.** Use the graphs from Item 5 to analyze key features of power functions for which b is a positive odd integer.
   a. What are the domain and range of this type of power function?

   b. Describe the symmetry of the graph of this type of power function.

   c. What are the real zeros of this type of function, if any?

   d. How does the sign of a affect the end behavior of the function's graph?

   e. How does the sign of a affect the intervals over which the function is increasing and decreasing?

7. Graph the power functions $y = x^{\frac{1}{2}}$ and $y = x^{\frac{1}{3}}$ on the same graphing calculator screen.
   a. What is the domain of $y = x^{\frac{1}{2}}$?

   b. What is the domain of $y = x^{\frac{1}{3}}$?

   c. Write the equation of each function in radical form.

   d. **Make use of structure.** How do the radical forms of the functions help to explain the difference in the domains of the power functions $y = x^{\frac{1}{2}}$ and $y = x^{\frac{1}{3}}$?

MATH TIP

For a natural number n, the expression $x^{\frac{1}{n}}$ is equivalent to $\sqrt[n]{x}$.

8. a. Graph the power function $y = x^{-1}$ on the coordinate plane below.

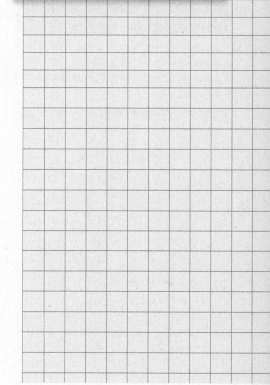

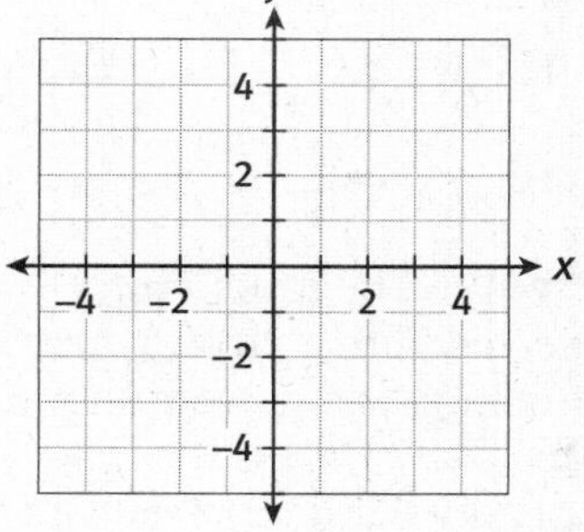

My Notes

b. How does the graph of this function differ from the graphs of the other power functions in this lesson?

c. Describe the end behavior of the function's graph.

d. Describe the behavior of the function as x approaches 0.

e. What are the asymptotes of the function's graph?

f. **Make use of structure.** Write the equation of the function without using an exponent. How does this form of the equation explain why the graph has a vertical asymptote?

Check Your Understanding

9. A power function of the form $y = ax^b$ has a positive integer exponent and a minimum value of 0.
  a. Is the value of b even or odd? How do you know?
  b. Is the value of a positive or negative? How do you know?

10. Make a conjecture about the domain of a power function of the form $y = x^{\frac{1}{n}}$, where n is a positive even integer. Explain the reasoning you used to make your conjecture.

11. **Critique the reasoning of others.** A student claims that the graphs of all power functions pass through the point (0, 0). Is the student correct? Explain.

ACADEMIC VOCABULARY

A *conjecture* is a mathematical statement that is based on evidence but has not yet been proven.

LESSON 7-2 PRACTICE

Make a table that describes key features of the graphs of the following power functions. The key features should include domain, range, symmetry, maximum or minimum, end behavior, and intervals over which the function is increasing or decreasing.

12. $y = -3x^7$ **13.** $y = x^{\frac{1}{4}}$ **14.** $y = 2x^6$

15. $y = -x^{\frac{1}{5}}$ **16.** $y = -\frac{2}{3}x^4$ **17.** $y = 16x^5$

18. **Reason quantitatively.** The function $f(x) = 0.0008x^{3.91}$ models the number of people infected with a virus, where x is the time in months.
  a. Explain why the function is a power function.
  b. Graph the function.
  c. Find $f(24)$ and explain what it represents in this situation.

ACTIVITY 7 PRACTICE

Write your answers on notebook paper.
Show your work.

Lesson 7-1

Students in a physics class collected the following data about a ball dropped from a height.

Distance Fallen by Dropped Ball

Time (s)	Distance Fallen (m)
0.10	0.04
0.16	0.11
0.22	0.22
0.28	0.36
0.34	0.54
0.40	0.75
0.46	0.99
0.52	1.28

1. Make a scatter plot of the data.

2. Perform a linear regression using the time and distance data.
  a. Give the equation of the regression line.
  b. Give the meaning of the slope and *y*-intercept of the model in terms of the context of the situation.
  c. What is the correlation coefficient? Interpret the meaning of this value.

3. Perform a transformation on the data to check whether a power function is a good model for the data.
  a. Make a table showing the results of the transformation.
  b. Tell how you transformed the data.

4. Perform a linear regression using the transformed data.
  a. Give the equation of the regression line.
  b. What is the correlation coefficient? Interpret the meaning of this value.

5. Is a linear function or a power function a better model for the original data set? Explain how you know.

6. Use the equation of the regression line of the transformed data to write the equation of a power function that models the original data set. List a property or give an explanation for each step in your work.

7. Graph the power function on the scatter plot of the original data.

8. The students in the physics class drop a ball from a height of 10 m.
  a. Use your model from Item 6 to determine how many seconds it will take for the ball to hit the ground.
  b. Explain how you used the precision of the original data set to decide how to round your answer in Part a.

9. In the absence of air resistance, the formula $d = \frac{1}{2}gt^2$ gives the distance d in meters an object falls in t seconds, where g is the acceleration due to gravity in m/s^2.
  a. Use your model from Item 6 to approximate the acceleration due to gravity. Explain how you determined your answer.
  b. The actual acceleration due to gravity is about 9.8 m/s^2. Did the students' data lead to a good approximation of the acceleration due to gravity? Explain.

Lesson 7-2

Graph each power function.

10. $f(x) = \frac{1}{2}x^3$

11. $f(x) = 3x^{\frac{1}{3}}$

12. $f(x) = -2x^4$

13. $f(x) = 4x^{-1}$

14. Which could be the equation of the power function graphed below?

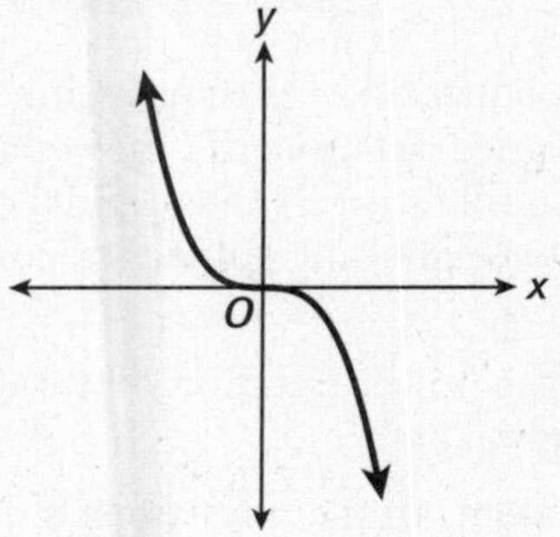

A. $y = -\frac{1}{3}x^4$ **B.** $y = -\frac{1}{4}x^3$

C. $y = \frac{1}{4}x^3$ **D.** $y = \frac{1}{3}x^4$

15. Explain how you determined your answer to Item 14.

16. The graph of which of these power functions is symmetric with respect to the y-axis?

A. $y = -3x^5$ **B.** $y = -3x^4$

C. $y = x^{\frac{1}{3}}$ **D.** $y = x^{\frac{1}{2}}$

17. Which of these power functions has a minimum of 0?

A. $f(x) = -2x^7$ **B.** $f(x) = -4x^2$

C. $f(x) = 3x^6$ **D.** $f(x) = 5x^3$

18. How does the sign of a affect the range of the power function $y = ax^{\frac{1}{4}}$?

State whether or not each function is a power function. Then explain your reasoning.

19. $f(x) = -4x^{\frac{2}{3}}$ **20.** $f(x) = -\frac{5}{x}$

21. $f(x) = x^3 - 2x^2$ **22.** $f(x) = 0.6x^{2.5}$

23. $f(x) = 3\sqrt{2x}$ **24.** $f(x) = 4(3^x)$

25. Which description matches the power function $y = 6x^6$?

A. decreasing throughout its domain
B. increasing throughout its domain
C. decreasing for $x < 0$ and increasing for $x > 0$
D. increasing for $x < 0$ and decreasing for $x > 0$

Describe the end behavior of each real-world model of a power function without first graphing the function.

26. $f(x) = -2x^7$ **27.** $f(x) = -\frac{2}{3}x^8$

28. $f(x) = 0.3x^6$ **29.** $f(x) = x^9$

30. Which of these power functions has no real zeros?

A. $f(x) = -4x^{-1}$ **B.** $f(x) = x^{\frac{1}{6}}$

C. $f(x) = 3x^{0.5}$ **D.** $f(x) = 6x^7$

The Beaufort scale is a numerical scale that indicates wind speed. On this scale, 0 represents calm or no wind, and 12 represents a hurricane. The function $v = 1.87B^{1.5}$ can be used to determine the wind speed v in mi/h, where B is the Beaufort scale number.

31. Explain why the function that describes the Beaufort scale is a power function.

32. Graph the function that describes the Beaufort scale.

33. What is the wind speed during a strong gale that measures 9 on the Beaufort scale?

MATHEMATICAL PRACTICES
Look For and Express Regularity in Repeated Reasoning

34. For a power function of the form $y = ax^b$, the coefficient a is negative and the exponent b is a positive even integer. Based on this information, draw four conclusions about the graph of the power function.

Search and Rescue

Lesson 8-1 Composition of Functions

My Notes

Learning Targets:

- Determine the composition of two functions.
- Determine the inverse of a function.

SUGGESTED LEARNING STRATEGIES: Think Aloud, Create Representations, Look for a Pattern, Group Presentation, Work Backward

A hiker who was last seen at a visitor center in a national park has been reported missing. A search-and-rescue (SAR) team estimates that the hiker would have been walking at a rate of 2 mi/h. The SAR team needs to determine the possible search area in which to look for the hiker.

1. The theoretical search area is circular. Write the equation of a function $f(x)$ that gives the number of square miles in the search area when its radius is x miles.

→ $A = \pi r^2$

$f(x) = \pi x^2$

2. Write the equation of a function $g(x)$ that gives the distance in miles the hiker could have walked in x hours at a rate of 2 mi/h.

→ $d = rt$

$g(x) = 2x$

You have seen that the operations of addition, subtraction, multiplication, and division can be applied to functions. Another operation with functions is the ***composition*** of one function with another. The composition of the function f with the function g is written $f \circ g$ or $(f \circ g)(x) = f(g(x))$. The domain of $(f \circ g)$ is the set of all x in the domain of g so that the values of $g(x)$ are in the domain of f.

$(f \circ g)(x) = f(g(x))$ $(g \circ f) = g(f(x))$

MATH TERMS

The **composition** of functions is an operation that combines functions in such a way that the output of one function is used as the input for the other.

3. Use the equations you wrote in Items 1 and 2 to find the composition $(f \circ g)(x)$.

$f(g(x))$ $f(x) = \pi x^2$ $x(2x)^2$ $\pi(2^2x^2)$ $4\pi x^2$

4. Reason quantitatively. What does the input of the composition $(f \circ g)(x)$ represent in this situation? How do you know?

The number of hours the hiker walked. The input quantity for $f(g(x))$ is the same as the input quantity for $g(x)$

READING MATH

$f \circ g$ is read "f of g." $(f \circ g)(x)$ and $f(g(x))$ are read "f of g of x."

My Notes

5. **Reason quantitatively.** What does the output of the composition $(f \circ g)(x)$ represent in this situation? How do you know?

6. What is the reasonable domain of $(f \circ g)(x)$ in this situation? Explain.

7. **Model with mathematics.** The SAR team will use the distance in miles that the hiker could have walked as the radius of the theoretical search area. Explain why the composition $(f \circ g)(x)$ is a good model for the SAR team to use for calculating the number of square miles in the theoretical search area.

CONNECT TO STATISTICS

SAR teams rely on statistics to help them focus on the portions of the possible search area where the probability of finding a missing person is greatest. For example, data collected about the behavior of other lost hikers can help rescuers make predictions about where a hiker is most likely to be found.

8. The hiker was last seen walking away from a visitor center at the park 6 hours ago. What is the theoretical search area in square miles? Explain how you used the composition $(f \circ g)(x)$ to find your answer.

9. Use the equations you wrote in Items 1 and 2 to find the composition $(g \circ f)(x)$.

$g(x) = 2x$

$2(\pi x^2)$

$= 2\pi x^2$

10. Is $(f \circ g)(x)$ equivalent to $(g \circ f)(x)$? What does this tell you about whether composition of functions is commutative?

no they are not equivalent.
so, the composition of fns is not necessarily commutative

MATH TIP

An operation on functions is commutative if the order of the functions within the operation does not matter.

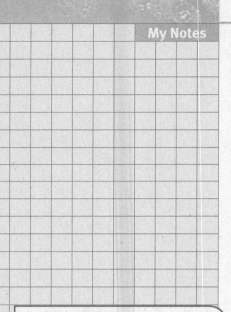

One way to transform a function involves composition with the absolute-value function.

11. Express regularity in repeated reasoning. For each function listed below, use graphs to compare $f(x)$ with $g(f(x))$, where $g(x) = |x|$. Describe the effects of this absolute-value transformation.

a. $f(x) = x^3$ **b.** $f(x) = x^2 - 4$

c. $f(x) = x^5 + 2x^3$ **d.** $f(x) = \frac{1}{x}$

e. $f(x) = \sin x$ **f.** $f(x) = \ln x$

My Notes

TECHNOLOGY TIP

Graph $f(x)$ as Y1 and abs(Y1) as Y2. Turn Y1 on and off or trace each function to see ordered pairs as well as where the graphs differ or coincide. Use ZOOM Trig for the window for part e. It is also helpful to use the calculator's TABLE function.

12. Express regularity in repeated reasoning. For each function listed below, use graphs to compare $f(x)$ with $f(g(x))$, where $g(x) = |x|$. Describe the effects of this absolute-value transformation.

a. $f(x) = x^3$ **b.** $f(x) = \ln x$

c. $f(x) = x^5 + 2x^3$ **d.** $f(x) = e^x$

e. $f(x) = \sin x$ **f.** $f(x) = \sqrt{x}$

TECHNOLOGY TIP

Graph $f(x)$ as Y1 and Y1(abs(x)) as Y2. Turn Y1 off and on as needed.

13. A function f is defined on the closed interval from -4 to 4 and has the graph shown.

a. Sketch the graph of $y = g(f(x))$, where $g(x) = |x|$.

b. Sketch the graph of $y = f(g(x))$, where $g(x) = |x|$.

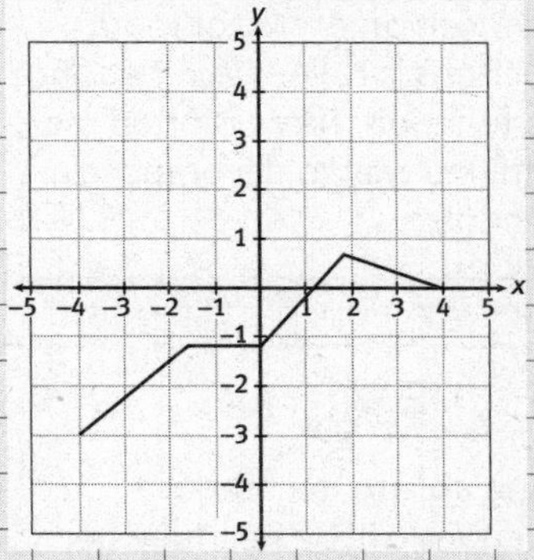

My Notes

c. Sketch the graph of $y = g(f(x))$, where $g(x) = -x$.

d. Sketch the graph of $y = f(g(x))$, where $g(x) = -x$.

You can often write the equation of a given function as a composition of two other simpler functions.

Example A

Given $h(x) = \log(3x - 4)$, write the equations of two functions $f(x)$ and $g(x)$ so that $f(g(x)) = h(x)$.

Step 1: Analyze $h(x)$. To evaluate $h(x)$, you start with x and find the value of $3x - 4$. Then you find the common logarithm of the result.

Step 2: Write the equation for $g(x)$. $g(x)$ is evaluated first in the composition $f(g(x))$, so let $g(x) = 3x - 4$.

Step 3: Write the equation for $f(x)$. Let $f(x) = \log x$.

Step 4: Check by finding $f(g(x))$.

$$\begin{aligned} f(g(x)) &= f(3x - 4) \\ &= \log(3x - 4) \\ &= h(x) \end{aligned}$$

Solution: $f(x) = \log x$ and $g(x) = 3x - 4$

Try These A

Write the equations of two functions $f(x)$ and $g(x)$ so that $f(g(x)) = h(x)$.

a. $h(x) = \frac{1}{2}x - 5$

b. $h(x) = \frac{1}{x^2 + 3}$

c. $h(x) = 2^{x+1}$

d. $h(x) = x^2 + 6x + 9$

MATH TIP

Writing a function as the composition of two or more functions is called *decomposing* the function. There is often more than one way to decompose a function.

CONNECT TO AP

Being able to decompose functions will be helpful when solving some types of problems in calculus.

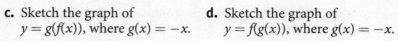

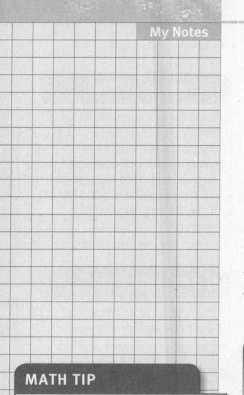

My Notes

Check Your Understanding

14. **Critique the reasoning of others.** Given that $h(x) = 3x + 5$, a student claims that $(h \circ h)(x) = (3x + 5)^2$. What mistake did the student make? Write the correct equation for $(h \circ h)(x)$.
15. Explain how to determine the range of $f(g(x))$ given $f(x)$ and $g(x)$.
16. Given that $q(x) = 2x + 4$ and $p(q(x)) = \sqrt{2x + 5}$, what is the equation of $p(x)$? Explain how you determined your answer.
17. a. Given the functions $f(x) = \ln x$ and $g(x) = -|x|$, find the composition $f(g(x))$.
    b. What is the domain of the composition? What does the domain indicate about the composition?

MATH TIP

You can compose a function with itself. So, for example, $(f \circ f)(x) = f(f(x))$.

LESSON 8-1 PRACTICE

Find $f(g(x))$ and $g(f(x))$ for each pair of functions. State the domain.

18. $f(x) = x^2 - 4$, $g(x) = x - 2$
19. $f(x) = \frac{1}{x}$, $g(x) = x^2 + 3x - 4$
20. $f(x) = x^2 + 3$, $g(x) = \sqrt{x - 5}$
21. $f(x) = e^{x-3}$, $g(x) = \ln x + \ln 3$

Write the equations of two functions $f(x)$ and $g(x)$ so that $f(g(x)) = h(x)$.

22. $h(x) = |x - 2| + 4$
23. $h(x) = (x + 1)^4 + (x + 1)$

Gold has a density of 19.3 g/cm^3. On a certain date, gold is valued at \$55.62 per gram. Use this information for Items 24–27.

24. Write the equation of a function $f(x)$ that gives the value in dollars of an object made of gold with a mass of x grams.
25. Write the equation of a function $g(x)$ that gives the mass in grams of a cube of gold with a side length of x cm.
26. **Reason quantitatively.** Find the composition $f(g(x))$. State its reasonable domain. What does the composition represent in this situation?
27. What is the value of a cube of gold having a side length of 20 cm? Explain how you used the composition $f(g(x))$ to find your answer.

My Notes

Learning Targets:

- Find the inverse of a function.
- Restrict the domain of a function so that its inverse is also a function.

SUGGESTED LEARNING STRATEGIES: Marking the Text, Discussion Groups, Create Representations, Look for a Pattern, Quickwrite

MATH TERMS

If $f(x) = y$, then the function f^{-1} is the **inverse function** of f if $f^{-1}(y) = x$. The domain of f is the range of f^{-1}, and the range of f is the domain of f^{-1}.

READING MATH

The notation f^{-1} is read as "the inverse of f." Note that the -1 in this notation does not represent an exponent.

The function $f(x) = 2.5(x - 5)$ gives the distance in miles that a search-and-rescue helicopter can travel within x minutes of receiving an emergency call.

A search-and-rescue operator wants to develop the equation of a new function that will give the time in minutes from receiving an emergency call that it will take the helicopter to travel x miles. This new function will be the ***inverse function*** of f.

1. Complete the table of values for $f(x)$. Then use it to complete the table of values for the inverse function $f^{-1}(x)$.

Time (min), x	7	9	11	13	15
Distance (mi), $f(x)$					

Distance (mi), x					
Time (min), $f^{-1}(x)$	7	9	11	13	15

2. The coordinate grid below shows the graph of $f(x)$. Use the table of values from Item 28 to help you graph $f^{-1}(x)$ on the same coordinate grid.

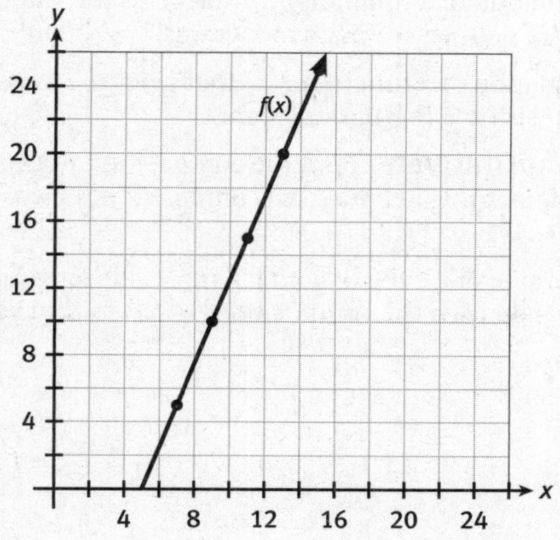

My Notes

A reflection of the graph of a function over the line $y = x$ causes the x- and y-coordinates of the points on the graph to be switched.

3. Use a dashed line to graph $y = x$ on the coordinate grid on the previous page. Does the graph of $f^{-1}(x)$ appear to be a reflection of the graph of $f(x)$ over the line $y = x$? Explain.

4. Why does it make sense that the graph of the inverse of a function is a reflection of the graph of the function over the line $y = x$?

5. a. Reason abstractly. The search-and-rescue operator determines that $f(53) = 120$. Based on this information, what is $f^{-1}(120)$? Explain how you know.

b. Reason quantitatively. Explain the meanings of $f(53)$ and $f^{-1}(120)$ in the context of the situation.

6. Write the equation of $f^{-1}(x)$. Explain how you determined your answer.

My Notes

You can test whether two functions are inverses by using compositions. Because inverse functions undo each other, their compositions should equal the original input variable. In other words, if $f(g(x)) = x$ and $g(f(x)) = x$, then f and g are inverse functions.

7. Use compositions to check whether the equation you wrote in Item 6 is the inverse of the function $f(x) = 2.5x(x - 5)$.

Sometimes the inverse of a function is not itself a function. In such cases, you may be able to restrict the domain of the original function so that its inverse will be a function.

Example A

Find the inverse function of $f(x) = (x - 2)^2$. Restrict the domain of f if needed, and describe the restriction. Then state the domain and range of the inverse function.

Step 1: Determine whether the inverse of f is a function.

Graph $f(x) = (x - 2)^2$.

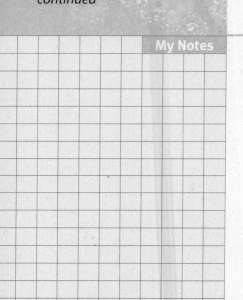

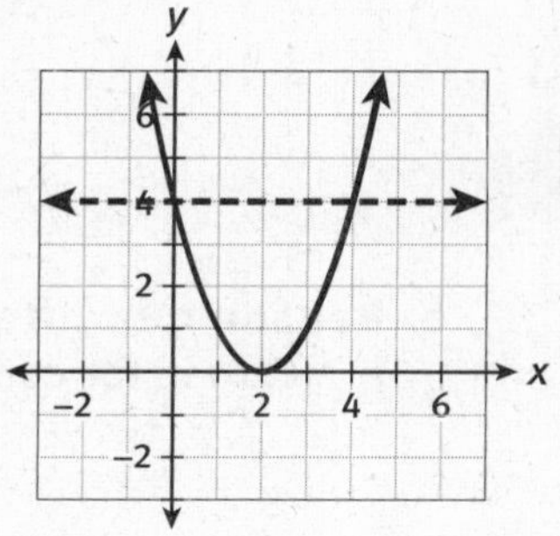

Notice that for any y-value greater than 0, a horizontal line passes through more than one point on the graph. Therefore, the inverse of f is not a function.

Step 2: Restrict the domain of f if needed.

If you restrict the domain to include only the right half of the parabola (shown in bold), the inverse of f will be a function. So, restrict the domain of f to $\{x \mid x \geq 2\}$.

Step 3: Find the inverse function.

$f(x) = (x - 2)^2$	
$y = (x - 2)^2$	Replace $f(x)$ with y.
$x = (y - 2)^2$	Switch y and x to find the inverse function.
$\sqrt{x} = y - 2$	Take the positive square root of both sides.
$\sqrt{x} + 2 = y$	Add 2 to both sides.
$\sqrt{x} + 2 = f^{-1}(x)$	Replace y with $f^{-1}(x)$.

MATH TIP

If a horizontal line passes through more than one point on the graph of a function, then the function has more than one x-value for the same y-value. As a result, the inverse of the function will have more than one y-value for the same x-value, which means that the inverse is not a function.

MATH TIP

When you restrict the domain of f to $x \geq 2$, you also restrict the range of its inverse to $y \geq 2$. So, when you are finding the equation of the inverse, you know that the quantity $y - 2$ will always be nonnegative. As a result, you can ignore the negative square root in the calculations in Step 3.

Step 4: Check by graphing.

Each graph represents a function, and the graphs are reflections of each other across the line $y = x$. So, f^{-1} is the inverse function of f.

Solution: $f^{-1}(x) = \sqrt{x} + 2$ is the inverse function of $f(x) = (x - 2)^2$, where the domain of f is $\{x \mid x \geq 2\}$. The domain of f^{-1} is $\{x \mid x \geq 0\}$, and the range is $\{y \mid y \geq 2\}$.

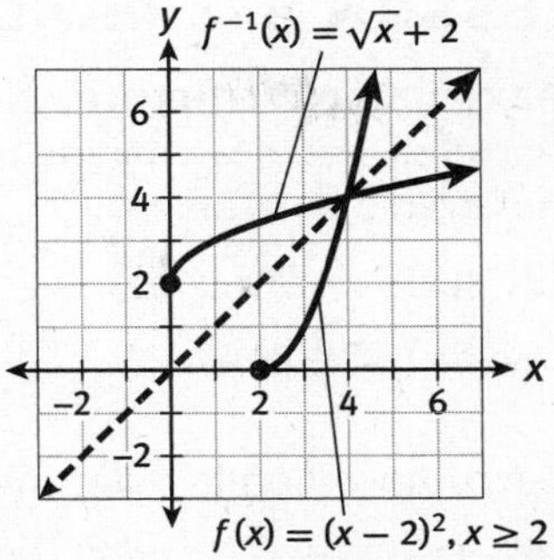

My Notes

TECHNOLOGY TIP

To graph a function with a restricted domain on a graphing calculator, enter the function rule in parentheses followed by the domain restriction in parentheses. For example, to graph $f(x) = (x - 2)^2$ with the domain restricted to $x \geq 2$, you would enter $((X - 2)^2)\ (X \geq 2)$ as Y1. To enter inequality symbols in a function rule, press 2nd TEST.

Try These A

Find the inverse function. Restrict the domain of f if needed, and describe the restriction. Then state the domain and range of the inverse function.

a. $f(x) = \frac{1}{2}x^3$ **b.** $f(x) = (x + 4)^4 - 1$

c. $f(x) = \log_2 x$ **d.** $f(x) = \sqrt{x + 3}$

Check Your Understanding

8. Explain how you can use a graph of the function $f(x) = 5x - 6$ to determine whether its inverse is a function.

9. **Make use of structure.** How would you restrict the domain of $f(x) = |x| + 4$ so that its inverse is a function? Explain how you decided on the domain restriction.

10. The graph shows a function f. Sketch the graph of its inverse function f^{-1}, and explain how you determined the coordinates of points on the graph of f^{-1}.

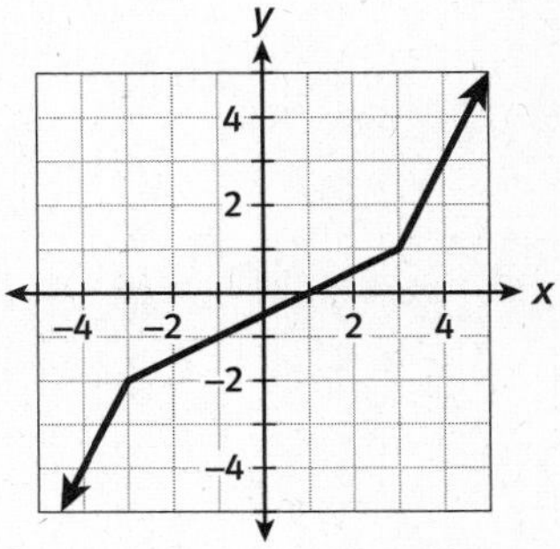

11. Find the inverse function of $f(x) = \frac{1}{x}$. What relationship do you notice between f and f^{-1} in this case?

My Notes

LESSON 8-2 PRACTICE

Make use of structure. Find the inverse function. Restrict the domain of f if needed, and describe the restriction. Then state the domain and range of the inverse function.

12. $f(x) = -2(x + 1)^2 - 4$

13. $f(x) = e^{2x}$

14. $f(x) = \frac{2}{x} + 4$

15. $f(x) = |x - 3| + 2$

Use composition to determine whether each pair of functions are inverses.

16. $f(x) = 2x - 3$ and $g(x) = \frac{1}{2}x + 3$

17. $f(x) = (x - 4)^2 + 5$ for $x \geq 4$ and $g(x) = \sqrt{x - 5} + 4$

The function $f(x) = \frac{4}{3}\pi x^3$ gives the volume in cm^3 of a sphere with a radius of x cm. Use this information for Items 18–20.

18. Write the equation of the inverse of f, and explain what the inverse represents in this situation.

19. Graph the inverse function.

20. **Reason quantitatively.** Find $f(12)$ and $f^{-1}(12)$, and explain what each represents in this situation.

ACTIVITY 8 PRACTICE

Write your answers on notebook paper.
Show your work.

Lesson 8-1

Yvonne earns \$9 per hour for the first 40 hours she works in a week. She earns \$13.50 per hour after that. Each week she deposits 15 percent of her earnings into her college savings account.

1. Write the equation of a function $f(x)$ that can be used to determine Yvonne's weekly earnings when she works x hours and $x \geq 40$.
2. Write the equation of a function $g(x)$ that can be used to determine the amount Yvonne deposits in her savings account when her weekly earnings are x dollars.
3. Find the composition $g(f(x))$. What does the composition represent in this situation?
4. Last week, Yvonne deposited \$60.08 in her savings account. How many hours did she work that week? Explain how you used the composition $g(f(x))$ to find your answer.

The function $f(x) = 331.4 + 0.6x$ gives the speed of sound in m/s in dry air, where x is the temperature in °C. The function $g(x) = \frac{5}{9}(x - 32)$ converts a temperature x in °F to °C.

5. Find $f(g(x))$, and tell what this composition represents in this situation.
6. What is the speed of sound in dry air when the temperature is 98°F? Explain how you determined your answer.

Find $f(g(x))$ and $g(f(x))$ for each pair of functions. State the domain.

7. $f(x) = 3x - 7$, $g(x) = -8x - 9$
8. $f(x) = \frac{1}{x^2}$, $g(x) = \sqrt{x - 4}$
9. $f(x) = \ln x$, $g(x) = 2x - 3$
10. $f(x) = x^2 + 3x - 1$, $g(x) = x + 4$

Write the equations of two functions $f(x)$ and $g(x)$ so that $f(g(x)) = h(x)$.

11. $h(x) = (x - 3)^2 - 5$
12. $h(x) = 16x^4$
13. $h(x) = 2\sqrt{x + 8}$
14. $h(x) = \frac{x + 2}{x + 5}$
15. The function $t(d)$ models the high temperature in °F in a certain city on day d of the year. The function $n(t)$ models the number of visitors to a pool in the city on a day when the high temperature is t °F. What does the composition $n(t(d))$ represent in this situation?

Use the tables to find each value.

x	1	3	5	7
$f(x)$	2	4	6	8

x	2	6	8	10
$g(x)$	3	7	11	15

16. $f(g(2))$
17. $g(f(5))$
18. $f(g(6))$

Given that $f(x) = x^2$ and $g(x) = 3x + 1$, find each value.

19. $f(g(4))$
20. $g(f(-2))$
21. $f(g(0))$

A function f has the graph shown. Use the graph for Items 22–23.

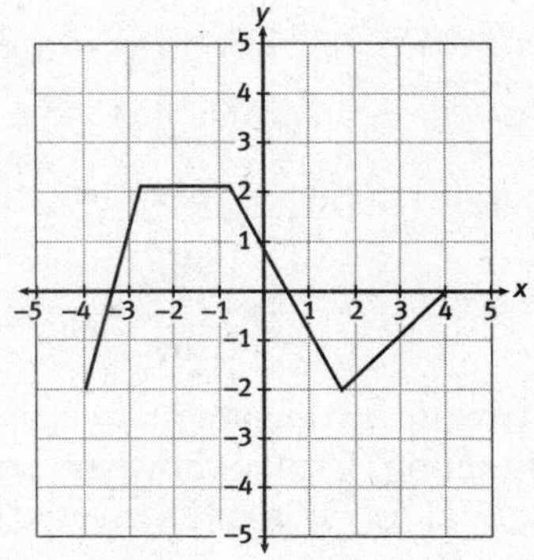

22. Sketch the graph of $y = g(f(x))$, where $g(x) = |x|$.
23. Sketch the graph of $y = f(g(x))$, where $g(x) = |x|$.

Lesson 8-2

24. Based on the table below, what is $f^{-1}(10)$?

x	0	5	10	20
$f(x)$	0	10	20	30

A. 0 **B.** 5
C. 10 **D.** 20

The graph represents a function $f(x)$. Use the graph for Items 25 and 26.

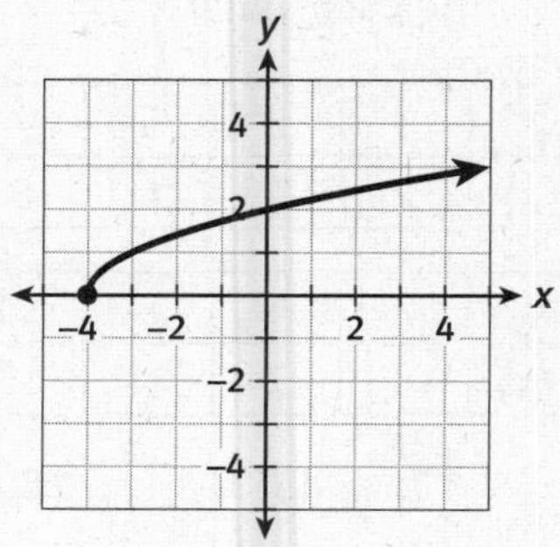

25. For what value of x is $f^{-1}(x) = -4$? Explain how you know.

26. Sketch a graph of $f^{-1}(x)$.

Find the inverse function. Restrict the domain of f if needed, and describe the restriction. Then state the domain and range of the inverse function.

27. $f(x) = 2x^2 + 4$ **28.** $f(x) = -3\log(x + 2)$

29. $f(x) = \sqrt[3]{x - 6}$ **30.** $f(x) = (x + 1)^4 - 1$

31. Given that $f(x) = \frac{2x - 1}{4}$, what is $f^{-1}(3)$?

A. $\frac{11}{2}$ **B.** $\frac{13}{2}$
C. 8 **D.** 26

32. Explain why the inverse of $f(x) = (x + 1)(x - 3)$ is not a function. Explain how you could restrict the domain of $f(x)$ so that its inverse would be a function.

33. The table represents the function $g(x)$. Make a table that represents its inverse, $g^{-1}(x)$.

x	−5	−2	7	12
$g(x)$	−4	1	6	−10

Use composition to determine whether each pair of functions are inverses.

34. $f(x) = \log_3(x - 1)$ and $g(x) = 3^{x+1}$

35. $f(x) = \frac{1}{x + 2}$ and $g(x) = \frac{1}{x} - 2$

36. $f(x) = -4(x - 6)$ and $g(x) = -\frac{1}{4}(x - 24)$

The function $f(x) = \left(\frac{1}{2}\right)^x$ gives the probability of getting heads x times in a row when tossing a coin. Use this information for Items 37 and 38.

37. Write the equation of the inverse of f, and explain what the inverse represents in this situation.

38. Find $f^{-1}(0.01)$, and explain what it represents in this situation.

MATHEMATICAL PRACTICES
Make Sense of Problems and Persevere in Solving Them

39. Recall that the formula $A = Pe^{rt}$ gives the balance A in an account that earns continuously compounded interest, where P is the principal, r is the annual interest rate expressed as a decimal, and t is the time in years. Gilberto deposits \$1000 in an account that earns continuously compounded interest. After 1 year, the balance in the account is \$1030.45. How many years will it take for the balance in the account to reach \$1500? Show your work, and include in your answer both the equation of a function that gives the account balance after x years and the equation of a function that gives the number of years for the balance in the account to reach x dollars.

Transformations, Compositions, and Inverses

FEEDING FRENZY

Even when an animal is sitting still, its body is using energy. An animal's basal metabolic rate, or BMR, is a measure of the amount of energy the animal uses per day when at rest. An animal's BMR is related to its weight. In general, the more an animal weighs, the higher its BMR and the more food it needs to eat each day.

1. The function $f(x) = 70x^{\frac{3}{4}}$ can be used to estimate the BMR of mammals and many other types of animals. In this function, x is the mass of the animal in kilograms, and $f(x)$ is its BMR in kilocalories (kcal) per day. Note that 1 kcal is equal to 1 food Calorie.

a. The graph of the function $f(x) = 70x^{\frac{3}{4}}$ is given below. Write appropriate scales and labels for the axes.

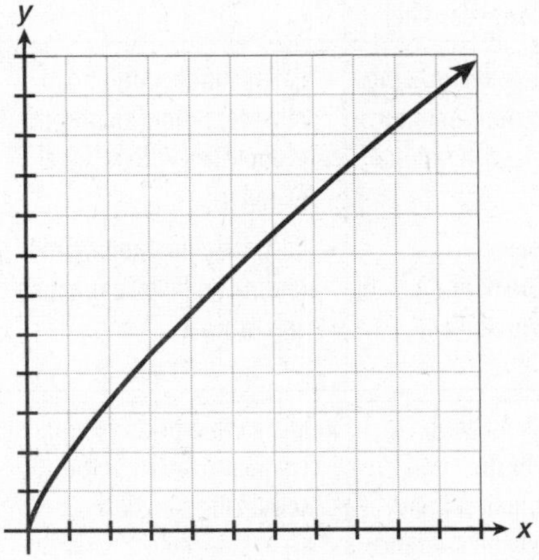

b. What are the domain and range of the function? Explain mathematically why the domain is not all real numbers.

c. Does the value of the function increase or decrease over its domain? Why does it make sense in the context of the problem situation that the function behaves in this way?

d. Describe the graph of $f(x)$ as a transformation of the graph of $h(x) = x^{\frac{3}{4}}$. Explain how you identified the transformation.

2. A male Bengal tiger at a zoo has an estimated BMR of 4000 kcal/day, and a female Bengal tiger has an estimated BMR of 2850 kcal/day.

a. Find the inverse of $f(x) = 70x^{\frac{3}{4}}$, and explain what the inverse represents in this situation.

b. Predict how much greater the mass of the male tiger is than that of the female tiger. Explain how you determined your answer.

3. The howler monkeys at a zoo are fed a diet that contains 3.35 kcal/gram.

a. Write a function $g(x)$ that gives the mass of food in grams that a howler monkey must eat to obtain x kilocalories of energy.

b. Find $g(f(x))$, and tell what it represents in this situation.

c. One of the howler monkeys has a mass of 9 kg. How many grams of food must it eat each day just to meet the needs of its basal metabolic rate?

Transformations, Compositions, and Inverses

FEEDING FRENZY

Scoring Guide	Exemplary	Proficient	Emerging	Incomplete
	The solution demonstrates these characteristics:			
Mathematics Knowledge and Thinking (Item 2)	• Clear and accurate understanding of a monomial with a rational exponent and a clear understanding of inverse functions in this context	• A functional understanding of undoing a function to find a solution of a monomial with a rational exponent and also understanding of inverse operations to solve the word problem	• Partial understanding of functions using rational exponents and/or partial understanding of solving them	• Little or no understanding of functions with rational exponents or techniques to solve
Problem Solving (Items 1, 2, 3)	• An appropriate and efficient strategy that results in a correct answer	• A strategy that may include unnecessary steps but results in a correct answer	• A strategy that results in some incorrect answers	• No clear strategy when solving problems
Mathematical Modeling / Representations (Items 1, 2)	• Clear and accurate understanding of representations of graphs of monomials with rational exponents • Clear and accurate understanding of finding an inverse function and using it	• A functional understanding of representations of graphs of monomials with rational exponents • Mostly accurate understanding of finding an inverse function and using it	• Partial understanding of representations of graphs of monomials with rational exponents • Partial understanding of finding an inverse function and using it	• Little or no understanding of representations of graphs of monomials with rational exponents • Inaccurate or incomplete understanding of inverses
Reasoning and Communication (Item 3)	• Precise use of appropriate math terms and language to describe the composite function and its meaning in the context of the problem with appropriate units	• Correct characterization of the solution of the composite function (may not necessarily understand it completely in the context of the problem)	• Misleading or confusing characterization of the composite function	• Incomplete or inaccurate characterization of the composite function

Functions and Their Graphs

2

Unit Overview

In this unit you will study polynomial and rational functions, their graphs, and their zeros. You will also learn several theorems related to polynomials and their complex roots, whether rational or imaginary.

Key Terms

As you study this unit, add these and other terms to your math notebook. Include in your notes your prior knowledge of each word, as well as your experiences in using the word in different mathematical examples. If needed, ask for help in pronouncing new words and add information on pronunciation to your math notebook. It is important that you learn new terms and use them correctly in your class discussions and in your problem solutions.

Academic Vocabulary

- efficiency

Math Terms

- relative maximum
- relative minimum
- turning points
- polynomial function
- end behavior
- increasing
- decreasing
- multiplicity
- multiple root
- Fundamental Theorem of Algebra
- Linear Factorization Theorem
- Rational Root Theorem
- Factor Theorem
- Remainder Theorem
- Descartes' Rule of Signs
- Complex Conjugate Theorem
- bounded
- vertical asymptote
- horizontal asymptote
- parameter
- hole
- oblique asymptote

ESSENTIAL QUESTIONS

? How are zeros and end behavior of polynomial functions and their graphs related to the degree and the factors of the polynomial?

? How are rational functions used to model real-world problems?

EMBEDDED ASSESSMENTS

These assessments, following Activities 11 and 13, will give you an opportunity to demonstrate what you have learned about polynomial functions, rational functions, and exponential and logarithmic functions.

Getting Ready

Write your answers on notebook paper or grid paper. Show your work.

1. Simplify $\left(\dfrac{6x^2}{y^3}\right)^2$.

2. Multiply.

a. $(2x^2+1)(2x-1)$

b. $(x-2+3i)(x-2-3i)$

3. Factor x^2-6x+5. Then solve $x^2-6x+5=0$.

4. Evaluate. $\dfrac{3^{327}}{3^{323}}$.

5. Use synthetic division to divide x^3-7x-6 by $x+2$.

6. Find the x- and y-intercepts of $y=-2(x-3)^2+4$.

7. Describe the pattern displayed by 1, 2, 5, 10, 17, ...

8. A simple interest loan with a principal of \$5000 is paid back after $2\frac{1}{2}$ years. The total payment is \$5875. What was the annual rate of interest on the loan?

9. Draw the fourth stage of the figure below. Explain how you would create any figure in the pattern and find the number of squares.

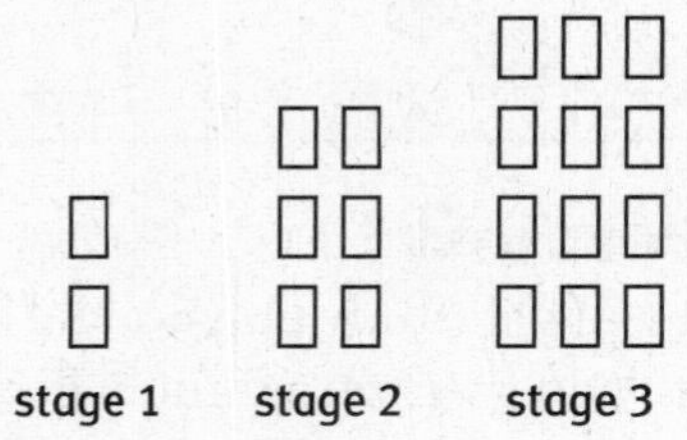

10. Find a linear regression model for the data.

x	y
1	4
3	8
4	10
5	13

Polynomials

Sunspots

Lesson 9-1 Data and Polynomial Models

My Notes

Learning Targets:

- Compare models to best fit a data set.
- Use a polynomial regression to make predictions.

SUGGESTED LEARNING STRATEGIES: Summarizing, Paraphrasing, Look for a Pattern, Create Representations, Discussion Groups, Quickwrite

Dark areas called *sunspots* appear on the surface of the Sun. Sunspots last from a few days to a few weeks. Scientists who study sunspots have found that there appears to be a relationship over time between the number of sunspots and the year in which they occur.

The following data represent the number of sunspots for 1991 through 2000. Data were obtained from the National Geophysical Data Center.

Year	Years Since 1990	Sunspots
1991		146
1992		94
1993		55
1994		30
1995		18
1996		9
1997		22
1998		64
1999		93
2000		120

CONNECT TO SCIENCE

Sunspots appear in pairs. They are intense magnetic fields that break through the surface of the sun. The field lines leave through one sunspot and re-enter through another.

Sunspots were observed as early as 200 B.C. by the Chinese. It was not until the mid-nineteenth century that Rudolf Wolf devised a method for estimating daily solar activity.

1. **Model with mathematics.** Fill in the table. Explain why a linear function would not be an appropriate model to represent the number of sunspots given the number of years since 1990.

2. Would an exponential function be a good model for the data? Explain your reasoning.

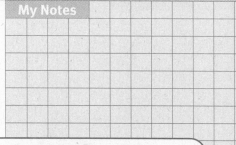

My Notes

3. Graph the data from the table for the number of sunspots as a function of the number of years since 1990. Label both axes on the graph with an appropriate scale.

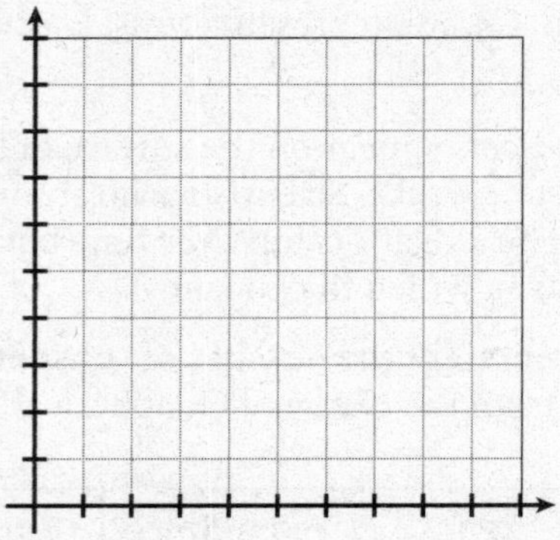

4. Examine the table and graph. What type of function could be used to model the data? Explain your reasoning.

5. Use the regression capabilities of your graphing calculator. Find a model that best represents the data.

6. List the important features of the graph of this function.

7. According to the model, in which year are the sunspot occurrences at a minimum?

TECHNOLOGY TIP

A graphing calculator can be used to find the maximum or the minimum values of a quadratic function.

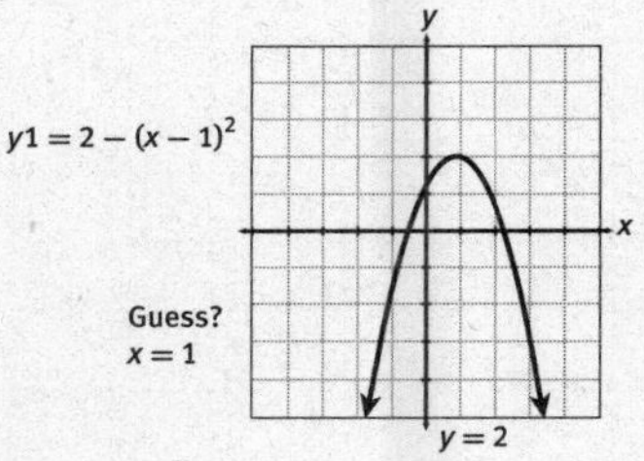

MATH TIP

The quadratic formula is

$$x = \frac{-b \pm \sqrt{b^2 - 4ac}}{2a}.$$

My Notes

8. Use the model you found in Item 5 to determine the year(s) in which the number of sunspots is 200.

9. Reason quantitatively. Do you think the quadratic model is accurate for the distant past and future? Explain.

The table below shows sunspot data from the year 1991 to 2005.

Year	Sunspots
1991	146
1992	94
1993	55
1994	30
1995	18
1996	9
1997	22
1998	64

Year	Sunspots
1999	93
2000	120
2001	111
2002	104
2003	64
2004	40
2005	30

MATH TERMS

A function value $f(a)$ is a **relative maximum** of f if there is an interval around a where, for any x in that interval, $f(a) \geq f(x)$.

A function value $f(a)$ is a **relative minimum** of f if there is an interval around a where, for any x in that interval, $f(a) \leq f(x)$.

Relative maxima and minima are often referred to as **turning points**.

10. Graph the data from the table for the number of sunspots as a function of the year since 1990. Label both axes on the graph with an appropriate scale.

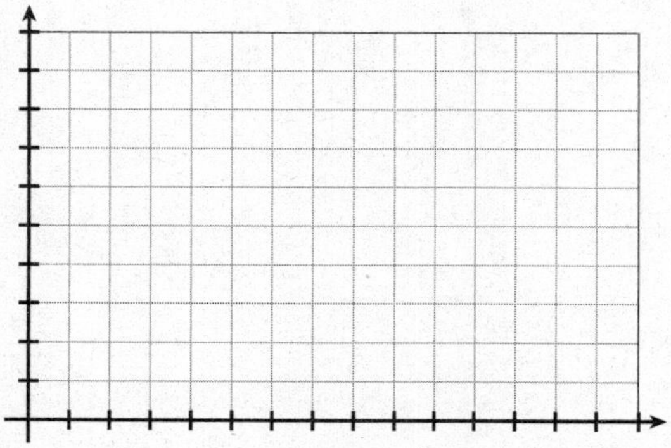

My Notes

11. What type of function could best be used to model the data? Explain your reasoning.

TECHNOLOGY TIP

Be sure to begin with a viewing window within which all the points of the table will be included. Then expand it to see your function without domain restrictions.

12. Use appropriate tools strategically. Use the regression capabilities of your graphing calculator to find a model to represent the data.

TECHNOLOGY TIP

A graphing calculator can be used to find the turning points of a polynomial function. Use the same method that you would use to find a maximum or a minimum of a quadratic function.

13. List the important features of the graph of the function you found in Item 12 without the domain restrictions of the context. In other words, look at the graph of the function defined over the set of real numbers.

14. Do you think the model from Item 12 would be appropriate for predicting sunspot data 25 years into the future? Explain.

15. Could you use this model to predict the number of sunspots observed by the Chinese in 200 B.C.? Explain.

ACTIVITY 6 PRACTICE

Write your answers on notebook paper. Show your work.

Lesson 6-1

Identify the transformation of $f(x)$ that each function represents.

1. $g(x) = f(x - 5)$
2. $g(x) = 3f(x)$

Describe each function as one or more transformations of its parent function.

3. $g(x) = \log(x + 4)$
4. $g(x) = -x^2 - 3$
5. $g(x) = \dfrac{2}{x+5}$
6. $g(x) = e^{-4x}$

Use the table below to help you create a table of values for each transformation of $f(x)$.

x	−8	−5	−1	0	4	9
$f(x)$	17	14	10	9	5	10

7. $y = -2f(x)$
8. $y = f(x - 4)$

Use the graph of $f(x)$ for Items 9–12. Sketch each transformation of $f(x)$.

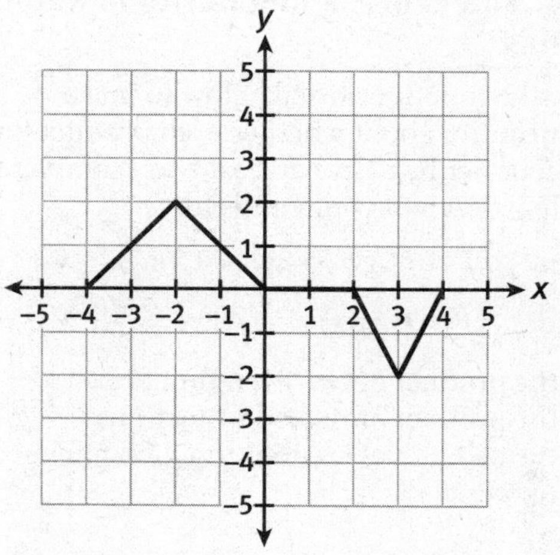

9. $y = \frac{1}{2}f(x)$
10. $y = f(x - 3)$
11. $y = -f(x)$
12. $y = f(x) - 2$

Determine if the following functions are odd, even, or neither. Then describe the symmetry of the graph of the function, if any.

13. $f(x) = |x^5|$
14. $f(x) = e^{x-5}$
15. $f(x) = \sqrt[3]{x}$
16. $f(x) = \dfrac{x}{x^2+1}$
17. Explain how the real-world models of functions $p(x) = 4r(x)$ and $q(x) = r(4x)$ differ.

Use the given information to write the equation of $g(x)$, and then graph $g(x)$.

18. The graph of $g(x)$ is a translation 2 units to the right of the graph of $f(x) = e^x$ followed by a reflection over the x-axis.
19. The graph of $g(x)$ is vertical stretch of the graph of $f(x) = x^2 + 4x$ by a factor of 2 followed by a translation 4 units down.
20. The function $f(x) = -(x - 25)^2 + 625$ gives the area in square feet of a rectangular pen that can be enclosed by a small roll of fencing, where x is the length of the pen. The function $g(x)$ gives the area in square feet of a rectangular pen that can be enclosed by a large roll of fencing. The graph of $g(x)$ is a translation 25 units to the right and 1875 units up of the graph of $f(x)$.
    a. Write the equation of $g(x)$.
    b. Graph $f(x)$ and $g(x)$ on the same coordinate grid.
    c. What is the perimeter of a rectangular pen enclosed with a small roll of fencing? What is the perimeter of a rectangular pen enclosed with a large roll? Explain how you know.
21. The function $f(x) = 2000e^{0.03x}$ models the amount in dollars in an investment account after x years for an initial investment of \$2000. The function $g(x)$ models a second investment account. The graph of $g(x)$ is a horizontal compression of the graph of $f(x)$ by a factor of $\frac{3}{5}$.
    a. Write the equation of $g(x)$.
    b. In which account would you rather invest your money, the one modeled by $f(x)$ or the one modeled by $g(x)$? Justify your choice.

22. The points $(2, -1)$ and $(4, -8)$ lie on the graph of $f(x)$. Assuming that $f(x)$ is odd, which of the following points must also lie on the graph of $f(x)$?

A. $(-1, 2)$ **B.** $(-4, -8)$
C. $(-2, 1)$ **D.** $(8, -4)$

Lesson 6-2

Find the sum, difference, product, and quotient of the functions in each item below. State the domain.

23. $f(x) = 3x - 7, g(x) = -8x - 9$

24. $f(x) = \frac{1}{x^2}, g(x) = \sqrt{x - 4}$

25. $f(x) = x^2 - x - 6, g(x) = x + 2$

26. $f(x) = \begin{cases} 3x - 1 & \text{if } x \le 2 \\ -4x & \text{if } x > 2 \end{cases}, g(x) = 2x - 5$

Graph each piecewise-defined function. Determine and analyze any key features such as domain, range, relative extrema, and zeros.

27. $f(x) = \begin{cases} -2 & \text{if } x < -1 \\ 2 & \text{if } -1 \le x \le 1 \\ 4 & \text{if } x > 1 \end{cases}$

28. $f(x) = \begin{cases} x^2 - 3 & \text{if } x \le 0 \\ 2x - 3 & \text{if } 0 < x < 5 \\ 7 & \text{if } x \ge 5 \end{cases}$

Use the function $f(x) = \begin{cases} -x + 5 & \text{if } x \le 2 \\ (x - 4)^2 & \text{if } x > 2 \end{cases}$ and the given information to write the equation of $g(x)$, and then graph $g(x)$.

29. The graph of $g(x)$ is a translation 5 units left of the graph of $f(x)$.

30. The graph of $g(x)$ is a vertical stretch of the graph of $f(x)$ by a factor of 3.

31. The graph of $g(x)$ is a reflection of the graph of $f(x)$ over the x-axis.

32. What is the domain of $\left(\frac{f}{g}\right)(x)$ given that $f(x) = \sqrt{x - 3}$ and $g(x) = (x + 2)^2$?

A. $[0, \infty)$ **B.** $[3, \infty)$
C. $\{x \mid x \neq -2\}$ **D.** $\mathbb{R}$

33. The cost in dollars of ordering x football jerseys from a company is given by

$$f(x) = \begin{cases} 35x & \text{if } 0 < x \le 10 \\ 32x & \text{if } x > 10 \end{cases}.$$

a. The function $g(x)$ is a vertical compression of $f(x)$ by a factor of 0.9. Write the equation of $g(x)$. Then tell what $g(x)$ represents in this situation.

b. The function $h(x) = 2x$ gives the discount in dollars that a returning customer receives when buying x jerseys. Find $f - h$, and tell what it represents in this situation.

34. The function $f(x) = 3.6x$ gives the cost in dollars of buying x gallons of gasoline. The function $g(x) = 30x$ gives the distance in miles Anuja can drive her car on x gallons of gasoline. Find $\frac{f}{g}$, and tell what it represents in this situation.

MATHEMATICAL PRACTICES
Look For and Express Regularity in Repeated Reasoning

35. Use the functions listed below to make conjectures about whether each product is even, odd, or neither. Give at least two examples to support each of your conjectures.

Even: $f(x) = x^2, g(x) = x^2 + 1, h(x) = x^4$

Odd: $p(x) = x^3, q(x) = \frac{1}{x}, r(x) = \frac{1}{2}x^3$

a. the product of two even functions
b. the product of two odd functions
c. the product of an even function and an odd function

My Notes

Check Your Understanding

Use notebook paper to write your answers.

16. Find a model to represent the data.

x	−4	−3	−1	0	1	4	6
y	−3	0	1	1.5	1	−2	−8

17. Graph the equation you found in Item 16. List the important features of the graph.

18. Describe the characteristics of a data set that could be accurately modeled by a linear function.

LESSON 9-1 PRACTICE

19. Examine the data in the table. What type of function could be used to model the data? Explain your reasoning.

x	1	2	3	4	5	6	7	8	9	10
y	49	22	16	12	10	14	19	17	10	3

20. Use the regression capabilities of your graphing calculator to find a model that best represents the data in Item 19.

21. **Attend to precision.** Graph the equation you found in Item 19. List the important features of the graph. Approximate any values to three decimal places.

22. An insect population doubles each month. What type of function could be used to model the data for the number of insects as a function of the number of months since January 2012? Explain your reasoning.

23. **Critique the reasoning of others.** Jenna says the graph on her calculator, as shown below, must represent a quadratic function. Is she correct? Explain your reasoning.

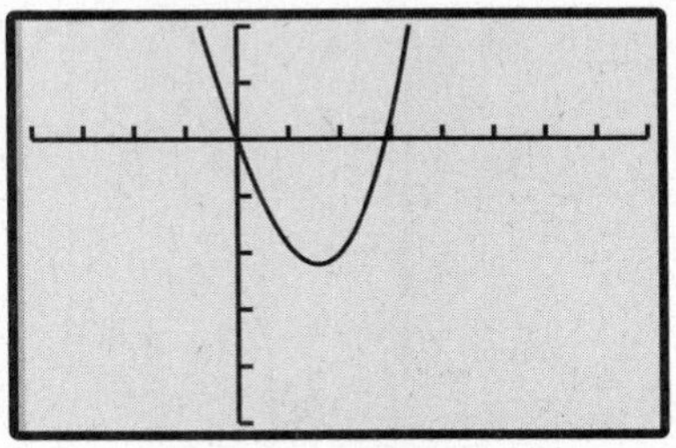

My Notes

Learning Targets:

- Describe and analyze graphs of polynomial functions.
- Graph polynomial functions using technology.

SUGGESTED LEARNING STRATEGIES: Think-Pair-Share, Group Presentations, Look for a Pattern, Quickwrite

MATH TERMS

End behavior of a function can be determined by seeing what happens to the graph of a function on the extreme left and right ends of the *x*-axis. See what happens to *y* as *x* approaches $-\infty$ and ∞.

You used a quadratic function and a cubic function to model the sunspot data. These are examples of *polynomial functions*. A **polynomial function** of degree n is one that can be written in the form

$$f(x) = a_n x^n + a_{n-1}x^{n-1} + \ldots + a_1 x + a_0$$

where n is a nonnegative integer and the coefficients $a_0, a_1, \ldots a_n$ are real numbers with a leading coefficient $a_n \neq 0$.

MATH TIP

Some important features of graphs are the *x*-intercept(s) or zeros of a function, the *y*-intercept, and the turning points, also known as the relative maximum and minimum values of a function.

MATH TERMS

A function is said to be **increasing** on intervals of the domain where the graph is rising and **decreasing** on intervals of the domain where the graph is falling.

1. **Make sense of problems.** Describe the important features of the graphs below.

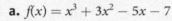

a. $f(x) = x^3 + 3x^2 - 5x - 7$	Features of the Graph
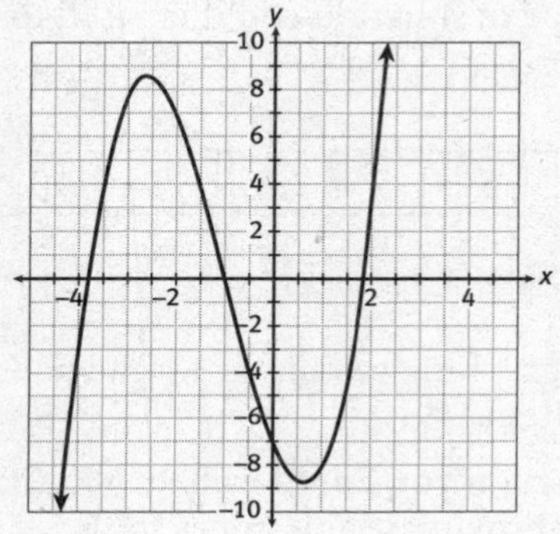	
b. $f(x) = x^3 + x^2 + x + 1$	Features of the Graph
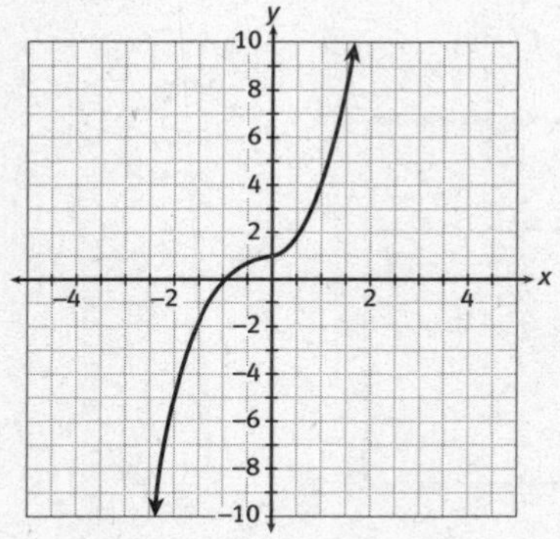	

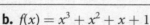

c. $f(x) = -2x^3 - 3x^2 + 8x + 3$	Features of the Graph
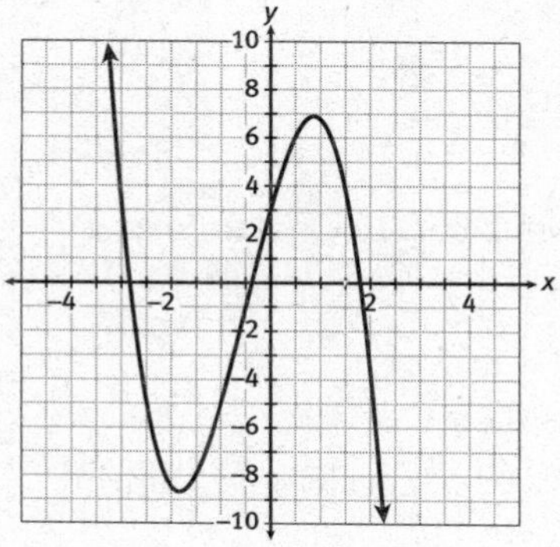	
d. $f(x) = -4x^3 - x^2 + x + 6$	Features of the Graph
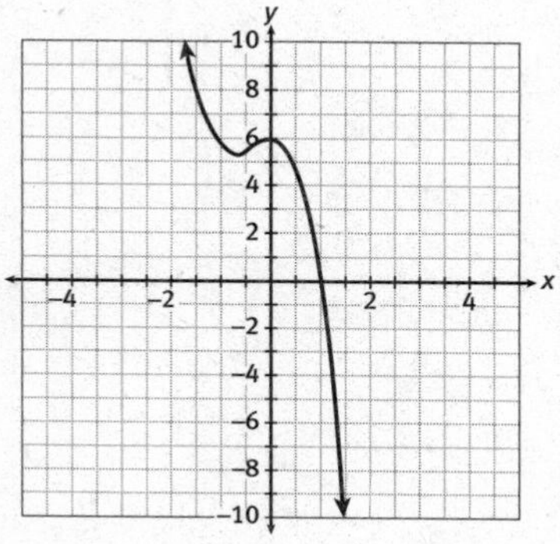	

2. Compare and contrast the end behavior of cubic functions to the end behavior of quadratic functions.

My Notes

DISCUSSION GROUP TIP

As needed, refer to the Glossary to review translations of key terms. Incorporate your understanding into group discussions to confirm your knowledge and use of key mathematical language.

My Notes

TECHNOLOGY TIP

A graphing calculator can be used to find the zeros, the relative maximum, and the relative minimum points on a graph.

$y = x^3 - 2x^2 - 9x + 18$

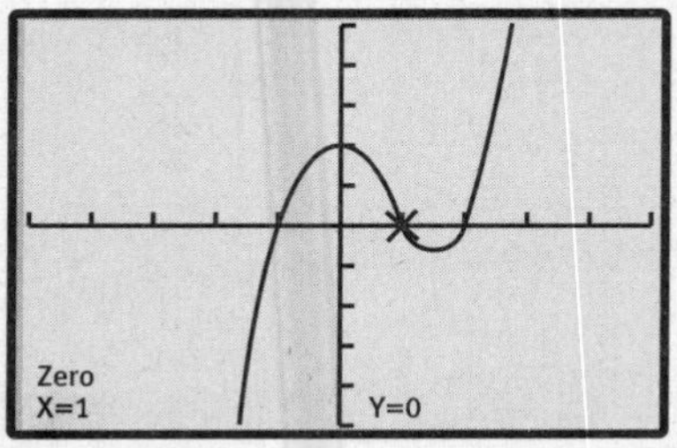

MATH TERMS

The number of times a given polynomial function has a factor is the **multiplicity** of the related root.

MATH TERMS

A **multiple root** occurs when a polynomial equation has a root with multiplicity of 2 or greater. For example, $f(x) = (x + 3)^2 (x - 3)^2$ has *double roots* at $x = 3$ and also at $x = -3$.

3. Use appropriate tools strategically. Use a graphing calculator to examine the graphs of the following functions. Determine the following:

- the degree of the polynomial
- the leading coefficient
- the end behavior of the polynomial function
- the maximum number of zeros
- the maximum number of turning points (relative maxima and minima)

a. $f(x) = -\frac{1}{2}x^2 - 4x$

b. $f(x) = x(x + 2)^2 (x - 2)^2$

c. $f(x) = x(x - 1)^2 (x + 2)^2$

d. $f(x) = -2x^4 + 6x^2 + 4$

e. $f(x) = x^2 + 5x + 7$

f. $f(x) = -2x^5 - 3x^3 + 8x$

g. $f(x) = 4x^5 - 8x^4 - 5x^3 + 10x^2 + x - 1$

h. $f(x) = -\frac{1}{4}x^4 + 3x^2 - 3$

i. $f(x) = x^4 + 2$

My Notes

4. For each of the functions in Items 3a to 3d, find the domain and the range of the function, the zeros, the relative maximum and relative minimum points, and the intervals of the domain where the function is increasing and decreasing.

5. What is the relationship between double roots of a polynomial and relative maximum and minimum values?

Check Your Understanding

Use notebook paper to write your answers.

6. Reason abstractly. List the important features of the graph below. Approximate any values to three decimal places.

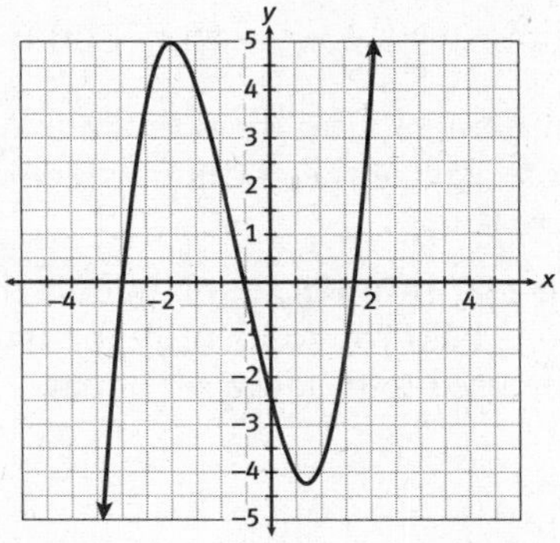

7. Without using a calculator, list end behavior and x- and y-intercepts of the function.

$f(x) = (x + 2)(x - 2)(x + 5)(x - 5)(x + 7)$

8. Use a graphing calculator to find the zeros, turning points, y-intercepts, and end behavior.

$f(x) = x^5 + 5x^4 - 68x^3 - 340x^2 + 256x + 1280$

9. Compare and contrast the end behavior of linear functions to the end behavior of quadratic functions.

My Notes

LESSON 9-2 PRACTICE

10. List the degree of each function below.

a. $x^2 + 2x - 4$

b. $x(x - 1)^2$

c. $x(x - 1)^2(x + 1)^2$

d. $(x + 1)(x^2 + 2x - 4)$

11. List the important features of the graph below. Approximate any values to three decimal places.

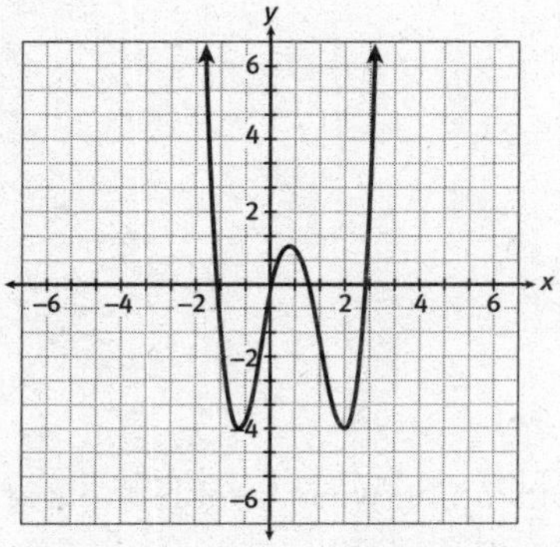

12. Without using a calculator, determine the end behavior and *x*- and *y*-intercepts of the function.

$$f(x) = (x + 4)(x - 4)(x + 1)(x - 1)$$

13. Without using a calculator, find the end behavior, maximum possible zeros, and maximum possible turning points.

$$f(x) = -2x^8 + 2x^5 - x^4 + 5x^2 - 9$$

14. Use appropriate tools strategically. Use a graphing calculator to find the zeros, turning points, *y*-intercepts, and end behavior.

$$f(x) = x^5 + x^4 - 25x^3 - 25x^2 + 144x + 144$$

15. For the function in Item 13, find the domain and the range of the function and the intervals of the domain where the function is increasing and decreasing.

16. Construct viable arguments. Explain how the important features of polynomial functions help you to identify the type of polynomial function that can be used to model a set of data.

ACTIVITY 9 PRACTICE

Write your answers on notebook paper.
Show your work.

Lesson 9-1

1. Examine the data in the table. What type of function could be used to model the data? Explain your reasoning.

x	−6	−5	−4	−3	−2	−1	0	1	2	3
y	−5	−1	5	9	10	6	5	−1	−7	−13

2. Use the regression capabilities of your graphing calculator to find a model that best represents the data in Item 1.

3. Graph the equation you found in Item 2. List the important features of the graph. Approximate any values to three decimal places.

4. Use the regression capabilities of your graphing calculator to create a model to represent the data in the table.

x	−1	0	1	2	3	5
y	−3	3	3.5	1	−1.5	5

5. Graph the function you found in Item 4 and list the important features of the graph.

6. The graph of data in a data table falls along a curve. Which type of function is *not* an appropriate model for the data in the table?
   A. linear
   B. exponential
   C. quadratic
   D. cubic

7. A small community theater makes slight changes to Saturday night ticket prices each week for 6 weeks. They record the data each week. The table below shows total ticket revenue, in dollars, as a function of ticket price.

Ticket Price (*x*)	10	15	20	25	30	35
Total Revenue (*y*)	450	645	800	925	780	700

   a. Use the regression capabilities of your graphing calculator to find a model that best represents this situation.
   b. Use your calculator to graph the equation you found in part a.
   c. The theater wants to set ticket prices at the price that will maximize revenue based on the data they recorded. What is the optimal ticket price? Explain your reasoning.

Lesson 9-2

8. List the degree of each function below.
   a. $12x^2 + 3x^6 - 14x$
   b. $x^3(x - 3)^2$
   c. $(x + 7)^2(x - 2)^2$

9. List the important features of each graph. Approximate any values to three decimal places.
   a. $f(x) = -2x^3 - 2x^2 + 9x + 1$

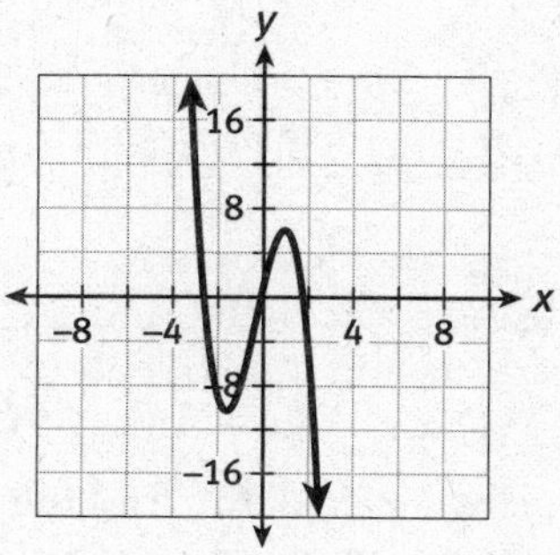

b. $f(x) = x^3 + 6x^2 + 11x + 6$

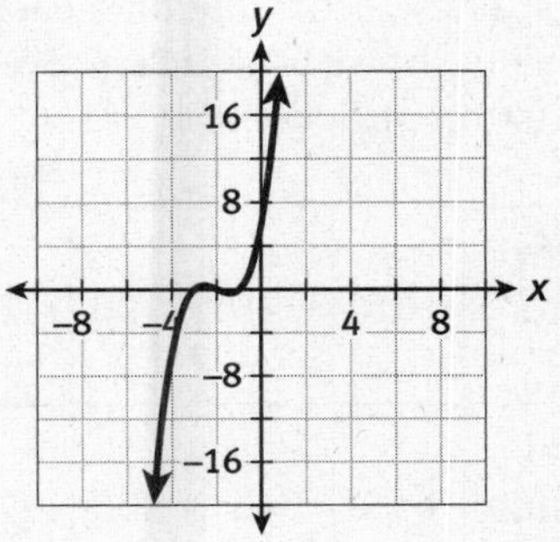

c. $f(x) = x^4 + 2$

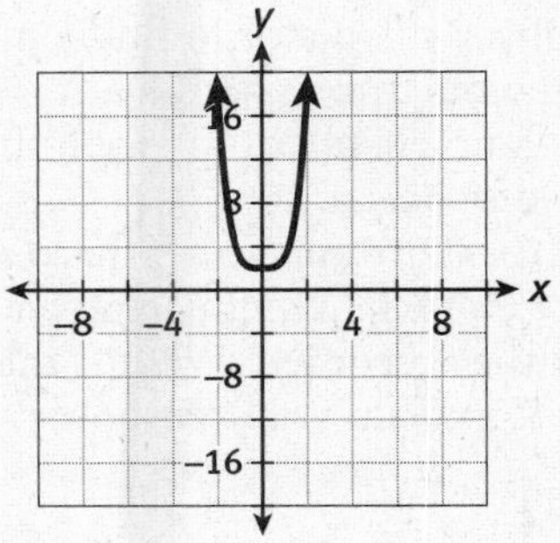

d. $f(x) = x^4 - 3x^2 - 6$

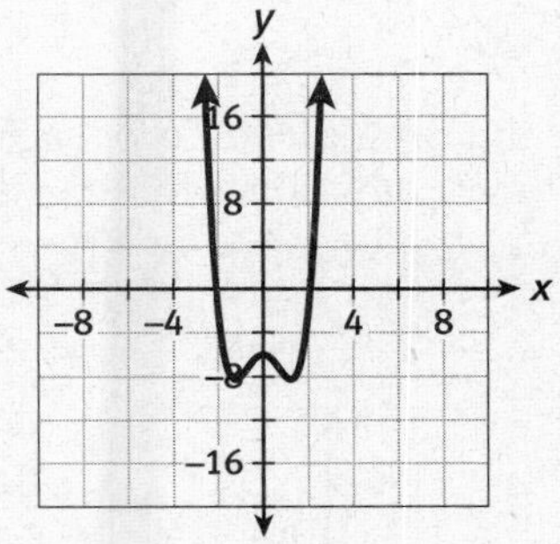

10. Without using a calculator, find the end behavior and x- and y-intercepts of $f(x) = (x + 4)(x - 3)(x + 3)(x - 9)(x + 2)$.

11. Without using a calculator, find the end behavior, maximum possible zeros, and maximum possible turning points of $f(x) = 5x^9 + 6x^5 - 3x^3 + 5x - 4$.

12. Use a graphing calculator to find the zeros, turning points, y-intercepts, and end behavior of $f(x) = x^4 - 5x^3 - 30x^2 + 40x + 64$.

13. Use a graphing calculator to examine the graphs of the following functions. Determine

- the degree of the polynomial
- the leading coefficient
- the end behavior of the polynomial function
- the maximum number of zeros
- the maximum number of turning points (relative maxima and minima)

a. $f(x) = \frac{1}{2}x^2 + 2x$
b. $f(x) = x(x + 1)^2(x - 1)^2$
c. $f(x) = x^3 + 10x^2 + 31x + 30$

14. For the functions in Item 13, parts a–c, find the domain and the range of the function, zeros, relative maximum and relative minimum points, and the intervals of the domain where the function is increasing and decreasing.

15. Roberto claims that if he knows the degree of a polynomial function, he can correctly determine exactly how many turning points are in the function's graph. Is Roberto correct? If not, explain his error.

16. Write to another student describing a pattern you have recognized among polynomials of different degrees. Write to explain how the pattern is related to features of the various functions.

MATHEMATICAL PRACTICES
Look For and Make Use of Structure

17. Explain how zeros and end behavior of polynomial functions and their graphs are related to the degree and the factors of the polynomial.

Analyzing Polynomial Functions

ACTIVITY 10

Graph It

Lesson 10-1 Sketching Graphs of Polynomial Functions

My Notes

Learning Targets:

- Analyze end behavior and zeros to sketch polynomial functions.
- Understand the Fundamental Theorem of Algebra.
- Understand the Linear Factorization Theorem.

SUGGESTED LEARNING STRATEGIES: Discussion Groups, Guess and Check, Look for a Pattern, Think-Pair-Share, Summarizing, Paraphrasing

Use the graphs of $f(x)$ and $g(x)$ and the following polynomials for Items 1–4.

a. $x^8 - 4x^2 + 2$ **b.** $-x^6 + 4.5x^2 + 2$
c. $x^5 - 4x^2 + 2$ **d.** $x^4 - 4.5x^2 + 2$
e. $-x^4 - 5x^2 + 3$ **f.** $x^6 - 5x^2 + 3$

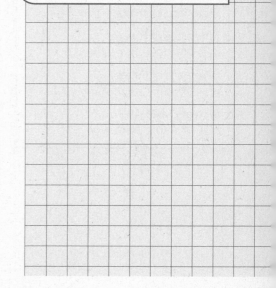

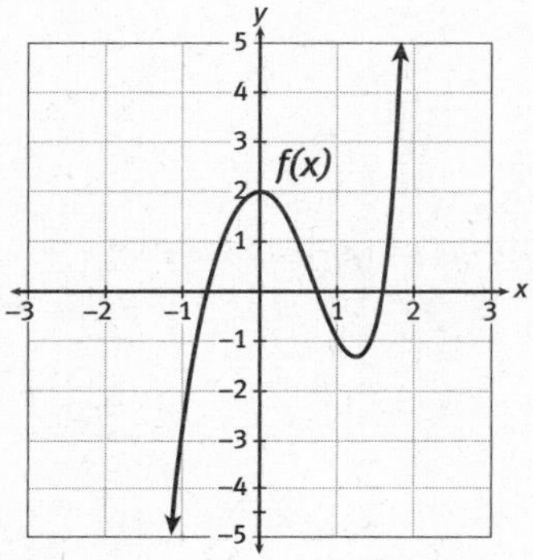

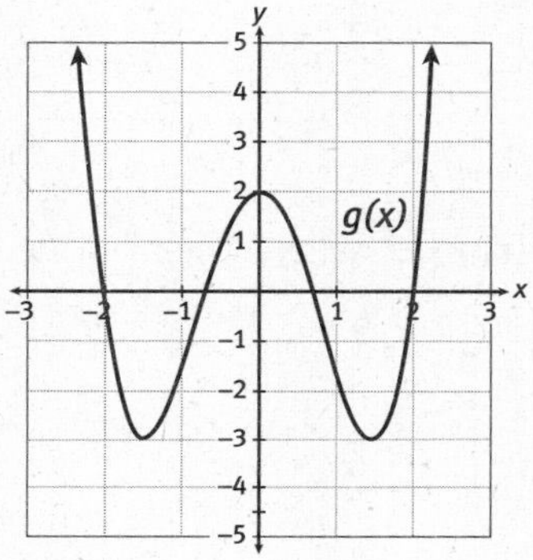

1. Without using a calculator, determine which polynomial function represents the graph of $f(x)$.

2. Which features of the graph and functions did you use to help determine which function matched the graph?

3. Without using a calculator, determine which polynomial function represents the graph of $g(x)$.

4. Which features of the graph and functions did you use to help determine which function matched the graph?

CONNECT TO AP

In AP Calculus, you will learn that a type of polynomial called a Taylor Polynomial can be used to approximate other types of functions including exponential functions and trigonometric functions.

My Notes

MATH TIP

To find the x-intercepts of a function, set the function equal to zero and solve for x. To find the y-intercept of a function, evaluate the function at $x = 0$.

MATH TIP

The quadratic formula is $x = \frac{-b \pm \sqrt{b^2 - 4ac}}{2a}$.

MATH TIP

Factoring shortcuts

Difference of Squares
$a^2 - b^2 = (a + b)(a - b)$

Difference of Cubes
$a^3 - b^3 = (a - b)(a^2 + ab + b^2)$

Sum of Cubes
$a^3 + b^3 = (a + b)(a^2 - ab + b^2)$

Graphs of polynomials can be sketched by plotting the x- and y-intercepts and considering the end behavior of a function.

5. Make use of structure. Use what you know about end behavior and zeros of a function to sketch a small graph of each function.

a. $f(x) = x + 3$

b. $g(x) = (x + 5)(x - 5)$

c. $h(x) = (x + 4)(x - 4)(x + 1)$

d. $k(x) = (x + 2)(x - 2)(x + 1)(x - 1)$

If $x = a$ is a *zero* of a function f, then

- $x = a$ is a *solution* or *root* of the polynomial equation $f(x) = 0$,
- $(x - a)$ is a *factor* of the polynomial $f(x)$, and
- $(a, 0)$ is an *x-intercept* of the graph of f.

6. Find the real zeros of the following quadratic functions:

a. $f(x) = x^2 - x - 20$

b. $f(x) = 2x^2 - 9x - 18$

c. $f(x) = 25 - x^2$

d. $f(x) = x^2 - 5$

e. $f(x) = x^2 - 2x - 3$

f. $f(x) = x^2 + 10x + 25$

My Notes

7. Find the real zeros for the following polynomials:

a. $f(x) = x^4 - 81$

b. $f(x) = x^3 + 2x^2 - 8x$

c. $f(x) = x^3 - 27$

d. $f(x) = x^3 + 125$

8. Use appropriate tools strategically. Use your graphing calculator to find the real zeros for $f(x) = 3x^3 - 22x^2 + 6.5x + 15$.

Check Your Understanding

Use notebook paper to write your answers.

9. What is a polynomial function that could have the zeros $x = -3$, $x = -2$, and $x = 1$? Is this polynomial unique? If not, give an example of another polynomial with the same zeros.

10. A polynomial function has zeros at $x = 3$ and $x = -1$. If the function is shifted four units to the left, what are the zeros of the transformed function?

11. Make sense of problems. Explain to another student the effect that a transformation has on the zeros of a polynomial.

Taken together, the ***Fundamental Theorem of Algebra*** and the ***Linear Factorization Theorem*** guarantee that every polynomial function of degree n with real coefficients has exactly n complex zeros.

MATH TERMS

Let $p(x)$ be a polynomial function of degree n with real coefficients. The **Fundamental Theorem of Algebra** states that $p(x)$ has at least one zero in the complex number system.

The **Linear Factorization Theorem** states that $p(x)$ has precisely n linear factors.

Example A

Determine the number of zeros of $f(x) = x^2 + 5 + 2x^3 + 10x$. Then find the real zeros.

$f(x)$ has degree 3, therefore it has three complex zeros.	Determine the degree.
$2x^3 + x^2 + 10x + 5 = 0$	Set the function equal to 0.
$(2x^3 + x^2) + (10x + 5) = 0$	Factor completely.
$(x^2 + 5)(2x + 1) = 0$	
$x^2 + 5 = 0$ or $2x + 1 = 0$	
$x = \pm i\sqrt{5}$ or $x = -\frac{1}{2}$	Solve for x.

My Notes

Try These A

Factor and find the zeros of each function.

a. $f(x) = 3x^3 - 2x^2 + 12x - 8$

b. $f(x) = x^2 + 2x^3 + 4 + 8x$

c. $f(x) = x^4 - x^3 - 20x^2$

d. $f(x) = 4x^4 + 12x^2 + 8$

LESSON 10-1 PRACTICE

Determine the y-intercept and the end behavior of the following functions.

12. $y = 5x^5 - x^4 + 4x^3 + 2x + 5$

13. $y = 5x^{12} + 43x^8 - 14x^5 + 12x^2 + 8x$

Use what you know about end behavior and zeros to graph the following functions.

14. $f(x) = x(x - 5)(x - 3)(x + 2)(x + 4)$

15. $f(x) = (x - 3)^2 (x + 2)^2 (x + 4)^2$

Factor and find the zeros of each function.

16. $f(x) = 4x^3 - 3x^2 + 16x - 12$

17. $f(x) = -x^2 + 2x^3 - 9 + 18x$

18. $f(x) = x^4 + 3x^3 - 18x^2$

19. $f(x) = 2x^4 + 12x^2 + 16$

20. Graph $f(x) = (x^2 + 4x + 4)(x - 1)$.

21. Graph $f(x) = (x - 1)^3(x + 1)^2$.

22. **Construct viable arguments.** Make a conjecture about how the multiplicity of a root affects the graph of a polynomial function.

My Notes

Learning Targets:

- Apply the Rational Root Theorem to find zeros.
- Use the Factor Theorem.
- Apply the Remainder Theorem.

SUGGESTED LEARNING STRATEGIES: Create Representations, Discussion Groups, Marking the Text, Summarizing, Paraphrasing, Note Taking

The Rational Root Theorem is a useful tool for factoring higher-order polynomials.

The ***Rational Root Theorem*** states that if a polynomial $f(x) = a_nx^n + a_{n-1}x^{n-1} + \ldots + a_0$, where $a_n \neq 0$, has integer coefficients, then every rational zero of f has the form $\frac{p}{q}$, where p is a factor of a_0, and q is a factor of a_n. The Rational Root Theorem determines the possible rational roots of the polynomial.

Example A

Find all possible rational roots of $f(x) = 2x^3 - 3x^2 - 18x - 8$.

q: $\pm1, \pm2$
p: $\pm1, \pm2, \pm4, \pm8$

Find the factors of the leading coefficient and the constant term, q and p respectively.

$\pm\frac{1}{1}, \pm\frac{2}{1}, \pm\frac{4}{1}, \pm\frac{8}{1}, \pm\frac{1}{2}, \pm\frac{2}{2}, \pm\frac{4}{2}, \pm\frac{8}{2}$

Write all combinations of $\frac{p}{q}$.

$\pm1, \pm\frac{1}{2}, \pm2, \pm4, \pm8.$

Write all possible rational zeros.

The ***Factor Theorem*** provides one way of testing the possible rational roots to determine which, if any, are zeros of a given polynomial.

MATH TERMS

The **Factor Theorem** states that a polynomial $f(x)$ has a factor $(x - k)$ if and only if $f(k) = 0$.

Example B

Use the Factor Theorem to find the real zeros of $f(x) = 2x^3 - 3x^2 - 18x - 8$.
Test possible rational zeros to find a zero of the function.

Test $x = 1$:

$f(1) = 2(1)^3 - 3(1)^2 - 18(1) - 8 = -27$

1 is not a zero, but a point exists at $(1, -27)$.

Test $x = -2$:

$f(-2) = 2(-2)^3 - 3(-2)^2 - 18(-2) - 8 = 0$

-2 is a zero, so $(x + 2)$ is a factor of $f(x)$.

My Notes

You can also determine which of the possible roots of a polynomial are zeros by using synthetic division. We will continue this example using synthetic division.

Example C

Use the Factor Theorem and synthetic division to find the real zeros and factor $f(x) = 2x^3 - 3x^2 - 18x - 8$.

From the list of possible rational roots, test $x = -1$:
Divide $(2x^3 - 3x^2 - 18x - 8)$ by $(x + 1)$.

$$\begin{array}{r|rrrr} -1 & 2 & -3 & -18 & -8 \\ & & -2 & 5 & 13 \\ \hline & 2 & -5 & -13 & 5 \end{array}$$

← Remainder indicates not a root.

By the ***Remainder Theorem***, $f(-1) = 5$. So -1 is not a zero.
Continue this process, finding values of the polynomial or zeros for each of the possible roots.

Divide $(2x^3 - 3x^2 - 18x - 8)$ by $\left(x + \frac{1}{2}\right)$.

$$\begin{array}{r|rrrr} -\frac{1}{2} & 2 & -3 & -18 & -8 \\ & & -1 & 2 & 8 \\ \hline & 2 & -4 & -16 & 0 \end{array}$$

← 0 remainder indicates a root.

$-\frac{1}{2}$ is a zero. $f(x)$ can be factored: $f(x) = \left(x + \frac{1}{2}\right)(2x^2 - 4x - 16)$.

Once you have divided so that you have a quadratic factor, factor it, if possible, or use the quadratic formula.

$$f(x) = \left(x + \frac{1}{2}\right)(2x^2 - 4x - 16)$$

$$f(x) = 2\left(x + \frac{1}{2}\right)(x - 4)(x + 2).$$

The zeros are $-\frac{1}{2}$, 4, and 2.

MATH TERMS

The **Remainder Theorem** states that if a polynomial $f(x)$ is divided by $(x - k)$, then the remainder r is $f(k)$.

MATH TIP

Use the reduced polynomial. Find the new p and q values and continue to test possible roots. If the reduced polynomial is quadratic, factor or use the quadratic formula.

Try These A–B–C

Use the Rational Root Theorem to find the possible real zeros and the Factor Theorem to find the zeros.

a. $f(x) = x^4 - 9x^2 + 4x + 12$

b. $f(x) = 2x^3 - 3x^2 - 8x - 3$

My Notes

Use the Rational Root Theorem and synthetic division to find the real zeros.

c. $f(x) = -4x^3 + 15x^2 - 8x - 3$

MATH TIP

A possible rational root may work more than once if the root has a multiplicity greater than 1.

d. $f(x) = 8x^4 - 34x^2 + 8$

Check Your Understanding

1. For $f(x) = x^4 + 2x^2 + 4$, how many real numbers could be solutions to the equation $f(x) = 0$? Explain.
2. For $f(x) = x^3 + 2x^2 + 8x + 1$, how many possible real numbers could be solutions to the equation $f(x) = 0$? Explain.

LESSON 10-2 PRACTICE

Use the Rational Root Theorem to find the possible real zeros and the Factor Theorem to find the zeros.

3. $f(x) = x^4 + x^3 - 6x^2 - 4x + 8$
4. $f(x) = 2x^3 + 7x^2 - 17x - 10$

Use the Rational Root Theorem and synthetic division to find the real zeros.

5. $f(x) = 3x^3 - 2x^2 - 7x - 2$
6. $f(x) = x^4 - 10x^2 + 9$
7. **Use appropriate tools strategically.** The polynomial function $f(x) = 2x^4 - 4x^2 - 4$ is graphed on a calculator as shown.
   a. Use the Rational Root theorem to write all possible rational roots of the polynomial.
   b. Based on the graph, how many of these possible roots will actually be rational zeros? Explain your reasoning.
   c. What is a transformation that would result in the polynomial having exactly four rational zeros? Explain your reasoning.

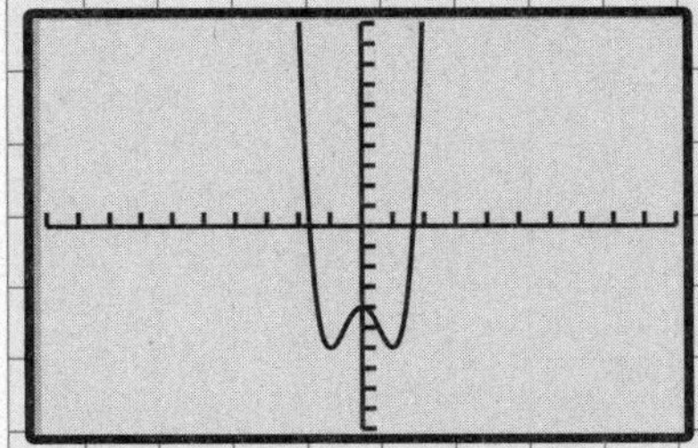

8. Determine all of the rational zeros of $f(x) = x^4 - 2x^2 - 4x + 5$.
9. Explain to another student how a graphing calculator can be used to confirm the results predicted by the Remainder Theorem.
10. **Express regularity in repeated reasoning.** When using the Rational Root Theorem and synthetic division, why is it more efficient to use the reduced polynomial to find additional zeros?

My Notes

Learning Targets:

- Use Descartes' Rule of Signs.
- Accurately graph polynomial functions.

SUGGESTED LEARNING STRATEGIES: Marking the Text, Note Taking, Close Reading

If $f(x)$ is a polynomial function in standard form with real coefficients and a nonzero constant term, then ***Descartes' Rule of Signs*** states

- The number of *positive* real zeros of $f(x)$ equals the number of sign changes in the terms of $f(x)$, or is less than this number by an even integer, and
- The number of *negative* real zeros of $f(x)$ equals the number of sign changes of the terms of $f(-x)$, or is less than this number by an even integer.

DISCUSSION GROUP TIP

As you share ideas in your group, ask your group members or your teacher for clarification of any language, terms, or concepts that you do not understand.

Example A

Find the number of positive real zeros and negative real zeros of $f(x) = 2x^3 - 3x^2 - 18x - 8$.

Step 1: Determine the sign changes in $f(x)$. $\quad f(x) = 2x^3 - 3x^2 - 18x - 8$

There is one sign change between the first and second terms (from + to −); so there is one positive real zero.

Step 2: Determine the sign changes in $f(-x)$.

$$f(-x) = 2(-x)^3 - 3(-x)^2 - 18(-x) - 8$$
$$= -2x^3 - 3x^2 + 18x - 8$$

There is one sign change between the second and the third terms and another between the third and the fourth terms, so there are either two negative real zeros or none.

Try These A

Determine the number of positive and negative real zeros.

a. $h(x) = x^3 - 4x^2 + x + 5$

My Notes

b. $z(x) = -3x^5 - 4x^3 + 5x + 7$

c. $g(x) = x^5 + 9x^4 + 16x^3 - 60x^2 - 224x - 192$

MATH TIP

The signs of the terms in a polynomial can help eliminate some of the possible rational roots that were found using the Rational Root Theorem.

All of the tools you have learned throughout this activity can help you to sketch a graph of a polynomial function without a calculator.
To graph a polynomial function without a calculator, use the following steps.

- Find the y-intercept.
- Consider the end behavior.
- Find the real zeros and plot them.
- Plot any additional points found while determining the zeros.
- Sketch the graph.

1. Sketch a graph of the polynomial functions.

a. $h(x) = 2x^3 + x^2 - 5x + 2$

b. $g(x) = x^5 + x^3 + 2x^2 - 12x + 8$

Check Your Understanding

2. Could the polynomial function $f(x) = -x^4 + x^3 - 6x^2 + 4x - 8$ have three positive real zeros? Explain your reasoning. As you prepare your explanation, remember to use words that will help your classmates understand the situation. Be careful to communicate mathematical terms correctly.

My Notes

ACADEMIC VOCABULARY

In Item 2, ***efficiency*** is referring to reaching the answer in a way that requires the fewest number of steps.

3. If you are using the Factor Theorem and synthetic division to find real zeros of a given polynomial, how can Descartes' Rule of Signs increase the ***efficiency*** of the process?

4. In the graph below, the function $f(x) = -x^2 - 2$ is translated 3 units up to become $g(x) = -x^2 + 1$. Discuss how this transformation affects the number of zeros for each function as indicated by Descartes' Rule of Signs.

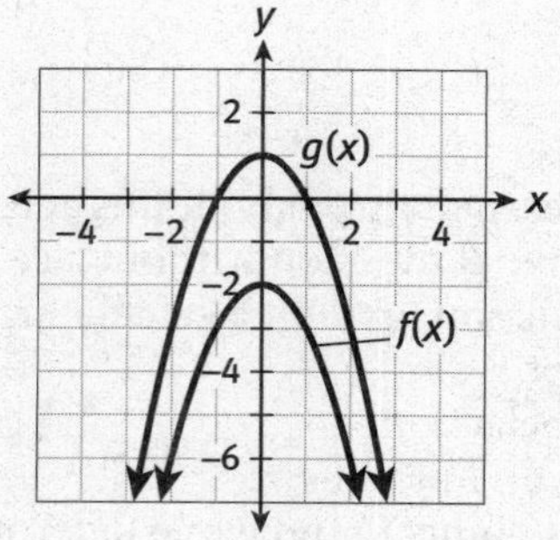

LESSON 10-3 PRACTICE

5. Arrange the functions below in order from least number of sign changes to greatest number of sign changes.

$f(x) = 4x^3 - 2x^2 - 5x + 2$ $\quad g(x) = 4x^3 - 2x^2 + 5x - 2$
$h(x) = -4x^3 + 2x^2 + 5x + 2$

Determine the number of positive and negative real zeros.

6. $f(x) = 4x^3 - 2x^2 + 3x + 7$

7. $h(x) = 4x^5 + 2x^3 + x^2 - 5x + 2$

8. $g(x) = -5x^4 + 2x^3 - 6$

9. $h(x) = -x^3 + 3x^2 - 7x - 6$

Sketch a graph of the polynomial functions.

10. $f(x) = x^3 - 2x^2 - 4x + 5$

11. $f(x) = x^3 - 5x^2 - \frac{x}{16} + \frac{5}{16}$

12. Critique the reasoning of others. Carla is using the Rational Root Theorem and synthetic division to find real roots of polynomial functions and sketch their graphs. She says she has wasted her time when she tests a possible root and finds a nonzero remainder instead. Do you agree with her statement? Explain your reasoning.

13. Use appropriate tools strategically. How can proficiency in factoring help when graphing polynomial functions without using a calculator?

ACTIVITY 10 PRACTICE

Write your answers on notebook paper.
Show your work.

Lesson 10-1

Use the graph to answer Items 1 and 2.

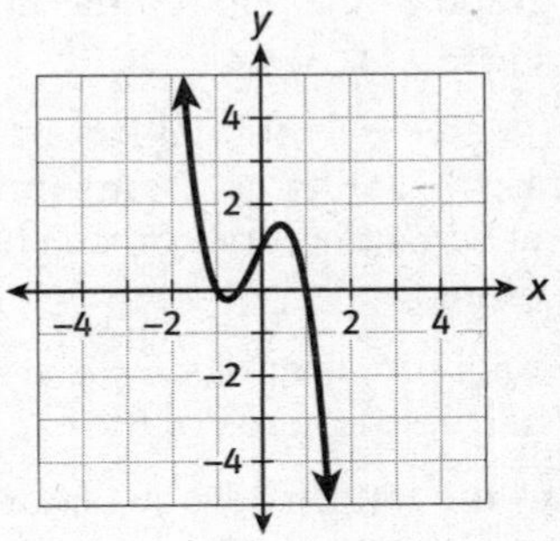

1. Which of the following polynomial functions represents the graph of $f(x)$?

A. $f(x) = 2x^3 + x^2 - 2x - 1$
B. $f(x) = -2x^3 - x^2 + 2x + 1$
C. $f(x) = x^2 - 2x - 1$
D. $f(x) = -x^2 + 2x + 1$

2. Which features of the graph and functions did you use to help determine which function matched the graph?

Determine the y-intercept and end behavior of each function.

3. $y = 4x^7 - 2x^3 + 8x + 6$

4. $f(x) = -3x^{11} + 4x^9 - 4x^4 + 10x^3 + 9$

Use what you know about end behavior and zeros of a function to sketch a small graph of each function.

5. $f(x) = (x - 2)(x - 6)(x + 2)(x + 7)$

6. $f(x) = (x - 1)^2(x + 1)(x - 3)^2$

Find the real zeros of the following quadratic functions.

7. $f(x) = x^2 - 3x - 28$

8. $f(x) = x^2 + 12x + 36$

9. $f(x) = x^2 - 3$

10. $f(x) = 4 - x^2$

Find the real zeros of the following polynomials.

11. $f(x) = x^3 + 5x^2 - 9x - 45$

12. $f(x) = x^3 + 64$

13. $f(x) = x^3 - 8$

14. $f(x) = x^4 - 16$

Factor and find the real zeros.

15. $f(x) = 4x^3 - x^2 + 36x - 9$

16. $f(x) = 3x^3 + 2x^2 + 27x + 18$

17. $f(x) = x^4 - 3x^3 - 28x^2$

18. $f(x) = x^4 - 34x^2 + 225$

Lesson 10-2

Use the Rational Root Theorem to find the possible real zeros for each function.

19. $f(x) = 3x^3 - 6x^2 + 6x + 1$

20. $f(x) = x^4 - 3x^3 - 28x^2$

Use the Rational Root Theorem to find the possible real zeros and the Factor Theorem to find the zeros.

21. $f(x) = 2x^3 + x^2 - 18x - 9$

22. $f(x) = x^3 + x^2 - 4x - 4$

23. $f(x) = x^4 - 26x^2 + 25$

24. $f(x) = x^5 - x^4 - 26x^3 + 26x^2 + 25x - 25$

Use the Rational Root Theorem and synthetic division to find the zeros.

25. $f(x) = x^3 + 3x^2 - 10x - 24$

26. $f(x) = x^3 + 3x^2 - 9x - 27$

27. $f(x) = x^3 + 9x^2 + 27x + 27$

28. $f(x) = x^4 - 8x^2 + 16$

29. For $f(x) = 3x^2 + 8$, how many real numbers could be solutions to the equation $f(x) = 0$? Explain.

30. For $f(x) = x^3 + 5x^2 - 2x - 24$, how many possible real numbers could be solutions to the equation $f(x) = 0$? Explain.

31. Which of the following polynomial functions could have zeros of $x = \pm 3$ and $x = -\frac{1}{2}$?

A. $f(x) = \frac{1}{2}x^2 - 3x + 3$
B. $f(x) = -2x^3 + x^2 - 6x - 3$
C. $f(x) = 2x^3 + x^2 - 18x - 9$
D. $f(x) = x^4 - 18x^2 + 81$

Lesson 10-3

Determine the number of sign changes in each function.

32. $f(x) = x^3 + 9x^2 + 27x + 27$

33. $g(x) = -x^3 + 9x^2 - 27x + 27$

34. $f(x) = x^4 - 8x^2 + 16$

Determine the number of positive and negative real zeros.

35. $f(x) = x^3 + 9x^2 + 27x + 27$

36. $g(x) = 2x^3 + x^2 - 18x - 9$

37. $h(x) = 4x^5 + 2x^3 + x^2 - 5x + 2$

38. Sketch a graph of the polynomial function $f(x) = -4x^3 - 13x^2 - 6x - 3$.

39. A fourth-degree polynomial has a zero with a multiplicity of 2. What is the maximum number of different zeros the function can have? Explain your reasoning.

40. A polynomial function has zeros at $x = -2$ and $x = 2$. What are the zeros of $f(x - 3)$? Explain.

41. Derek uses the Rational Root Theorem and synthetic division to find the zeros of $f(x) = x^3 - 2x^2 - 9x + 18$. His work is shown below. Is his solution correct? If not, correct his errors.

possible zeros: $\pm 1, \pm 2, \pm 3, \pm 6, \pm 9, \pm 18$
Test $x = -2$.

$$\begin{array}{r|rrrr} 2 & 1 & -2 & -9 & 18 \\ & & 2 & 0 & -18 \\ \hline & 1 & 0 & -9 & \mid 0 \end{array} \qquad -2 \text{ is a zero.}$$

Factor $f(x) = (x - 2)(x^2 - 9)$
$f(x) = (x - 2)(x + 3)(x - 3)$
zeros are $-2, \pm 3$

MATHEMATICAL PRACTICES
Use Appropriate Tools Strategically

42. This activity featured strategies for sketching the graph of a polynomial function without a calculator. Describe one advantage of graphing polynomials with a calculator. Then describe one advantage of graphing polynomials without a calculator.

Complex Polynomial Roots and Inequalities

Open Question

Lesson 11-1 Writing a Polynomial Function

My Notes

Learning Targets:

- Maximize volume in applications.
- Apply the Complex Conjugate Theorem.

SUGGESTED LEARNING STRATEGIES: Create Representations, Look for a Pattern, Quickwrite, Create Representations, Identify a Subtask

MetalBox Manufacturing Company makes metal boxes to house electronic equipment by cutting squares and rectangles from a 10-inch-by-20-inch piece of metal, as shown. Each box goes through a pneumatic press to bend it into a rectangular prism, and the corners are welded.

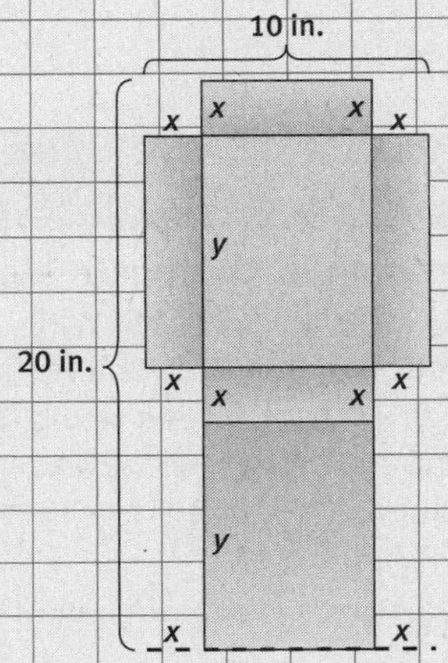

1. What is the length y in terms of x?

2. Write a formula for the volume of the box in terms of x.

3. Choose a value of x. Use this value of x to find the dimensions and volume of the box.

4. What domain makes sense for the problem situation? Explain.

5. Sketch and label a graph of the volume function over this domain.

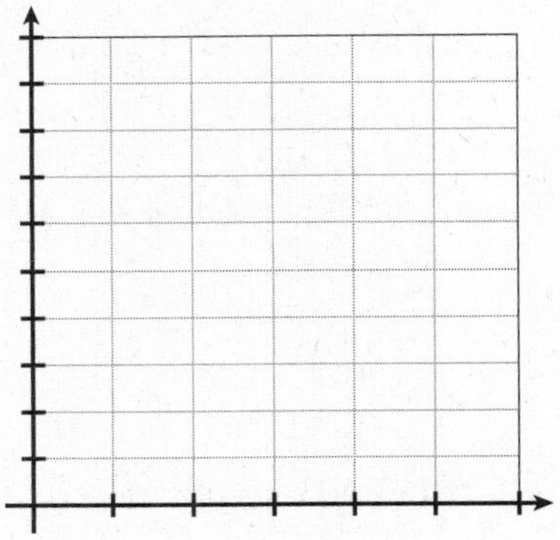

6. Use a graphing calculator to find the maximum volume of the box. What are the dimensions of the box with a maximum volume, and what is its volume?

My Notes

When you developed the function for the volume of the box, you created a polynomial function from its factors. It is also possible to create polynomials from their zeros.

Recall that the general form for a polynomial function is $f(x) = a_n x^n + a_{n-1}x^{n-1} + \ldots + a_1 x + a_0$ and the factored form of a polynomial function is $f(x) = a(x - r_1)(x - r_2)(x - r_3)\,(x - r_4)\ldots(x - r_n)$.

Example A

Find a fourth-degree polynomial function with real coefficients that has 2, −2, and $1 + 3i$ as zeros.

Step 1: Find the other complex zero.
By the ***Complex Conjugate Theorem***, $1 - 3i$ is also a root.
So, $f(x) = a(x - 2)(x + 2)(x - (1 + 3i))(x - (1 - 3i))$
For simplicity, let $a = 1$.

Step 2: Expand the polynomial. $f(x) = (x^2 - 4)((x - 1) - 3i)((x - 1) + 3i)$

Use the difference of squares pattern. $f(x) = (x^2 - 4)((x - 1)^2 - (3i)^2)$
$f(x) = (x^2 - 4)(x^2 - 2x + 1 + 9)$

Use the Distributive Property. $f(x) = x^4 - 2x^3 + 6x^2 + 8x - 40$

MATH TERMS

The **Complex Conjugate Theorem** states that for a polynomial function with real coefficients, if $a + bi$ is a root, with a and b real numbers, then its complex conjugate $a - bi$ is also a root of the polynomial.

Try These A

Find a polynomial function of lowest degree with real coefficients and the given zeros.

a. Degree: 3, Zeros: 3, 3, 5

b. Degree: 4, Zeros: 1, −1, 3, −3

c. Degree: 3, Zeros: 2, $3i$

d. Degree: 4, Zeros: 1, −3, $1 + 2i$

e. Degree: 5, Zeros: −4 (Use the Binomial Theorem.)

My Notes

Check Your Understanding

7. You know that a fourth-degree polynomial with real coefficients has -3, $1 + 2i$, and $1 - 2i$ as zeros. Do you have sufficient information to write the polynomial? Why or why not?

8. Use the Binomial Theorem to write in standard form a polynomial that has 3 as a zero with multiplicity 5.

9. Explain the Complex Conjugate Theorem to another student. Describe how the theorem can be used to find zeros of polynomial functions.

10. **Construct viable arguments.** Is it possible for a polynomial of degree 3 to have 4, 2, and $1 + 2i$ as roots? Why or why not?

MATH TIP

The Binomial Theorem states that for positive integers n,

$$(a+b)^n = \sum_{k=0}^{n} \binom{n}{k} a^{n-k} b^k.$$

LESSON 11-1 PRACTICE

The ACME box company has an order for rectangular boxes from the Speedy Delivery Company. Speedy Delivery Company's policy has limits on the size a box can be. They use rectangular pieces of cardboard that are 24 inches long by 36 inches wide to make these boxes. The boxes are made by cutting a section of size x by x out of each corner of the cardboard.

11. Write an equation that represents the volume of the box.

12. Use the equation you wrote in Item 11 to determine the maximum volume of a box that the Speedy Delivery Company is allowed to deliver.

13. Determine the possible domain for the construction of these boxes.

Find a polynomial with real coefficients of given degree with the given zeros.

14. Degree: 3, Zeros: $-2, 3, 7$

15. Degree: 4, Zeros: $-1, -1, 3, 3$

16. Degree: 3, Zeros: $x = -4, 4, 15$

17. Degree: 5, Zeros: $x = -5, -3, -1, 0, 4$

18. **Use appropriate tools strategically.** After finding a polynomial with real coefficients of a given degree with given zeros, how could you use a graphing calculator to check your answer?

19. **Reason abstractly.** A polynomial function only has complex zeros. Can it be determined whether the number of zeros will be odd or even? Explain.

My Notes

Learning Targets:

- Rewrite polynomial functions in factored form.
- Find all of the zeros of a polynomial function.

SUGGESTED LEARNING STRATEGIES: Note Taking, Think-Pair-Share, Create Representations, Simplify the Problem, Discussion Groups

The previous example had complex zeros. A quadratic factor can be factored over the integers, real numbers, and complex numbers.

$x^2 - 2$ is not factorable over the rational numbers, but it is factorable over the real numbers: $(x + \sqrt{2})(x - \sqrt{2})$.

$x^2 + 2$ is factorable over the complex numbers: $(x + i\sqrt{2})(x - i\sqrt{2})$.

Example A

Find the zeros of $f(x)$ and write the function as a product of complex factors. $f(x) = x^2 + 5$.

Set the function equal to zero. $x^2 + 5 = 0$

Solve for x.
$$x^2 = -5$$
$$x = \pm\sqrt{-5}$$
$$x = \pm i\sqrt{5}$$

Rewrite as a product of linear factors. $f(x) = (x - i\sqrt{5})(x + i\sqrt{5})$

Try These A

Find the zeros of the following polynomials and write them as a product of complex factors.

a. $f(x) = x^2 - 8$

b. $f(x) = x^2 + 11$

c. $f(x) = (x^2 + 9)(x^2 - 4)$

Example B

Rewrite the polynomial function $f(x) = x^4 - 5x^2 - 14$ as a product of complex factors and find the zeros.

Factor the polynomial into a product of quadratics. $f(x) = (x^2 + 2)(x^2 - 7)$

Factor over the real numbers. $f(x) = (x^2 + 2)(x + \sqrt{7})(x - \sqrt{7})$

Write in completely factored form. $f(x) = (x + i\sqrt{2})(x - i\sqrt{2})(x + \sqrt{7})(x - \sqrt{7})$

Use the Zero Product Property to solve for the zeros.
$$0 = (x + i\sqrt{2})(x - i\sqrt{2})(x + \sqrt{7})(x - \sqrt{7})$$
$$x = \pm i\sqrt{2}, \pm\sqrt{7}$$

MATH TIP

The Zero Product Property says that for any product $(a_1)(a_2)(a_3)\ldots(a_n) = 0$, $a_1 = 0$ or $a_2 = 0$ or $a_3 = 0$ or $\ldots a_n = 0$. This is true for polynomial factors as well as real numbers.

Try These B

Rewrite each polynomial function as a product of complex factors and find the zeros.

a. $f(x) = x^4 - 16$

b. $f(x) = x^3 - x^2 + x - 1$

c. $f(x) = 2x^3 - x^2 + 8x - 4$

d. $f(x) = x^4 - 6x^2 + 5$

Example C

Find all of the zeros for $f(x) = x^3 - 1$.

Factor the polynomial so it is not factorable over the real numbers.	$f(x) = (x - 1)(x^2 + x + 1)$
Use the Zero Product Property to find the zeros.	$(x - 1) = 0$ or $(x^2 + x + 1) = 0$
Use the Quadratic Formula if necessary.	$x = 1, x = -\frac{1}{2} - \frac{\sqrt{3}}{2}i, -\frac{1}{2} + \frac{\sqrt{3}}{2}i$

Try These C

Find all of the zeros for the following functions.

a. $f(x) = x^2 + 3x + 11$

b. $f(x) = 3x^4 - 6x^3 + 21x^2$

Example D

Find all of the zeros of $f(x) = x^4 - 3x^3 + x^2 + 7x - 30$ given that $1 + 2i$ is a zero of the function.

Two factors are $x - (1 + 2i)$ and $x - (1 - 2i)$.

Rewrite and multiply.

$((x - 1) - 2i)((x - 1) + 2i)$

$(x - 1)^2 - (2i)^2$

$x^2 - 2x + 5$

My Notes

Use long division to divide $f(x)$ by $x^2 - 2x + 5$.

$$\begin{array}{r} x^2 - x - 6 \\ x^2 - 2x + 5 \overline{) x^4 - 3x^3 + x^2 + 7x - 30} \\ \underline{x^4 - 2x^3 + 5x^2} \\ -x^3 - 4x^2 + 7x - 30 \\ \underline{x^3 + 2x^2 - 5x} \\ -6x^2 + 12x - 30 \\ \underline{-6x^2 + 12x - 30} \\ 0 \end{array}$$

$f(x) = (x^2 - 2x + 5)(x^2 - x - 6)$
$\quad = (x^2 - 2x + 5)(x + 2)(x - 3)$

The zeros are $x = -2$, $x = 3$, and $x = 1 \pm 2i$.

Try These D

Find all of the zeros of the function given one complex zero.

a. $f(x) = x^4 - 21x^2 - 100$ given $2i$ is a zero.

b. $f(x) = x^3 - 7x^2 + 12x - 10$ given $1 + i$ is a zero.

c. $f(x) = x^4 - 10x^3 + 42x^2 - 112x + 160$ given $1 - 3i$ is a zero.

Check Your Understanding

1. Is the quadratic factor $x^2 + 3$ factorable over the real numbers? Explain.

2. Will the polynomial function $f(x) = x^4 - x^2 - 6$ have complex zeros? Explain.

LESSON 11-2 PRACTICE

Write each polynomial function as a product of linear and complex factors and find the zeros.

3. $f(x) = x^2 - 12$

4. $f(x) = x^2 + 6$

Rewrite each polynomial function as a product of complex factors and find the zeros.

5. $f(x) = x^4 - 625$

6. $f(x) = 2x^4 - 7x^2 - 4$

Find the zeros of the functions.

7. $f(x) = x^2 - 3x + 10$

8. $f(x) = 5x^4 + 5x^3 + 30x^2$

9. Express regularity in repeated reasoning. Find the zeros of $f(x) = x^3 - 3x^2 + 16x - 48$ given $4i$ is a zero.

My Notes

Learning Targets:

- Solve polynomial inequalities.
- Represent solutions using interval notation and graphs.

SUGGESTED LEARNING STRATEGIES: Note Taking, Look for a Pattern, Quickwrite, Group Presentation, Think-Pair-Share

MetalBox Manufacturing would like to create boxes of different volumes from the same 10-inch-by-20-inch piece of metal. The volume must be at least 72 cubic inches.

1. Square corners are cut from the metal of length x. Write an inequality for the volume that satisfies the constraint above.

2. Use a graphing calculator to determine the interval over which the volume of the boxes is larger than 72 cubic inches.

One method of solving inequalities is to use sign patterns.

Solving Polynomial Inequalities

- Write the inequality in factored form.
- Identify the zeros.
- Pick one test value for x that falls between the intervals created by the zeros.
- Evaluate the polynomial at these values to test the sign of the inequality in each interval and determine the solution.
- State the solution intervals.

Example A

Solve $x^3 + 2x^2 \geq 3x$ algebraically.

Write the inequality in general form.

$x^3 + 2x^2 - 3x \geq 0$

Factor.

$x(x - 1)(x + 3) \geq 0$

The zeros, in increasing order, are -3, 0, and 1. These are solutions because the inequality symbol is $\geq$.

Test one value in each interval: $(-\infty, -3)$, $(-3, 0)$, $(0, 1)$, $(1, \infty)$.

Test -4: $(-4)(-4 - 1)(-4 + 3)$; Each factor is negative, so the product is negative.

Test -1: $(-1)(-1 - 1)(-1 + 3)$; Two factors are negative and one is positive, so the product is positive.

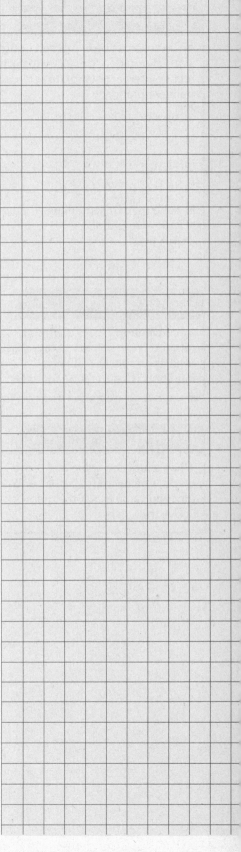

My Notes

MATH TIP

An interval can be expressed using interval notation. The following list relates interval notation to set builder notation.

$(a, b) = \{x \in \mathbb{R} | a < x < b\}$

$[a, b) = \{x \in \mathbb{R} | a \le x < b\}$

$(a, b] = \{x \in \mathbb{R} | a < x \le b\}$

$[a, b] = \{x \in \mathbb{R} | a \le x \le b\}$

$\mathbb{R}$ is the set of real numbers
$\in$ "is an element of"
| "such that"

WRITING MATH

By convention, $[1, \infty)$ is written, rather than $[1, \infty]$, to indicate that there is no specific value for infinity. $\cup$ is set notation for *union*.

MATH TIP

When a function value is < 0, the graph is below the *x*-axis. When a function value is > 0, the graph is above the *x*-axis.

Continue this process and record the results in a table.

Interval	$x < -3$	$-3 < x < 0$	$0 < x < 1$	$x > 1$
Test value	-4	-1	$\frac{1}{2}$	2
Sign	$-$	$+$	$-$	$+$

A number line can help you organize the information.

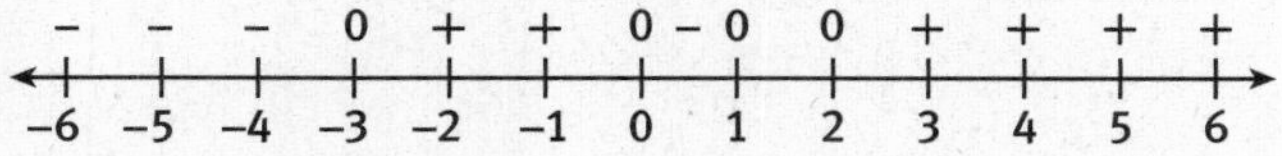

The solutions are the intervals of x where the inequality is greater than or equal to 0. So, x-values of the zeros are included in the solution.

Solution intervals: $[-3, 0] \cup [1, \infty)$

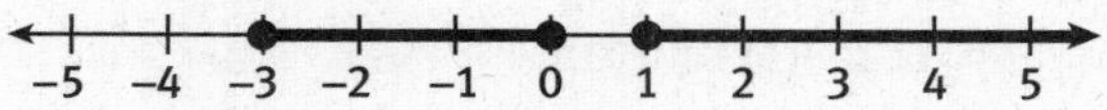

You can graph the related function to verify the solutions.

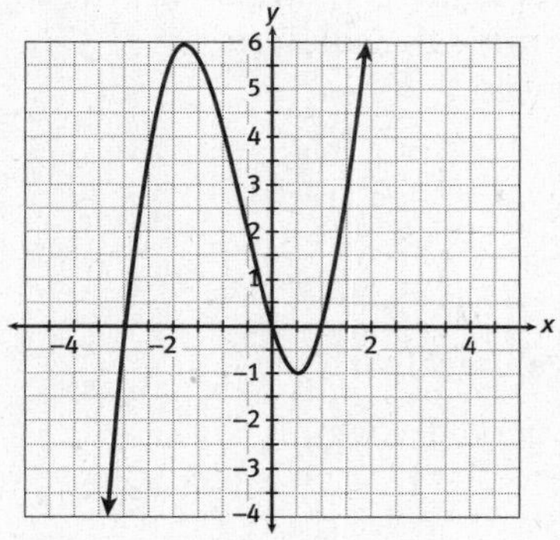

3. Summarize how graphs can be used to find solutions to polynomial inequalities.

Try These A

Use a sign pattern to solve each inequality and write the solution interval.

a. $x^2 - x - 2 < 0$

b. $x^4 - 81 \ge 0$

c. $x^3 - x^2 > 4x - 4$

d. $2x^3 + 48 \le 3x^2 + 32x$

My Notes

4. **Model with mathematics.** Use what you know about polynomial functions to solve the following problem.

The Harrisons have contracted to have a fence installed around their pool. They want to use 300 feet of fencing, and they plan to attach the fence to the house as shown. The back of the house is 90 feet long, but they will use whatever portion of the house will maximize the area of the rectangular enclosure.

What are the length and width of the fenced area?

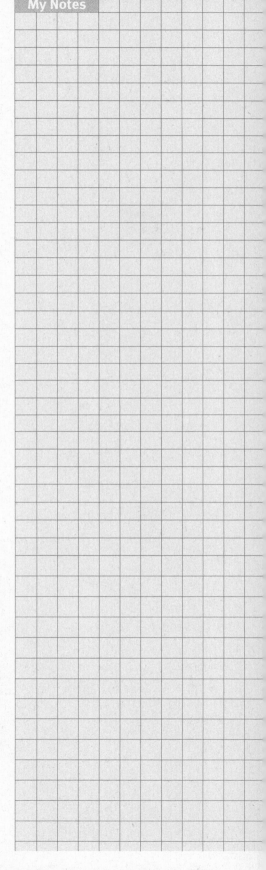

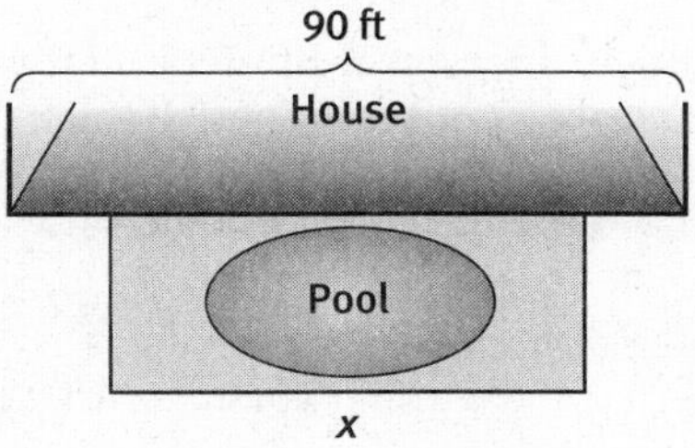

5. **Critique the reasoning of others.** Tom says that a fifth-degree polynomial function with real coefficients must have at least one real zero because complex zeros come in pairs. Janet says that it must have at least one real zero because of end behavior. Who is correct? Explain your reasoning.

Check Your Understanding

6. When using sign patterns to solve a polynomial inequality, is there a way to tell the maximum number of intervals created by the zeros? Explain.
7. What are the intervals that would need to be tested to solve $-x^3 + 7x^2 > 10x$?
8. Describe the solution of a polynomial inequality represented by the notation $(-4, 0) \cup (2, \infty)$.
9. A polynomial inequality is factored as $x(x - 2)(x + 1) \leq 0$. How can the inequality be solved by graphing its related function?

My Notes

LESSON 11-3 PRACTICE

10. MetalBox Manufacturing also makes boxes from 5-inch-by-40-inch pieces of metal. As with the 10-inch-by-20-inch pieces of metal, square corners of length x are cut from each piece. The volume of the box must be at least 56 cubic inches. Write an inequality for the volume that satisfies the constraint.

11. Use a graphing calculator to determine the interval over which the volume of the boxes made from the 5-inch-by-40-inch pieces of metal is larger than 56 cubic inches.

12. Using the 5-inch-by-40-inch piece of metal, is it possible to make a box with a volume of at least 72 cubic inches? Explain.

Solve each inequality and write the solution interval.

13. $x^2 + 12x \geq -35$

14. $x^4 - 256 \geq 0$

15. $x^2 - 6x \leq 91$

16. $x^2 - 15x + 54 > 0$

17. **Model with mathematics.** Keisha is having a fence installed around a corral for her horses. She wants to use 600 feet of fencing, and she plans to attach the fence to the barn as shown. The back of the barn is 150 feet long, but she will use whatever portion of the barn will maximize the area of the rectangular enclosure. What are the length and width of the fenced area? What is the area of the corral? Justify your answers.

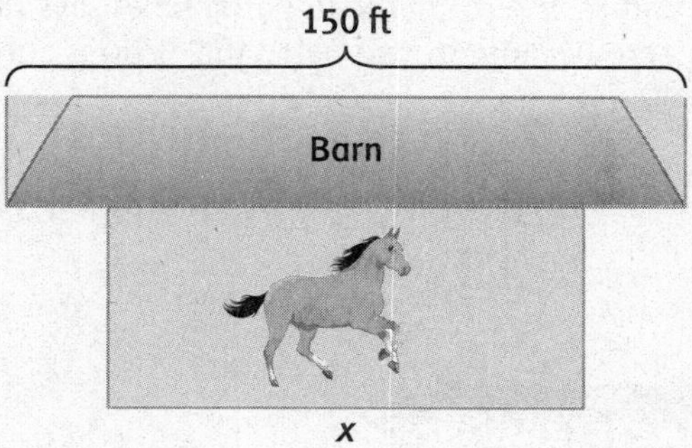

18. **Use appropriate tools strategically.** The function $y = x^3 + 4x^2 - 20x - 48$ is graphed on a calculator, as shown below. How can the graph be used to solve the polynomial inequality $x^3 + 4x^2 - 20x - 48 < 0$ without factoring?

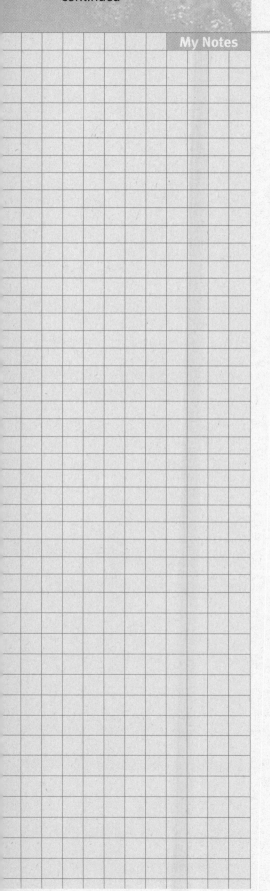

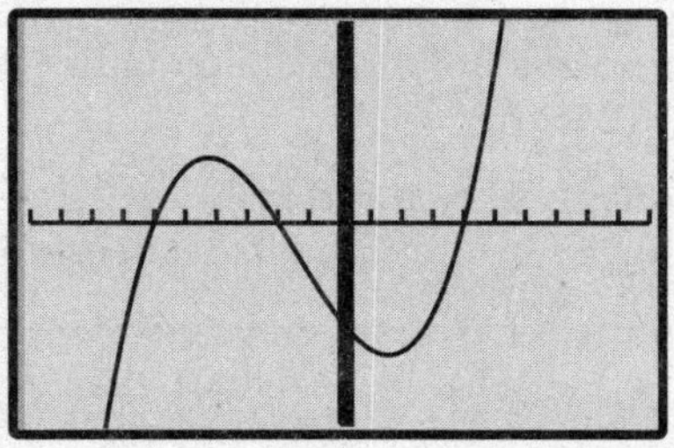

ACTIVITY 11 PRACTICE

Write your answers on notebook paper.
Show your work.

Lesson 11-1

Use the diagram below to answer Items 1 through 5.

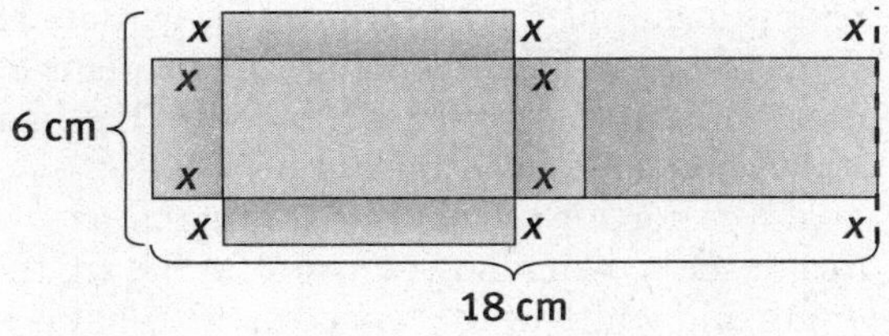

1. Best Boxes, Inc. makes boxes by cutting square corners of length x from pieces of cardboard. What is a polynomial function that represents the volume of the box in terms of x when it is assembled?
2. What are the dimensions and volume of the box when $x = 2$?
3. What domain makes sense for this problem situation? Explain.
4. Use a graphing calculator to find the maximum volume of the box. What are the dimensions of the box with a maximum volume? What is its volume?
5. What is the factored form of a third-degree polynomial function with real coefficients that has -5, 0, and 5 as zeros?
6. What is the factored form of a fourth-degree polynomial function with real coefficients that has -3, 1, and $1 + 5i$ as zeros?

   A. $f(x) = (x + 3)(x - 1)(x - (1 + 5i))$

   B. $f(x) = (x + 3)(x - 3)(x + 1)(x - (1 + 5i))$

   C. $f(x) = (x + 3)(x - 1)(x + 1)(x - (1 + 5i))$

   D. $f(x) = (x + 3)(x - 1)(x - (1 + 5i))(x - (1 - 5i))$

Find a polynomial of lowest degree with real coefficients and the given zeros.

7. Degree: 3, Zeros: $x = -4, 2, 5$
8. Degree: 3, Zeros: $x = 3, 6i$
9. Degree: 4, Zeros: $x = -2, 2, 1, 1$
10. Degree: 5, Zeros: $x = -6, -4, -2, 0, 3$
11. Use the Binomial Theorem to write in standard form a polynomial that has -2 as a zero with multiplicity 6.
12. **Make use of structure.** What is the maximum number of complex zeros a polynomial of degree 11 can have? Explain.

Lesson 11-2

13. Is $x^2 - 7$ factorable over the rational numbers? Why or why not?
14. Is $x^2 + 7$ factorable over the real numbers? Explain.

Find the zeros of the following polynomials and write them as a product of complex factors.

15. $f(x) = x^2 + 15$
16. $f(x) = x^2 - 13$
17. $f(x) = x^2 + 13$
18. $f(x) = x^2 + 9$

Rewrite the polynomial functions as a product of complex factors.

19. $f(x) = x^4 - 625$

20. $f(x) = 3x^3 + 18x^2 - x - 6$

21. $f(x) = x^4 - 12x^2 - 64$

22. $f(x) = x^4 + 2x^2 - 15$

Find the zeros of each function.

23. $f(x) = x^2 - 9x - 13$

24. $f(x) = 14x^3 - 77x^2 + 35x$

25. $f(x) = x^3 + 16x$

26. $f(x) = x^5 - 7x^3 - 44x$

27. Find all the zeros of $f(x) = x^3 + 3x^2 - 5x + 25$, given $1 + 2i$ is a zero.

28. Choose the other zeros of $x^3 - 5x^2 + 23x - 51$ if $x = 1 + 4i$ is a zero.

A. $x = 3, x = 1 + 4i$
B. $x = -3, x = 1 + 4i$
C. $x = 3, x = 1 - 4i$
D. $x = -3, x = 1 - 4i$

29. Will the zeros of the quadratic function $f(x) = x^2 + 9$ be real or complex? Explain how you know.

Lesson 11-3

30. Best Boxes, Inc. also makes boxes from 12-inch-by-20-inch pieces of cardboard. As with the 6-inch-by-18-inch pieces, square corners of length x are cut from each piece. The volume of the box must be at least 100 cubic inches. Write an inequality for the volume that satisfies the constraint.

31. Use a graphing calculator to determine the interval over which the volume of the boxes made from the 12-inch-by-20-inch pieces of metal is larger than 100 cubic inches.

Solve each inequality and write the solution interval.

32. $x^2 + x > 2$

33. $-x^2 > x - 2$

34. $x^3 - 5x^2 \geq 9x - 45$

35. $x^4 \geq 256$

36. Feng is installing a fence around his garden. He wants to use 48 feet of fencing, and he plans to attach the fence to the shed as shown. The back of the shed is 12 feet long, but he will use whatever portion of the shed will maximize the area of the rectangular enclosure. What are the length and width of the fenced area? What is the area of the garden?

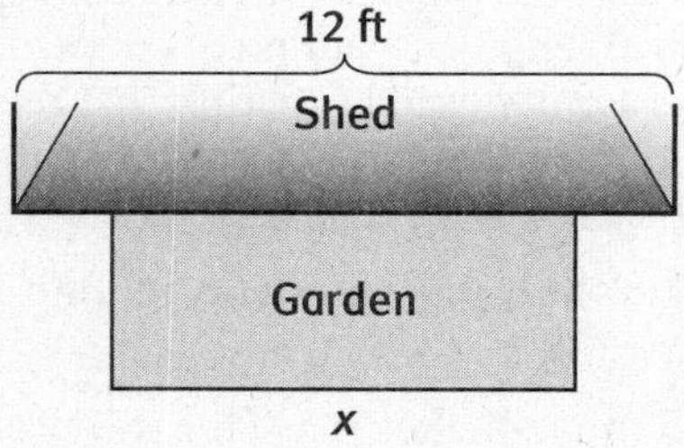

37. How can you check that the zeros you found for a polynomial function are, in fact, the correct zeros?

38. A polynomial function has the form $f(x) = x^n + 1$, where n is an even number. Bree says that it is possible for the function to have a real zero. Is she correct? Why or why not?

MATHEMATICAL PRACTICES
Reason Abstractly and Quantitatively

39. Explain how the degree of a polynomial relates to the number of strictly real or strictly complex zeros of the function.

Polynomial Functions
COFFEE TIME

The manager of the Caffo Coffee Shop tracked the number of customers that came to the shop every hour. She collected the data shown to help decide how many employees she needs and when breaks can be given.

Hours	Sales
1	123
2	156
3	125
4	92
5	83
6	90
7	94
8	103
9	115
10	123
11	126
12	93
13	51
14	35

1. Would a cubic function be an appropriate model for the data? Explain your reasoning.

2. Use a graphing calculator to find a quartic polynomial function that can be used to model the data.

3. Graph the quartic model. List the important features of the graph over the set of real numbers (i.e. without the domain restrictions of the context).

4. Could the manager of the coffee shop use this model to predict the best time for employee breaks? Explain.

Consider the function $f(x) = x^6 - x^4 - 16x^2 + 16$. Answer Items 5–9 without using a calculator.

5. What is the greatest possible number of x-intercepts for $f(x)$? Explain.

6. Why might the number of complex zeros and the number of intercepts differ?

7. What is the greatest possible number of turning points for $f(x)$? Explain.

8. Find $f(0)$, the y-intercept of $f(x)$.

9. Factor $f(x)$ and find the x-intercepts.

Use the graph to answer Items 10–11.

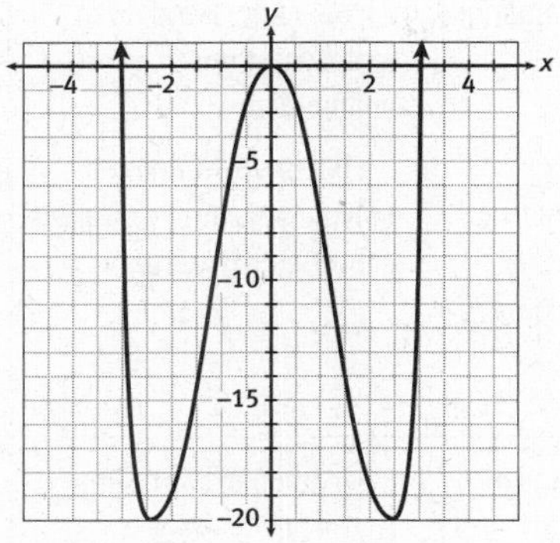

10. Write a possible function for the graph of $f(x)$.

11. If the function is shifted three units to the left, what are the zeros of the transformed function? Explain your reasoning.

12. Use the Binomial Theorem to write in standard form a polynomial that has 4 as a zero with multiplicity 5.

13. Sketch a possible graph of a fifth-degree polynomial function with only two zeros, at $x = 2$ and $x = 5$. What is the equation of your function?

14. Create an inequality from your function in Item 13. What is the solution set?

15. The manager of the Caffo Coffee Shop also collects data as she adjusts the prices of the Caffo Latte, a shop specialty item. The function $f(x) = -114.286x^2 + 825.714x - 210$ represents total daily Caffo Latte revenues as a function of price per cup. Use a graphing calculator to answer the following questions.

a. At what price per cup are total daily Caffo Latte revenues per day maximized?

b. Over what price range are total daily Caffo Latte revenues at least \$1200?

Scoring Guide	Exemplary	Proficient	Emerging	Incomplete
	The solution demonstrates these characteristics:			
Mathematics Knowledge and Thinking (Items 1, 4, 5, 6, 7, 8, 9, 14)	• Clear and accurate understanding of polynomial functions and their graphical behavior, including the Fundamental Theorem of Algebra and Descartes' Rule of Signs	• A functional understanding of polynomial functions and their graphical behavior – may or may not know Descartes' Rule of Signs	• Partial understanding of polynomial functions and their roots and shape	• Little or no understanding of polynomial functions and their roots and shape
Problem Solving (Items 4, 15)	• An appropriate and efficient strategy that results in a quartic polynomial that is then analyzed appropriately	• A strategy that may include unnecessary steps but results in a correct answer	• A strategy that results in some incorrect answers	• No clear strategy when solving problems
Mathematical Modeling / Representations (Items 2, 3, 4, 10, 11, 12, 13)	• Clear and accurate understanding of representations of polynomials • Clear and accurate understanding of creating a quartic regression and then understanding its meaning by analyzing it graphically	• A functional understanding of representations of polynomials • Mostly accurate understanding of a quartic regression – may or may not include ability to apply meaning	• Partial understanding of representations of polynomials • Partial understanding of polynomials but incomplete or ineffective reasoning	• Little or no understanding of representations of polynomials • Inaccurate or incomplete understanding of polynomials
Reasoning and Communication (Items 1, 6, 11)	• Precise use of appropriate math terms and language to express knowledge of the Fundamental Theorem of Algebra and the nature of real/complex roots	• Correct characterization of knowledge of the Fundamental Theorem of Algebra and the nature of real/complex roots	• Misleading or confusing characterization of polynomial behavior with some understanding demonstrated	• Incomplete or inaccurate characterization of polynomial behavior

Rational Expressions and the Reciprocal Function

Playing Catch-Up

Lesson 12-1 Writing Rational Functions

My Notes

Learning Targets:

- Write ratios of variable expressions.
- Write a rational function based on a real-world scenario.

SUGGESTED LEARNING STRATEGIES: Marking the Text, Close Reading, Graphic Organizer, Create Representations, Guess and Check, Simplify the Problem

Miguel and Cera have a son named Cory. Miguel teaches mathematics at Sci-fi High School, and he enjoys making up problems for his algebra students. Miguel used the following problem as a classroom warm-up exercise.

As of today, Miguel's age is five times Cory's age. Cera's age is three more than four times Cory's age.

Next year, Miguel's age will be 10 more than three times Cory's age then. As of today, how many times as old as Cory is Cera?

1. If y is used to represent Cory's current age in years, complete the following table by filling in the appropriate expressions in terms of the variable y.

	Current Age (years)	Age 1 Year From Now (years)
Cory	y	
Cera		
Miguel		

2. Write an equation in terms of y that could be used to solve Miguel's warm-up problem; then solve the problem using your equation.

3. Miguel's original problem asked "How many times as old as Cory is Cera?" He also could have asked "How much older is Cera than her son Cory?" Explain the difference in meaning between these two questions.

My Notes

4. Complete the table that follows to show the numerical ages, in years, of each family member now and in future years.

	Age Now	Age in 1 Year	Age in 5 Years	Age in 10 Years	Age in *x* Years
Cory					
Cera					
Miguel					

5. Which of the two possible questions posed in Item 3 will have an answer that remains constant regardless of how many years pass? Explain.

6. Assume that Cory, Cera, and Miguel could live for hundreds of years.

a. How much older than Cory would Cera be 75 years from now?

b. How many times as old as Cory would Cera be 75 years from now?

c. How much older than Cory would Cera be 500 years from now?

d. How many times as old as Cory would Cera be 500 years from now?

e. How much older than Cory would Cera be x years from now?

f. How many times as old as Cory would Cera be x years from now?

7. What operation did you compute between the ages of Cera and Cory in

a. parts a, c, and e of Item 6?

b. parts b, d, and f of Item 6?

My Notes

8. Describe what was constant or variable with regard to the operations in Items 7a and 7b that you computed for Item 6.

In the table in Item 4, x represented the number of years since Cory's sixth birthday. The table data implied that x had only positive values. Negative values of x can be used to represent the past. For example, $x = -1$ would be used to determine family member ages 1 year ago, and $x = -6$ would represent the precise day, 6 years ago, on which Cory was born.

9. Does $x = -5.5$ have any meaning in terms of the years since the present time? If so, find the ages of the family members for $x = -5.5$. If not, explain why it is not relevant in this setting.

10. Does $x = -7.5$ have any meaning in terms of the years since the present time? If so, find the ages of the family members for $x = -7.5$. If not, explain why it is not relevant in this setting.

11. Complete the following table in which x is measured in (past) years from now.

x	−1	−3	−5	−5.5	−5.9	−5.99
Cory's Age						
Cera's Age						
Ratio of Cera's Age to Cory's Age						

12. Let $R(x)$ represent the ratio of Cera's age in years to Cory's age in years, and let x represent the number of years from now, either past or future. Write R as a function of x.

My Notes

Check Your Understanding

13. Suppose you started solving the problem in Item 1 by using y to represent Miguel's age now in years instead of Cory's age now in years.
   a. What expression would represent Cory's age now?
   b. What expression would represent Cory's age 1 year from now?
   c. What equation could you write and solve to find Miguel's age now?
   d. Reason quantitatively. Would this change the function you wrote in Item 12? Explain.

14. Explain how using inverse operations could help you check your answers to the "how many times as old" problems in parts b, d, and f of Item 6.

15. If x represents the number of years from now, what appears to happen to the ratio of Cera's age in years to Cory's age in years as x increases?

16. Suppose $Q(x)$ represents the ratio of Cory's age in years to Cera's age in years, where x represents the number of years from now. Write Q as a function of x.

LESSON 12-1 PRACTICE

17. Model with mathematics. Car A and Car B are traveling on the same road in the same direction at the same speed. Both cars have passed through point P. Right now, Car B is four times as many miles from point P as Car A is. After both cars travel 50 more miles, Car B will be two times as many miles from point P as Car A will be.

Let m represent Car A's current position in miles from point P. Complete the following table by filling in the appropriate expressions in terms of the variable m.

	Current Position (miles from Point P)	Position After 50 More Miles (miles from Point P)
Car A		
Car B		

18. Write and solve an equation to find m, the current position of Car A.

19. Let $R(x)$ represent the ratio of Car A's position in miles from point P to Car B's position in miles from point P, and let x represent the number of miles traveled from now, either past or future. Write R as a function of x.

20. What appears to happen to the ratio of Car A's position in miles from point P to Car B's position in miles from point P as x increases?

21. Reason abstractly. If the two cars could keep traveling on the same road in the same direction at the same speed forever, would Car A ever catch up to Car B? Explain your reasoning.

Learning Targets:

- Write equations for vertical and horizontal asymptotes.
- Sketch the graph of a rational function.

SUGGESTED LEARNING STRATEGIES: Create Representations, Look for a Pattern, Quickwrite, Identify a Subtask, Summarizing, Paraphrasing

The function $R(x) = \frac{27+x}{6+x}$ represents the ratio of Cera's age in years to Cory's age in years, where x represents the number of years from now, either past or future.

1. On the grid below, sketch a graph of the function $R(x)$ for $-6 < x \leq 18$.

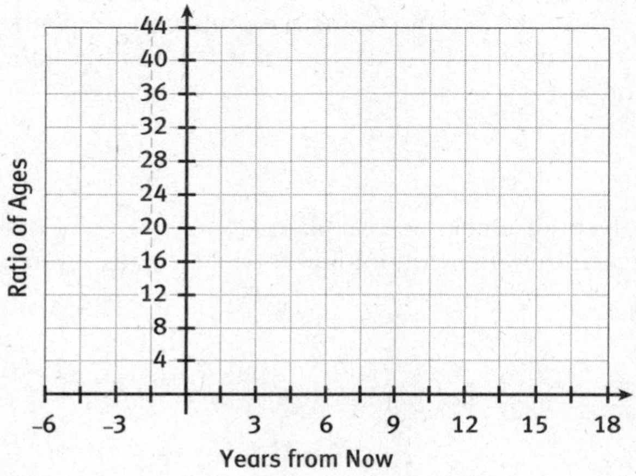

2. As $R(x)$ is evaluated for values of x closer and closer to -6, the ratio found by $R(x)$ gets larger and larger. Explain why this occurs.

The shape of the graph you drew in Item 13 became almost vertical near $x = -6$, because the function values increased without ***bound*** as x approached -6. If you were to observe the graph from a distance (or zoom out using a graphing calculator), it would appear that the graph merges with a vertical line as x approaches -6.

3. What is the equation of the vertical line, called a **vertical asymptote**, that your graph appears to be merging with as x-values are selected closer and closer to -6?

4. Explain why the graph of $y = R(x)$ is never actually vertical even though it may appear that way on your graph or in your calculator window.

My Notes

MATH TERMS

A function f is **bounded** on an interval if there is some constant M such that $|f(x)| < M$ for all x-values in that interval. So a function with consecutive turning points is bounded within that interval.

If a function is not bounded, it approaches positive infinity or negative infinity.

My Notes

5. Use a graphing calculator to determine what happens to $R(x)$ for extremely large values of x. As x increases without bound (that is, as $x \to \infty$), to what numerical value does $R(x)$ appear to converge?

6. What is the equation of the horizontal line, called a **horizontal asymptote**, that the graph approaches for very large values of x?

7. Reason quantitatively. How are the horizontal asymptote and the end behavior of $R(x)$ related?

8. Use the context of Cory and Cera's age problem to explain why the value of $R(x)$ can never actually reach the value you found on the calculator in Items 4 and 5.

9. Solve an algebraic equation to explain why the value of $R(x)$ can never actually reach the value you found on the calculator in Items 4 and 5.

The function R is a member of a family of functions known as **rational functions**. Rational functions are expressed as a ratio of two polynomials. In this activity, R is a ratio of two linear polynomials. Rational functions may have vertical and/or horizontal asymptotes.

If the absolute value of function f becomes very large as x approaches some number b, then the line $x = b$ is called a ***vertical asymptote*** of f.

If the values of function f approach some number a as the absolute value of x becomes very large, then the line $y = a$ is called a ***horizontal asymptote*** of f.

The simplest rational function is the reciprocal function $f(x) = \frac{1}{x}$.

10. Sketch the graph of $f(x) = \frac{1}{x}$ on the grid below and make a table of values for x and the corresponding values of $f(x)$.

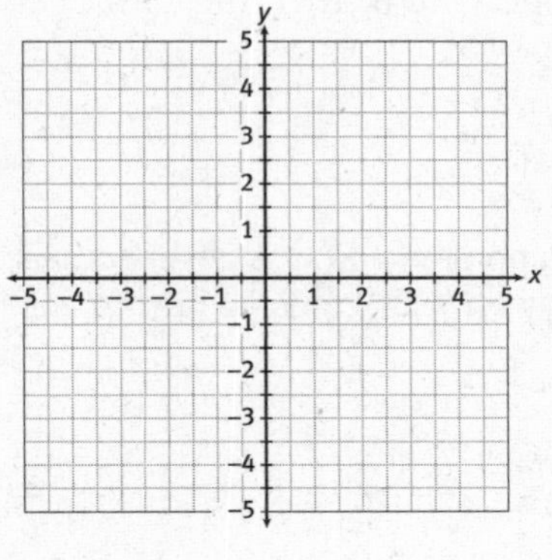

MATH TIP

Notice that $f(x) = \frac{1}{x}$ is the ratio of two polynomial functions. The numerator is the constant polynomial function $y = 1$, and the denominator is the linear polynomial function $y = x$.

x	$f(x) = \frac{1}{x}$

11. Describe the features of the graph and properties of $f(x) = \frac{1}{x}$.

My Notes

TECHNOLOGY TIP

Use a calculator to graph the parent function $y = \frac{1}{x}$. To see how the calculator represents the vertical asymptote, enter 2ND CALC and then 1: VALUE to calculate the y-value for $x = 0$. You can also use the calculator's TRACE function to see what happens as x goes from -1 to 1.

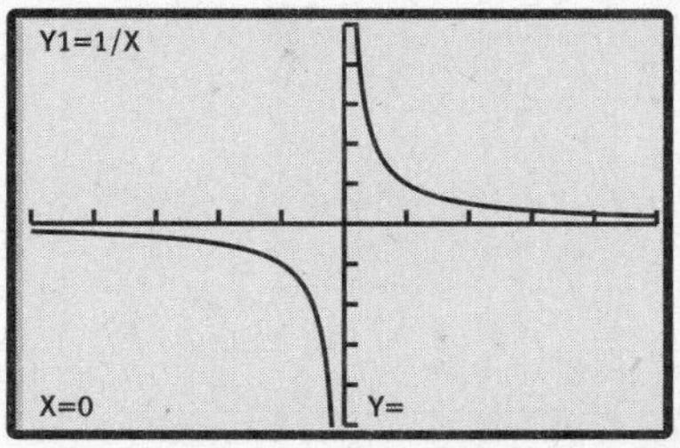

Check Your Understanding

Use a graphing calculator to help with the following problems.

12. Determine where the function $R(x) = \frac{3x-2}{x+7}$ increases or decreases without bound.

13. Find the equation of the vertical asymptote of $R(x) = \frac{3x-2}{x+7}$.

14. Find the equation of the horizontal asymptote of $R(x) = \frac{3x-2}{x+7}$.

15. Make use of structure. Without using a graphing calculator, what can you tell about the vertical asymptote of the graph of $R(x) = \frac{3x-2}{x+7}$ simply by looking at the equation? Explain.

TECHNOLOGY TIP

When entering rational functions into some calculators, remember that the division bar acts as a grouping symbol. So, $y = \frac{x-5}{x-7}$ is entered as $y = (x - 5)/(x - 7)$.

My Notes

LESSON 12-2 PRACTICE

16. $R(x) = \dfrac{45 + x}{15 + x}$ represents the ratio of Arturo's age in years to his son's age in years, where x represents the number of years from now, either past or future. Sketch a graph of the function R for $-15 < x \leq 18$.

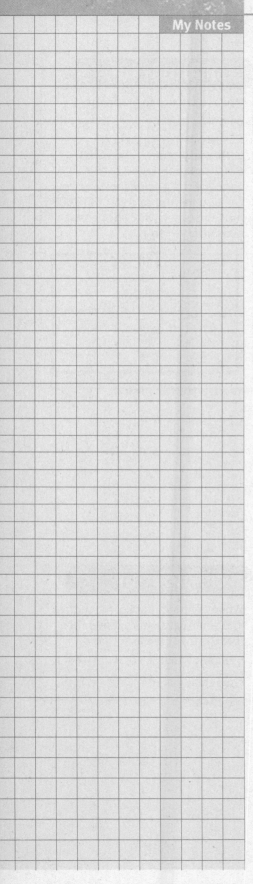

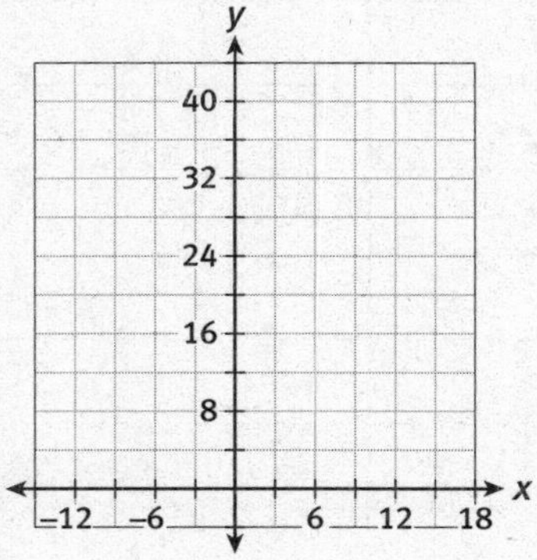

17. What is the equation of the vertical asymptote? Explain how you know.

18. What happens to $R(x)$ for extremely large values of x?

19. How is the graph of $R(x)$ for extremely large values of x related to its horizontal asymptote? That is, analyze the behavior of $R(x)$ around its horizontal asymptote.

20. Write an algebraic equation and solve. Explain why the value of $R(x)$ will never actually reach the value you found in Items 18–19.

Use a graphing calculator and $R(x) = \dfrac{x + 3}{x - 5}$ for Items 21–23.

21. Determine where the function is unbounded.

22. Find the equation of the vertical asymptote.

23. Find the equation of the horizontal asymptote.

24. In Items 17–19 of Lesson 12-1, you found that the function $R(x) = \dfrac{25 + x}{100 + x}$ represents the ratio of Car A's position in miles from point P to Car B's position in miles from point P, where x represents the number of miles traveled from now, either past or future. What is the equation of the vertical asymptote of $R(x) = \dfrac{25 + x}{100 + x}$?

25. What is the equation of the horizontal asymptote of $R(x) = \dfrac{25 + x}{100 + x}$?

26. Construct viable arguments. Demonstrate why the value of $R(x)$ will never actually reach the value you found in Item 25.

27. Make use of structure. The graph of the parent function $f(x) = \dfrac{1}{x}$ is translated 5 units up. Write the equation of the transformed function. What are the vertical and horizontal asymptotes of the transformed function?

28. Reason abstractly. The title of this activity is "Playing Catch-Up." Write to explain to another student why this title might have been chosen for a lesson on rational functions.

ACTIVITY 12 PRACTICE

Write your answers on notebook paper.
Show your work.

Lesson 12-1

Use the following information for Items 1–7.

Anita is four times as old as her daughter Nia. Nine years from now, Anita will be two and a half times as old as Nia.

1. If y is used to represent Nia's current age in years, complete the following table by filling in the appropriate expressions in terms of the variable y.

	Current Age (years)	Age 9 Years from Now (years)
Nia		
Anita		

2. Write and solve an equation to find y, the age of Nia.

3. What is Anita's age?

4. Let $R(x)$ represent the ratio of Anita's age in years to Nia's age in years, and let x represent the number of years from now, either past or future. Write R as a function of x.

5. What is the domain of $R(x)$ for all numbers of years, either past or future? What domain makes sense in a real-world context?

6. If you were to graph the ratio of Anita's age and Nia's age in years, where $x = 0$ represents the present, at what value of x would the graph appear to become vertical? What does this mean in terms of their ages?

7. What is the end behavior of $R(x)$?

Use the following information for Items 8–10.

Train A and Train B are traveling on the same track in the same direction at the same speed. Both trains have passed Station S. Right now, Train A is 10 times as many kilometers from Station S as Train B is. After both trains travel 20 more kilometers, Train A will be eight times as many kilometers from Station S as Train B will be.

8. Let k represent Train B's current position in kilometers from Station S. Write and solve an equation to find k, the current position of Train B.

9. What is the current position of Train A?

10. Let $R(x)$ represent the ratio of Train A's position in kilometers from Station S to Train B's position in kilometers from Station S, and let x represent the number of kilometers traveled from now, either past or future. Write R as a function of x.

11. Clint is three times as old as Fiona. In 3 years, Clint will be two times as old as Fiona. Which function represents the ratio of Clint's age in years to Fiona's age in years, where x represents the number of years from now?

A. $R(x) = \frac{2+x}{3+x}$

B. $R(x) = \frac{6+x}{2+x}$

C. $R(x) = \frac{9+x}{3+x}$

D. $R(x) = \frac{12+x}{6+x}$

12. If Rosa is five times as old as Raoul now, could she be six times as old as Raoul 5 years from now? Explain your reasoning.

13. Tim is 10 years old and his brother John is 5 years old. Make a table showing both brothers' ages now, 1 year from now, 2 years from now, and 3 years from now. What patterns do you notice?

Lesson 12-2

Use the following information for Items 14–19.

As of today, Jeff's age is three times Ming's age. Tina's age is four more than two times Ming's age. Next year, Jeff's age will be seven more than two times Ming's age.

14. As of today, how many times as old as Ming is Tina? Justify your response.

15. Let $R(x)$ represent the ratio of Tina's age in years to Ming's age in years, and let x represent the number of years from now, either past or future. Write R as a function of x.

16. Copy the grid below on graph paper. Sketch a graph of the function R for $-8 < x \leq 36$.

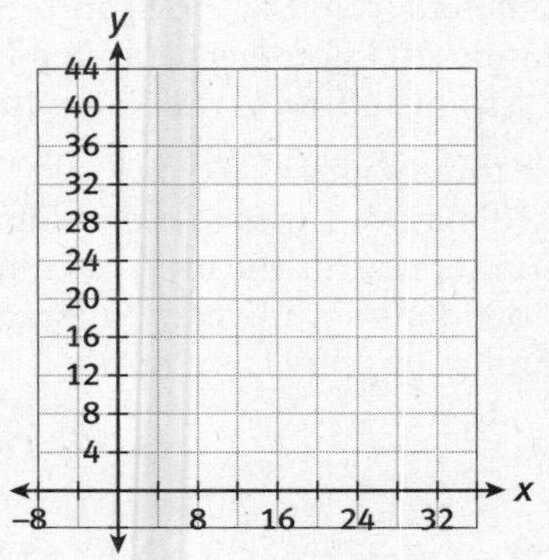

17. What is the equation of the vertical asymptote?

18. What is the equation of the horizontal asymptote? Analyze the behavior of $R(x)$ around this asymptote.

19. What is the meaning of the horizontal asymptote in the context of Tina and Ming's age problem?

Use a graphing calculator for Items 20–22.

20. Determine where the function $R(x) = \dfrac{x+7}{x-2}$ is unbounded.

21. Find the equation of the vertical asymptote of $R(x) = \dfrac{x+7}{x-2}$.

22. Find the equation of the horizontal asymptote of $R(x) = \dfrac{x+7}{x-2}$.

23. Which of the following are the asymptotes of the graph of $y = \dfrac{1+x}{x}$?

I. $x = 0$
II. $y = 0$
III. $y = 1$

A. I only
B. II only
C. I and II only
D. I and III only

24. What will the graph of $f(x) = \dfrac{1}{x+2}$ look like? Use a graphing calculator to help you describe features.

25. How can you check that the function you found to represent the ratio of two ages in an age problem is correct?

MATHEMATICAL PRACTICES
Reason Abstractly and Quantitatively

26. Compare and contrast polynomial functions to rational functions. Describe how the graph of a rational function is different from the graph of a polynomial function.

Rational Functions

Rationalizing Water Collection

Lesson 13-1 Transformations of Rational Functions

My Notes

Learning Targets:

- Compare and contrast graphs of rational functions.
- Write and sketch graphs of transformations of rational functions.

SUGGESTED LEARNING STRATEGIES: Activating Prior Knowledge, Create Representations, Quickwrite, Look for a Pattern

Rainwater harvesting is becoming a viable alternative for supplying households and businesses with water. In many countries rainwater harvesters collect the runoff from roofs and store it for later use. Rain collects in gutters that channel the water into a cistern, or rain barrel.

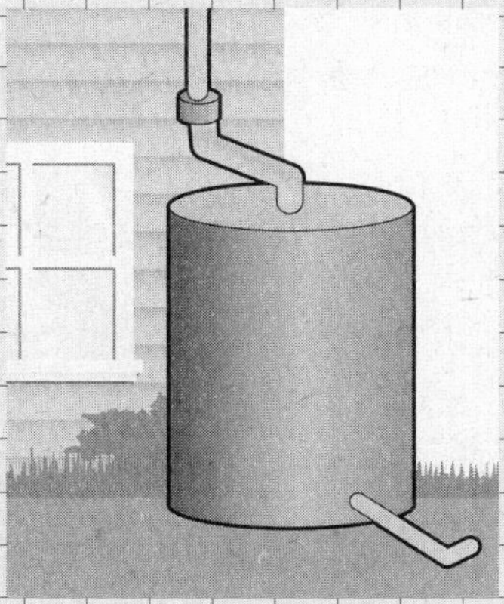

To determine the most economical cistern size, you must evaluate the annual house demand for water and the amount of rainfall in your area.

For a cistern that is used in a house that is lived in year-round, the volume should be approximately 25 cubic meters.

1. Given a cylindrical cistern that holds 25 m^3 of water, write a function for the height $h(x)$ of the cistern given the radius x.

2. What type of function is $h(x)$?

3. Describe the features of the graph of $h(x)$.

MATH TIP

The volume of a cylinder is given by the formula $V = \pi r^2 h$, where r is the radius and h is the height.

4. What are the domain and range of $h(x)$ in terms of the cistern problem?

5. A second cistern that also holds 25 m^3 of water is in the shape of a rectangular prism. The function $p(x) = \dfrac{25}{x^2 + 2x}$ gives the height of the cistern for a rectangular base with length x meters.

a. Reason quantitatively. How are the length and width of the rectangular base of the cistern related? Explain your reasoning.

b. Describe the features of the graph of $p(x)$.

c. What are the domain and range of $p(x)$ in terms of the cistern problem?

My Notes

TECHNOLOGY TIP

Be sure to insert parentheses if needed when graphing rational functions to assure correct order of operations.

Using a graphing calculator, investigate the graphs of $f(x) = \frac{1}{x}$, $g(x) = \frac{2}{x}$, $k(x) = \frac{3}{x}$, $p(x) = \frac{4}{x}$, $d(x) = \frac{-1}{x}$, and $u(x) = \frac{1}{x^2}$.

6. What can you conclude about the asymptotes of the general function $R(x) = \frac{A}{x}$?

7. Compare and contrast the graphs of $f(x) = \frac{1}{x}$ and $u(x) = \frac{1}{x^2}$.

8. Graph $h(x)$ from Item 1 and $u(x) = \frac{1}{x^2}$ on the grid below.

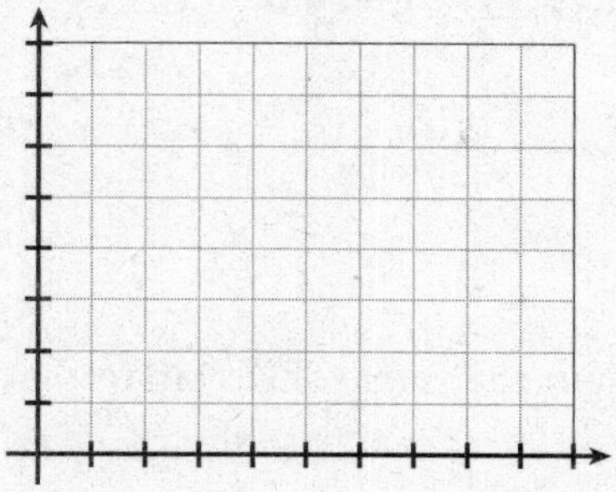

9. How could the graph of $h(x)$ be obtained from the graph of $u(x) = \frac{1}{x^2}$?

In the following items, you will analyze how several transformations affect the graph of the function $f(x) = \frac{1}{x}$.

10. Investigate the graphs of $f(x) = \frac{1}{x}$, $g(x) = \frac{1}{x+2}$, $h(x) = \frac{1}{x-2}$, $p(x) = \frac{1}{x-4}$, and $z(x) = \frac{1}{x^2+1}$. If you use a graphing calculator, select a viewing window of ± 23.5 for x and ± 15.5 for y.

At what values in the domain did vertical asymptotes occur for each of the functions? Explain why the vertical asymptotes occur at these values.

MATH TIP

The graph of a rational function has a vertical asymptote $x = c$ when c is a zero of the denominator only.

My Notes

11. Given $f(x) = \frac{1}{x}$, graph $f(x)$ and $f(x - 3)$. Describe the transformation to obtain the graph of $f(x - 3)$ from the graph of $f(x)$. What is the vertical asymptote?

12. Investigate the graphs of $f(x) = \frac{1}{x}$, $g(x) = \frac{1}{2x-1}$, $h(x) = \frac{1}{2x-6}$, and $p(x) = \frac{1}{2x-12}$. What conclusion can you make for a function of the form $f(x) = \frac{1}{Bx-C}$?

13. Graph $f(x) = \frac{1}{x}$ and $k(x) = \frac{1}{2x+5}$. How is the graph of $k(x)$ obtained from the graph of $f(x)$? What is the vertical asymptote of $k(x)$?

14. Use appropriate tools strategically. Use a graphing calculator and a viewing window of ± 23.5 for x and ± 15.5 for y. Graph each pair of functions and the sum $f(x) + g(x)$. What conclusions can you make about the graphs of the sums?

a. $f(x) = \frac{1}{x}$ and $g(x) = 2$

b. $f(x) = \frac{1}{x}$ and $g(x) = -3$

c. $f(x) = \frac{1}{x}$ and $g(x) = 5$

15. Standard transformations can be used to help graph rational functions of the form $f(x) = \frac{A}{Bx-C} + D$. Explain how the ***parameters*** A, B, C, and D relate to the graph of the rational functions.

MATH TERMS

A **parameter** is a constant in an equation that varies in other equations of the same general form. For example, in the equation $y = ax^2 + bx + c$, a, b, and c are parameters.

My Notes

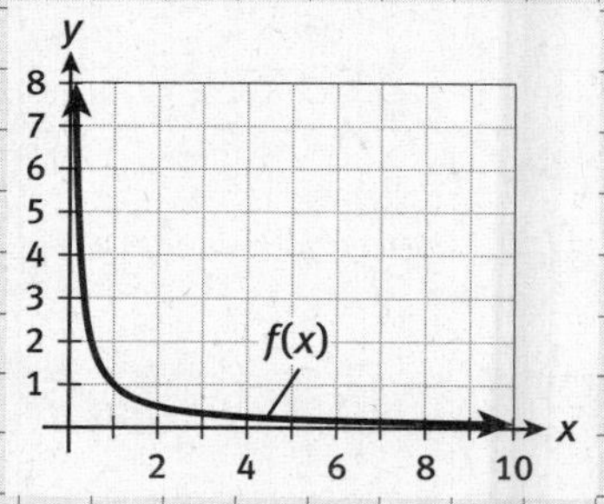

16. Given $f(x) = \frac{1}{x}$, use the information obtained from Item 15 to write a real-world model for $m(x)$, the transformation of $f(x)$ when it is translated $1\frac{1}{2}$ units to the right and $\frac{1}{2}$ unit up, stretched vertically by a factor of 2, and stretched horizontally by a factor of 2. What is the vertical asymptote of $m(x)$?

Check Your Understanding

17. The function $h(x) = \frac{42}{x^2}$ gives the height of a cistern in the shape of a rectangular prism with a square base of side length x that holds 42 m^3 of water. Describe the features of the graph of $h(x)$.

18. Explain how the graph of $g(x) = \frac{3}{4x - 20} + 1$ can be obtained from the graph of the parent function $f(x) = \frac{1}{x}$.

LESSON 13-1 PRACTICE

Sketch a graph of each function or pair of functions.

19. $f(x) = \frac{1}{x}$ and $g(x) = -\frac{5}{x}$.

20. $p(x) = \frac{1}{x + 4}$

21. $u(x) = \frac{1}{3x - 1}$

22. $z(x) = \frac{-2}{x - 4} + 3$

23. On the grid below, graph $f(x) = \frac{1}{x}$ and $g(x)$, the transformation of $f(x)$ translated 3 units to the right, compressed horizontally by a factor of 3, and stretched vertically by a factor of 0.5. Write $g(x)$. What is the vertical asymptote of $g(x)$?

24. Attend to precision. Write to explain to another student how to obtain the graph of $u(x) = \frac{1}{4(x - 12)}$ from the graph of $f(x) = \frac{1}{x}$.

25. Critique the reasoning of others. Carrie says that the graph of $g(x) = \frac{1}{x + 3} + 2$ is a translation 2 units up and 3 units to the right of the graph of $f(x) = \frac{1}{x}$. Is she correct? If not, correct any errors.

My Notes

Learning Targets:

- Determine horizontal, vertical, or oblique asymptotes.
- Accurately graph rational functions.
- Solve rational inequalities.

SUGGESTED LEARNING STRATEGIES: Look for a Pattern, Group Presentation, Think-Pair-Share, Self Revision/Peer Revision, Note Taking

Rational functions that are not in the form $f(x) = \dfrac{A}{Bx - C} + D$ still have patterns that can help you to graph them.

1. Use your calculator to graph $f(x) = \dfrac{x+5}{x^2 - 4}$. How does this graph differ from graphs of rational functions?

MATH TIP

Recall that you can determine where a function graph has x-intercepts by solving $f(x) = 0$.

2. Use a graphing calculator and the ZDecimal window to graph each function. Look for patterns to complete the statements that follow.

$$g(x) = \frac{2x+1}{x^2 - 1}; \quad h(x) = \frac{7x^2 - 3}{5x^4 + 1}$$

a. Make a conjecture about how to find a horizontal asymptote for a rational function where the degree of the denominator is greater than the degree of the numerator. Explain.

b. Create a rational function of your own where the degree of the denominator is greater than the degree of the numerator and use it to test your conjecture in part a.

3. For each rational function, use a graphing calculator and the standard ZDecimal window to graph the function and look for patterns to complete the statements that follow. $u(x) = \dfrac{6x+1}{x-1}; \quad v(x) = \dfrac{2x^2+3}{2x^2-3}$

a. Make a conjecture about how to find a horizontal asymptote for a rational function where the degree of the denominator is equal to the degree of the numerator. Explain.

b. Create a rational function of your own and use it to test your conjecture. Explain your findings.

4. Find the y-intercepts of each function in Items 2 and 3.

5. Find the x-intercepts of each of the functions in Item 3.

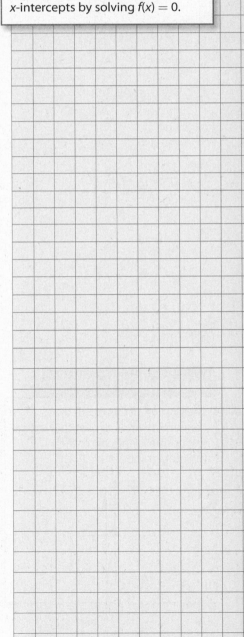

My Notes

6. **Reason abstractly.** What relationship does the numerator of a rational function have to the zeros of a rational function?

When graphing rational functions, determining the features of the graph can be helpful.

To Graph a Rational Function

- Find the intercepts, if they exist.
- Find the horizontal asymptote, if it exists.
- Find the vertical asymptote(s), if they exist.
- Determine the behavior of the graph in the regions formed by the vertical asymptotes.
- Choose a calculator window so that vertical asymptotes will be evaluated, or recognize that a graph that connects points over an asymptote is inaccurate for the value of the asymptote.

Example A

Sketch a graph of $f(x) = \frac{x+2}{x^2-9}$.

- Find and plot the intercepts, if they exist.

$$f(0) = \frac{0+2}{0-9} = -\frac{2}{9} \text{ and } 0 = \frac{x+2}{x^2-9},\ x = -2$$

- Find and sketch the horizontal asymptote, if it exists.

Because the degree of the denominator is greater than that of the numerator, the horizontal asymptote is $y = 0$.

- Find and sketch the vertical asymptote(s), if they exist.

$$x^2 - 9 = 0, \text{ so } x = \pm 3.$$

- Determine the behavior of the graph in the regions formed by the vertical asymptotes. Test points in the regions, and sketch the function.

$$f(-4) = \frac{-4+2}{(-4)^2-9} = -\frac{2}{7},\ f(-2) = 0,\ f(-2.5) = \frac{2}{11},$$

$$f(2) = -\frac{4}{5},\quad f(4) = \frac{6}{7}$$

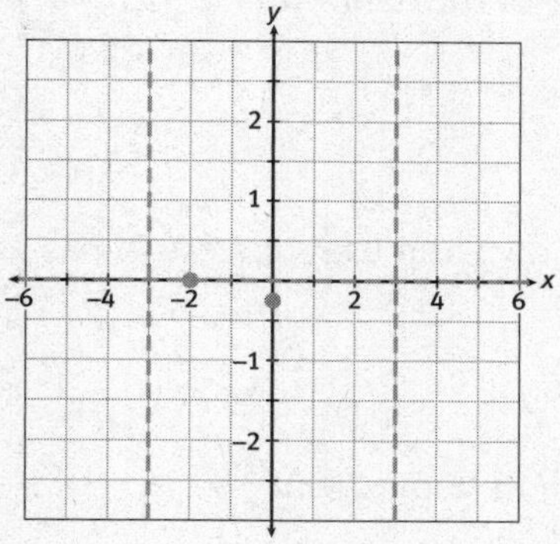

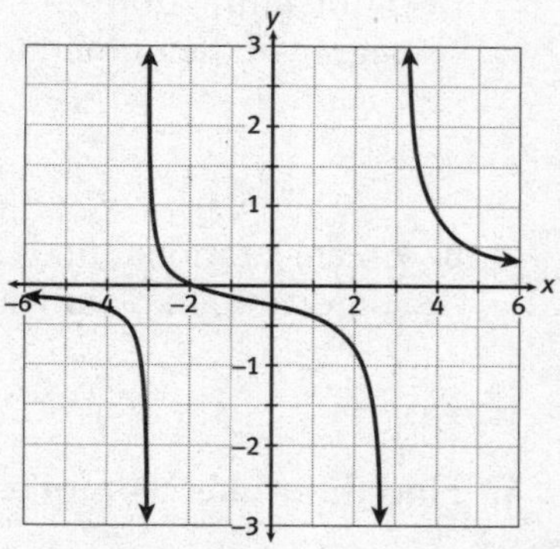

Notice the graph can actually cross the horizontal asymptote. The horizontal asymptote is the behavior of the graph as $x \to \pm\infty$. It does not necessarily represent the behavior of the function over the entire domain.

TECHNOLOGY TIP

The portion of this graph that connects the points over the vertical asymptote is not part of the function graph.

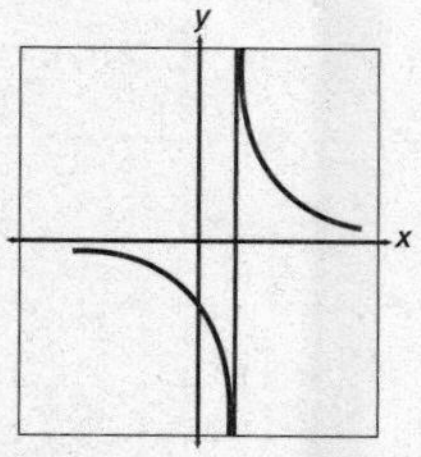

My Notes

Try These A

Graph.

a. $f(x) = \dfrac{x}{x^2 - 2x - 15}$

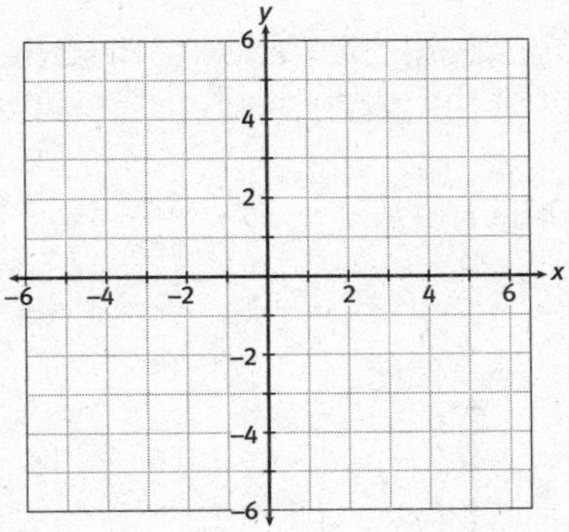

b. $f(x) = \dfrac{x^2 - 5}{x^2 - 4}$

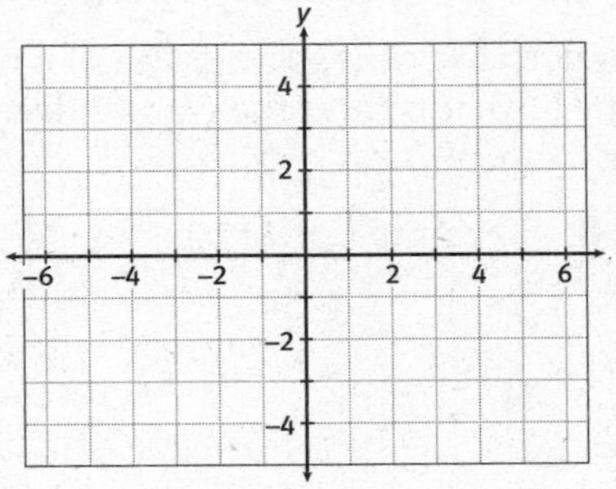

Not all rational functions have vertical asymptotes.

7. For each function, use a graphing calculator and a window set to $-9.4 \le x \le 9.4$ and $-6.2 \le y \le 6.2$ to graph.

Simplify each rational function algebraically. What generalizations can you make about the functions?

a. $f(x) = \dfrac{x^2 + 3x}{x}$

b. $f(x) = \dfrac{x^2 - 4}{x - 2}$

c. $f(x) = \dfrac{(x+2)(x-3)}{(x-3)(x+4)}$

d. $f(x) = \dfrac{(x+2)x}{(x+3)(x+2)(x-1)}$

MATH TIP

The first step in working with rational functions is to simplify and determine if there are any discontinuities.

Vertical asymptotes divide the graph into regions from left to right. Graph at least one point in each region and use it to determine whether the graph will be above or below the horizontal asymptote.

My Notes

MATH TERMS

If a value of x makes the numerator and denominator 0, then a **discontinuity** or *hole* in the graph occurs. If a value of x only makes the denominator 0, then a vertical asymptote occurs.

Discontinuities are those x-values for which a rational function is undefined. Because division by zero is undefined, a discontinuity occurs at any value of x that causes the denominator of the fraction to be zero. If a value of x causes both the numerator and denominator to be zero, then there will be a hole in the graph at that value of x. If only the denominator is zero, then the graph will have a vertical asymptote at that value of x.

When describing the graph of a rational function, one feature to describe is the left-sided and the right-sided behavior of the graph of a function around discontinuities.

8. The graph of $k(x) = \dfrac{1}{x^2 + x - 6}$ is shown below.

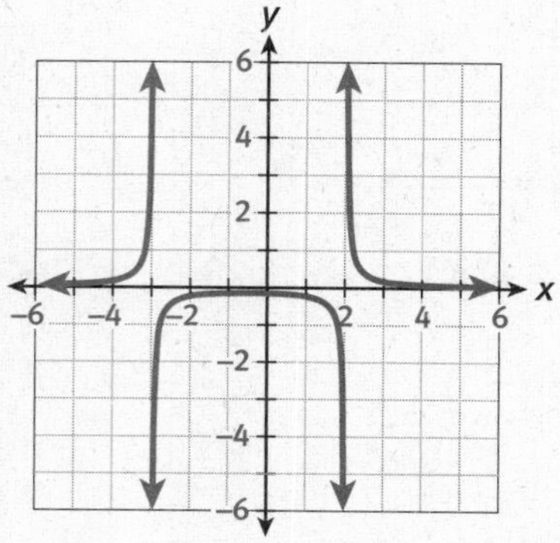

a. What are the discontinuities in $k(x)$?

b. Explain how you can determine the discontinuities algebraically.

c. Describe the left-sided and the right-sided behavior of the graph of $k(x)$ around each of the discontinuities.

9. For each part below, use a graphing calculator and a standard window to graph each pair of functions and their sum. What generalization can you make about the graphs?

a. $f(x) = x$ and $g(x) = \frac{1}{x}$

b. $f(x) = 3x$ and $g(x) = \frac{1}{x}$

c. $f(x) = -2x + 1$ and $g(x) = \frac{1}{x}$

My Notes

10. What are the asymptotes for the graph of $f(x) = 2x + 1 + \frac{2}{x}$?

11. Rewrite $f(x) = \frac{x^2 + 3x - 2}{x + 4}$ to express it in the same form as the function in Item 10. What are the asymptotes of the graph of this function?

Check Your Understanding

12. Explain how to find the horizontal asymptote of $g(x) = \frac{x + 4}{2x + 7}$.

13. Do all rational functions have vertical asymptotes? Why or why not? If not, give an example of a rational function that lacks a vertical asymptote.

14. The degree of the numerator of a rational function is exactly one greater than the degree of the denominator. How can you find the slant asymptote of the function?

LESSON 13-2 PRACTICE

Find the horizontal asymptote.

15. $g(x) = \frac{x - 9}{x^3 + 5x^2 - 7}$

16. $f(x) = \frac{8x - 7}{4x + 3}$

17. $g(x) = \frac{x^2 + 2 + 6x^4 + 1 - 4x}{3x^3 + 3x^4 - 5x^2}$

18. Find the *x*- and *y*-intercepts.

a. $f(x) = \frac{x^2 + 2x + 1}{3 + 3x^2}$

b. $g(x) = \frac{2x^3 - 16x}{4x^2 + 3x^3}$

Sketch a graph of each function without using a graphing calculator.

19. **a.** $f(x) = \frac{x - 1}{x + 1} + 2$

b. $g(x) = \frac{x}{x^2 + 7x - 8}$

20. **a.** $f(x) = \frac{x^2 - 2x + 1}{x - 1}$

b. $g(x) = \frac{x^2 - 8x + 15}{x - 3}$

21. Find the equation of the slant asymptote. Analyze the behavior of each function at its slant asymptote.

a. $f(x) = \frac{x^2 + 4}{x + 3}$

b. $g(x) = \frac{x^2 + 4x + 5}{x + 2}$

22. **Construct viable arguments.** The graph of a rational function has exactly two vertical asymptotes. Is that sufficient information to determine that the polynomial in the denominator has a degree of 2? Give an example to justify your answer.

23. **Make sense of problems.** Compare the strategies of graphing rational functions by transforming the parent rational function $f(x) = \frac{1}{x}$ and graphing rational functions by determining the features of the graph such as intercepts and asymptotes.

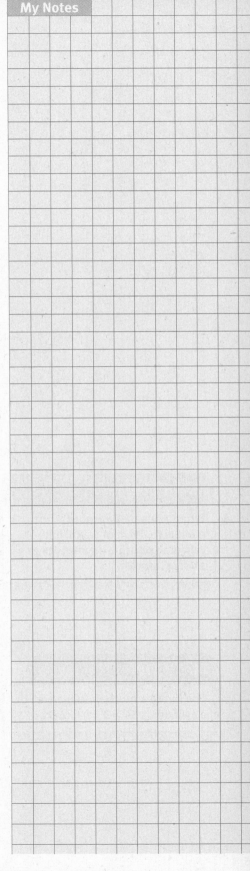

My Notes

Learning Targets:

- Write the equation of a rational function given certain attributes.
- Solve rational inequalities.

SUGGESTED LEARNING STRATEGIES: Create Representations, Group Presentation, Look for a Pattern, Quickwrite, Think-Pair-Share

So far, you have determined features of rational functions by looking at their graphs and their algebraic representations. It is also possible to write a rational function given a description of some of its attributes.

1. Write a function that has asymptotes of $y = 2 - 3x$ and $x = 1$.

2. Write a function for each of the following conditions.

a. a function whose graph is a line with a hole at $x = 1$

b. a function whose graph has an asymptote, the line $y = x + 3$, and has vertical asymptotes at $x = \pm 3$

c. a function whose graph has an asymptote, the line $y = 4 - 2x$, and has exactly one vertical asymptote, $x = 1$

3. Consider the function $y = \dfrac{x^2 + 3x - 2}{x + 4}$. Describe how to graph the function in as much detail as it would take for another person to sketch the graph from your description.

MATH TERMS

When a linear asymptote is not parallel to the *x*- or *y*-axis, it is called an **oblique asymptote** or a *slant asymptote*.

A manufacturer of cisterns needs to use the least amount of material to build a cistern in order to maximize profits.

4. For a cylindrical cistern that has a volume of 25 cubic meters, create an equation that represents the total surface area of aluminum that it would take to build the cistern in terms of the radius x.

MATH TIP

The formula for the surface area of a cylinder is $SA = 2\pi rh + 2\pi r^2$.

5. Using your graphing calculator with a window set to $0 \le x \le 5$ and $0 \le y \le 150$, determine the intervals on this window in which the function is increasing or decreasing.

6. What is the minimum amount of aluminum needed to build this cistern, to the nearest whole number?

My Notes

Rational inequalities can be solved by a variety of techniques. Some rational inequalities can be easily solved algebraically.

7. Solve $12 < \dfrac{9n+51}{n-4}$.

Rational inequalities can also be solved in much the same way as polynomial inequalities, with a few additional steps required because of the possibility of having zeros in the denominator. Sign patterns can be used to solve rational inequalities as well as polynomial inequalities.

Solving Rational Inequalities with Sign Patterns

- Write the inequality so that polynomials in the numerator and denominator are in factored form.
- Identify the zeros of the function from the numerator.
- Find the undefined points from the denominator.
- Pick one test value for x that falls between each of the intervals created by the zeros and the undefined points.
- Evaluate the rational function at these values to test the sign of the inequality in each interval and determine the solution.
- State the solution intervals.

Example A

Solve $\dfrac{x^2+3x-4}{x^2-4} > 0$.

Factor the polynomials in the numerator and the denominator.

$$\frac{(x+4)(x-1)}{(x+2)(x-2)} > 0$$

The zeros and undefined points in increasing order are -4, -2, 1, and 2. Note that the zeros are not solutions because the inequality symbol is $>$.

Next, use these four values to divide the number line into five intervals and test one value in each interval: $(-\infty, -4)$, $(-4, -2)$, $(-2, 1)$, $(1, 2)$, and $(2, \infty)$.

Test -5: $\dfrac{(-5+4)(-5-1)}{(-5+2)(-5-2)}$. Both factors in the numerator are negative, so the product is positive. Both factors in the denominator are negative, so the product is positive. A positive divided by a positive is positive, so the quotient is positive.

Test -3: $\dfrac{(-3+4)(-3-1)}{(-3+2)(-3-2)}$. Factors in the numerator are positive and negative, so the product is negative. Both factors in the denominator are negative, so the product is positive. A negative divided by a positive is negative, so the quotient is negative.

My Notes

Continue this process and record the results in a table.

Interval	$x < -4$	$-4 < x < -2$	$-2 < x < 1$	$1 < x < 2$	$2 < x$
Test value	-5	-3	0	$\frac{3}{2}$	3
Sign	$+$	$-$	$+$	$-$	$+$

A number line can help you organize the information. Note that zeros are indicated by **0** and undefined points are defined by **u**.

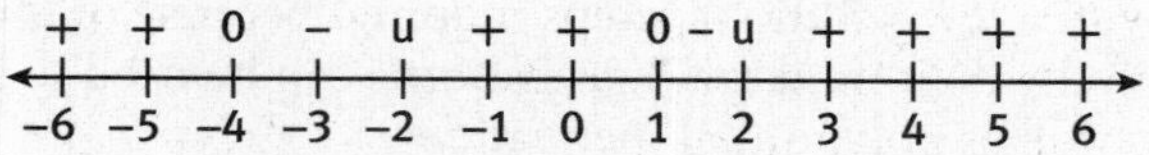

The solution is the intervals of x where the inequality is greater than 0. So, x-values of the zeros are not included in the solution.

Solution intervals: $(-\infty, -4) \cup (-2, 1) \cup (2, \infty)$

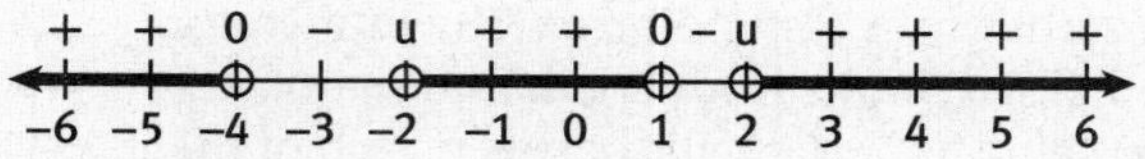

You can use a calculator to graph the related function to verify the solution.

$$\frac{x^2 + 3x - 4}{x^2 - 4} > 0$$

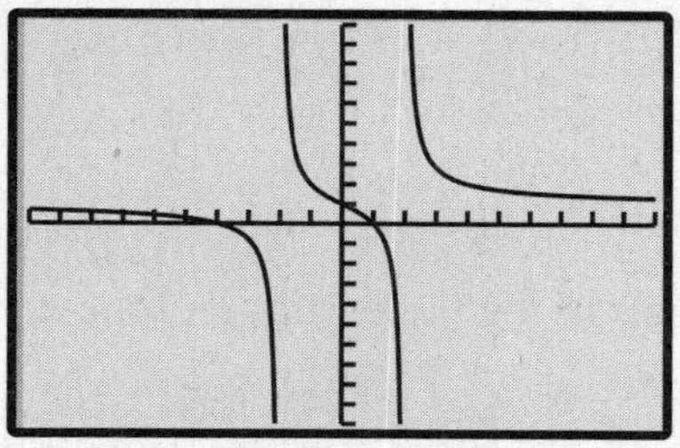

Try These A

Solve each inequality and write the solution interval.

a. $\dfrac{x^2 - 2x - 15}{x - 4} \le 0$

b. $\dfrac{x - 1}{x^2 - 9} > 0$

8. Explain how graphs can be used to find the solutions to polynomial inequalities.

My Notes

Rational inequalities can also be used to solve real-world problems.

The manufacturer of the cisterns in Items 4–6 has decided that acceptable profit levels can be obtained if the amount of aluminum needed to build the cistern is no more than 50 m^2.

9. Use the formula for surface area to write a rational inequality to determine the range of cisterns that would meet this requirement in terms of radius x.

10. Write the inequality from Item 9 in the form of a fraction that is less than zero.

11. Are there any undefined values of x? If so, what are they?

12. Use appropriate tools strategically. How could you use a graphing calculator to find the zeros? Explore the limitations of the graphing calculator as it relates to the behavior of the function around discontinuities.

13. Interpret the zeros in the context of the cistern problem.

My Notes

Check Your Understanding

14. Is it possible to write two different functions whose graphs are each lines with a hole at $x = 2$? Justify your answer.

15. If the symbol in a rational inequality is $>$, are the ( ) symbols used if the solution intervals are written in interval notation? Explain.

LESSON 13-3 PRACTICE

16. Write a function whose graph has an asymptote, the line $y = 2$, and vertical asymptotes at $x = \pm 4$.

17. Write a function whose graph has an asymptote, the line $y = 3 + 4x$, and exactly one vertical asymptote, $x = 2$.

18. Solve $\frac{x^3 - 2x^2 - 3x}{x + 1} \geq 0$ and write the solution intervals.

19. **Critique the reasoning of others.** Tom was asked to write a function whose graph has an asymptote, the line $y = 2x$, and exactly one vertical asymptote, $x = 5$. He wrote $f(x) = 2x + \frac{5}{x^2 - 25}$. Is Tom's answer correct? If not, explain and correct his error.

20. **Reason abstractly.** How is solving a rational inequality different from solving a polynomial inequality?

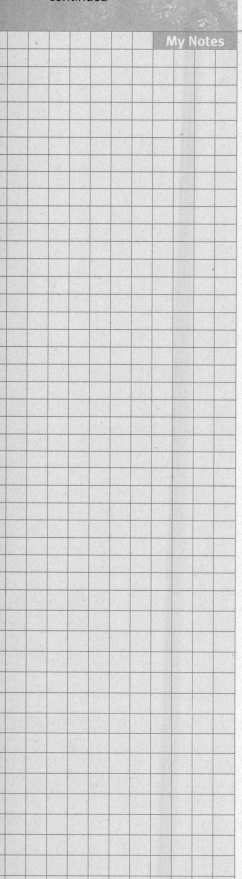

ACTIVITY 13 PRACTICE

Write your answers on notebook paper.
Show your work.

Lesson 13-1

1. The function $h(x) = \frac{120}{x^2 - 3x}$ gives the height in centimeters of a box in the shape of a rectangular prism, where x is the length of the box's rectangular base. How can the function be interpreted in the context of the problem?

2. Describe the features of the graph of $h(x)$ in Item 1.

3. Sketch a graph of $f(x) = \frac{1}{x}$ and $g(x) = \frac{8}{x}$.

4. Sketch a graph of $h(x) = \frac{1}{x - 5}$.

5. Sketch a graph of $k(x) = \frac{3}{2x + 1} - 4$. Describe how the graph of $k(x)$ could be obtained from the graph of $f(x) = \frac{1}{x}$.

6. Given $f(x) = \frac{1}{x}$, describe the transformation to obtain the graph of $f(x + 4)$ from the graph of $f(x)$. What is the vertical asymptote?

7. If $f(x) = \frac{1}{x}$ and $h(x) = \frac{1}{4x - 1}$, how is the graph of $h(x)$ obtained from the graph of $f(x)$? What is the vertical asymptote of $h(x)$?

8. If $f(x) = \frac{1}{x}$ and $g(x) = -5$, what is the effect of adding $g(x)$ to $f(x)$?

9. The graph of $g(x)$ is a transformation of $f(x) = \frac{1}{x}$ translated 2 units to the right, compressed horizontally by a factor of 3, and stretched vertically by a factor of 4.
a. Graph $f(x)$ and $g(x)$.
b. Write $g(x)$.
c. What is the vertical asymptote of $g(x)$?

10. If $g(x) = \frac{4}{0.5x + 4}$, explain how you can determine the number of units the graph would be translated left or right from the graph of the parent rational function $f(x) = \frac{1}{x}$.

Lesson 13-2

Find the horizontal asymptote.

11. $f(x) = \frac{x - 6}{5x^3 + 4}$

12. $g(x) = \frac{4x^2 + x^3 + 1 - 4x}{5x^3 + 3x - 7x^2 + 8}$

13. Which function does not have a horizontal asymptote of 0?

A. $f(x) = \frac{x^2 + 8}{2x^4 - 3x^2 - 1}$

B. $g(x) = \frac{x^3 + 5x^2 + x^4 - 2}{4x^4 - 2x^2 + 1}$

C. $h(x) = \frac{x^3 + 5x^2 + 4x - 2}{4x^4 - 2x^2 + 1}$

D. $k(x) = \frac{x^3 + 8}{2x^4 - 3x^2 - 1}$

14. Find the x- and y-intercepts of $g(x) = \dfrac{x^2 - x - 6}{3x + 7}$.

15. Sketch a graph without using a graphing calculator.

a. $f(x) = \dfrac{2x - 1}{x}$ **b.** $g(x) = \dfrac{x}{x^2 - x - 2}$

16. Graph. Explore the limitations of a graphing calculator as it relates to the behavior of each function around its discontinuities.

a. $f(x) = \dfrac{x^2 + x}{x + 1}$ **b.** $g(x) = \dfrac{x^2 + x - 12}{x + 4}$

17. Find the equation of the slant asymptote.

a. $f(x) = \dfrac{x^2 - 4x - 5}{x - 3}$ **b.** $g(x) = \dfrac{x^2 - 9}{x - 3}$

18. The graph of a rational function $f(x)$ has a horizontal asymptote of $y = 0$. Is it possible for the graph of $f(x)$ to cross the x-axis? Explain your reasoning.

19. Is it possible for the graph of a rational function to have both a hole and a vertical asymptote? If so, give an example.

20. Consider the function $k(x) = \dfrac{1}{x^2 + x - 12}$.

a. What are the discontinuities in the graph of $k(x)$?

b. Describe the behavior of the graph of $k(x)$ around the discontinuities (hint: the left-sided and the right-sided behavior).

Lesson 13-3

21. Write a function that has asymptotes of $y = 5 - x$ and $x = 3$.

22. Write a function whose graph has an asymptote, the line $y = x + 1$, and vertical asymptotes at $x = \pm 2$.

23. Write a function whose graph has an asymptote, the line $y = 2 + 6x$, and exactly one vertical asymptote, $x = -1$.

24. If $f(x) = \dfrac{16 - x^2}{x - 4}$, what value does $f(x)$ approach as x approaches $-\infty$?

A. $-\infty$
B. -4
C. 0
D. ∞

25. When solving a rational inequality, why are zeros and undefined values used to define the intervals for testing x-values?

26. In Item 1, the function $h(x) = \dfrac{120}{x^2 - 3x}$ gave the height in centimeters of a box in the shape of a rectangular prism.

a. Identify the domain of $h(x)$ in the context of the problem.

b. Write a rational inequality to find the possible values for the length and width of the base of the box if the height is less than 10 inches.

c. Solve the rational inequality.

d. Interpret the solution intervals in the context of the problem.

MATHEMATICAL PRACTICES
Look for and Make Use of Structure

27. Describe the different breaks in graphs of rational functions. Explain how these breaks can be used to solve a rational inequality.

Taneytown High School is hosting a reunion for its alumni. The reunion committee decides to rent a large hall and have the dinner catered. The hall costs $750 for the evening, and each dinner is an additional $20. The three oldest alumni will not be charged for their tickets but will be included in the total cost to the committee. The committee will set the ticket price to cover their costs; they will not make a profit.

1. Complete the table to explore ticket price options for different numbers of ticket sales.

People Attending Dinner and Dance	30	50	100	200
Attendees Paying for Tickets	27			
Total Cost to the Committee	$1350			
Cost per *Paying* Attendee	$50			

2. a. Write a rule for the total cost to the committee, $C(n)$, based on the total number of alumni, n, who will attend the event.

b. What does the function $C(n) = \frac{20n + 750}{n - 3}$ mean in the context of the problem? What is the domain of $C(n)$ within the context of this problem?

3. What is the minimum number of people who would need to attend the reunion to keep the cost to less than $25 per paying attendee? Show or describe your work and reasoning.

4. The graph of $C(n)$ has a horizontal asymptote. Give the equation of this asymptote and explain its meaning within the context of this problem.

5. In $u(x) = \frac{c}{ax - b} + d$, a, b, c, and d are positive real numbers. How could the graph of $u(x)$ be obtained from the graph of $f(x) = \frac{1}{x}$?

6. In $f(x) = \frac{x^2 - c^2}{(x + a)(x - b)(x + c)}$, a, b, and c are positive real numbers.

Show your work for each step below.

a. Find the y-intercept of $f(x)$.
b. Identify the x-values of any holes in the graph of $f(x)$.
c. Find the vertical asymptote(s) of $f(x)$.
d. Find the x-intercept(s) of $f(x)$.
e. Find any horizontal asymptotes of $f(x)$.

f. Using the graph, which point is the correct location for a hole in the graph of $f(x)$?

g. Describe the left-sided and the right-sided behavior of the graph of $f(x)$ around each of the vertical asymptotes.

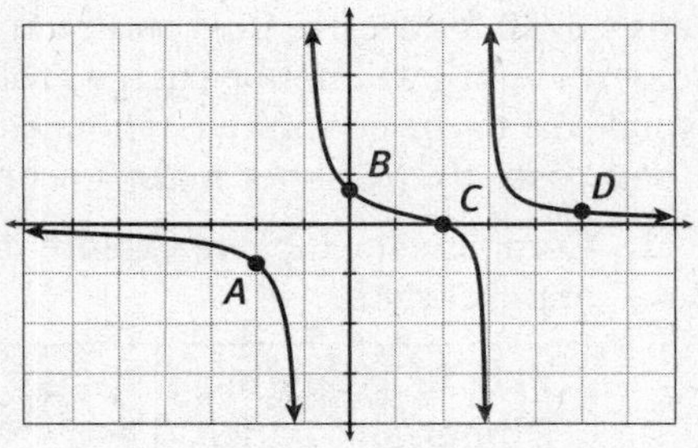

Scoring Guide	**Exemplary**	**Proficient**	**Emerging**	**Incomplete**
	The solution demonstrates these characteristics:			
Mathematics Knowledge and Thinking (Items 2b, 4, 5)	• Clear and accurate understanding of writing and graphing rational functions, graphical transformations, and intercepts	• A functional understanding of writing and graphing rational functions, graphical transformations, and intercepts	• Partial understanding of writing and graphing rational functions	• Little or no understanding of writing and graphing rational functions
Problem Solving (Items 1, 2, 3)	• An appropriate and efficient strategy that results in a correct answer	• A strategy that may include unnecessary steps but results in a correct answer	• A strategy that results in some incorrect answers	• No clear strategy when solving problems
Mathematical Modeling / Representations (Items 4, 6)	• Clear and accurate understanding of representations of rational functions and their graphs • Clear and accurate understanding of creating rational graphs, vertical and horizontal asymptotes, and interpreting their meaning in context	• A functional understanding of representations of rational functions • Mostly accurate interpretation of asymptotic behavior, discontinuities, roots and *y*-intercepts as they pertain to graphs of rational functions	• Partial understanding of representations of rational functions • Partial understanding of asymptotic behavior, discontinuities, roots and *y*-intercepts as they pertain to graphs of rational functions	• Little or no understanding of representations of rational functions • Inaccurate or incomplete understanding of asymptotic behavior, discontinuities, roots and *y*-intercepts as they pertain to graphs of rational functions
Reasoning and Communication (Items 5, 6)	• Precise use of appropriate math terms and language to describe translations of graphs of rational functions and the key characteristics of rational functions – potentially using limits	• Correct characterization of translations of graphs of rational functions and the key characteristics of rational functions	• Misleading or confusing characterization of rational functions, their graphs and discontinuities	• Incomplete or inaccurate characterization of graphs of rational functions

Trigonometric Functions

3

Unit Overview

In this unit you will build on your understanding of right triangle trigonometry as you study angles in radian measure, trigonometric functions, and circular functions. You will investigate in depth the graphs of the sine and cosine functions and extend your knowledge of trigonometry to include tangent, cotangent, secant, and cosecant, as well as solving trigonometric equations.

Key Terms

As you study this unit, add these and other terms to your math notebook. Include in your notes your prior knowledge of each word, as well as your experiences in using the word in different mathematical examples. If needed, ask for help in pronouncing new words and add information on pronunciation to your math notebook. It is important that you learn new terms and use them correctly in your class discussions and in your problem solutions.

Academic Vocabulary

- subtend

Math Terms

- initial side
- terminal side
- standard position
- coterminal angles
- subtend
- radian
- angular velocity
- linear velocity
- reference triangle
- periodic function
- period
- amplitude
- phase shift
- trigonometric functions
- sine
- unit circle
- tangent
- cosecant
- secant
- tangent
- concentric circles
- one-to-one function
- inverse trigonometric function
- reference angle

ESSENTIAL QUESTIONS

? What type of real-world problems are modeled and solved using trigonometry?

? How are graphic representations of trigonometric functions useful in understanding real-life phenomena?

EMBEDDED ASSESSMENTS

This unit has two embedded assessments, following Activities 18 and 20. These assessments will give you an opportunity to demonstrate what you have learned about trigonometric functions and their inverses, the graphs of sinusoidal curves, and writing and solving trigonometric equations.

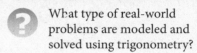

Getting Ready

Write your answers on notebook paper.
Show your work.

1. Find the measure of each angle of triangle ABC, given $AC = 6$, $CB = 2\sqrt{3}$, and $AB = 4\sqrt{3}$.
2. Which equation could you use to find the measure of x in the figure below?

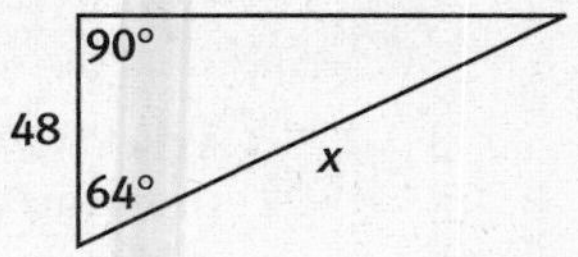

   A. $\sin 64° = \frac{x}{48}$
   B. $\cos 64° = \frac{x}{48}$
   C. $\tan 64° = \frac{x}{48}$
   D. $\sin 64° = \frac{48}{x}$
   E. $\cos 64° = \frac{48}{x}$
3. In $\triangle DEF$, $m\angle D = 70°$, $m\angle E = 90°$, and $EF = 10$. Find, to the nearest whole number, the measure of the hypotenuse of $\triangle DEF$.
4. In $\triangle GHI$, $GH = 166$ ft, $HI = 112$ ft, and $m\angle H = 90°$. Find the measure of $\angle G$ and the length of $\overline{GI}$.
5. Explain this statement: The inverse of a function is sometimes a function. Use examples in your explanation.
6. Consider the function $f(x) = \sqrt{x-1}$.
   a. Give the domain and the range.
   b. Sketch a graph of the function.

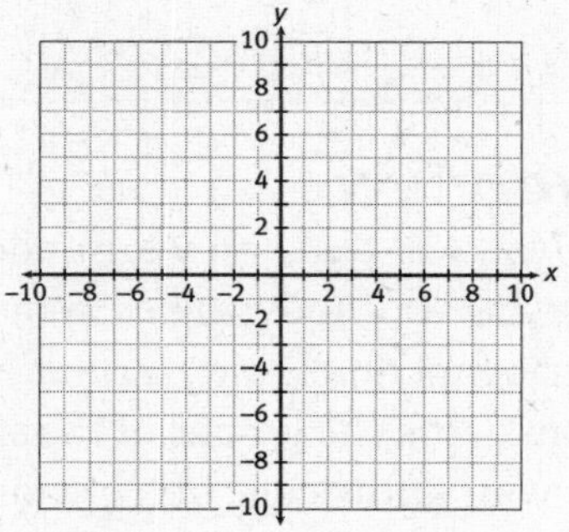

   c. Write the inverse function.
   d. Give the domain and the range of the inverse function.
   e. Sketch a graph of the inverse function on the same coordinate grid as in Item 6b.
7. Determine whether $f(x) = \frac{x}{4} + 1$ and $g(x) = 4x - 4$ are inverse functions. Justify your answer.
8. Explain how the graph of $y = 2(x-1)^2 + 3$ differs from the graph of $y = x^2$. Explain how you can determine the differences without graphing.

Angles and Angle Measure

What's My Angle Measure?

Lesson 14-1 Angle Measures in Standard Position

My Notes

Learning Targets:

- Draw angles in standard position.
- Find the initial side and terminal side of an angle in standard position.
- Identify coterminal angles.

SUGGESTED LEARNING STRATEGIES: Activating Prior Knowledge, Summarizing, Paraphrasing, Vocabulary Organizer, Create Representations, Think-Pair-Share

In geometry, an angle has two fixed rays with a common endpoint.

1. **Attend to precision.** Draw an example of each of the following types of angles, and give the degree measure of the angle. Then state the possible range of measures for all angles of that type.

   a. acute angle

   b. obtuse angle

   c. right angle

   d. straight angle

In trigonometry, an angle consists of a fixed ray, called the ***initial side***, and a rotating ray, called the ***terminal side***. An angle is in ***standard position*** when the vertex is at the origin and the initial side is on the positive x-axis. A counterclockwise rotation represents an angle with positive measure. A clockwise rotation represents an angle with negative measure.

CONNECT TO HISTORY

Dividing a circle into 360 parts can be traced to the ancient city of Babylon. The Babylonians used a base-60 number system instead of the base-10 system we use today.

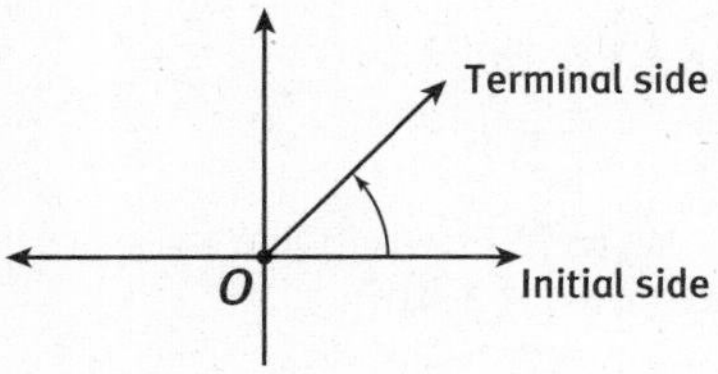

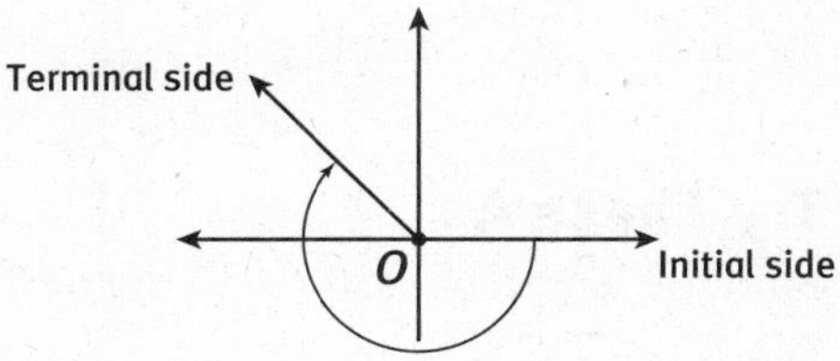

2. Draw each angle described below in standard position, and then give the degree measure of the angle.
   a. one-fourth of a complete counterclockwise rotation
   b. one-half of a complete clockwise rotation
   c. one complete counterclockwise rotation (the angle formed by rotating the initial side counterclockwise until it coincides with itself)
   d. one-eighth of a complete clockwise rotation
   e. two and one-third complete counterclockwise rotations

My Notes

MATH TERMS

The 125° angle and the −235° angle shown below are formed by different rotations, yet they have the same initial and terminal sides. Therefore, they are **coterminal angles**.

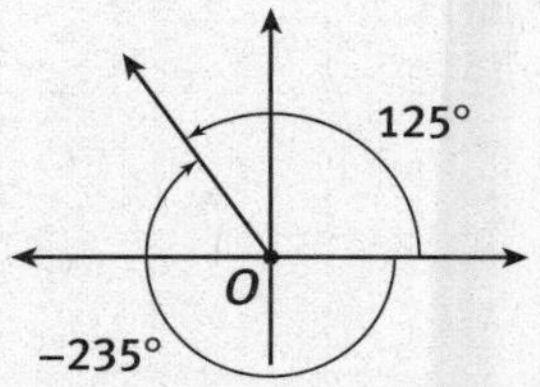

MATH TERMS

When the sides of an angle pass through the endpoints of an arc, the angle **subtends** the arc. In the figure below, the arc $\overset{\frown}{PQ}$ is subtended by angle POQ.

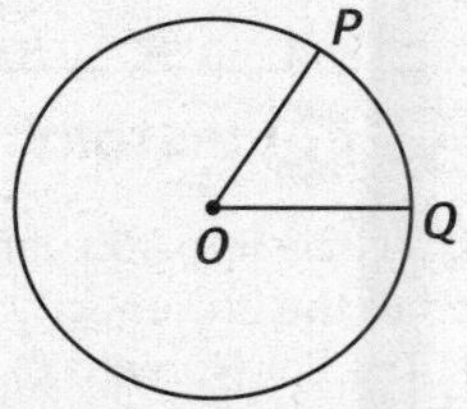

Coterminal angles are angles formed by different rotations but with the same initial and terminal sides. To find measures of coterminal angles, add or subtract multiples of 360°.

3. Make use of structure. For each angle in standard position, find two positive angles and two negative angles that are coterminal with the given angle.

a. 60° **b.** −100°

4. Find an angle between 0° and 360° that is coterminal with the given angle.

a. 890° **b.** −1350°

The circumference of a circle is equal to $2\pi r$, where r is the radius of the circle. The length of an arc ***subtended*** by a central angle of n degrees is equal to $\frac{n}{360}(2\pi r)$.

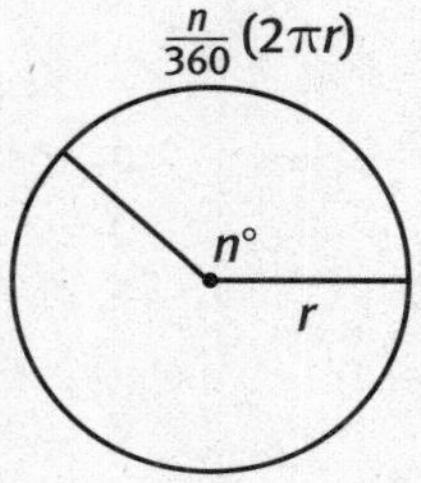

Example A

A pet gerbil runs the length of an arc on a circular wheel with radius 12.5 cm which subtends a central angle of 40°. What length did the gerbil travel?

$\frac{40}{360}(2\pi(12.5))$	Substitute the radius and angle measure.
8.7 cm	Simplify.

Try These A

Find the length of each arc to the nearest hundredth of a unit.

a.

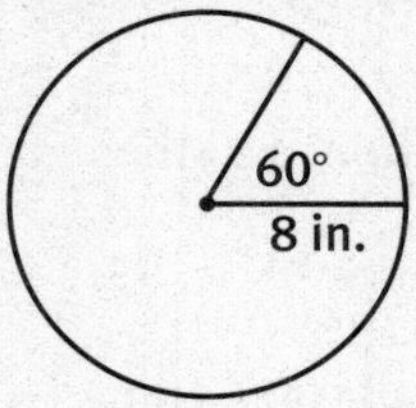

b.

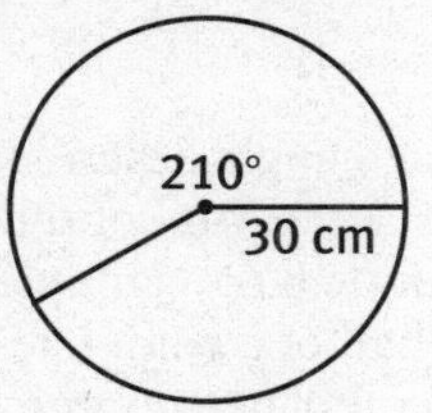

5. Make sense of problems. A wheel with a radius of 20 inches rotated 80° as it rolled along the ground. How far did the wheel travel?

My Notes

CONNECT TO GEOGRAPHY

A nautical mile is approximately equal to the length of a $\frac{1}{60}$-degree arc on a great circle of the earth line of longitude.

6. The second hand of a clock is 6 inches long.

a. How many degrees does the second hand rotate in $4\frac{1}{2}$ minutes?

b. How far does the tip of the second hand travel in $4\frac{1}{2}$ minutes?

7. What is the length of the major arc $\overset{\frown}{AB}$?

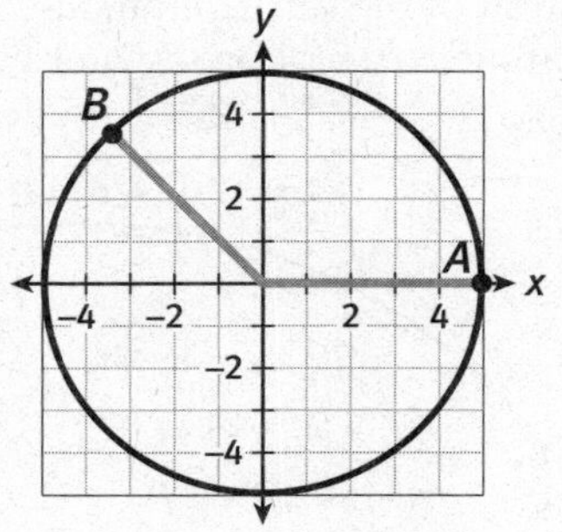

Check Your Understanding

8. Express regularity in repeated reasoning. Write an expression that generates every angle coterminal with a 78° angle.

9. Which arc has a greater length: an arc subtended by a 30° angle on a circle with radius 14 cm or an arc subtended by a 45° angle on a circle with radius 12 cm?

LESSON 14-1 PRACTICE

10. An angle of 291° is drawn on a coordinate plane with its vertex at the origin and its initial side on the positive x-axis. In which quadrant does the terminal side lie?

11. Find an angle between 0° and 360° that is coterminal with the given angles.

a. −110° **b.** 430°

12. What is the perimeter of each figure?

a. **b.**

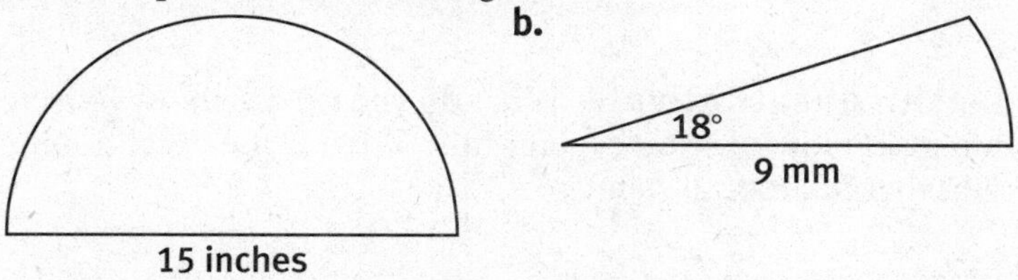

13. The end of a pendulum with a length of 21 cm travels an arc length of 24 cm. How many degrees does the pendulum swing?

14. Critique the reasoning of others. Neil believes the two arcs subtended by a 195-degree angle and by a −165-degree angle in a circle with a radius of 10 inches will have the same length. Explain Neil's mistake.

My Notes

Learning Targets:

- Measure angles in radians.
- Convert angle measures from degrees to radians.
- Recognize trigonometric ratios to complete reference triangles.

SUGGESTED LEARNING STRATEGIES: Use Manipulatives, Create Representations, Vocabulary Organizer, Think-Pair-Share, Group Presentations

Degrees are not the only unit of measure for angles. To find out about another unit of angle measure, complete the following questions concerning circles *A* and *B*, shown below.

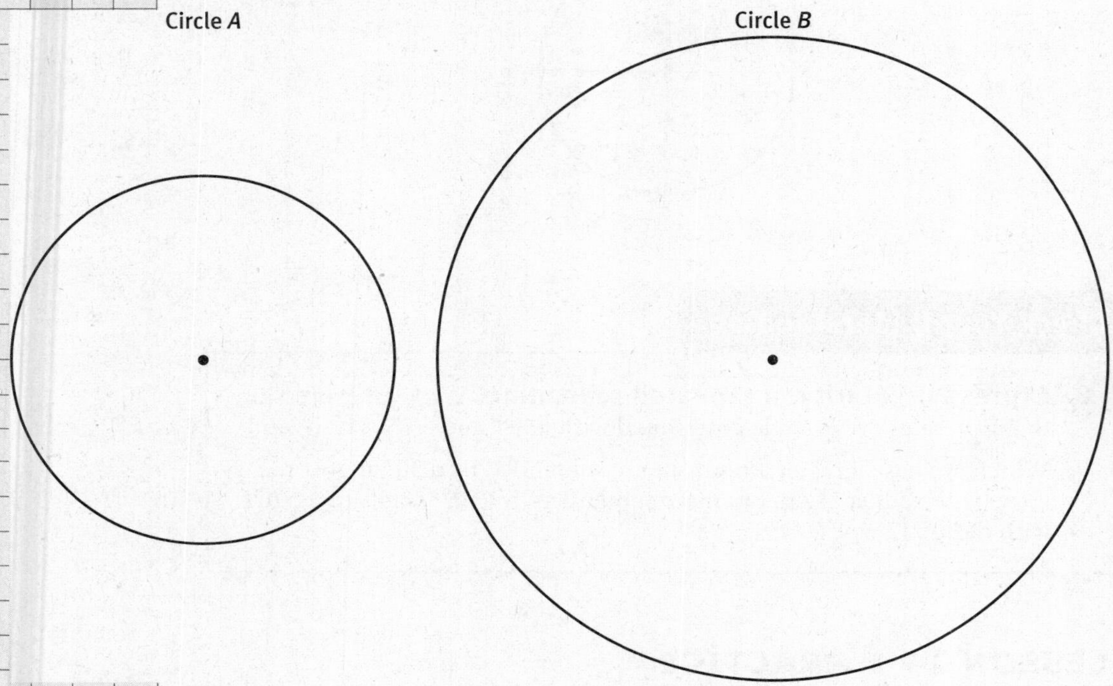

1. Cut a piece of string equal in length to the radius of each circle.

a. Bend the string around each circle and mark off as many arcs as possible that are equal in length to the radii. Write the approximate number of radii that fit around each circle.
Circle *A*: Circle *B*:

b. **Reason quantitatively.** What do you notice about your answers in part a? How can you explain this? What is the exact number of radii that fit around each circle?

c. In each circle, mark off a central angle that intercepts an arc with the same length as the radius of the circle.

Angles may be measured in ***radians*** as well as in degrees. One radian is the measure of a central angle which intersects an arc equal in length to the radii.

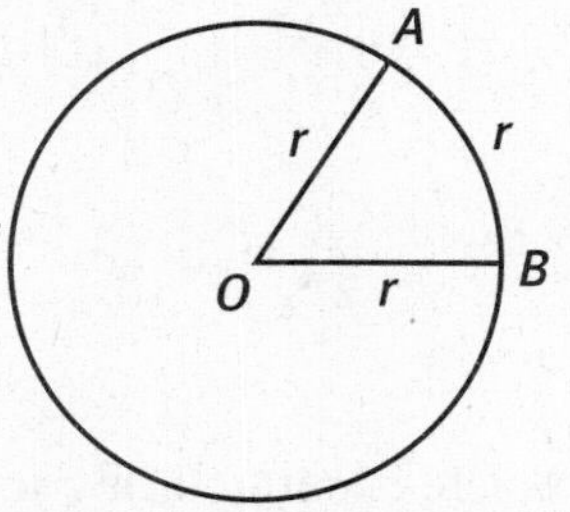

$m\angle AOB = 1$ radian

My Notes

MATH TERMS

A central angle of a circle which subtends an arc equal to the length of the radius of the circle has a measure of one **radian**.

CONNECT TO AP

In calculus, angles are measured in radians, since proofs of major theorems are based on radian measure.

2. Suppose that angle θ is in standard position and formed by one complete counterclockwise rotation.

a. What is the measure of angle θ in degrees?

b. What is the measure of angle θ in radians? Give an exact answer in terms of π.

3. Use your answers to Item 2 to complete the following.

A full rotation = ______________ degrees = ______________ radians

1 degree = ______________ radians

1 radian = ______________ degrees

WRITING MATH

Degree measure is denoted using the degree symbol (°), while radian measure is written without any symbol.

4. Convert each degree measure to radians. Give exact answers.

a. $45°$ **b.** $-210°$ **c.** $15°$

5. Convert each radian measure to the nearest degree.

a. $\frac{\pi}{2}$ **b.** $\frac{2\pi}{3}$ **c.** 4

6. Name the quadrant or axis where the terminal side of each angle lies.

a. $\frac{\pi}{5}$ **b.** $-\frac{4\pi}{7}$

c. $\frac{3\pi}{2}$ **d.** $\frac{11\pi}{8}$

MATH TIP

When the terminal side of an angle lies in a certain quadrant or on a certain axis, we say that the angle lies in that quadrant or on that axis.

My Notes

7. Draw each angle in standard position. Write the radian measure.
   a. one-fourth of a complete clockwise rotation

   b. two-thirds of a complete counterclockwise rotation

   c. one and three-fourths counterclockwise rotations

8. **Express regularity in repeated reasoning.** Explain how to find angles coterminal to a given angle measured in radians.

9. For each angle in standard position, find one positive angle and one negative angle that is coterminal with the given angle.

   a. $\frac{3\pi}{5}$

   b. $-\frac{2\pi}{3}$

10. Find an angle between 0 and 2π that is coterminal with each angle.

    a. 13π

    b. $-\frac{32\pi}{5}$

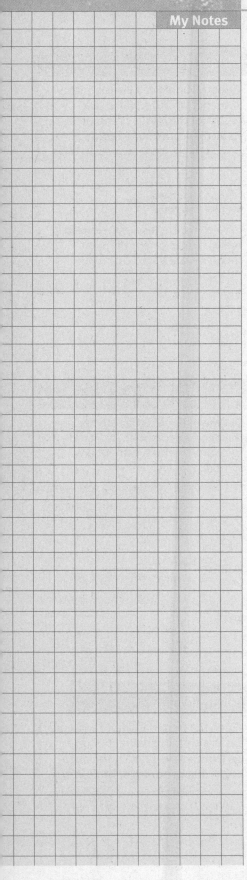

An object rotating about a point has both ***angular velocity*** and ***linear velocity***. Angular velocity is the rate of change in angle measure as the object rotates. Linear velocity is the rate at which location changes as the object rotates.

Example A

A Ferris wheel with a radius of 45 feet rotates at a speed of 2.5 revolutions per minute (rpm). Find the angular velocity, in radians per minute, and the linear velocity, in miles per hour, of a point on the outer edge of the Ferris wheel.

Angular velocity is the ratio of radians rotated to time.

$2.5(2\pi) = 5\pi$ — Find the number of radians in 2.5 revolutions.

$\frac{5\pi \text{ radians}}{1 \text{ minute}}$ — Express angular velocity as a ratio.

Linear velocity is the ratio of feet traveled to time in hours.

$2.5(2\pi(45)) \approx 706.86$ feet — Find the approximate distance traveled by multiplying the number of revolutions by the circumference.

$\frac{706.86 \text{ feet}}{1 \text{ minute}}$ — Express linear velocity as a ratio.

$\frac{706.86 \text{ feet}}{1 \text{ minute}} \times \frac{1 \text{ mile}}{5280 \text{ feet}} \times \frac{60 \text{ minutes}}{1 \text{ hour}}$ — Multiply to change the units.

8.03 miles per hour — Simplify.

Try These A

a. Find the linear velocity, in centimeters per second, of an object rotating at 9 rpm around a point 12 centimeters away.

b. **Reason quantitatively.** A bicycle is ridden at a constant speed of 6 miles per hour. What is the angular velocity, in radians per second, of its wheels if they have a diameter of 24 inches?

11. The propeller blades of a single-engine aircraft rotate at a speed of 2,220 rpm at takeoff. What is the angular velocity of the blades in radians per second?

12. Two pulleys, one with a radius of 6 inches and the other with a radius of 9 inches, are connected by a belt. The larger pulley has an angular velocity of 60 rpm.

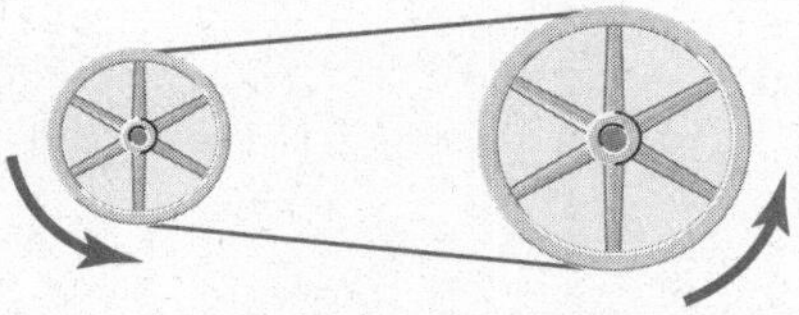

a. What is the linear speed of the belt in feet per second?

b. What is the angular velocity of the smaller pulley in revolutions per minute?

13. The second hand of a clock is 5 inches long. What is the linear speed of the tip of the second hand in feet per hour?

My Notes

MATH TERMS

Angular velocity, *w*, is equal to the measure, in radians, of the angle of rotation divided by time: $w = \frac{\theta}{t}$. **Linear velocity**, *v*, is equal to the length of the arc subtended by the angle of rotation divided by time: $v = \frac{\theta r}{t}$.

MATH TIP

1 mile = 5,280 feet

DISCUSSION GROUP TIPS

If you do not understand something in group discussions, ask for help or raise your hand for help. Describe your questions as clearly as possible, using synonyms or other words when you do not know the precise words to use.

My Notes

Given an angle in standard position, a ***reference triangle*** is formed by drawing a perpendicular segment from a point on the terminal side of the angle to the x-axis.

14. Each figure below shows an angle θ in standard position. Draw a perpendicular segment from point P to the x-axis to form a reference triangle.

a.

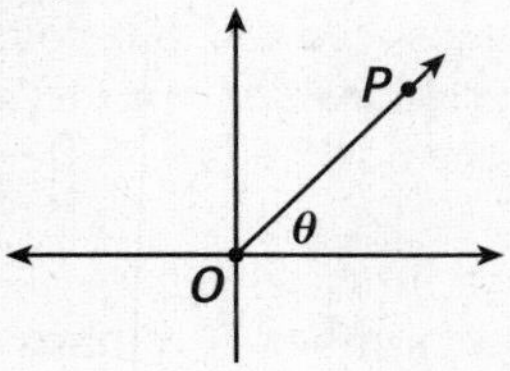

b.

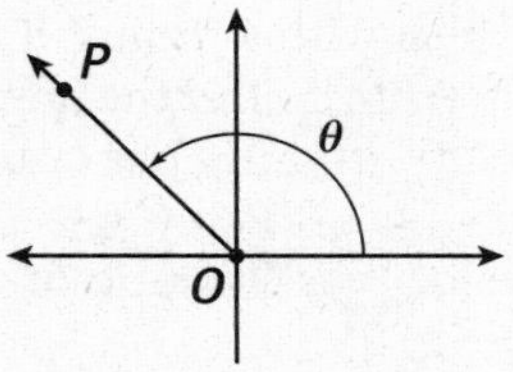

c.

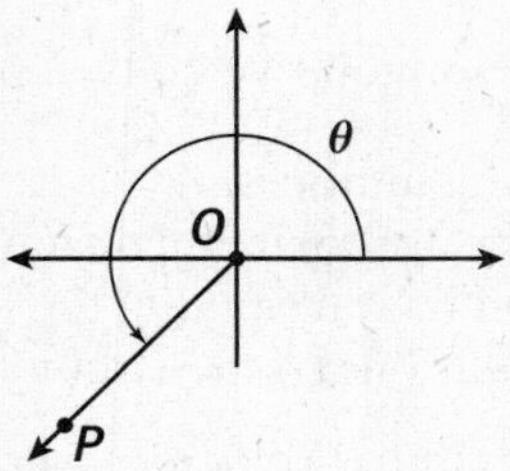

d.

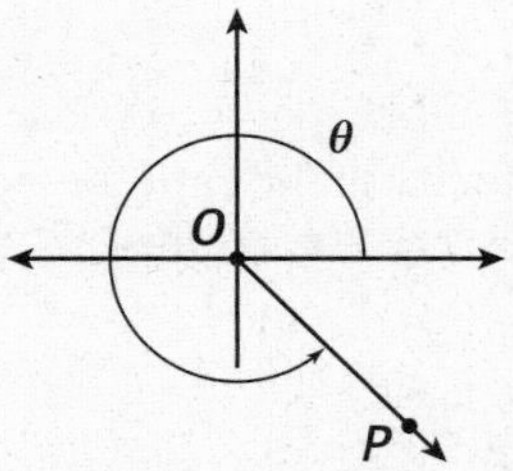

15. Draw a reference triangle and find the missing value for each figure.

a. Find OP.

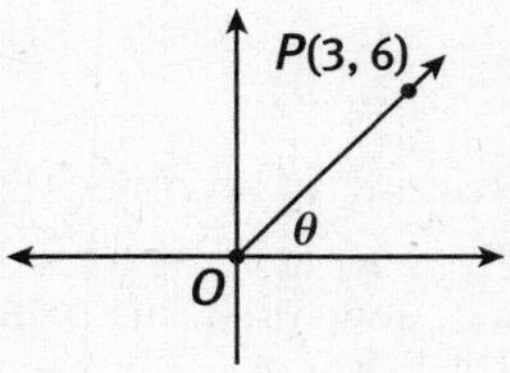

b. Find OP.

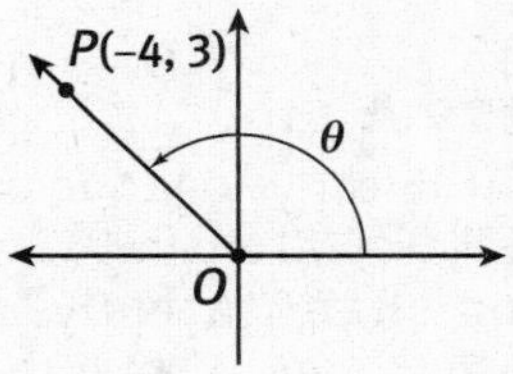

c. $OP = 6$; Find x.

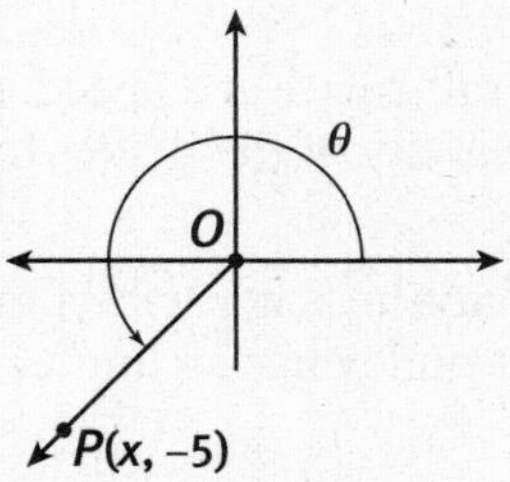

d. $OP = 10$; Find y.

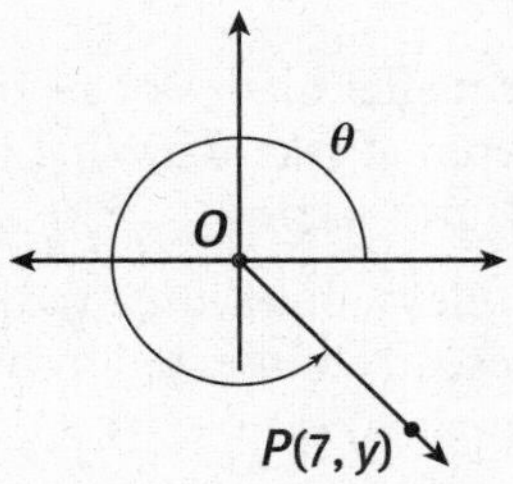

Recall the following right triangle trigonometric ratios.

$\sin\theta = \frac{\text{opposite leg}}{\text{hypotenuse}}$ $\cos\theta = \frac{\text{adjacent leg}}{\text{hypotenuse}}$

$\tan\theta = \frac{\text{opposite leg}}{\text{adjacent leg}}$ $\cot\theta = \frac{\text{adjacent leg}}{\text{opposite leg}}$

$\csc\theta = \frac{\text{hypotenuse}}{\text{opposite leg}}$ $\sec\theta = \frac{\text{hypotenuse}}{\text{adjacent leg}}$

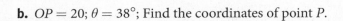

16. Given that θ is an angle in standard position, O is the origin, and P is a point on the terminal side of θ. For each of the following, draw a figure with a reference triangle. Then find the missing value, correct to three decimal places.

a. $P(3, y)$; $\theta = 70°$; Find y.

b. $OP = 20$; $\theta = 38°$; Find the coordinates of point P.

c. $P(6, 6)$; Find θ.

d. $OP = 12$; $\theta = 220°$; Find the coordinates of point P.

My Notes

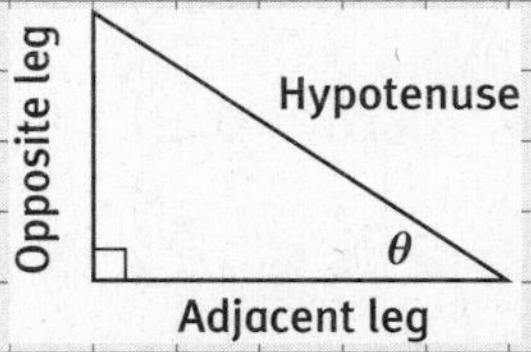

TECHNOLOGY TIP

Most calculators can evaluate trigonometric functions for angle measures in either degrees or radians. Be sure to have your calculator in the correct mode when solving problems.

CONNECT TO HISTORY

Although the study of trigonometric ratios dates back more than 2,000 years, the term *trigonometry* was coined in 1595 and is derived from the Greek word *trigonometria*, meaning "triangle measuring."

My Notes

Check Your Understanding

17. Explain how to find each coordinate of P.

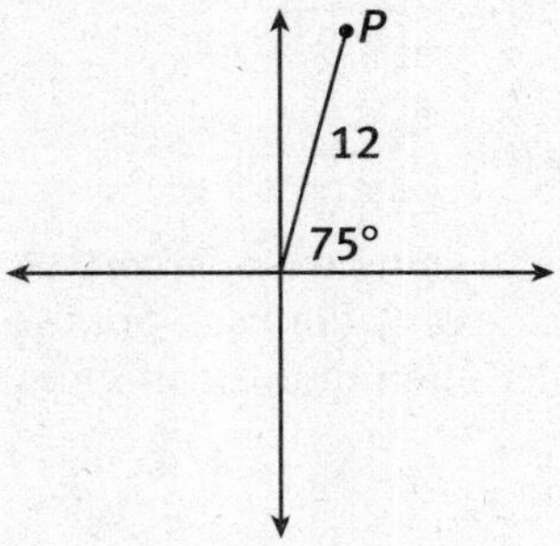

a. the x-coordinate of P
b. the y-coordinate of P

18. State two angles in radians, between -2π and 2π, that are coterminal with a $75°$ angle.

LESSON 14-2 PRACTICE

19. An angle of $\frac{5\pi}{9}$ radians is drawn on a coordinate plane, with its vertex at the origin and its initial side on the positive x-axis. In which quadrant does the terminal side lie?

20. Find an angle between 0 and 2π that is coterminal with the given angles.

a. $\frac{32\pi}{9}$ **b.** $-\frac{\pi}{6}$ **c.** 23π

21. The blade of a circular saw has a radius of 3 inches. The blade spins at 5,400 rpm.

a. What is the angular velocity of the blade in radians per second?
b. What is the linear velocity of the teeth at the end of the blade in miles per hour?

22. Find the coordinates of P to three decimal places.

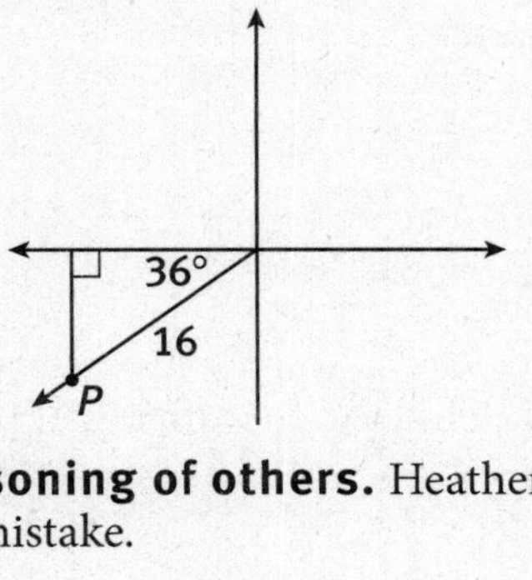

23. Critique the reasoning of others. Heather believes $OP = \sqrt{11}$. Explain Heather's mistake.

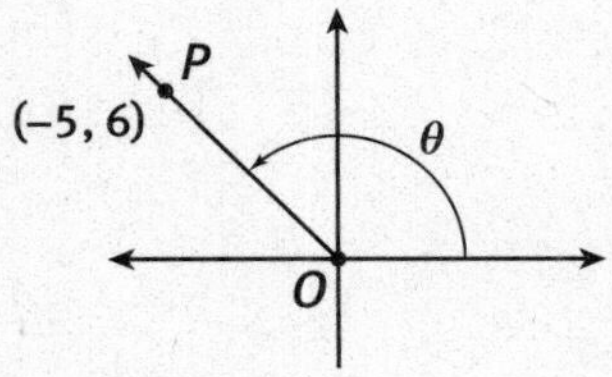

ACTIVITY 14 PRACTICE

Write your answers on notebook paper.
Show your work.

Lesson 14-1

1. Draw one-third of a complete counterclockwise rotation as an angle in standard position, and then give the measure of the angle in degrees.
2. Draw two and one-eighth complete clockwise rotations as an angle in standard position, and then give the measure of the angle in degrees.
3. Find an angle between $0°$ and $360°$ that is coterminal with a $905°$ angle.
4. Find an angle between $0°$ and $360°$ that is coterminal with a $-423°$ angle.
5. Which pair of angles is coterminal?
   A. $-600°$ and $600°$
   B. $-540°$ and $540°$
   C. $-480°$ and $480°$
   D. $-370°$ and $370°$
6. An angle of $143°$ is drawn on a coordinate plane, with its vertex at the origin and its initial side on the positive x-axis. In which quadrant does the terminal side lie?
7. Find the perimeter of the shaded region in the figure below, correct to three decimal places.

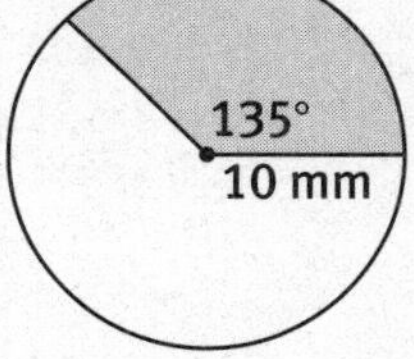

8. What is the value of x in the figure below, correct to three decimal places?

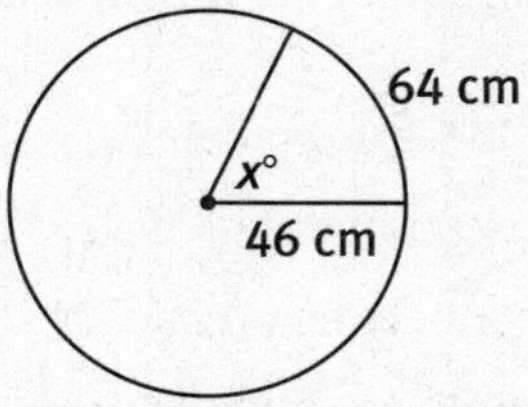

9. The end of a pendulum with a length of 12 inches travels an arc length of 10 inches. How many degrees, correct to three decimal places, does the pendulum swing?

Lessons 14-2 and 14-3

10. Convert each degree measure to radians. Give exact answers in terms of π.
    a. $150°$
    b. $630°$
    c. $-1{,}090°$
11. Convert each radian measure to degrees.
    a. $\frac{\pi}{2}$
    b. $\frac{19}{12}\pi$
    c. $-\frac{7}{10}\pi$
12. Draw three-eighths of a complete counterclockwise rotation as an angle in standard position, and then give the measure of the angle in radians.

13. Draw one and two-thirds of a complete counterclockwise rotation as an angle in standard position, and then give the measure of the angle in radians.

14. Find an angle between 0 and 2π that is coterminal with an angle of $\frac{37}{12}\pi$ radians.

15. Find an angle between 0 and 2π that is coterminal with an angle of $-\frac{11}{15}\pi$ radians.

16. A washing machine drum rotates at a speed of 1,500 rpm during the spin cycle. What is the angular velocity of the drum in radians per second?

A. $\frac{25}{2}\pi$ radians per second
B. 50π radians per second
C. $45{,}000\pi$ radians per second
D. $180{,}000\pi$ radians per second

17. A conveyor belt rolls on cylindrical bearings that have a radius of 1.4 inches. The belt has a velocity of 26.6 inches per minute. Find the angular velocity of the roller bearings in radians per minute, correct to three decimal places.

18. A pulley 8 inches in diameter rotates with an angular velocity of 150 rpm. Find the linear velocity, in feet per second, of a cable attached to the pulley, correct to three decimal places.

19. Draw a reference triangle and find OP.

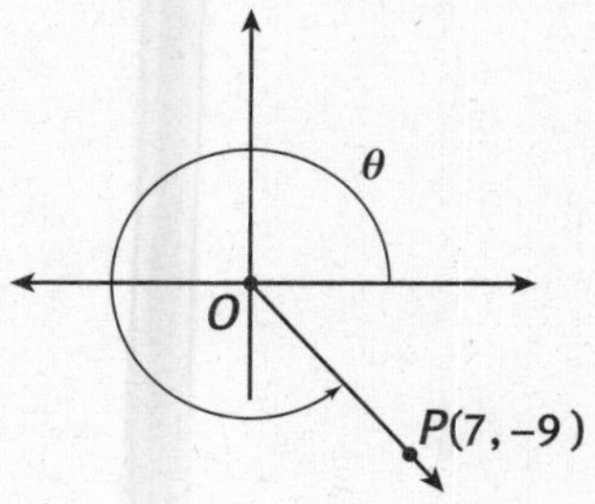

20. Let O be the origin and P be a point on the terminal side of θ, an angle in standard position. Find OP when P is $(-4, 11)$.

21. Let O be the origin and P be a point on the terminal side of θ, an angle in standard position. Find the coordinates of P when $OP = 20$ and $\theta = 24°$, correct to three decimal places.

22. Let O be the origin and P be a point on the terminal side of θ, an angle in standard position. Find OP when the x-coordinate of P is 12 and $\theta = 50°$, correct to three decimal places.

23. Let O be the origin and P be a point on the terminal side of θ, an angle in standard position. Find θ in degrees when $P(10, 10)$.

MATHEMATICAL PRACTICES
Reason Abstractly and Quantitatively

24. Two groups of students built catapults in their science classes. The catapults were identical in design with one exception. In both catapults, the arm of the catapult rotated about a fixed point to launch the projectile, and in both catapults, the arm rotated through the same measure arc with the same angular velocity. However, the arm of Group A's catapult was 6 inches longer than the arm of Group B's catapult. Which catapult launches items with the greater linear speed? Explain why this is true.

Sinusoidal Functions

Bicycle Wheels

Lesson 15-1 Exploring Periodic Data

My Notes

Learning Targets:

- Recognize situations that involve periodic data.
- Sketch a graph of periodic data.

SUGGESTED LEARNING STRATEGIES: Summarizing, Paraphrasing, Create Representations, Visualization, Use Manipulatives, Group Presentation, Quickwrite

As you read, mark the text to identify key information and parts of sentences that help you make meaning from the text.

Stacy has a new bike. The bike has 24-inch-diameter wheels and 6-inch-diameter training wheels. The horizontal distance between the center of the 24-inch front wheel and the center of one 6-inch training wheel is 36 inches. Stacy is riding at a steady pace, and the 24-inch wheels rotate once every 4 seconds. As Stacy is riding down the street, her bike runs over a freshly painted parking stripe, and each wheel picks up a narrow strip of fresh paint that leaves marks on the pavement.

MATH TIP

In one rotation, a wheel will travel a distance equal to the length of the circumference of the wheel.

1. **Model with mathematics.** The figure at the right represents the front wheel and a training wheel on Stacy's bike. Label the length of each of the three segments shown in the figure, and then summarizeany additional information given in the opening paragraph.

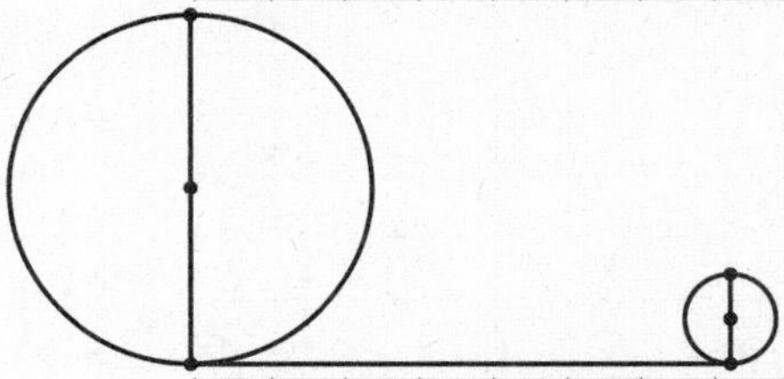

2. Let $t = 0$ seconds represent the time when Stacy's front wheel first crosses the freshly painted stripe. Sketch a graph of the height above the pavement of the paint spot on the front wheel as a function of the number of seconds for the first 8 seconds after $t = 0$.

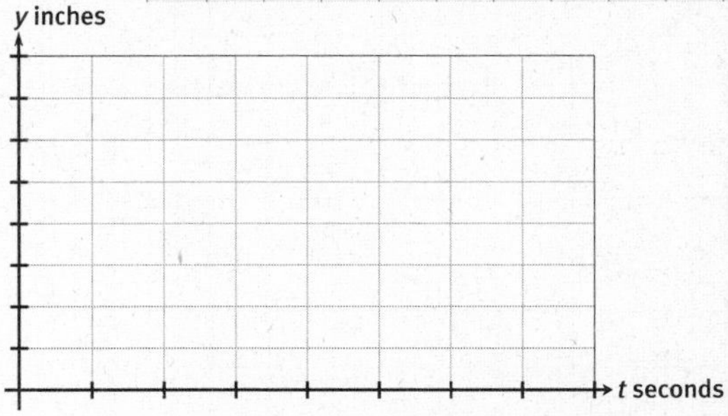

3. Assume that Stacy's bicycle is on a path that runs perpendicular to the paint stripe.
   a. Find the distance that the front wheel travels in 4 seconds. Then use this information to find how long it takes for the training wheel to make one complete revolution.

My Notes

b. How many seconds will it take from $t = 0$ seconds until the training wheel first runs over the freshly painted stripe?

c. On the grid in Item 2, sketch a graph of the height of the paint spot on the training wheel as a function of the number of seconds elapsed since $t = 0$.

4. Use the sketch from Item 3c to estimate the first time that the paint spots on the front wheel and on the training wheel will be exactly the same height above the pavement.

5. A more accurate graph would give a better approximation of the time you found in Item 4.

a. How many seconds after hitting the wet stripe will the paint spot first be in this position on the front wheel?

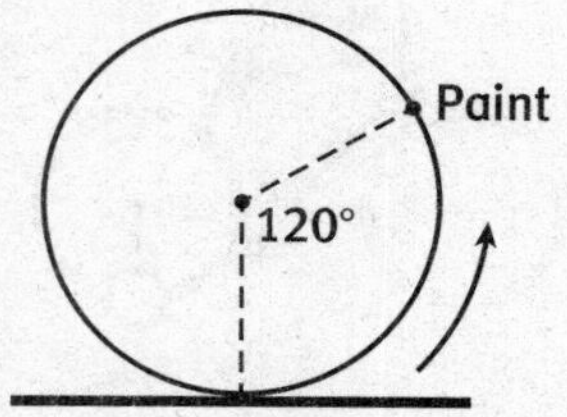

b. Make use of structure. Explain how special right triangles can be used to find the height of the paint spot.

c. Find the height of the paint spot to the nearest tenth of an inch.

d. Is there any other instance during the first revolution of the wheel where the paint spot is at this same height? How long after hitting the stripe does this happen?

e. For each value of t, draw a central angle with a vertical initial side showing the position of the paint spot and the angle of rotation since passing the stripe. Then determine the height of the paint spot to the nearest tenth of an inch. Assume the wheel spins counterclockwise as Stacy rides.

$t = \frac{1}{3}$ sec | $t = \frac{2}{3}$ sec | $t = 1$ sec

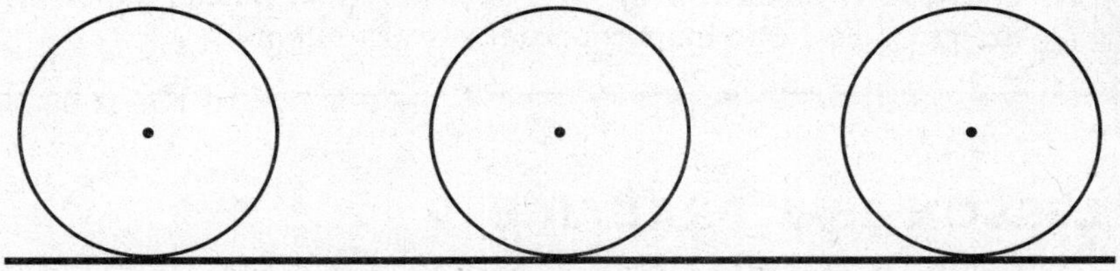

$t = 1\frac{1}{3}$ sec | $t = 1\frac{2}{3}$ sec | $t = 2$ sec

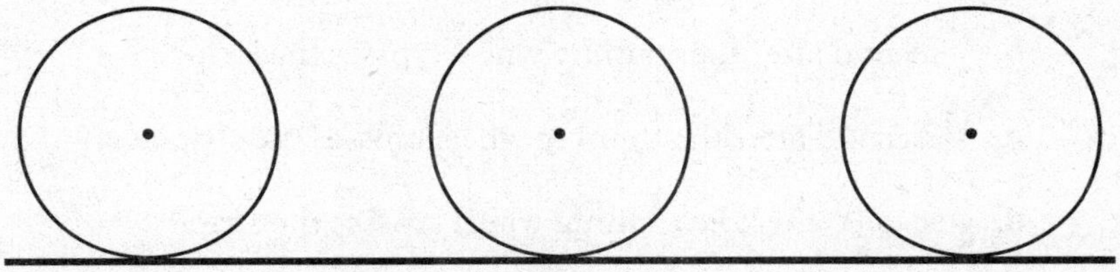

$t = 2\frac{1}{3}$ sec | $t = 2\frac{2}{3}$ sec | $t = 3$ sec

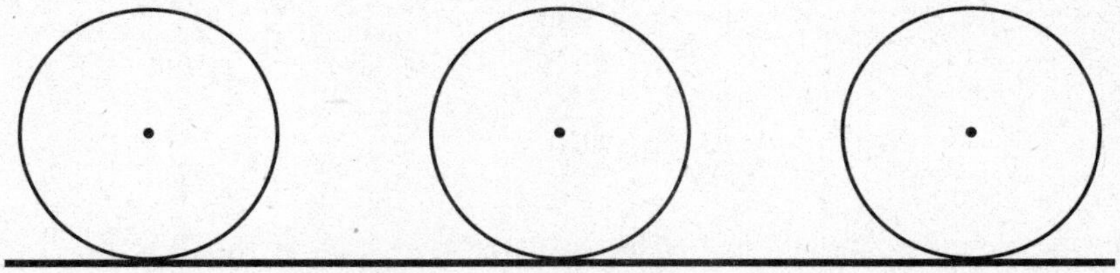

$t = 3\frac{1}{3}$ sec | $t = 3\frac{2}{3}$ sec | $t = 4$ sec

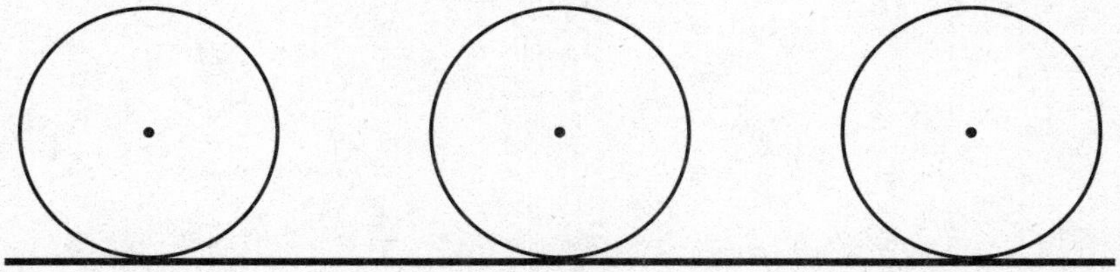

My Notes

MATH TIP

Special Right Triangles

30° – 60° – 90°

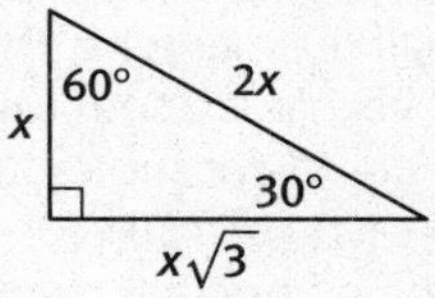

45° – 45° – 90°

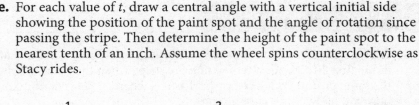

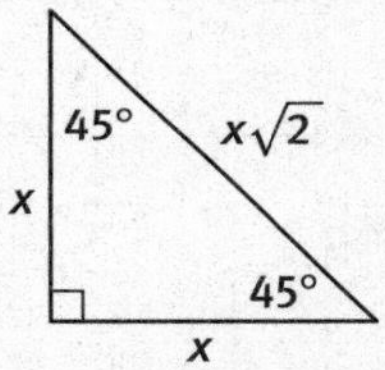

My Notes

Check Your Understanding

6. **Express regularity in repeated reasoning.** Find three other instances in the first 20 seconds after passing the stripe when the paint spot is in the same position on Stacy's wheel as it is when $t = 2$ seconds. Explain how you know this.
7. **Critique the reasoning of others.** Why would a graph with straight sides be an inappropriate answer to Item 2?

MATH TIP

The height of the center of each circle is half the diameter. The height of each paint spot can be found by adding or subtracting the length of a side of a 30°-60°-90° right triangle from that measure.

LESSON 15-1 PRACTICE

8. What is the height, to the nearest tenth of an inch, of the paint spot on the training wheel at the following times? Justify your answers.
   a. $\frac{1}{3}$ second after the training wheel crosses the stripe
   b. $\frac{1}{2}$ second after the training wheel crosses the stripe
   c. $\frac{11}{12}$ second after the training wheel crosses the stripe
   d. $\frac{1}{8}$ second after the training wheel crosses the stripe
   e. $2\frac{1}{4}$ seconds after the training wheel crosses the stripe

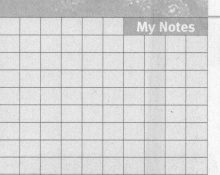

My Notes

Learning Targets:

- Explore how a change in parameters affects a graph.
- Determine the period, amplitude, or phase shift of a periodic function.

SUGGESTED LEARNING STRATEGIES: Create Representations, Quickwrite, Think-Pair-Share

1. Recall that Stacy has a bike with 24-inch-diameter wheels and 6-inch-diameter training wheels. The horizontal distance between the center of the 24-inch front wheel and the center of one 6-inch training wheel is 36 inches, and the 24-inch wheels rotate once every four seconds. t represents the time, in seconds, since Stacy's front wheel first crossed a freshly painted stripe of wet paint, making a spot on her wheel.

a. Use the results from Item 5e in Lesson 15-1 and the axes below to construct a detailed graph of the height above the pavement of the paint spot on the front wheel as a function of the number of seconds that have elapsed since time $t = 0$ seconds for the first 8 seconds.

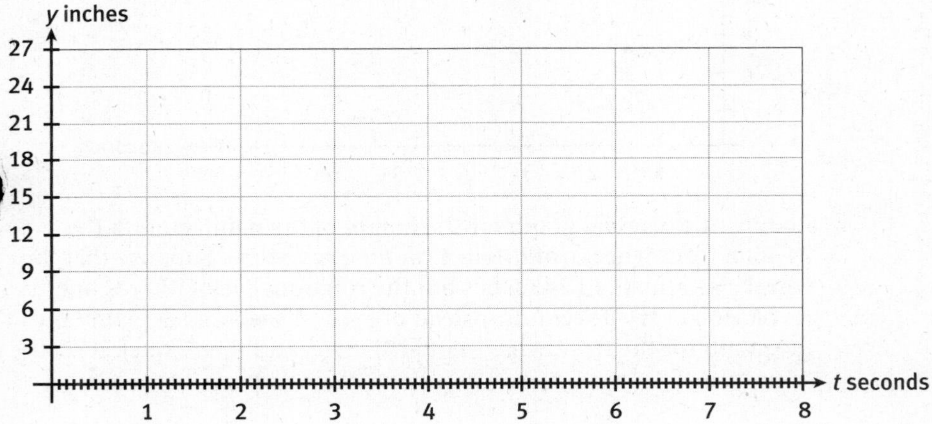

b. Describe your graph. How does it compare to your initial graph from Item 1 in Lesson 15-1?

c. If the graph were extended to include the first minute elapsed since $t = 0$, describe what the graph would look like.

d. On the axes in part a, construct a graph for the training wheel. Include heights of the paint spot on the training wheel at $\frac{1}{12}$-second intervals for the first 2 seconds after the training wheel tire first picks up the paint.

e. Use the graph in part a to approximate the first time the paint spots on the front wheel and on the training wheel will be exactly the same height above the pavement.

My Notes

Now we will explore how changes in parameters affect the graph of the height of the paint spot on the front wheel.

2. Review your work from Item 5 in Lesson 15-1.

a. Redraw the graph for the height of the paint spot on the 24-inch front wheel from Item 1 on the axes below. Suppose that the front wheel of Stacy's bike had a diameter of 18 inches inches instead of 24 but still rotated once every 4 seconds. Explain how this would change the graph, and then sketch it on the same axes.

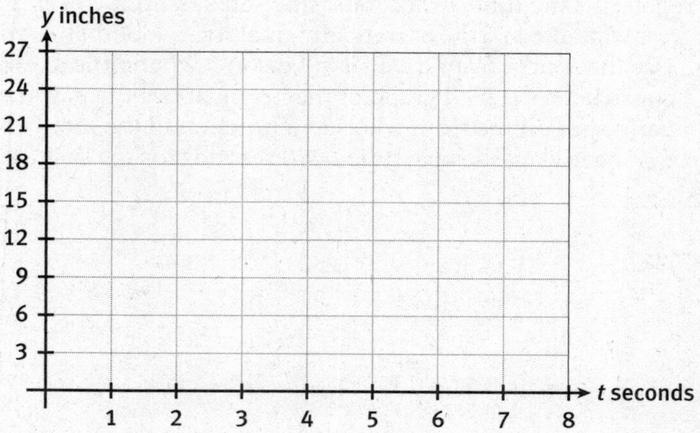

b. Redraw the original graph for the height of the paint spot on the 24-inch front wheel from Item 1 on the axes below. Suppose that the wheel size remained 24 inches but the rotational velocity was one revolution every 3 seconds instead of every 4 seconds. Explain how the graph for the front wheel would change, and then sketch it on the same axes.

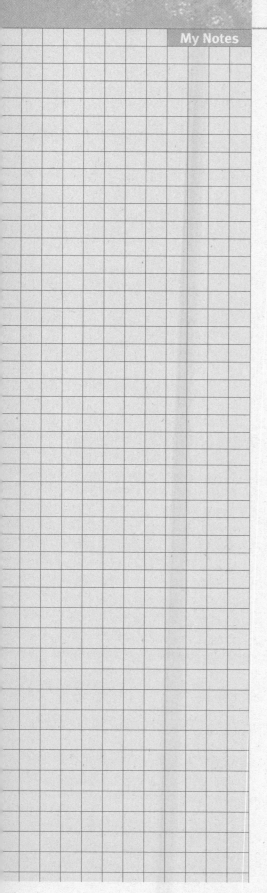

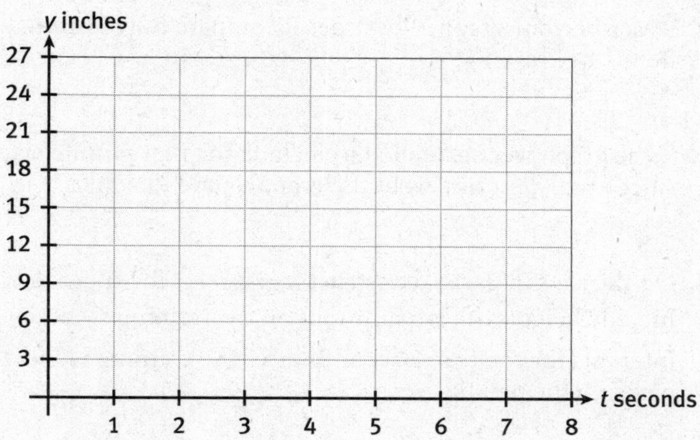

My Notes

3. How would the original graphs for both wheels have differed if the heights of the paint marks on the tires had been measured as a vertical distance above or below a line through the center of the 24-inch wheel and parallel to the ground? Explain, and make a sketch to illustrate your answer.

4. How would the original graphs for both wheels have differed if the heights of the paint marks on the tires had been plotted as a distance above the pavement and as a function of time elapsed since the training wheel first crossed the fresh paint? Explain, and make a sketch to illustrate your answer.

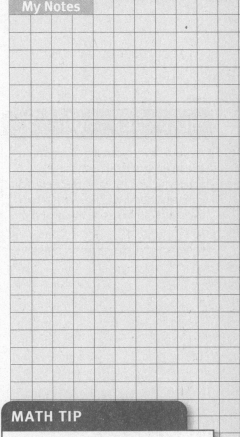

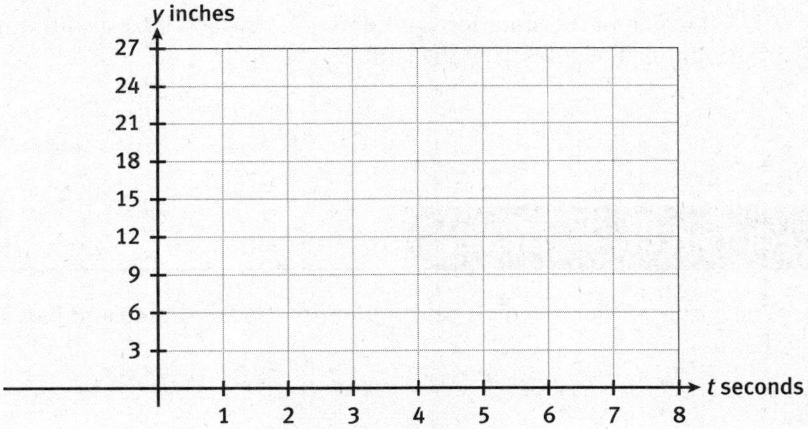

MATH TIP

The time it takes the training wheel to travel d inches is equal to $\frac{d}{6\pi}$ seconds.

My Notes

A function f is a ***periodic function*** if there is a positive number p such that $f(x) = f(x + p)$ for all x in the domain of f. The number p is the ***period*** of the function. If a periodic function has a maximum and minimum value, then the ***amplitude*** of the function is half the difference of the maximum and the minimum values. A ***phase shift*** is a horizontal translation of a periodic function.

DISCUSSION GROUP TIPS

As your share your ideas, be sure to use mathematical terms and academic vocabulary precisely. Ask your teacher if you need help to express your ideas to the group or class.

5. Consider the functions that model the height of the paint spot on the front wheel.

a. Explain why the function that models the original situation with the 24-inch wheel is periodic, and give the period of the function. Then tell which of the situations in Items 2–4 changed the period of the function, and give the new value of the period.

b. Give the amplitude of the function that models the original situation with the 24-inch wheel. Then tell which of the situations in Items 2–4 changed the amplitude of the function, and give the new value of the amplitude.

c. Tell which of the situations in Items 2–4 caused a vertical translation of a function. Then describe the translation.

d. Tell which of the situations in Items 2–4 caused a phase shift of a function. Then describe the shift.

Check Your Understanding

6. The graph of $g(x)$ is shown below. Identify the amplitude and period of the function.

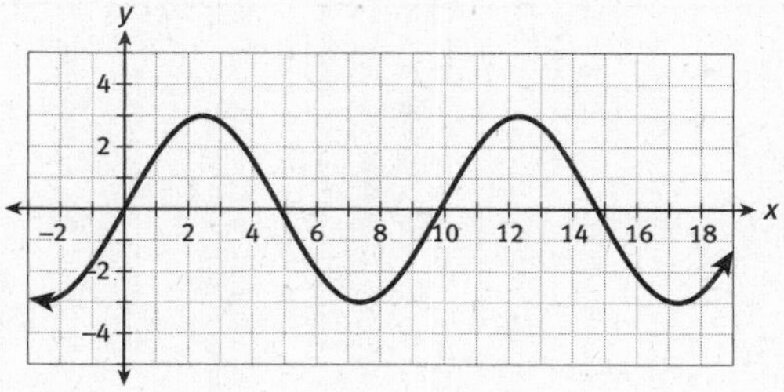

7. Let $h(x) = h(x + 10)$ for all x in the domain of h. What does this imply about the function $h(x)$?

LESSON 15-2 PRACTICE

8. Given the graph of $f(x)$ below, state the period and amplitude of $f(x)$.

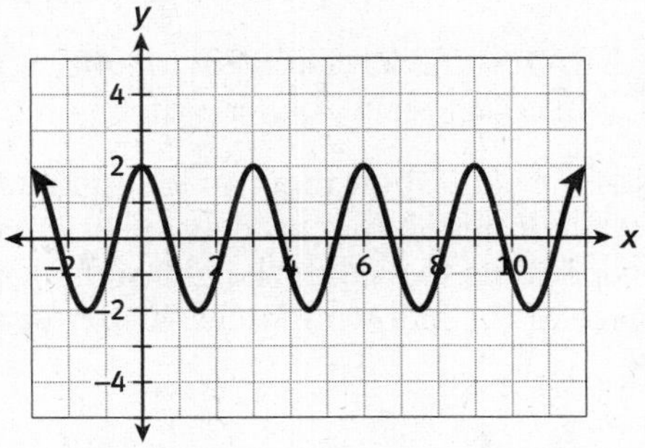

9. Let $p(x)$ be a vertical translation up 1 unit of $f(x)$ from Item 8.
a. Sketch $p(x)$.
b. What is the period of $p(x)$?
c. What is the amplitude of $p(x)$?

10. Use appropriate tools strategically. Marcus is using a graphing calculator to study $k(x)$, a periodic function centered vertically about the line $y = 5$. The period of $k(x)$ is 8, and the amplitude is 6. The settings of his viewing window are shown below. What changes should Marcus make to the viewing window settings in order to better study the function? Explain.

WINDOW
Xmin=−3
Xmax=17
Xscl=1
Ymin=−10
Ymax=10
Yscl=1
Xres=1

My Notes

CONNECT TO TECHNOLOGY

In the window settings,

Xmin is the minimum value displayed on the *x*-axis.

Xmax is the maximum value displayed on the *x*-axis.

Xscl is the distance between the tick marks on the *x*-axis.

Ymin is the minimum value displayed on the *y*-axis.

Ymax is the maximum value displayed on the *y*-axis.

Yscl is the distance between the tick marks on the *y*-axis.

Xres is the pixel resolution.

My Notes

Learning Targets:

- Graph a periodic function with various domains.
- Compare the graph of $y = \sin x$ to periodic graphs.

SUGGESTED LEARNING STRATEGIES: Identify a Subtask, Create Representations, Think-Pair-Share, Quickwrite

MATH TIP

For the periodic function $y = f(x)$ with period p, you know that $f(x) = f(x + p)$ for all x in the domain of f.
Furthermore, if $x = c + kp$, where k is any integer, then
$f(x) = f(c + kp)$
$= f(c)$.

1. Use the heights of the paint spots that you found in Item 5e in Lesson 15-1 and the fact that the function that models the original situation with the 24-inch wheel is periodic to find the height of the paint spot on the front wheel at each of the following times. Justify your answers.

a. 12 seconds

b. 14 seconds

c. 19 seconds

d. $8\frac{2}{3}$ seconds

e. $49\frac{1}{3}$ seconds

2. Suppose that the height of the paint spot is measured as a vertical distance above or below the center of the 24-inch wheel and that the paint mark starts at a point on the same horizontal line as the center of the wheel at $t = 0$. Suppose also that the wheel turns in the direction shown by the arrow in the figure at the same rate as before (one revolution in 4 seconds). Draw a graph of the height of the spot as a function of time for $0 \le t \le 8$.

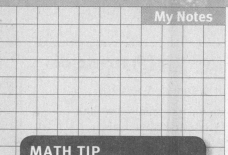

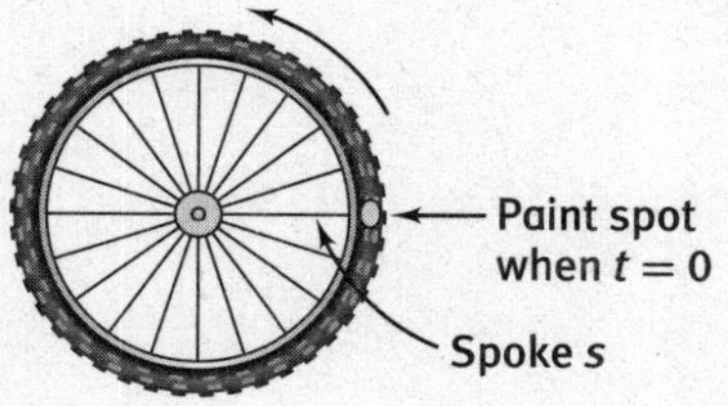

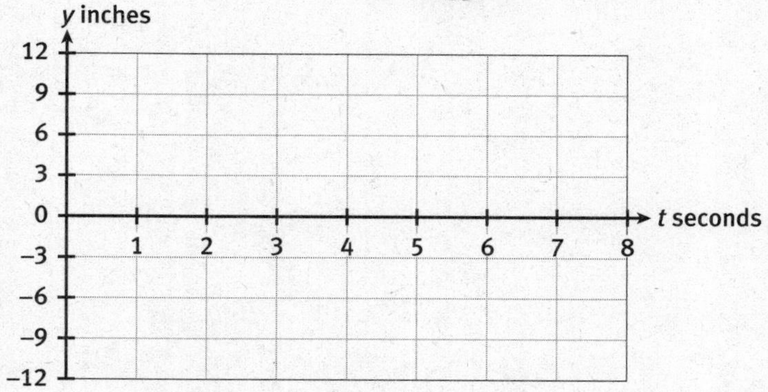

My Notes

3. What happens if the unit of measure is feet rather than inches? Copy the graph in Item 2 and label the axes to illustrate the change.

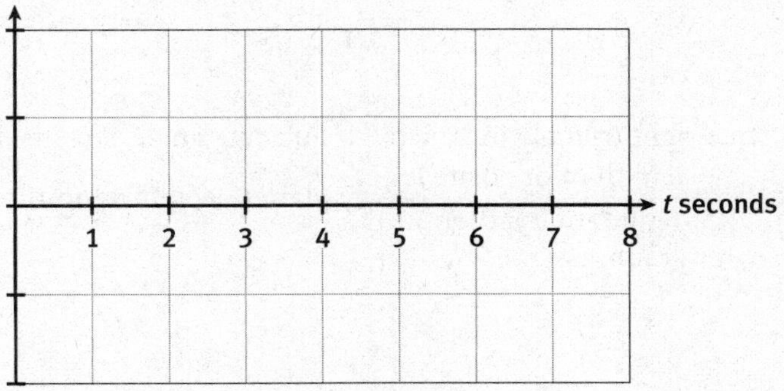

4. Instead of defining the function as height versus time, consider defining it as the height of the paint spot in feet versus the angle of rotation, measured in degrees, of spoke *s*. Through how many degrees will the spoke rotate in 8 seconds? Copy the graph in Item 3 and label both axes to reflect the change.

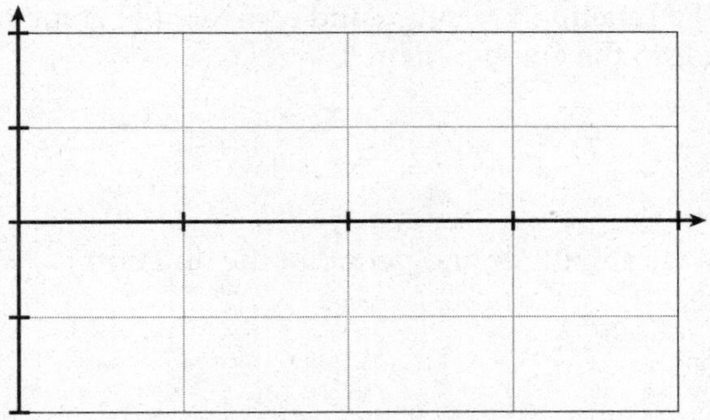

5. Copy the graph from Item 4 and label the axes so that the graph illustrates the height of the paint spot, in feet, as a function of the angle of rotation of spoke *s*, measured in radians.

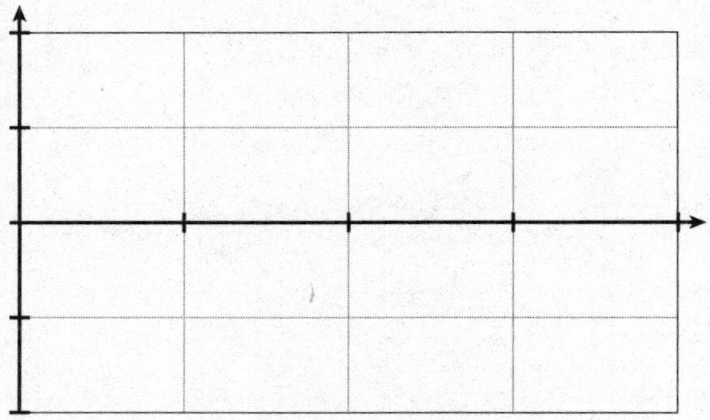

My Notes

MATH TERMS

The functions $y = \sin(x)$, $y = \cos(x)$, and $y = \tan(x)$ are examples of **trigonometric functions**.

The **sine** function is defined as follows:

$\sin\theta = \frac{y}{r}$,

where $x^2 + y^2 = r^2$.

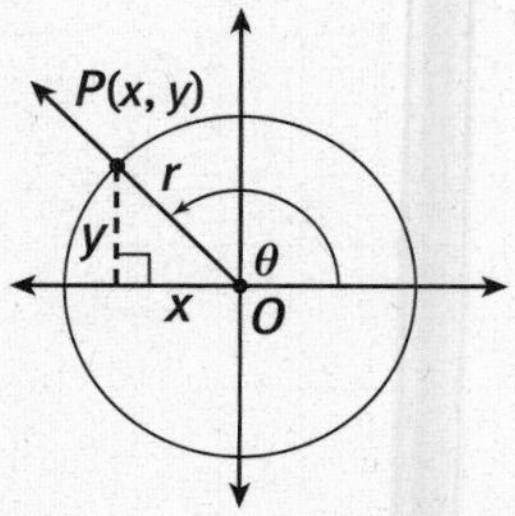

6. Put your graphing calculator in degree mode and set the window to match the graph in Item 4.

a. Graph the function $y = \sin(x)$ and compare the graph on your calculator to the graph in Item 4.

b. In a right triangle in which θ is an acute angle, $\sin\theta$ is defined as the ratio $\frac{\text{length of opposite leg}}{\text{length of hypotenuse}}$. Explain how this definition applies to your graph.

7. Put your graphing calculator in radian mode and set the window to match the graph in Item 5.

a. Graph the function $y = \sin(x)$ and compare the graph on your calculator to the graph in Item 5.

b. Identify the amplitude and period of the function $y = \sin(x)$.

c. If $P(x, y)$ is any point on the terminal side of an angle θ in standard position, then the ***sine*** of θ is defined as $\sin\theta = \frac{y}{r}$, where $x^2 + y^2 = r^2$. Explain how this definition of sine applies to your graph.

My Notes

Check Your Understanding

8. **Express regularity in repeated reasoning.** Suppose $y = g(x)$ is a periodic trigonometric function with a period of 5π radians and amplitude of 6π feet when x is measured in radians. What would be the period and amplitude of $g(x)$ if x were measured in degrees and y were measured in yards?

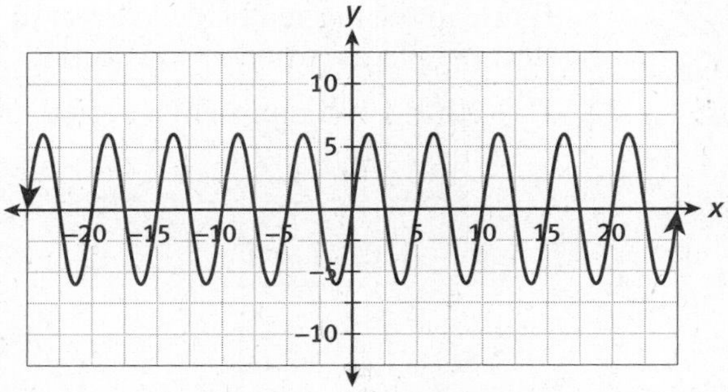

LESSON 15-3 PRACTICE

9. **Reason quantitatively.** Jenna created the periodic function $y = h(x)$ to model the depth of the water at the local marina during high and low tide. In Jenna's function, x is the number of hours that have passed since midnight, and y is the number of inches the water level at the marina is above or below 48 inches. Describe the effect each of the following changes has on the graph of $y = h(x)$.
   a. x is measured in minutes instead of hours.
   b. x is the number of hours before or after 6 p.m. instead of after midnight.
   c. y is measured in feet instead of inches.
   d. y is the depth of the water instead of the difference from 48 inches.

MATH TIP

1 radian $= \dfrac{180}{\pi}$ degrees

ACTIVITY 15 PRACTICE

Write your answers on notebook paper.
Show your work.

Lesson 15-1

Use this information for Items 1–12. A waterwheel has a diameter of 6 feet. The center of the wheel is 3 feet below the edge of a flume, and the wheel rotates at a steady rate of 10 revolutions per minute.

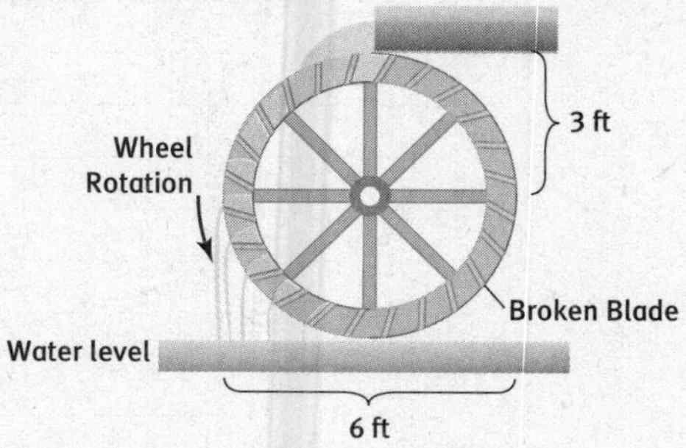

1. How long does it take the wheel to complete one revolution?
2. One of the blades of the waterwheel is broken. Let $y = d(t)$ be a function relating y, the vertical distance of the broken blade above or below the bottom of the flume, to time, t. Let $t = 0$ seconds represent the time when the broken blade is first touching the flume wheel. Sketch a graph of $y = d(t)$ for the first 30 seconds after $t = 0$.
3. What is the vertical distance the broken blade is from the bottom of the flume, correct to three decimal places, when $t = 4$ seconds?
4. What is the vertical distance the broken blade is from the bottom of the flume, correct to three decimal places, when $t = 5$ seconds?
5. At what value of t is the broken blade of the wheel first at the point farthest from the flume?
6. At which two instances is the broken blade in the same position in its rotation?
   A. $t = 11$ and $t = 16$ **B.** $t = 11$ and $t = 19$
   C. $t = 11$ and $t = 21$ **D.** $t = 11$ and $t = 23$

Lesson 15-2

7. Is $y = d(t)$ a periodic function?
8. What is the amplitude of $y = d(t)$?
9. If y were changed to be the vertical distance of the broken blade above or below the center of the wheel, how would the graph of y differ from the original graph in Item 2?
10. If the wheel slows to a steady rate of 6 revolutions per minute, how would the graph of y differ from the original graph in Item 2?
11. Which change in the scenario would result in a phase shift of the original function?
    A. changing the definition of $t = 0$
    B. changing the units of t
    C. using a faster wheel
    D. using a larger wheel

Lesson 15-3

12. Give the vertical distance from the bottom of the flume to the broken blade, correct to three decimal places, when $t = 13$ seconds.
13. Does this graph represent a periodic function?

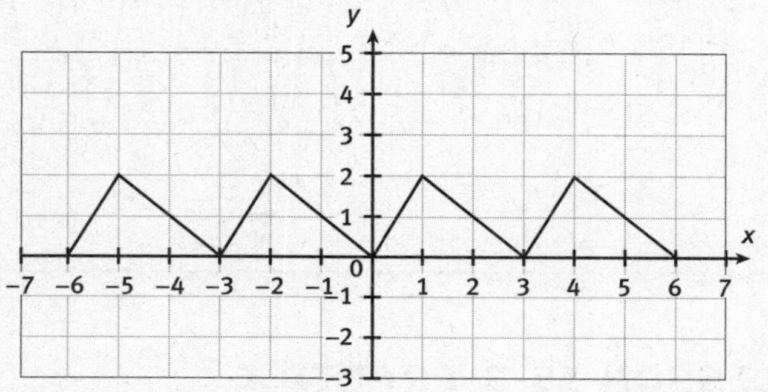

14. Suppose that the graph in Item 13 is a graph of $y = f(x)$. Find $f(22)$ and justify your answer.
15. Sketch an example of a periodic function with a period of 8 and amplitude of 6.
16. P is a point on the terminal side of a 50° angle in standard position. Find the coordinates of P, correct to three decimal places, given $x^2 + y^2 = 4$.

MATHEMATICAL PRACTICES
Reason Abstractly and Quantitatively

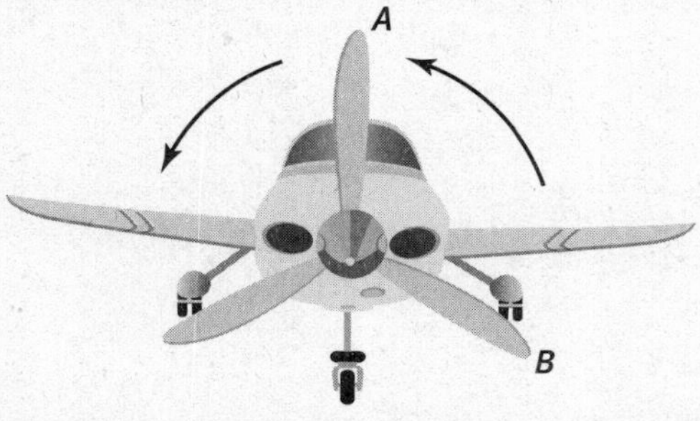

17. The blades of a propeller extend 3 feet from the center of an engine. Carlos created two graphs depicting the vertical distance of points A and B above or below the center of the engine as the blades spin at a constant rate. In both graphs, Carlos let $t = 0$ represent the time the engine began spinning.

    Use the vocabulary from this activity to describe any similarities and explain any differences between the two graphs.

Trigonometric Functions and the Unit Circle
Wheels Revisited
Lesson 16-1 The Unit Circle
ACTIVITY 16

My Notes

Learning Targets:

- Label points on the unit circle.
- Use the unit circle to find trigonometric values.

SUGGESTED LEARNING STRATEGIES: Summarizing, Paraphrasing, Create Representations, Look for a Pattern, Quickwrite

Suppose that a two foot–diameter wheel has a paint mark at a point on the same horizontal line as the center of the wheel at a time $t = 0$ and that the spoke aligned with the paint spoke is denoted as spoke s. Suppose also that the wheel turns in the direction shown by the arrow in the figure below.

1. Let the origin represent the center of the bicycle wheel and the position of spoke s at $t = 0$ represent the initial side of an angle θ in standard position. As the bicycle wheel rotates, let spoke s represent the terminal side of angle θ.

a. Some degree measures of the angle of rotation of spoke s are shown in the figure below. Use the symmetry of the figure to label the angle of rotation for each of the other positions shown for spoke s.

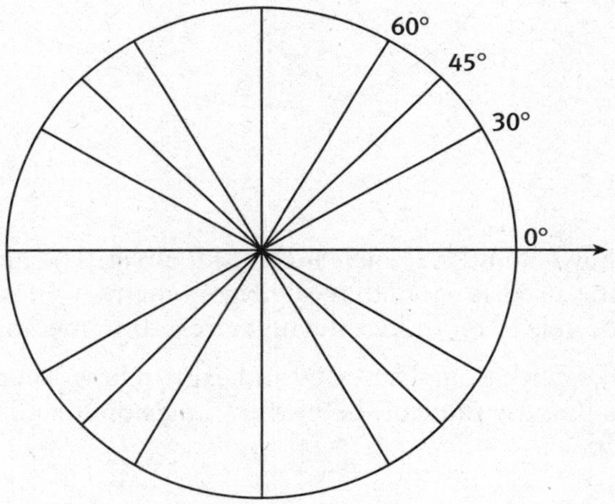

b. Convert each of the degree measures in the figure above to radians and record the answers on the figure in part a.

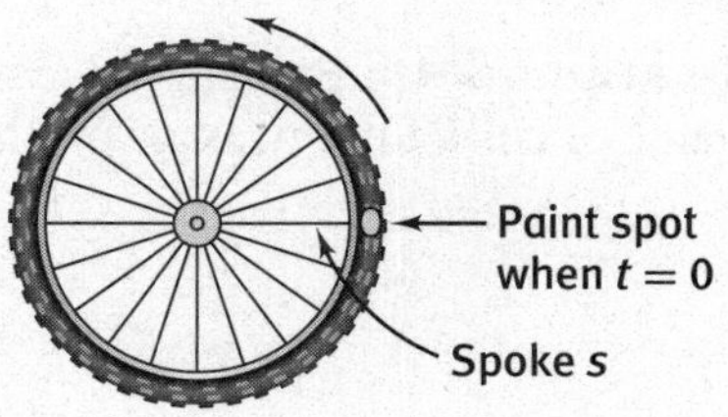

My Notes

The x-coordinate of the position of the paint spot is the horizontal distance to the right or left of the center of the wheel. The y-coordinate is the vertical distance above or below the center of the wheel. Once again, label the rotation of spoke s in both degrees and radians. Then use your knowledge of special right triangles and the symmetry of the figure to label the coordinates of the paint spot for each of the rotations shown in the figure.

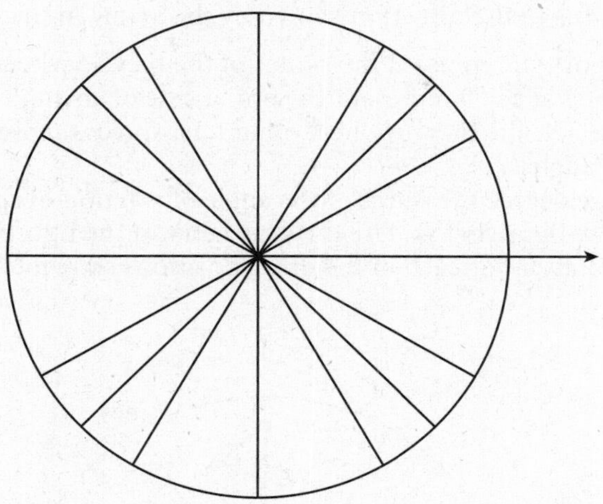

MATH TERMS

A circle with a radius of 1, centered at the origin, is known as a **unit circle**.

The figure shown above is known as the ***unit circle***. The unit circle is a circle of radius 1. It is used as a tool to recall trigonometric values of special angles. You should be able to reproduce the unit circle from memory quickly.

2. Recall the definition of sine of θ and explain how you can use the unit circle to find the value of sin θ for any angle on the unit circle.

MATH TIP

The trigonometric functions **cosine** and **sine** are defined as follows:

$\cos\theta = \frac{x}{r}$ where $x^2 + y^2 = r^2$

$\sin\theta = \frac{y}{r}$ where $x^2 + y^2 = r^2$

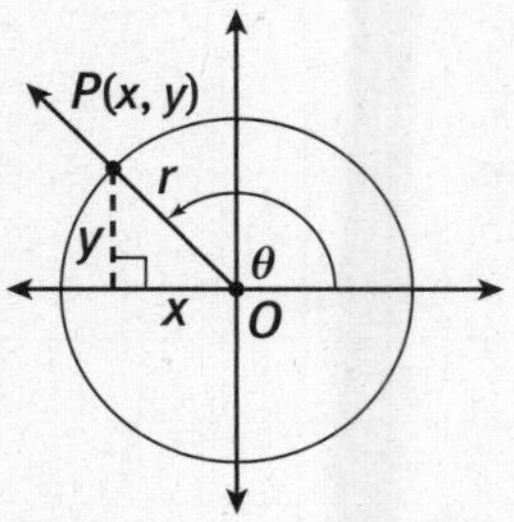

If $P(x, y)$ is any point on the terminal side of an angle θ in standard position, then **cosine** of θ is defined as $\cos\theta = \frac{x}{r}$ where $x^2 + y^2 = r^2$.

3. **Construct viable arguments.** Explain how you can use the unit circle to find the value of cos θ for any angle on the unit circle.

4. Use the unit circle to give the exact value of each of the following.

a. $\cos 45°$ **b.** $\sin\frac{2\pi}{3}$

c. $\sin 180°$ **d.** $\cos\frac{7\pi}{6}$

My Notes

5. Once again, consider the paint spot on the bicycle wheel and the rotation of spoke *s*.
   a. Give the exact value of the slope of spoke *s* for each angle given in the table below and the value of the slope correct to three decimal places. Then use your calculator to evaluate the tangent of the angle correct to three decimal places.

Angle θ	Exact slope	Approximate slope	tan θ
$\frac{\pi}{6}$			
135°			
$\frac{4\pi}{3}$			

   b. **Express regularity in repeated reasoning.** Based on observations from the table in part a, write a definition for **tangent** of θ in terms of x, y, and r.

6. Use the unit circle and the definition of tangent of θ to give the exact value of each of the following.
   a. tan 45°
   b. $\tan \frac{2\pi}{3}$
   c. tan 180°
   d. $\tan \frac{7\pi}{6}$

7. Compare the values of tan 0° and tan 90°.

8. Compare the values of tan 0° and tan 180°.

MATH TIP

When using a calculator to find trigonometric values, always choose the correct mode, either radians or degrees.

CONNECT TO AP

According to the AP Calculus course description, students must "know the values of the trigonometric functions at the numbers 0, $\frac{\pi}{6}, \frac{\pi}{4}, \frac{\pi}{3}, \frac{\pi}{2}$, and their multiples." Being able to give these values quickly and accurately in a wide variety of problem settings is a useful skill in AP Calculus.

MATH TIP

Recall that the slope of a line is defined as $\frac{y_2 - y_1}{x_2 - x_1}$, where (x_1, y_1) and (x_2, y_2) are any two points on the line.

My Notes

Do you notice a pattern in the x- and y-coordinates of points on the unit circle?

In this figure, each of the four points, P_1, P_2, P_3, and P_4, can be described by an angle of measure θ, using different initial sides and rotation in different directions.

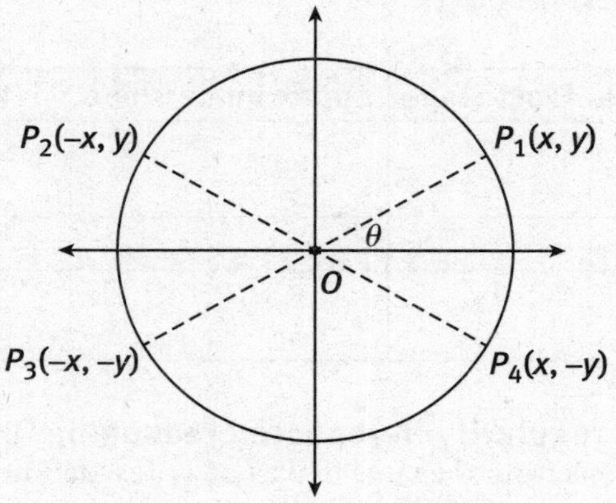

P_1 is a point on the terminal side of a counterclockwise rotation of an angle in standard position of θ degrees.

P_2 is a point on the terminal side of an angle in standard position (a counterclockwise rotation of measure $180 - \theta$ degrees from the positive x-axis) or a clockwise rotation of θ degrees from the negative x-axis.

P_3 is a point on the terminal side of an angle in standard position (a counterclockwise rotation of measure $180 + \theta$ degrees from the positive x-axis) or a counterclockwise rotation of θ degrees from the negative x-axis.

P_4 is a point on the terminal side of a clockwise rotation of θ degrees or a counterclockwise rotation of $-\theta$ degrees from the positive x-axis.

Example A

Given a 12° angle in standard position that intersects a unit circle with point $P(0.978, 0.208)$ on the terminal side of a 12° angle, the points of intersection for the terminal sides of three other angles can be found.

A 168° angle intersects the unit circle at $P(-0.978, 0.208)$, because $168 = 180 - 12$.

A 192° angle intersects the unit circle at $P(-0.978, -0.208)$, because $192 = 180 + 12$.

A 348° angle intersects the unit circle at $P(0.978, -0.208)$, because $348 = 360 + (-12)$.

Using the definitions of sine, $\sin\theta = \frac{y}{r}$, we see that $\sin 12° = \sin 168°$, $\sin 12° = -\sin 192°$, and $\sin 12° = -\sin 348°$.

My Notes

Try These A

For these items, use a well-labeled drawing to justify your answer.

a. **Make use of structure.** Given that $P(0.423, 0.906)$ is the point where the terminal side of a 65° angle in standard position intersects a unit circle, find sin 245° and cos 245°, correct to three decimal places.

b. Given that $\cos\frac{\pi}{12} = \frac{\sqrt{6}+\sqrt{2}}{4}$, find the exact values of $\cos\frac{11\pi}{12}$ and $\cos\frac{23\pi}{12}$.

9. Given $\sin\frac{\pi}{10} = 0.309$, find x between $\frac{\pi}{2}$ and 2π such that $\sin x = 0.309$.

MATH TIP

Recall that 180° = π radians.

10. Given $\tan\frac{3\pi}{5} = -3.078$, find $\tan\frac{8\pi}{5}$.

11. Given $P(-0.385, 0.923)$ is the point where the terminal side of an $n°$ angle in standard position intersects a unit circle, find sin n, cos n, and tan n.

Check Your Understanding

12. **Express regularity in repeated reasoning.** Write an equation that relates $\tan\theta°$ and $\tan(180 - \theta)°$.

13. Given that $P(0.924, 0.383)$ is the point associated with a $\frac{\pi}{8}$ radian angle on the unit circle, what angle between 0 and 2π is represented by the point $P(-0.924, -0.383)$?

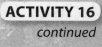

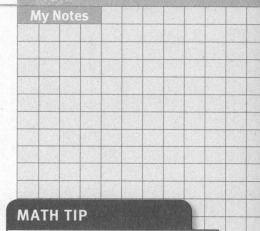

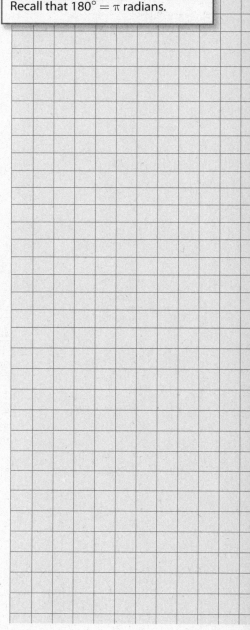

My Notes

LESSON 16-1 PRACTICE

14. Given $\cos 72° = 0.342$, explain how you can use the Pythagorean Theorem to find the coordinates of the point representing 72° on the unit circle.

15. Use appropriate tools strategically. Explain how you can use the trigonometry functions on your calculator to find the coordinates of the point representing 52° on the unit circle.

16. Given $0 < t < \frac{\pi}{2}$, $\sin t = p$, and $\cos t = q$, complete the table. Let x be an angle between 0 and 2π.

x	$\pi - t$	$\pi + t$	
$\sin x$			$-p$
$\cos x$			q
$\tan x$			

17. Critique the reasoning of others. Dylan believes that for every angle x, $0 < x < 2\pi$, there is a second angle y, $0 < y < 2\pi$, such that $x \neq y$ and $\cos x = \cos y$. Is Dylan correct? Explain. Be sure to use correct mathematical terms to support your reasoning and that your sentences are complete and grammatically correct.

My Notes

Learning Targets:

- Define the reciprocal trigonometric functions using the unit circle.
- Evaluate all six trigonometric functions for an angle in standard position.

SUGGESTED LEARNING STRATEGIES: Quickwrite, Think-Pair-Share, Identify a Subtask

The ***reciprocal functions*** of sine, cosine, and tangent are cosecant, secant, and cotangent, respectively.

1. Given that $P(x, y)$ is any point on the terminal side of an angle θ in standard position, and $x^2 + y^2 = r^2$. Define each of the six trigonometric functions in terms of x, y, and r.

sine of θ : $\sin \theta =$

cosecant of θ : $\csc \theta =$

cosine of θ : $\cos \theta =$

secant of θ: $\sec \theta =$

tangent of θ : $\tan \theta =$

cotangent of θ : $\cot \theta =$

2. Use the unit circle and the definitions of the reciprocal trigonometric functions to give the exact value of each of the following.

a. $\sec 45°$

b. $\cot \frac{2\pi}{3}$

c. $\sec 270°$

d. $\csc \frac{7\pi}{6}$

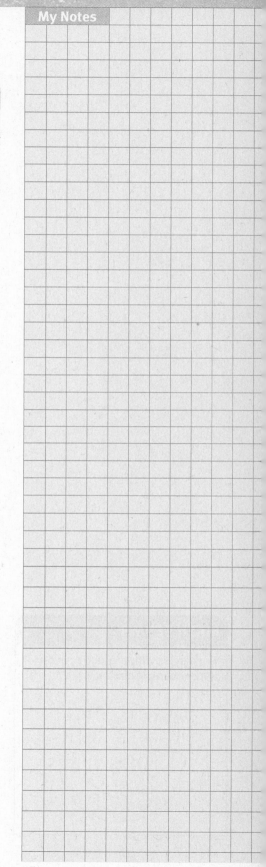

My Notes

So far we have only considered trigonometric values for angles on the unit circle. Here are some other examples for which the definitions of the trigonometric functions can be applied.

Example A

Let $(4, -3)$ be a point on the terminal side of θ, an angle in standard position. Find the values of sine, cosine, tangent, cosecant, secant, and cotangent of θ.

We know that $x = 4$ and $y = -3$. So

$$r = \sqrt{x^2 + y^2} = \sqrt{4^2 + (-3)^2} = \sqrt{25} = 5$$

Therefore, applying the definitions from Item 1, we know that

$$\sin\theta = -\frac{3}{5} \qquad \csc\theta = -\frac{5}{3}$$

$$\cos\theta = \frac{4}{5} \qquad \sec\theta = \frac{5}{4}$$

$$\tan\theta = -\frac{3}{4} \qquad \cot\theta = -\frac{4}{3}$$

Try These A

Given a point P on the terminal side of θ, an angle in standard position, find the exact values of sine, cosine, tangent, cosecant, secant, and cotangent of θ.

a. $P(-5, -12)$

b. $P(2, 4)$

MATH TERMS

Two circles with the same center are **concentric circles**.

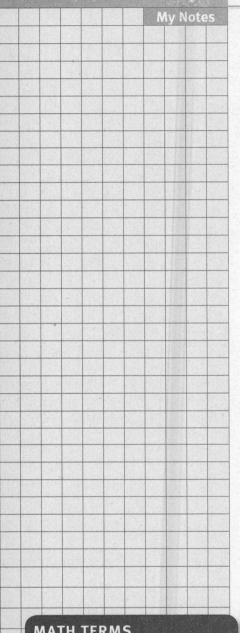

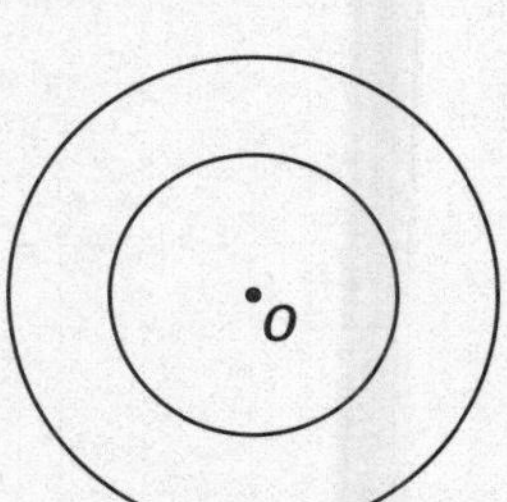

3. Given $P(6, -6)$ and $P(-4, 8)$ are points on ***concentric circles***. $(6, -6)$ is a point on the terminal side of x, an angle in standard position, and $(-4, 8)$ is a point on the terminal side of y, another angle in standard position. Both angles are between 0 and 2π.

a. Which point is on the larger of the two circles? Explain how you know.

b. Which angle has a greater measure? Explain how you know.

My Notes

Example B

Given that $\sin\theta = -\frac{2}{5}$ and that $\cos\theta < 0$, find the values of the other five trigonometric functions of θ. From the definition of sine, we know that $y = -2$ and $r = 5$. So $r^2 = x^2 + y^2 \Rightarrow 25 = x^2 + 4 \Rightarrow x = \pm\sqrt{21}$. Since $\cos\theta < 0$, we know that $x = -\sqrt{21}$. Therefore, applying the definitions from Item 1, we know that if $\sin\theta = -\frac{2}{5}$, then

$$\csc\theta = -\frac{5}{2}$$

$$\cos\theta = -\frac{\sqrt{21}}{5} \qquad \sec\theta = -\frac{5}{\sqrt{21}} \text{ or } -\frac{5\sqrt{21}}{21}$$

$$\tan\theta = \frac{-2}{-\sqrt{21}} = \frac{2}{\sqrt{21}} \text{ or } \frac{2\sqrt{21}}{21} \qquad \cot\theta = \frac{-\sqrt{21}}{-2} = \frac{\sqrt{21}}{2}$$

Try These B

Find the values of the six trigonometric functions of θ, given the following information.

a. $\tan\theta = \frac{4}{3}$; the terminal side of θ is in Quadrant III

b. $\sec\theta = \frac{6}{5}$; $\sin\theta < 0$

MATH TIP

Recalling that r is always positive, you can use the definitions of the trigonometric functions to determine the signs of the functions in each quadrant.

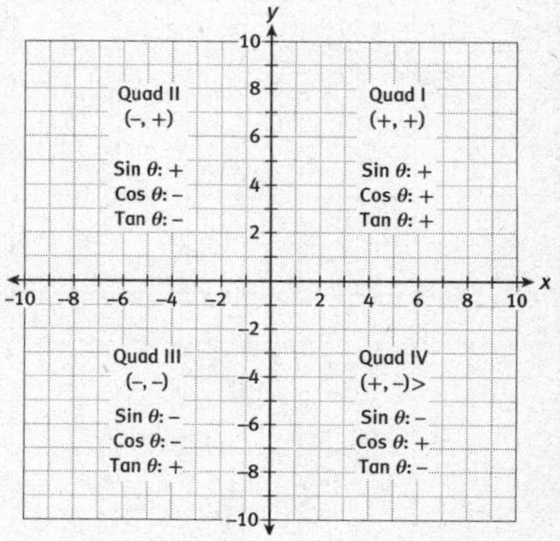

A function and its reciprocal function will have the same sign.

My Notes

4. Given $\sin x = \frac{\sqrt{11}}{4}$ and $\cos x = \frac{\sqrt{5}}{4}$, use the definitions of the reciprocal trigonometric functions to give the exact value of each of the following.
   a. $\sec x$

   b. $\cot x$

   c. $\csc x$

5. Given $\cos x = 0.265$ and $\tan x = -3.645$, use the definitions of the reciprocal trigonometric functions to give the value of each of the following, correct to three decimal places.
   a. $\sec x$

   b. $\cot x$

   c. $\csc x$

Check Your Understanding

6. Suppose $\cos x = -\frac{1}{4}$ and the terminal side of x is in Quadrant II. Explain why is it helpful to know in which quadrant the terminal side of x lies when finding the other five trigonometric functions.
7. **Make sense of problems.**
   a. When finding the six trigonometric functions, which functions have a range that includes negative values?
   b. When finding the six trigonometric functions, which functions have a range that includes 0?
   c. When finding the six trigonometric functions, which functions have a range that includes improper fractions?

LESSON 16-2 PRACTICE

8. Use the unit circle and the definitions of the reciprocal trigonometric functions to give the exact value of each of the following.
   a. $\cot 150°$
   b. $\csc \frac{5\pi}{3}$
9. Given $P(-\sqrt{10}, -7)$ is a point on the terminal side of x, an angle in standard position. Find the exact values of the six trigonometric functions.
10. Find the exact values of the six trigonometric functions of θ, given $\sec\theta = -\frac{8}{5}$ and the terminal side of θ is in Quadrant III.

ACTIVITY 16 PRACTICE

Write your answers on notebook paper. Show your work.

Lesson 16-1

1. Without referring to your work in this activity, draw and label a unit circle from memory. Give the angle measures in both degrees and radians and the coordinates of each point.
2. Explain how to use the unit circle to find the values of each of the six trigonometric functions.
3. Which of the following is the value of sin 300°?
   A. $-\frac{1}{3}$
   B. $-\frac{1}{2}$
   C. $-\frac{\sqrt{2}}{2}$
   D. $-\frac{\sqrt{3}}{2}$
4. Find θ between 90° and 360° such that $\cos\theta = \cos 63°$.
5. Find x, $\frac{\pi}{2} < x < 2\pi$, such that $\tan x = \tan\frac{3\pi}{8}$.
6. For what value(s) of x, $0 < x < 2\pi$, is $\tan x = 1$?
7. For what value(s) of θ, between 0° and 360°, is $\sin\theta = \frac{1}{2}$?
8. Write an equation that relates each pair of functions.
   a. $\sin x$ and $\sin(\pi + x)$
   b. $\tan x$ and $\tan(-x)$
   c. $\cos(\pi - x)$ and $\cos(\pi + x)$
9. Given $\tan\frac{\pi}{7} = 0.482$, find x between $\frac{\pi}{2}$ and 2π such that $\tan x = 0.482$.
10. Given $\cos\frac{\pi}{15} = 0.978$, find $\cos\frac{16\pi}{15}$, correct to three decimal places.

Lesson 16-2

11. Use the unit circle and the definitions of the reciprocal trigonometric functions to give the exact value of each of the following.
    a. cot 30°
    b. $\sec\frac{7\pi}{4}$
12. Given a point P on the terminal side of θ, an angle in standard position, find the values of the six trigonometric functions of θ.
    a. $P(6, 8)$
    b. $P(-2, -3)$
13. Given $\cot x = \frac{6}{11}$ and $x < \pi$, what is the value of $\sin x$?
    A. $\frac{6}{\sqrt{157}}$
    B. $\frac{6}{\sqrt{85}}$
    C. $\frac{11}{\sqrt{157}}$
    D. $\frac{11}{\sqrt{85}}$

14. Find $\cot \theta$, given $\cos \theta = \frac{2}{7}$ and the terminal side of θ is in Quadrant IV.

15. Find $\tan \theta$, given $\csc \theta = \frac{11}{6}$ and the terminal side of θ is in Quadrant II.

16. Find $\sec \theta$, given $\cot \theta = \frac{9}{10}$ and the terminal side of θ is in Quadrant III.

17. Find $\csc \theta$, given $\sec \theta = \frac{15}{8}$ and the terminal side of θ is in Quadrant I.

18. Given $\cos x = 0.524$, find $\sec x$, correct to three decimal places.

19. Given $\sin x = 0.152$, find $\sec x$, correct to three decimal places.

20. Let $\tan x = \cot x$ and $\sin x > \cos x$.

a. Find the value of the six trigonometric functions of x.

b. Find the value of x, if $0 < x < 2\pi$.

MATHEMATICAL PRACTICES
Attend to Precision

21. Explain why a point, $P(x, y)$, on the terminal side of an angle in standard position always produces a sine value less than or equal to 1, even if the point is on a circle with a radius greater than 1.

Graphs of the Form $y = A \sin[B(x - C)] + D$

Trigonometric Graphs

Lesson 17-1 Trigonometric Graphs and Transformations

My Notes

Learning Targets:

- Graph a trigonometric function over a specified interval.
- Describe how changing parameters affect a trigonometric graph.

SUGGESTED LEARNING STRATEGIES: Activating Prior Knowledge, Create Representations, Predict and Confirm, Self Revision/Peer Revision, Quickwrite

The graph of the sine function is an example of a periodic function, which means it repeats at regular intervals. The graphs of the other trigonometric functions are periodic as well. Trigonometric functions can be used to model many real-world situations that have periodic behavior, such as the height of a paint spot on a wheel, average daily temperature, minutes of daylight, and motion of the tides.

1. Consider the function $f(x) = \sin x$.

a. Sketch a graph of $f(x) = \sin x$ by plotting values from the unit circle on the interval $[0, 2\pi]$. Then use the periodic nature of sine to extend the graph across the entire grid.

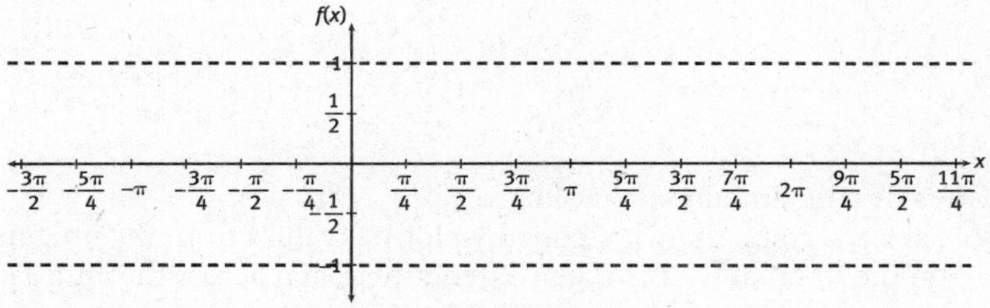

b. Complete the following information for $f(x) = \sin x$.

Domain:

Range:

Amplitude:

Period:

MATH TIP

Recall that the *amplitude* of a periodic function is defined to be one-half of the difference between the maximum and minimum function values.

c. Does the graph have any asymptotes? If so, identify them.

d. Identify the local minimum(s) of the function on the interval $[0, 2\pi]$.

My Notes

e. Use the graph to complete the table.

x	$-\frac{3\pi}{2}$	$\frac{\pi}{2}$	$\frac{5\pi}{2}$
$\sin x$			

f. Explain how these three radian measures are related on the unit circle.

g. Is the graph symmetric about the y-axis? Is the graph symmetric about the origin? Explain.

h. **Construct viable arguments.** Is the sine function odd, even, or neither? On what intervals is the function increasing or decreasing? Use specific values from the graph or unit circle to support your answer.

MATH TIP

Recall that a function is an *even function* if $f(-x) = f(x)$ for all x in the domain of f. Even functions are symmetric about the y-axis.

A function is an *odd function* if $f(-x) = -f(x)$ for all x in the domain of f. Odd functions are symmetric about the origin.

2. Consider the function $f(x) = \cos x$.

a. Sketch a graph of $f(x) = \cos x$ by plotting values from the unit circle on the interval $[0, 2\pi]$. Then extend the graph across the entire grid.

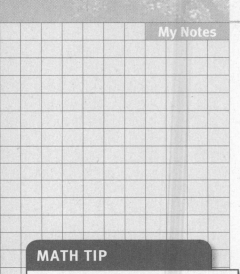

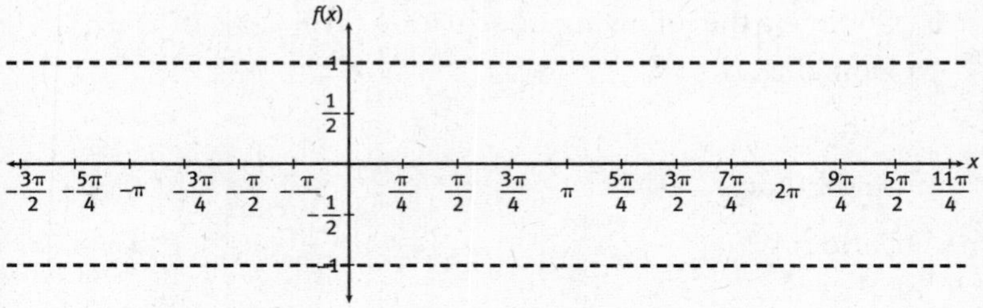

b. Complete the following information for $f(x) = \cos x$.

Domain: Range:

Amplitude: Period:

c. Identify the interval(s) on $[0, 2\pi]$ for which the cosine function is increasing.

d. Describe the symmetry of the graph. Is the function odd, even, or neither?

e. Describe the relationship between the graph of $f(x) = \cos x$ and $f(x) = \sin x$.

My Notes

3. Model with mathematics. Draw a quick sketch of a parent graph for sine and cosine by plotting the maximum and minimum values and the x-intercepts on the interval $[0, 2\pi]$. Label the scale on each axis.

a. $f(x) = \sin x$ **b.** $f(x) = \cos x$

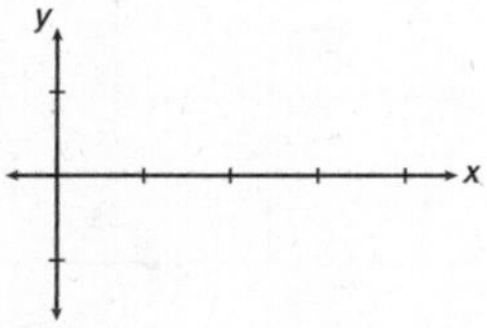

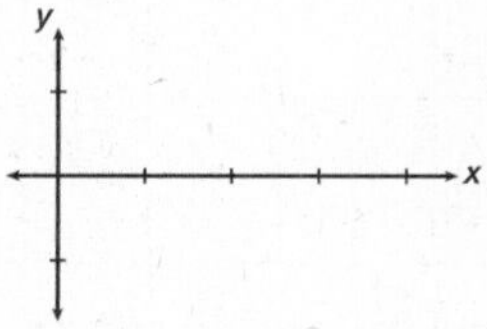

MATH TIP

Recall that the parent graphs for sine and cosine are the graphs of the most basic sine and cosine functions.

Families of sine and cosine graphs can be created by introducing parameters into the parent functions for sine and cosine. These parameters transform the base graph, producing periodic functions of the same general shape but with different amplitude, period, or other characteristics.

Example A

Sketch the graphs of $f(x) = \sin x$ and $g(x) = 2 \sin x$ and describe how the two graphs differ.

Solution:
Graph the parent graph, $y = f(x)$, labeling the scale of each axis. Use your knowledge of transformations, a calculator, or a table of values to graph $y = g(x)$. Extend the graphs across the entire grid.

x	0	$\frac{\pi}{2}$	π	$\frac{3\pi}{2}$	2π
$f(x)$	0	1	0	−1	0
$g(x)$	0	2	0	−2	0

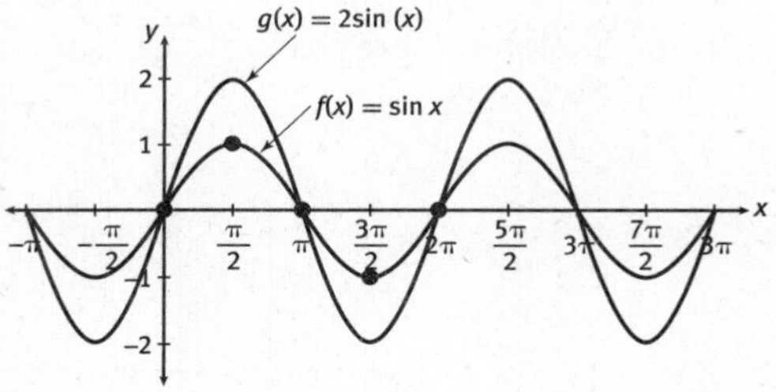

The graph of $g(x)$ is stretched vertically to twice the size of $f(x)$.

TECHNOLOGY TIP

If using a calculator to check your work, be sure the calculator is set for the correct mode: degrees or radians.

Try These A

a. Sketch the graphs of $f(x) = \cos x$ and $g(x) = \cos x + 2$, labeling each axis.

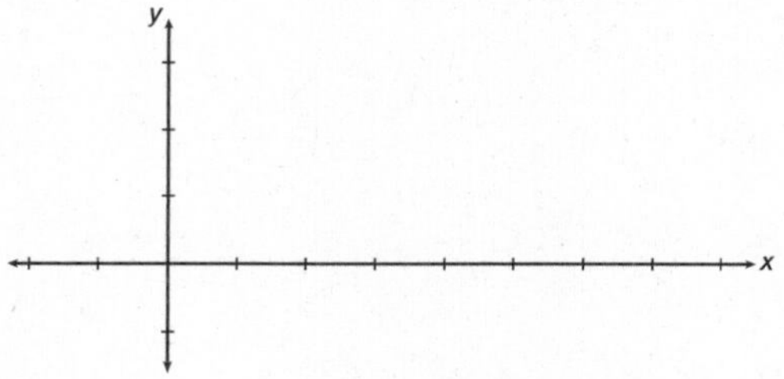

b. Describe the transformation that generates $g(x)$ from $f(x)$.

My Notes

4. a. Complete the table of values.

x	0	$\frac{\pi}{4}$	$\frac{\pi}{2}$	$\frac{3\pi}{4}$	π	$\frac{5\pi}{4}$	$\frac{3\pi}{2}$	$\frac{7\pi}{4}$	2π	$\frac{9\pi}{4}$
$\cos(x)$										
$\cos\left(x - \frac{\pi}{4}\right)$										

b. Sketch the graphs of $f(x) = \cos x$ and $g(x) = \cos\left(x - \frac{\pi}{4}\right)$, labeling each axis.

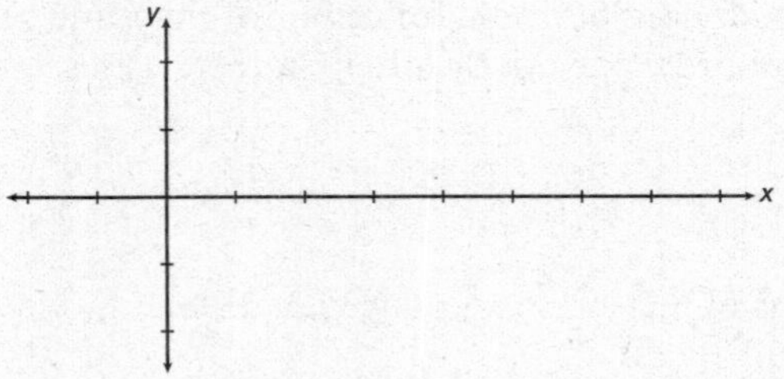

c. Describe the transformation that generates $g(x)$ from $f(x)$.

5. a. Sketch the graphs of $f(x) = \sin x$ and $g(x) = \sin\left(x + \frac{\pi}{2}\right)$, labeling each axis.

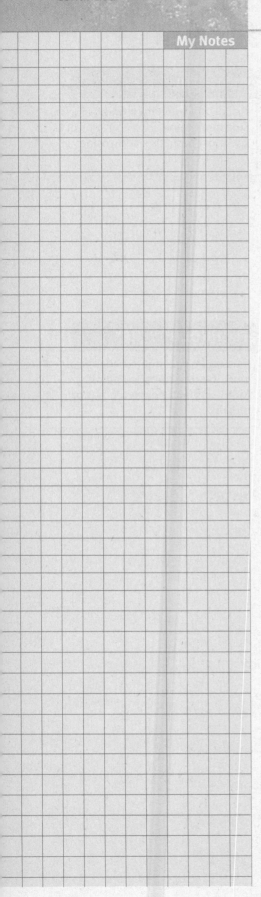

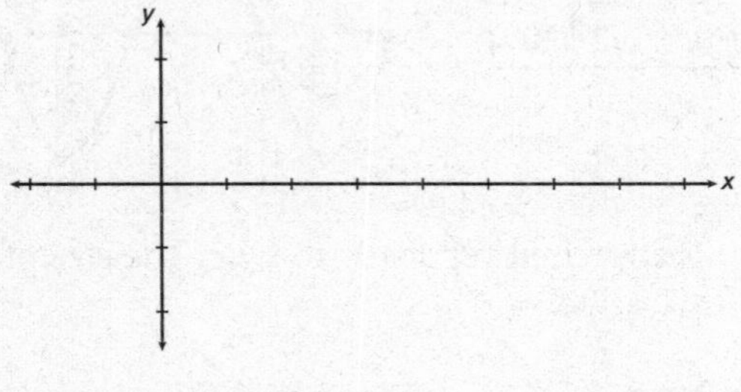

b. Describe the transformation that generates $g(x)$ from $f(x)$.

My Notes

Check Your Understanding

6. **Express regularity in repeated reasoning.** Explain how different values of the parameters A, C, and D in the functions $y = A \sin(x - C) + D$ and $y = A \cos(x - C) + D$ affect the graphs of the parent functions $y = \sin x$ and $y = \cos x$.

TECHNOLOGY TIP

Use a graphing calculator to check your graphs.

LESSON 17-1 PRACTICE

7. Complete the table using the unit circle.

x	0	$\frac{\pi}{4}$	$\frac{\pi}{2}$	$\frac{3\pi}{4}$	π	$\frac{5\pi}{4}$	$\frac{3\pi}{2}$	$\frac{7\pi}{4}$	2π
$\sin(x)$									
$\sin(2x)$									
$\sin\left(\frac{x}{2}\right)$									

8. Use the axes below to graph the functions in parts a and b.

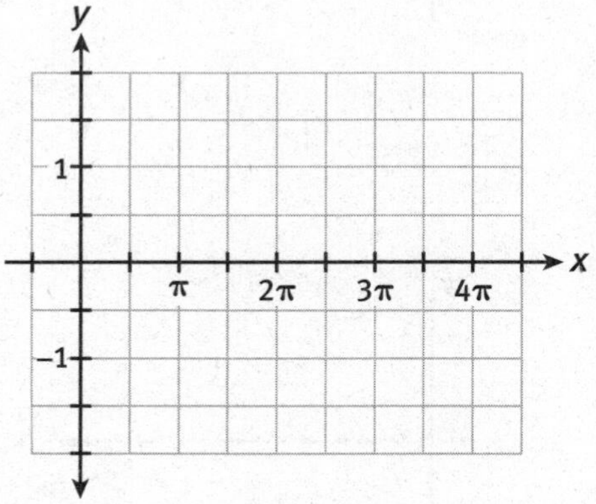

a. Graph $f(x) = \sin x$ over the interval $[0, 4\pi]$

b. Use the table in Item 7 and your understanding of periodic functions to graph $g(x) = \sin(2x)$ and $h(x) = \sin\left(\frac{x}{2}\right)$.

c. **Reason abstractly.** Explain how the parameter B in the function $y = \sin(Bx)$ affects the graph of the parent function $y = \sin x$.

d. State the amplitude and period for $g(x)$ and $h(x)$.

My Notes

Learning Targets:

- Find the amplitude and period of a trigonometric function.
- Write a trigonometric function given its graph.
- Model situations with trigonometric functions.

SUGGESTED LEARNING STRATEGIES: Activating Prior Knowledge, Create Representations, Predict and Confirm, Self Revision/Peer Revision, Quickwrite

1. Sine and cosine functions can be used to model real-world phenomena, including electric currents, radio waves, and tides. Based on your observations from Item 8 in Lesson 17-1, state the period of each function given below, and then sketch the graph of the function over one period. Be sure to label the axes carefully. After you have completed your answers, use a graphing calculator to verify results.

a. $f(x) = \cos(4x)$

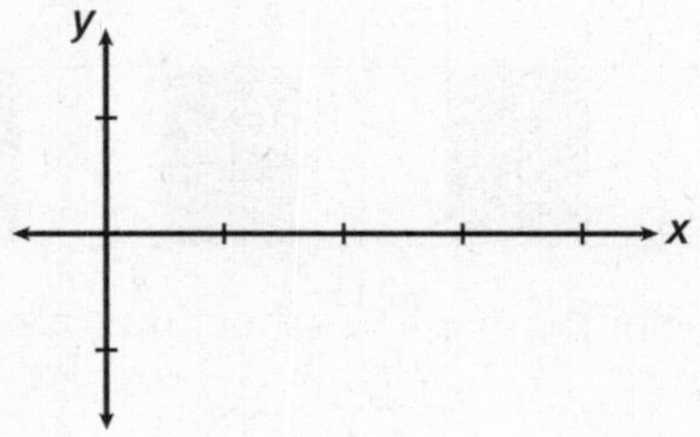

b. $f(x) = \sin(\pi x)$

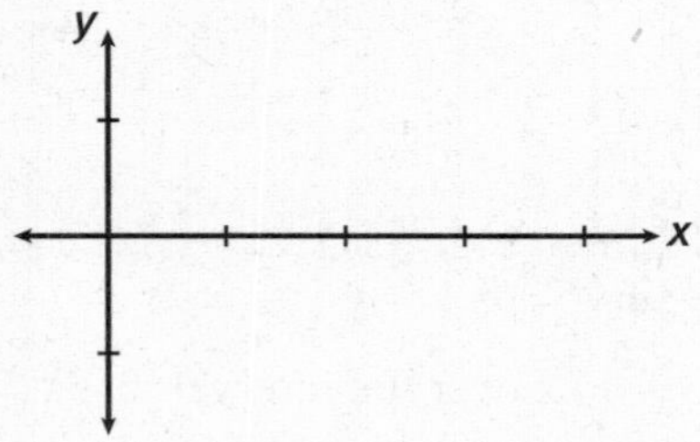

My Notes

2. Consider a function of the form $y = A\sin[B(x - C)] + D$ or $y = A\cos[B(x - C)] + D$.

a. What is the amplitude?

b. What is the period?

c. Which parameter can cause a vertical stretch or shrink or a reflection over the x-axis?

d. Which parameter causes a horizontal shift?

e. Which parameter causes a vertical shift?

3. State the period and amplitude of each function and describe any horizontal or vertical shifts. Sketch the graph of each function over one period. Carefully label the scale on each axis.

a. $y = 2\cos x$

b. $y = \sin(3x)$

c. $y = 3\sin x - 1$

d. $y = -\cos\left[2\left(x + \frac{\pi}{2}\right)\right]$

e. $y = \cos\left(\frac{\pi x}{2}\right)$

f. $y = 3\sin\left[\frac{1}{4}(x - \pi)\right] + 2$

g. $y = 4\cos(3x - \pi) + 1$

4. Make sense of problems. Write a set of ordered steps that explains how to graph functions of the form $y = A\sin[B(x - C)] + D$ and $y = A\cos[B(x - C)] + D$.

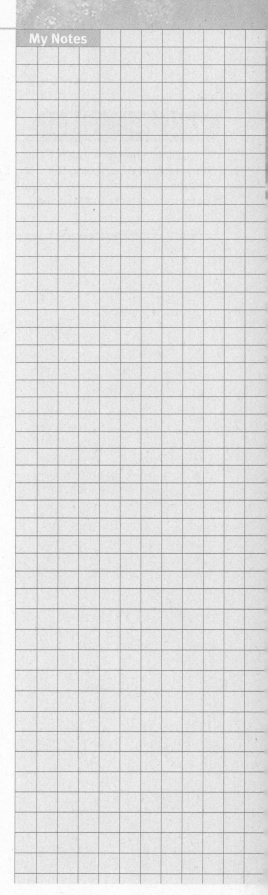

My Notes

MATH TIP

For cosine, a horizontal shift *C* can be determined by finding the distance a maximum (or minimum) point has been shifted from the *y*-axis.

When modeling real-world situations, it may be necessary to determine the equation of the sine or cosine function from a graph or a set of data.

Example A

Write an equation for the graph below in terms of sine.

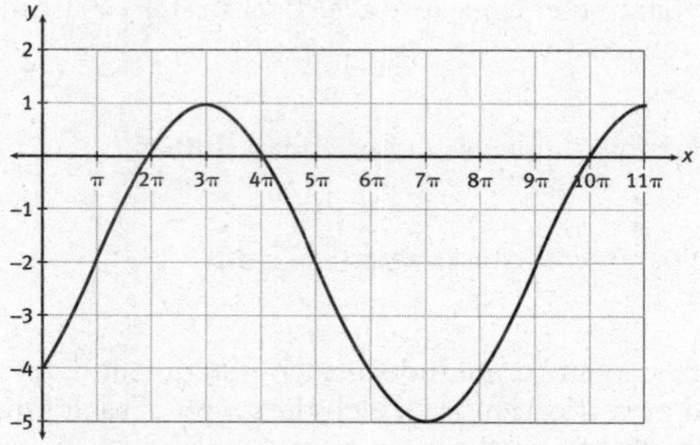

$y = A \sin B(x - C) + D$	
$\lvert A\rvert = \dfrac{\text{maximum} - \text{minimum}}{2}$	$\lvert A\rvert = \dfrac{1-(-5)}{2} = 3$
$D = \dfrac{\text{maximum} + \text{minimum}}{2}$	$D = \dfrac{1+(-5)}{2} = -2$
The period may be determined by finding the distance between two consecutive maximum values or two consecutive minimum values.	Period $= 11\pi - 3\pi = 8\pi$
$B = \dfrac{2\pi}{\text{period}}$	$B = \dfrac{2\pi}{8\pi} = \dfrac{1}{4}$
A horizontal shift *C* can be determined for sine by finding the *x*-coordinate of a point of intersection of the graph and the line $y = D$.	The graph intersects $y = -2$ at $(\pi, -2)$, so a possible value of C is π.
Determine whether *A* is positive or negative by determining whether or not there is a vertical reflection.	The first extrema for $x > \pi$ is a maximum. Therefore, there is no vertical reflection, and so $A = 3$.
$y = 3 \sin\left[\frac{1}{4}(x - \pi)\right] - 2$	

My Notes

Try These A

a. Write an equation for Example A in terms of cosine.

b. Write a second equation for Example A in terms of sine.

Check Your Understanding

5. Write two equations for the graph shown below, one in terms of sine and the other in terms of cosine.

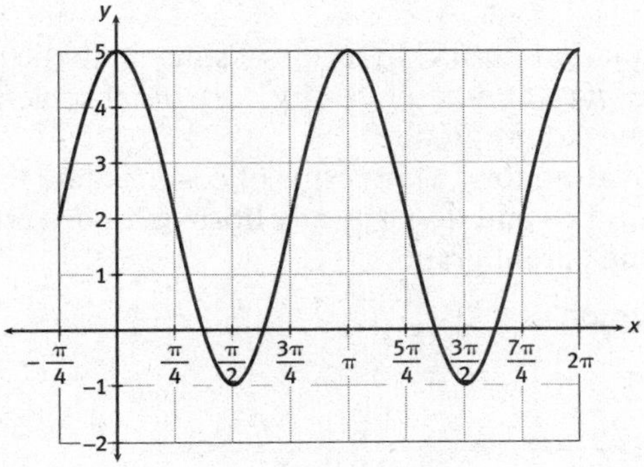

6. Write two equations for the graph shown below, one in terms of sine and the other in terms of cosine.

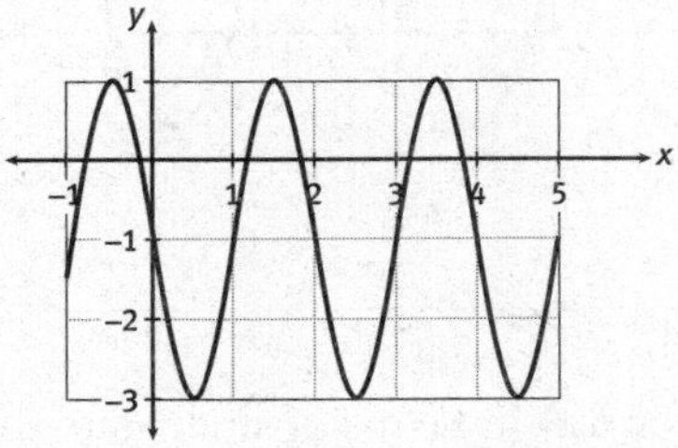

7. Suppose that the depth of the water at a popular surfing spot varies from 3 ft to 11 ft, depending on the time. Suppose that on Monday, high tide occurred at 6:00 a.m. and the next high tide occurred at 7:00 p.m.

a. Draw a graph to model the depth of water as a function of time t in hours since midnight on Monday morning.

b. Write an equation for the graph.

c. Use the equation in Item 6(b) to predict the depth of the water at 2 p.m., correct to three decimal places.

d. Reason quantitatively. Describe how the parameters of the equation that models this situation change if the depth of the water is measured in meters instead of feet.

CONNECT TO OCEANOGRAPHY

The depth of water at high and low tides follows a periodic pattern that can be modeled with a sine or cosine function.

My Notes

LESSON 17-2 PRACTICE

8. Consider the graph of $f(x)$.

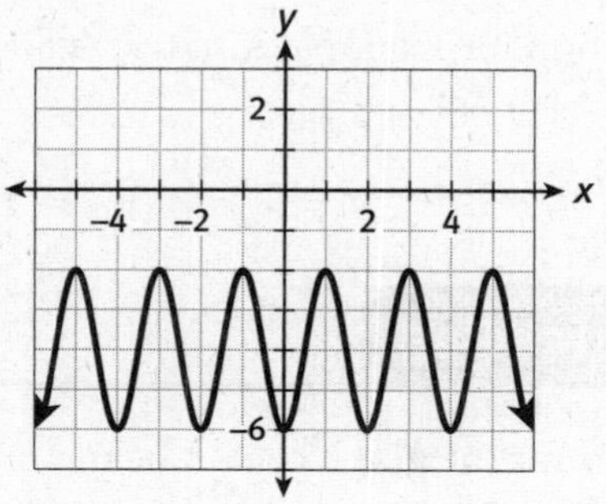

a. Write an equation for $f(x)$ in terms of sine. State the period and amplitude of $f(x)$, and describe any horizontal or vertical shifts relative to the parent graph.

b. Write an equation for $f(x)$ in terms of cosine. State the period and amplitude of $f(x)$, and describe any horizontal or vertical shifts relative to the parent graph.

9. Consider the graph of $f(x)$.

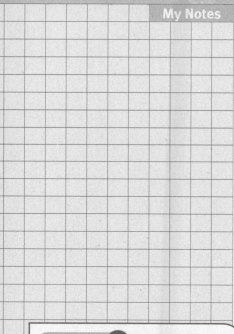

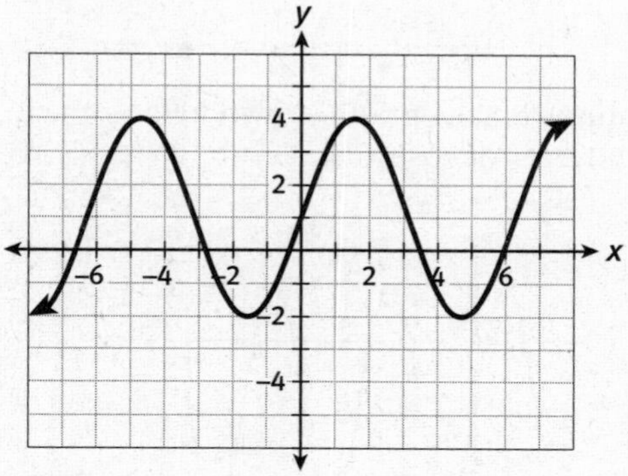

Write an equation for $f(x)$ in terms of sine. State the period and amplitude of $f(x)$, and describe any horizontal or vertical shifts relative to the parent graph.

CONNECT TO TECHNOLOGY

A graphing calculator can be used to check your answers. Use the TRACE or TABLE feature to see ordered pairs which satisfy the equation.

ACTIVITY 17 PRACTICE

Lesson 17-1

Write your answers on notebook paper. Show your work.

1. Identify the interval(s) on $[0, 2\pi]$ for which the sine function is increasing.
2. Identify the interval(s) on $[0, 2\pi]$ for which the cosine function is increasing.
3. a. Sketch the graphs of $f(x) = \sin x$ and $g(x) = \sin x - 1$ over at least one period, labeling each axis.
   b. State the period and amplitude of $g(x) = \sin x - 1$, and describe any horizontal or vertical shifts.
4. a. Sketch the graphs of $f(x) = \cos x$ and $g(x) = 4 \cos x$ over at least one period, labeling each axis.
   b. State the period and amplitude of $g(x) = 4 \cos x$, and describe any horizontal or vertical shifts.
5. a. Sketch the graphs of $f(x) = \sin x$ and $g(x) = \sin (x - \pi)$ over at least one period, labeling each axis.
   b. State the period and amplitude of $g(x) = \sin (x - \pi)$, and describe any horizontal or vertical shifts.
6. a. Sketch the graphs of $f(x) = \cos x$ and $g(x) = 2 \cos x + 1$ over at least one period, labeling each axis.
   b. State the period and amplitude of $g(x) = 2 \cos x + 1$, and describe any horizontal or vertical shifts.
7. Which pair of equations generates the same graph?
   A. $f(x) = \sin x - 3$ and $g(x) = \sin (x - 3)$
   B. $f(x) = \sin\left(x - \frac{\pi}{2}\right)$ and $g(x) = \sin\left(x + \frac{\pi}{2}\right)$
   C. $f(x) = -\cos x$ and $g(x) = \cos (x + \pi)$
   D. $f(x) = 2 \cos x$ and $g(x) = \cos \frac{1}{2}(x)$
8. Find a cosine equation which will generate the same graph as $f(x) = 2 \sin x - 2$.

Lesson 17-2

9. Write a sine equation that models the graph.

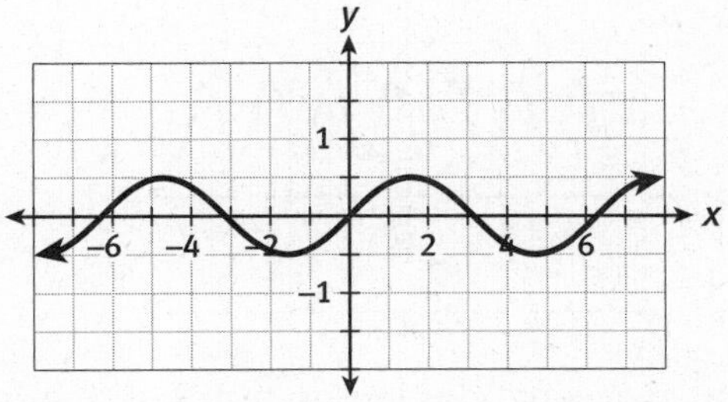

10. Write a cosine equation that models the graph.

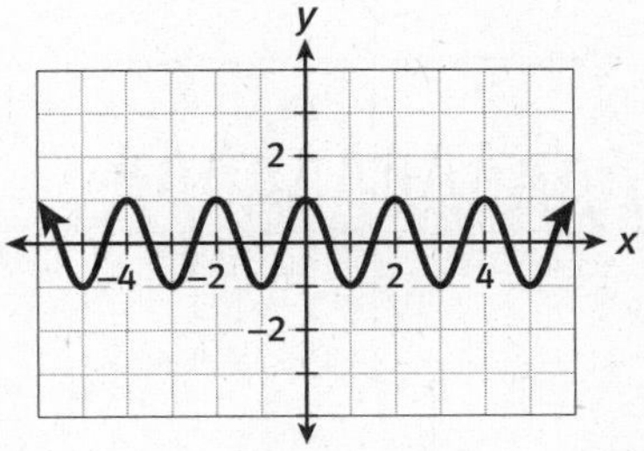

11. Write two equations, one in terms of sine and the other in terms of cosine, that model the graph.

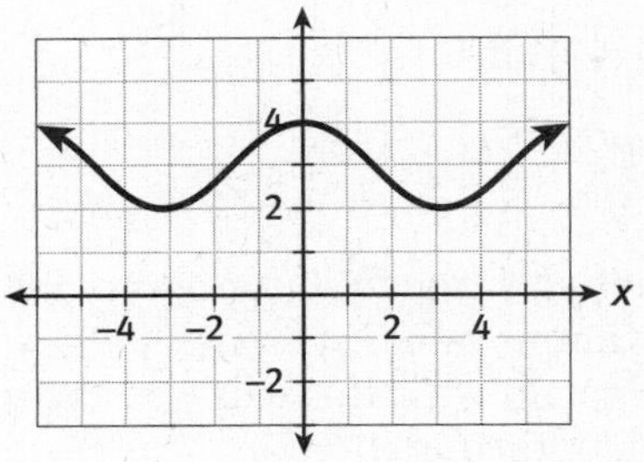

12. Write two equations, one in terms of sine and the other in terms of cosine, that model the graph.

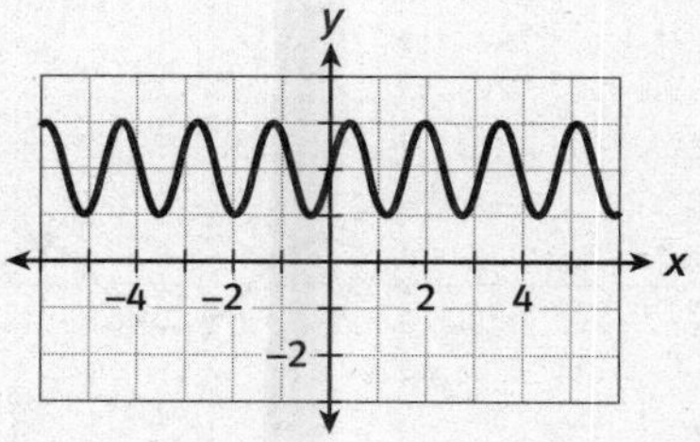

13. Write two equations, one in terms of sine and the other in terms of cosine, that model the graph.

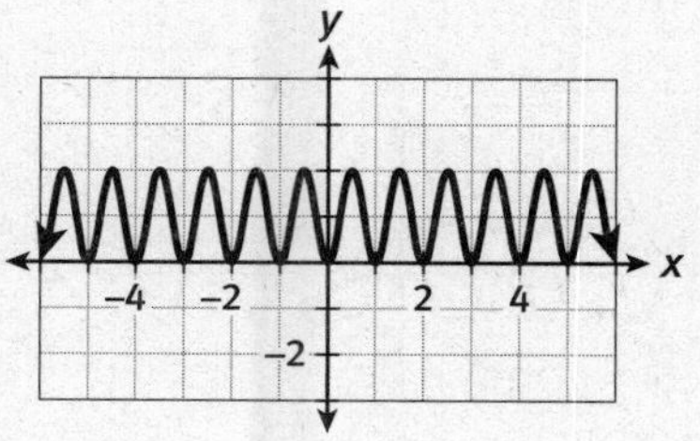

14. Which of the following functions has a period greater than the period of $f(x) = \sin x$?

A. $f(x) = \sin\frac{1}{5}(x)$

B. $f(x) = \frac{1}{5}\sin 5x$

C. $f(x) = \sin 5x$

D. $f(x) = 5\sin x$

15. The graph of a sine function shows the function has maximum values at $x = -3$, $x = 1$, $x = 5$, and $x = 9$. Explain what this tells you about the equation of the function.

16. The graph of a cosine function shows the function has maximum values at $x = -\frac{9\pi}{5}$, $x = -\frac{4\pi}{5}$, $x = \frac{\pi}{5}$, and $x = \frac{6\pi}{5}$. Explain what this tells you about the equation of the function.

17. The graph of a sine function has a maximum value of $y = 4$ and a minimum value of $y = 2$. Explain what this tells you about the equation of the function.

MATHEMATICAL PRACTICES
Make Sense of Problems and Persevere in Solving Them

18. A weight suspended from a spring vibrates vertically in a periodic pattern. The height of the weight relative to its rest position is $f(t)$ centimeters t seconds after the weight is at its lowest point.

Periodic Motion—Weight on a Spring

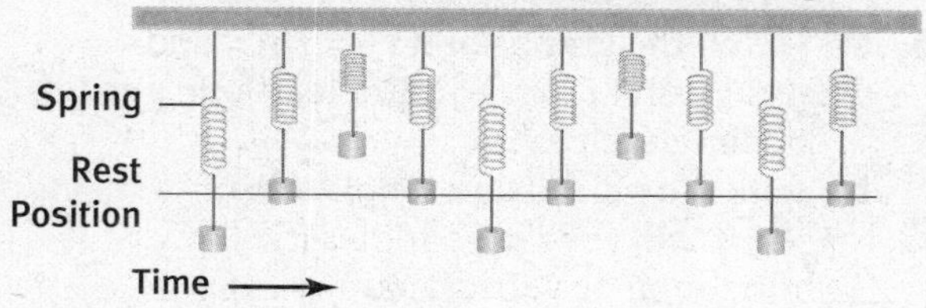

Explain why $f(t)$ could be a sine or cosine function, and identify any additional information needed to determine each of the parameters, A, B, C, and D.

Graphs of Other Trigonometric Functions

More Trigonometric Graphs

Lesson 18-1 Graphs of Reciprocal Trigonometric Functions

My Notes

Learning Targets:

- Sketch the graphs of $\csc x$, $\sec x$, $\tan x$, and $\cot x$.
- Find the period and locate asymptotes of reciprocal trig functions.
- Determine the domain and range of reciprocal trig functions.

SUGGESTED LEARNING STRATEGIES: Activating Prior Knowledge, Create Representations, Quickwrite

MATH TIP

The amplitude of a cosecant function is not defined because cosecant does not have a minimum and a maximum value.

The graphs of the sine and cosine functions are examples of periodic functions. The graphs of the other trigonometric functions are periodic as well.

1. Consider the function $f(x) = \csc x$.

a. How is the cosecant function related to the sine function?

b. Complete the table of values.

x	$\sin x$	$\csc x$
0		
$\frac{\pi}{4}$		
$\frac{\pi}{2}$		
$\frac{3\pi}{4}$		
π		
$\frac{5\pi}{4}$		
$\frac{3\pi}{2}$		
$\frac{7\pi}{4}$		
2π		

c. Attend to precision. Sketch a graph of $f(x) = \sin x$ by plotting values in the table, and then extend the graph across the entire grid.

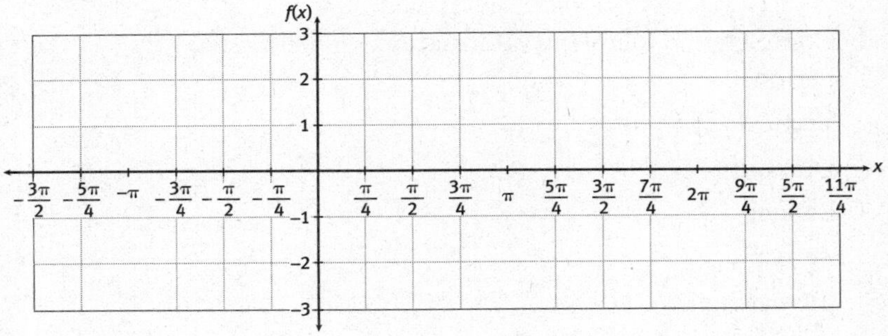

d. Explain how to locate vertical asymptotes of the graph of $f(x) = \csc x$ from features of the graph of $f(x) = \sin x$, and then draw the asymptotes on the axes above.

e. Sketch a graph of $f(x) = \csc x$ on the grid in part c.

f. Complete the following information for $f(x) = \csc x$.

Period:

Vertical asymptotes:

Domain:

Range:

Zeros:

Increasing:

Decreasing:

My Notes

2. Use the cosine function to develop the graph of $f(x) = \sec x$.

a. Sketch a graph of $f(x) = \cos x$ by plotting values from the unit circle on the interval $[0, 2\pi]$. Then extend the graph across the entire grid.

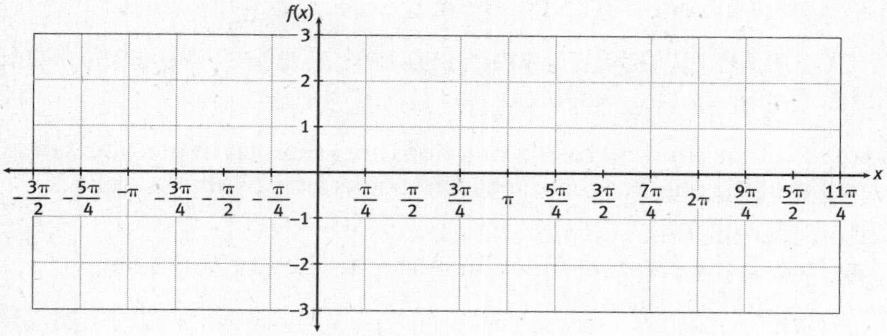

b. Explain how to locate vertical asymptotes of the graph of $f(x) = \sec x$ from features of the graph of $f(x) = \cos x$. Then draw the asymptotes on the axes above.

c. Sketch a graph of $f(x) = \sec x$ on the grid in part a by finding reciprocals of the y-coordinates on the graph of $f(x) = \cos x$.

d. Complete the following information for $f(x) = \sec x$.

Period:

Vertical asymptotes:

Domain:

Range:

Zeros:

Increasing:

Decreasing:

3. Consider the function $f(x) = \tan x$.

a. Use special angle values from the unit circle to sketch a graph of $f(x) = \tan x$ on the interval $[0, 2\pi]$. Then extend the graph across the entire grid. Draw vertical asymptotes where $f(x) = \tan x$ is undefined.

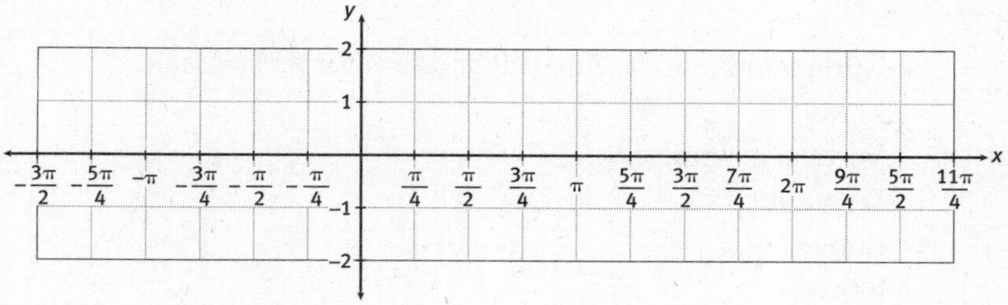

b. Complete the following information for $f(x) = \tan x$.
Period:
Vertical asymptotes:
Domain:
Range:
Zeros:
Increasing:
Decreasing:

4. Consider the function $f(x) = \cot x$.

a. Use special angle values from the unit circle to sketch a graph of $f(x) = \cot x$ on the interval $[0, 2\pi]$. Then extend the graph across the entire grid. Draw vertical asymptotes where $f(x) = \cot x$ is undefined.

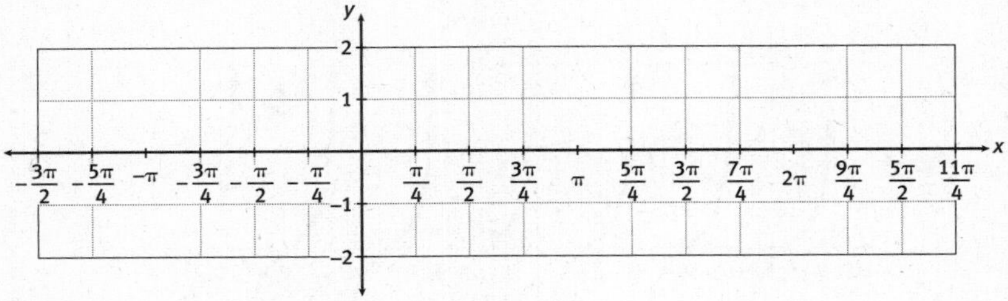

b. Complete the following information for $f(x) = \cot x$.

Period:

Vertical asymptotes:

Domain:

Range:

Zeros:
Increasing:
Decreasing:

My Notes

MATH TIP

Create an organized summary of the graphs of the trigonometric functions to use when sketching the transformations of the graphs.

Check Your Understanding

5. Classify each function as odd or even and describe its symmetry.

a. $\tan x$

b. $\cot x$

c. $\sec x$

d. $\csc x$

My Notes

LESSON 18-1 PRACTICE

6. Match each trigonometric function to its graph.

$y = \sec x$ $y = \csc x$ $y = \tan x$ $y = \cot x$

A.

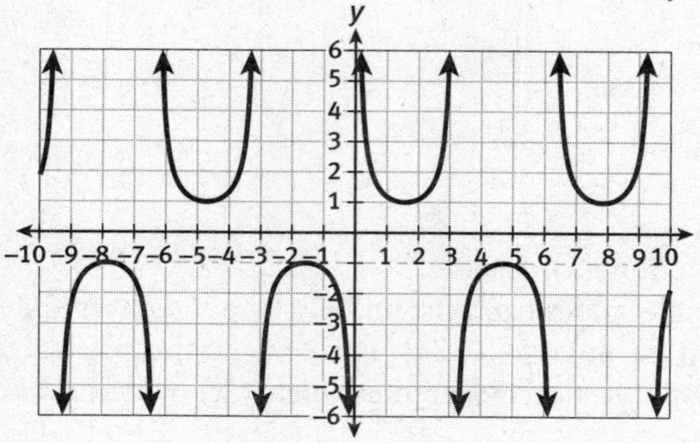

B.

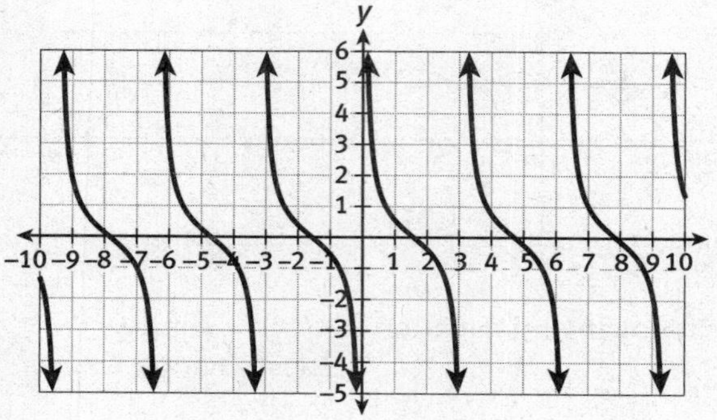

C.

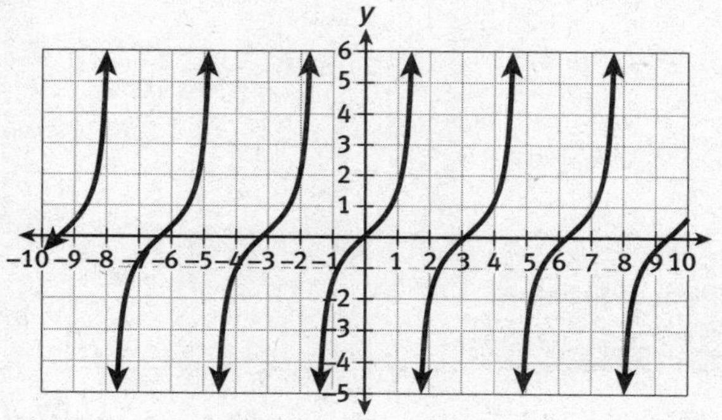

D.

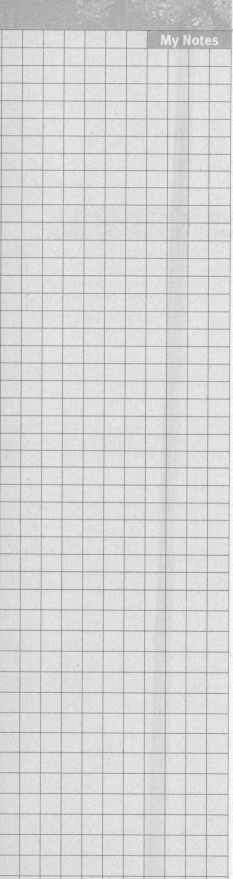

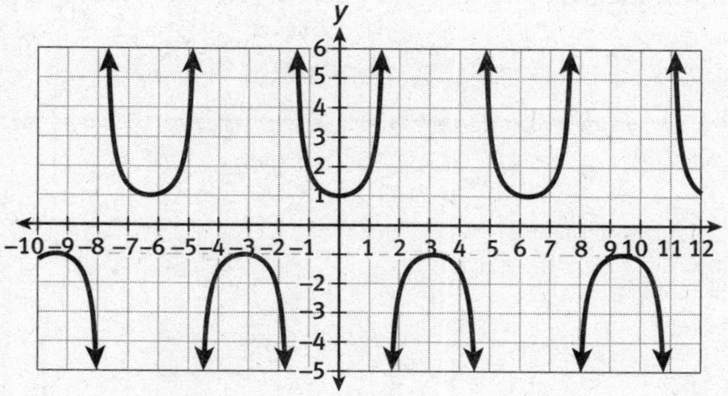

7. Reason abstractly and quantitatively. Explain why the function $f(x) = \csc x$ has no zeros.

My Notes

Learning Targets:

- Graph transformations of reciprocal trig functions.
- Describe how changing parameters affect a trigonometric graph.

SUGGESTED LEARNING STRATEGIES: Activating Prior Knowledge, Create Representations, Quickwrite, Think-Pair-Share

1. For each function given below, choose an interval on which to sketch a graph of one period of the function, and then sketch the graphs in My Notes. These graphs can serve as the parent graphs of the functions.

a. $f(x) = \csc x$ Interval:

b. $f(x) = \sec x$ Interval:

c. $f(x) = \tan x$ Interval:

d. $f(x) = \cot x$ Interval:

2. Look for and make use of structure. For each pair of trigonometric functions, graph the parent function $y = f(x)$. Then use your knowledge of transformations to graph $y = g(x)$. Extend the graph across the entire grid. Carefully label the scales on each axis. After you have completed all the graphs, use a graphing calculator to verify your answers.

a. $f(x) = \csc x$ and $g(x) = -2\csc x$

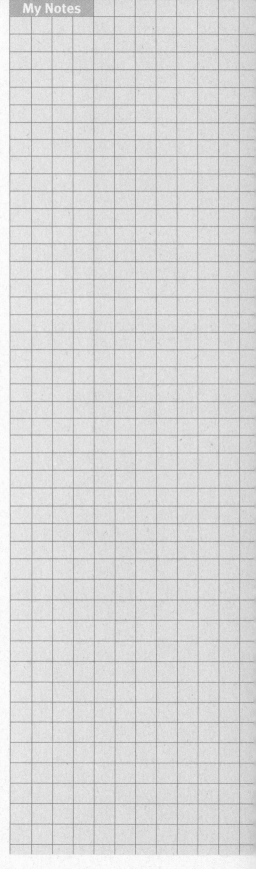

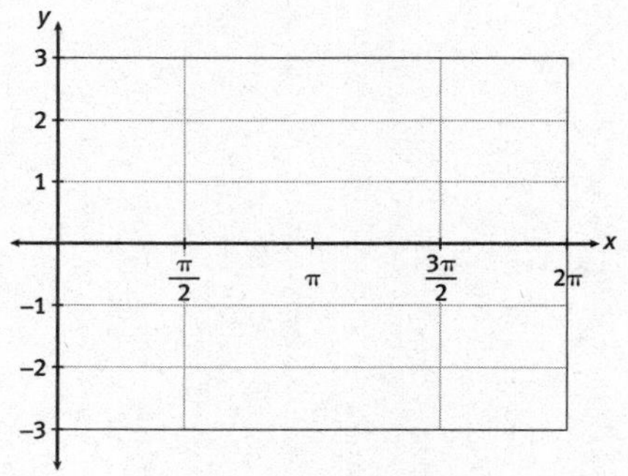

My Notes

b. $f(x) = \cot x$ and $g(x) = \cot\left(x - \frac{\pi}{4}\right)$

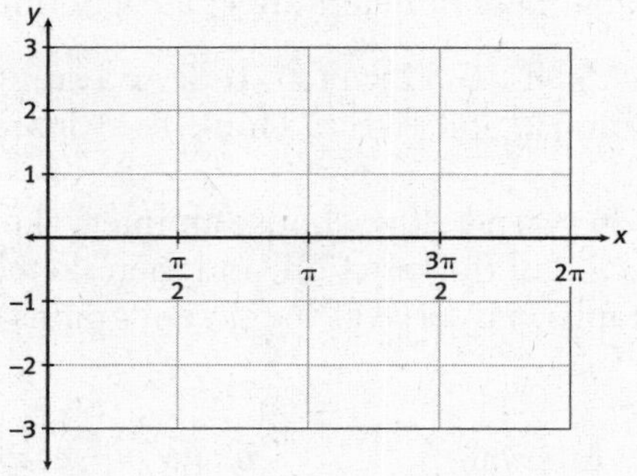

c. $f(x) = \tan x$ and $g(x) = \tan(x) + 2$

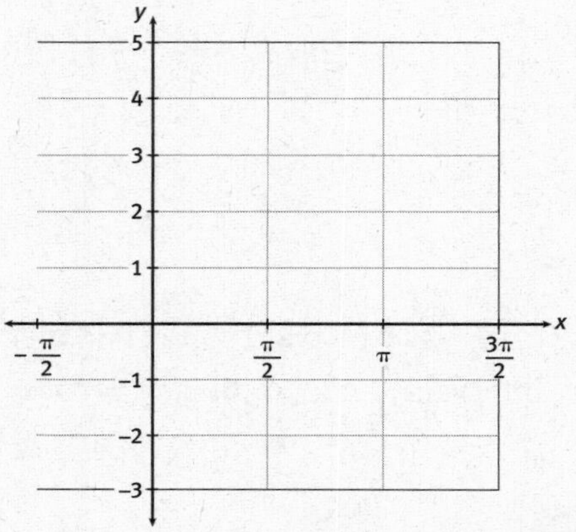

3. Express regularity in repeated reasoning. Consider all six trigonometric functions of the form $y = A\sin B(x - C) + D$. Summarize the effect of the parameters A, C, and D on the graphs of the parent functions.

My Notes

Consider trigonometric functions of the form $y = A\csc B(x - C) + D$. For sine, cosine, cosecant, and secant, the period of the function is $\frac{2\pi}{B}$. The period of tangent and cotangent is $\frac{\pi}{B}$.

4. State the period of each function and the amplitude, if it exists. Then graph each function over at least one period.

a. $y = 3\cos 4x$ **b.** $y = -2\sin(4\pi x)$

c. $y = 3\tan(2x) - 1$ **d.** $y = \csc(\pi x)$

e. $y = \cot\left[\frac{1}{4}(x - \pi)\right]$ **f.** $y = 4\sec(3x) + 1$

5. Which of the six trigonometric functions from Item 4 are even functions? Which are odd functions? Justify your answers.

6. **Make sense of problems.** Given a parent trigonometric function is odd or even, what effect will a horizontal shift have on it? Explain.

Check Your Understanding

7. **Reason quantitatively.** Describe each transformation in words.

a. $f(x) = \sec x$ to $f(x) = \sec\left(x - \frac{\pi}{2}\right)$

b. $f(x) = \csc x$ to $f(x) = \csc x + 2$

c. $f(x) = \tan x$ to $f(x) = -\tan x - 1$

d. $f(x) = \cot x$ to $f(x) = 2\cot(x + 1)$

LESSON 18-2 PRACTICE

8. Find the period of each function. Then graph the function over at least one period.

a. $y = -3\sec x$

b. $y = \tan\frac{1}{2}x$

c. $y = \cot\left(x + \frac{\pi}{4}\right)$

d. $y = \frac{1}{2}\csc x$

e. $y = \tan 2(x - \pi)$

9. **Reason abstractly.** Explain why the function $y = \cot\left[\frac{1}{4}(x - \pi)\right]$ is neither even nor odd.

ACTIVITY 18 PRACTICE

Write your answers on a separate sheet of grid paper.

Lesson 18-1

1. Which is the graph of $\frac{1}{\cos x}$?

A.

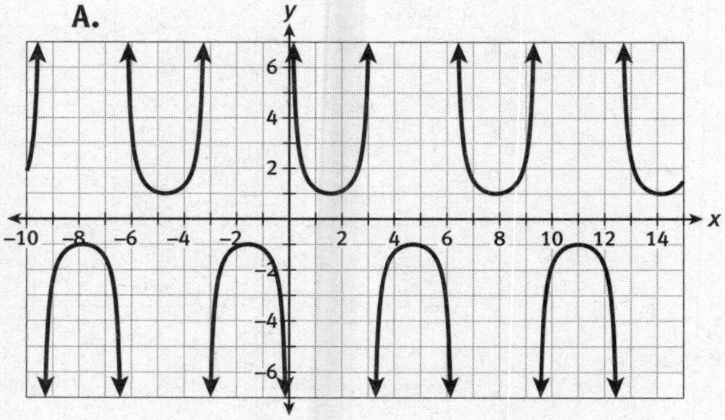

B.

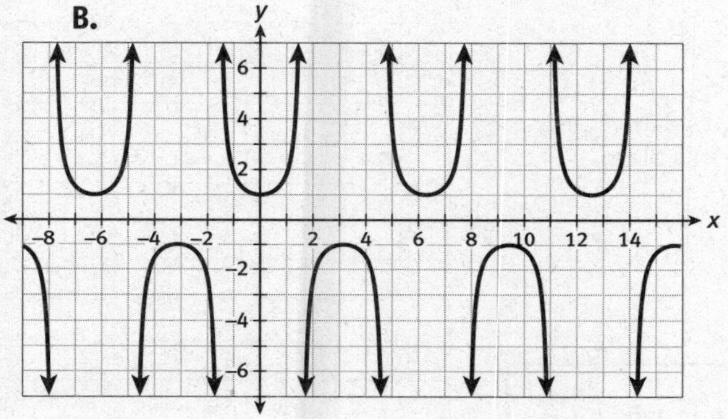

C.

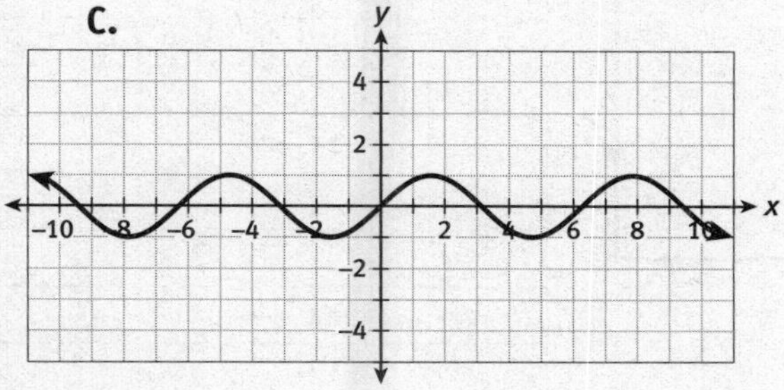

D.

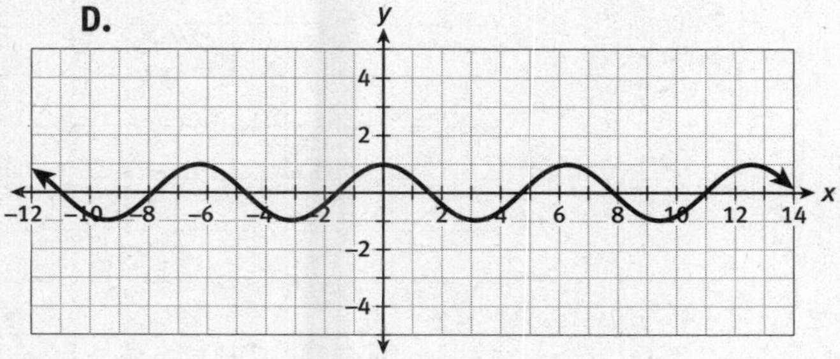

2. Which function has vertical asymptotes at $x = k\pi$, where k is any integer?

A. $f(x) = \csc x$ **B.** $f(x) = \sec x$
C. $f(x) = \tan x$ **D.** $f(x) = \cos x$

3. Which function has no zeros?

A. $f(x) = \cos x$ **B.** $f(x) = \sec x$
C. $f(x) = \tan x$ **D.** $f(x) = \cot x$

4. Explain why $y = \tan x$ is an odd function.

Lesson 18-2

5. Which describes the transformation of $f(x) = \sec x$ to $f(x) = -\frac{1}{2}\sec x$?

A. a reflection of $f(x) = \sec x$ over the x-axis and a vertical stretch of 2
B. a vertical compression of $f(x) = \sec x$ by $-\frac{1}{2}$
C. a reflection of $f(x) = \sec x$ over the x-axis and a vertical compression of $\frac{1}{2}$
D. a vertical stretch of $f(x) = \sec x$ by -2

6. Graph each of the following over the interval $[0, 2\pi]$.

a. $y = \tan(x) + 3$ **b.** $y = -3\csc(x)$
c. $y = \sec\left(x - \frac{\pi}{2}\right)$ **d.** $y = 2\cot(x) - 1$
e. $y = 2\cot x$ **f.** $y = -2\sec(x) + 3$
g. $y = \tan\left(x + \frac{\pi}{4}\right)$ **h.** $y = \csc(x) - 2$

7. State the period of each function. Then graph the function over at least one period.

a. $y = \sec 2x$
b. $y = -\csc\left(\frac{1}{4}x\right)$
c. $y = 3\tan(2x) - 1$
d. $y = 2\cot[\pi(x - 0.5)]$
e. $y = -\sin[2\pi(x - 1)] + 3$
f. $y = 2\csc 4x$
g. $y = -\tan(2\pi x)$
h. $y = 3\cot(2x) + 1$
i. $y = \sec(2x) - 3$
j. $y = -2\cos\left[4\left(x - \frac{\pi}{4}\right)\right] + 1$

MATHEMATICAL PRACTICES

Reason Abstractly and Quantitatively

8. Compare and contrast the graphs of the tangent and cotangent functions.

Angles, the Unit Circle, and Trigonometric Graphs
ORBITING SPACECRAFT

As a spacecraft orbits the earth, it is said to be at its apogee when it is farthest above the earth's surface and at its perigee when it is closest to the earth's surface.

1. Suppose that at time $t = 0$ minutes, a satellite is at its apogee. Then, 45 minutes later, it is at its perigee. The graph below models the satellite's approximate distance in kilometers from the surface of the earth at time t minutes.

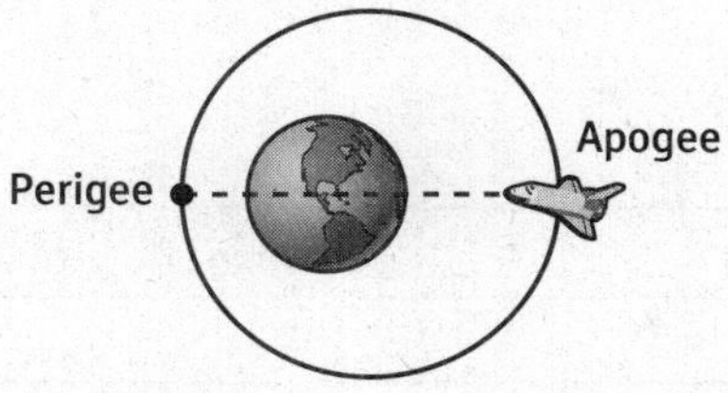

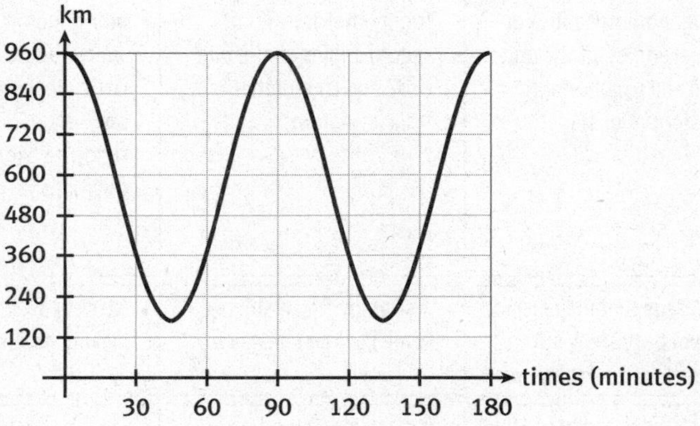

a. How far is the satellite from the earth's surface at its apogee and at its perigee?
b. State the period and amplitude for the model.
c. Write a function that models the situation.

2. Sketch the graph of each function over at least one period. Label the scale on each axis.
a. $f(x) = -3\cos\left[4\left(x - \frac{\pi}{8}\right)\right] + 2$
b. $f(x) = 2\tan(\pi x)$
c. $f(x) = \csc(2x) - 1$

3. Use the functions in Item 2 to answer each of the following.
a. Give the domain and range of each function.
b. Write the equation of the vertical asymptotes for each function.
c. Which functions are continuous? Explain why.
d. When is each function increasing and when is it decreasing?

4. Let θ be an angle is standard position with measure 948°.
a. Find an angle between 0° and 360° coterminal with θ.
b. Find the radian measure of angle θ.

5. An angle in standard position has a radian measure of $\frac{\pi}{5}$.
a. Find one positive angle and one negative angle that are coterminal with the given angle.
b. Find the degree measure of the angle.

6. Give the exact value of each trigonometric value.

a. $\sin 60°$ **b.** $\cos \frac{7\pi}{6}$ **c.** $\tan \frac{7\pi}{4}$

d. $\cot 270°$ **e.** $\csc 240°$ **f.** $\sec \frac{5\pi}{3}$

7. Point $P(2, -5)$ is on the terminal side of θ, an angle in standard position. Find sine, cosine, tangent, cosecant, secant, and cotangent of θ.

Scoring Guide	Exemplary	Proficient	Emerging	Incomplete
	The solution demonstrates these characteristics:			
Mathematics Knowledge and Thinking (Items 1, 2, 3, 5, 6)	• Clear and accurate understanding of trigonometric ratios of special angles on the unit circle and transforming trigonometric functions with amplitude, period, phase shift, and vertical shift	• A functional understanding of trigonometric ratios of special angles on the unit circle and trigonometric transformations	• Partial understanding of trigonometric ratios of special angles on the unit circle and trigonometric transformations	• Little or no understanding of trigonometric ratios of special angles on the unit circle, or of period, amplitude, or domain and range for trigonometric functions
Problem Solving (Item 1a)	• An appropriate and efficient strategy that results in a correct answer	• A strategy that may include unnecessary steps but results in a correct answer	• A strategy that results in some incorrect answers	• No clear strategy when solving problems
Mathematical Modeling / Representations (Items 1c, 2, 3)	• Clear and accurate understanding of representations of trigonometric graphs • Clear and accurate understanding of characteristics of trigonometric graphs	• A functional understanding of representations of trigonometric graphs given their equations • Mostly accurate representation of domain and range, continuity, and behavior	• Partial understanding of trigonometric transformations • Partial representations of trigonometric graphs given their equations • Partial understanding of domain, range, and behavior of trigonometric graphs	• Little or no understanding of representations of trigonometric functions • Inaccurate or incomplete understanding of domain, range, and graphical behavior of the trigonometric functions
Reasoning and Communication (Items 1, 2, 4, 5, 6, 7)	• Precise use of appropriate terms – *period, amplitude, coterminal,* and *radian;* demonstrates knowledge of the ratios for all six trigonometric functions if given a triangle with a central angle	• Correct characterization of period and amplitude, but mostly knows the special triangle ratios for the six trigonometric functions (may or may not be able to extend from the unit circle into using the ratios described in Item 7)	• Misleading or confusing characterization of the six trigonometric functions	• Incomplete or inaccurate characterization of trigonometric transformations and the six trigonometric ratios

Inverse Trigonometric Functions

ACTIVITY 19

Viewing Angle

Lesson 19-1 Inverse Cosine Function

My Notes

Learning Targets:

- Apply a trigonometric function to a real-world situation.
- Define and apply the inverse cosine function.

SUGGESTED LEARNING STRATEGIES: Close Reading, Summarizing, Paraphrasing, Marking the Text, Visualization, Think-Pair-Share, Create Representations, Quickwrite, Vocabulary Organizer

You can locate a point in a coordinate plane by using x- and y-coordinates. In the same way, a point on the curved surface of the earth can be specified by using lines of longitude and latitude. Imagine that the sky is the inner surface of a sphere that is much bigger than the earth. The coordinate system for the sky is similar to that for the earth, except that the lines of latitude are called lines of *declination* and the lines of longitude are known as lines of *right ascension*. In order to follow the path of an object as it moves across the sky, a telescope moves about two axes. In the figure below, θ represents the angle of declination, or the up-down motion of the telescope, and α represents the angle of right ascension, or the right-left motion of the telescope.

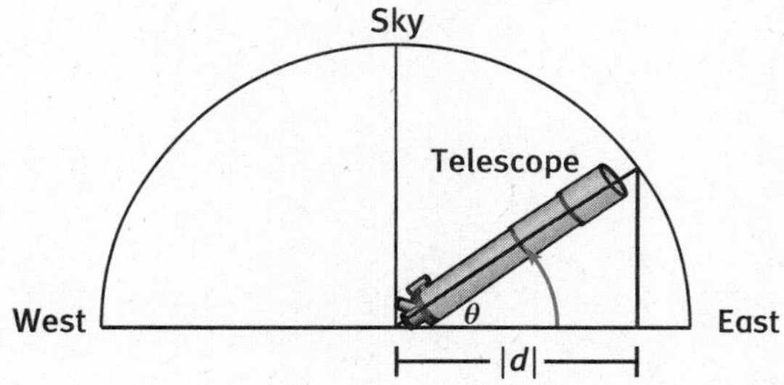

One telescope at the California Institute of Technology (Caltech) is 200 inches long. It is mounted to allow rotation about the two axes described above. Consider the angle of declination θ, shown in the figure at the right. The angle is formed by a horizontal ray, pointing due east, and the telescope. The horizontal distance from the viewing end of the telescope along the east-west line to the point at which a perpendicular line from the outer end of the telescope intersects the ray is $|d|$. The variable d represents a positive value when the horizontal distance is measured along the east ray and a negative value when the horizontal distance is measured along the west ray.

1. **Reason quantitatively.** As the telescope rotates, what are the possible values of θ, the angle of declination?

2. Use a trigonometric ratio and the length of the telescope to relate the variables θ and d.

DISCUSSION GROUP TIPS

In your discussion groups, read the text carefully to clarify meaning. Reread definitions of terms as needed to help you comprehend the meanings of words, or ask your teacher to clarify vocabulary terms.

My Notes

3. Find the value of d for each given value of θ.

a. 60°

b. 110°

c. Why is the value of d negative in part b?

Suppose that a local astronomy club has a one-meter telescope mounted in the same manner as the telescope previously described. Suppose also that the one-meter telescope rotates about the axis of declination. Let the angle of declination θ be measured in radians.

4. Find the value of d for each given value of θ.

a. $\frac{\pi}{4}$

b. $\frac{2\pi}{3}$

c. $\frac{\pi}{2}$

5. Model with mathematics. Sketch a graph below to show the relationship between θ and d as the telescope rotates counterclockwise.

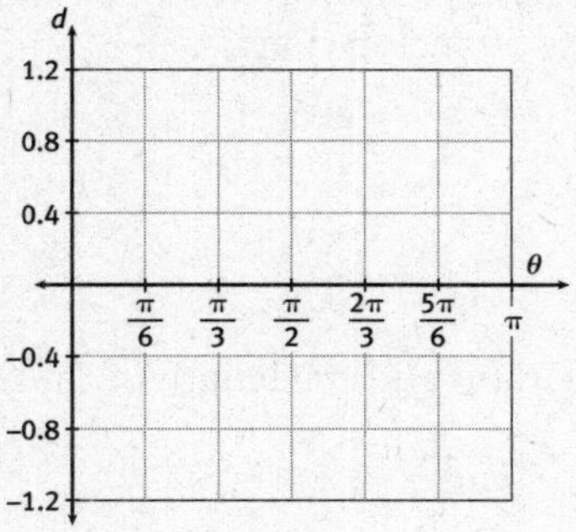

My Notes

6. Refer to the graph in Item 5 to answer parts a–d.

a. Write an equation for the graphed relation, and state the domain and range for the problem situation.

b. Reason abstractly. Is the relation a function over the stated domain? Explain why or why not.

c. Is the inverse of the relation a function over the stated domain? Explain why or why not.

d. Would the graph of the inverse of the relation be a function if the rotation were not limited to 0 to π? Explain your reasoning.

7. Complete the values for $y = \cos(x)$ in the table below. When answers are irrational, give both the exact value and an approximation, rounded to three decimal places.

x	y
0	
$\frac{\pi}{6}$	
$\frac{\pi}{4}$	
$\frac{\pi}{3}$	
$\frac{\pi}{2}$	
$\frac{2\pi}{3}$	
$\frac{3\pi}{4}$	
$\frac{5\pi}{6}$	
π	

My Notes

MATH TERMS

A **one-to-one** function is a function where each element of the range corresponds to exactly one element of the domain. Every function has an inverse relation, but only one-to-one functions have inverse functions.

MATH TERMS

The **inverse trigonometric functions** are the inverse functions of the trigonometric functions, with suitably restricted domains.

MATH TIP

$\cos^{-1}\left(-\frac{\sqrt{2}}{2}\right) = \theta$ means that

$\cos(\theta) = -\frac{\sqrt{2}}{2}$ and $0 \le \theta \le \pi$.

Therefore, $\cos^{-1}\left(-\frac{\sqrt{2}}{2}\right) = \frac{3\pi}{4}$.

Because the function $y = \cos(x)$ is ***one-to-one*** over the domain $0 \le x \le \pi$, the inverse of the function over this domain is a function and an example of an ***inverse trigonometric function***. Although there are other domains over which the cosine function is one-to-one, this is the function that mathematicians have chosen to use to define the inverse cosine function. The notation for the inverse cosine function is $y = \cos^{-1}(x)$, where $\cos(y) = x$ and $0 \le y \le \pi$.

8. **Use appropriate tools strategically.** Explain how you can use the table of values in Item 7 to obtain values for the function $y = \cos^{-1}(x)$.

9. State the domain and range of $y = \cos^{-1}(x)$.

10. Graph the function $y = \cos^{-1}(x)$ on the grid below.

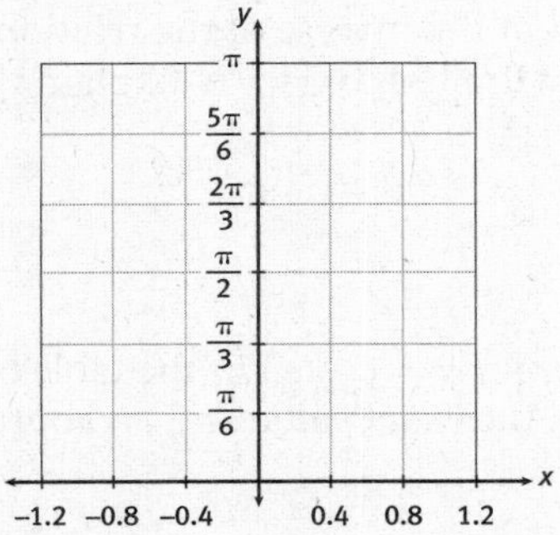

11. Complete the following information for $f(x) = \cos^{-1}(x)$.

Zeros:

Increasing:

Decreasing:

Check Your Understanding

12. **Reason abstractly.** Explain why the domain of the cosine function must be restricted to define the inverse cosine function.

13. Use your answer to Item 10 to find $\cos^{-1}\left(\frac{1}{2}\right)$ and $\cos^{-1}\left(-\frac{1}{2}\right)$.

My Notes

LESSON 19-1 PRACTICE

14. Which graph shows a function that has an inverse defined over its entire domain?

A.

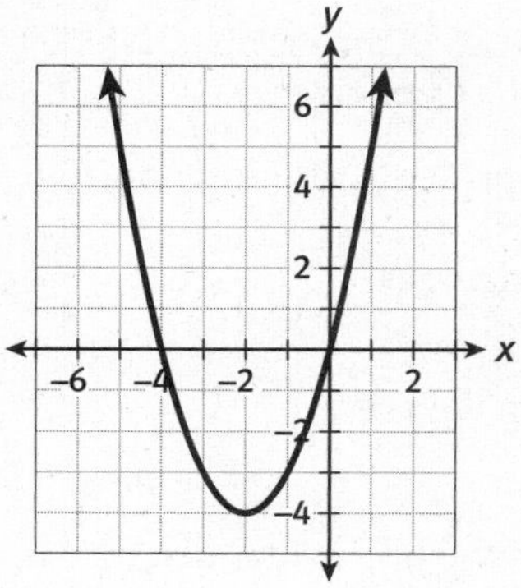

C.

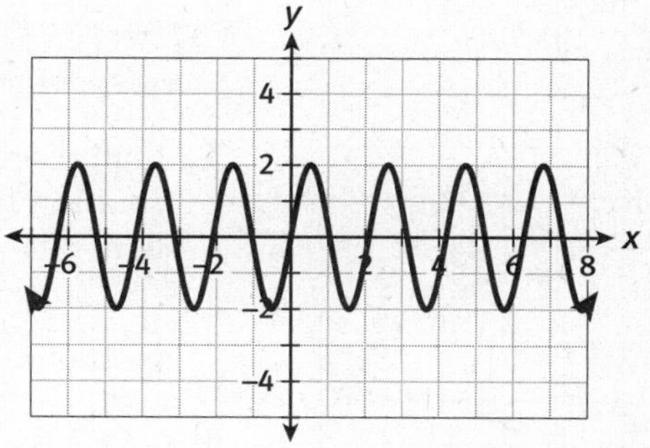

B.

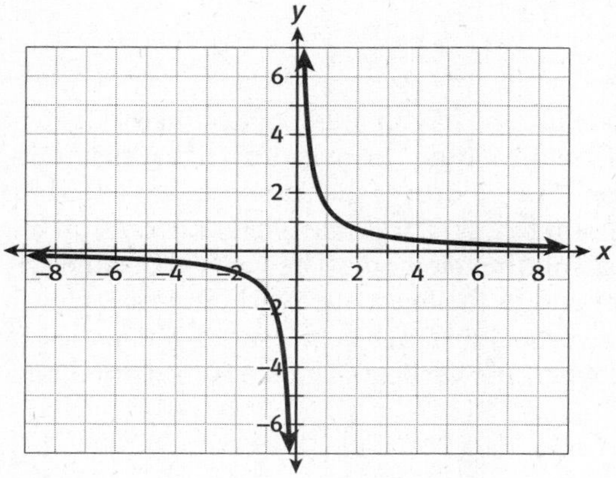

D.

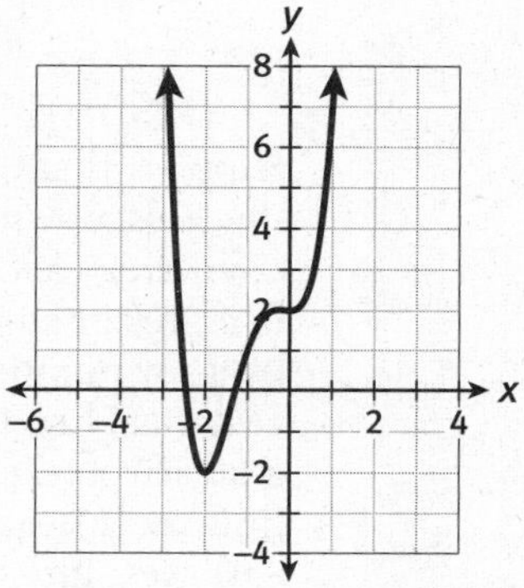

15. Find the exact value of each expression without using a calculator.

a. $\cos^{-1}(0)$ **b.** $\cos^{-1}(1)$

c. $\cos^{-1}\left(-\frac{1}{2}\right)$ **d.** $\cos^{-1}\left(\frac{\sqrt{3}}{2}\right)$

16. Use a calculator to evaluate the following expressions in radian measure, correct to three decimal places.

a. $\cos^{-1}(-0.65)$ **b.** $\cos^{-1}(0.20)$

c. $\cos^{-1}(-0.93)$ **d.** $\cos^{-1}(0.55)$

17. Carlos is on the street looking at the top of a flagpole. The line-of-sight distance between Carlos and the top of the flagpole is 50 feet.

a. Express the horizontal distance d between Carlos and the flagpole as a function of the angle of elevation θ.

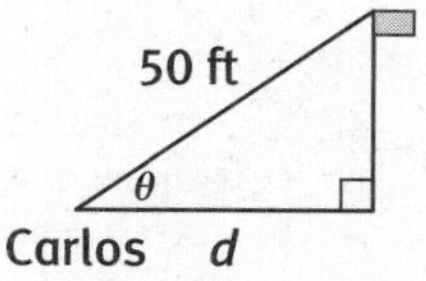

b. Express the angle of elevation θ as a function of the horizontal distance d to the flagpole.

c. If the horizontal distance between Carlos and the flagpole is 35 feet, what is the measure of the angle of elevation?

18. Reason abstractly. If the domain of the function $y = \cos x$ is restricted to the interval $[-\pi, 0]$, is $y = \cos^{-1}x$ a function? Explain why or why not. State a general rule for choosing a restricted domain for a trigonometric function so that the function is one-to-one.

My Notes

Learning Targets:

- Relate one-to-one functions to inverse trigonometric functions.
- Define and apply the inverse sine function.

SUGGESTED LEARNING STRATEGIES: Think-Pair-Share, Create Representations, Quickwrite, Vocabulary Organizer

1. Suppose the angle of declination θ represents a counterclockwise rotation for the Caltech 200-inch telescope.
a. If $d = 100$ inches, determine θ in degrees.

b. If $d = -150$ inches, determine θ in degrees.

c. If the radius of a telescope is r and the horizontal distance is d, write an expression for angle θ.

Suppose that the Caltech telescope has an angle of declination of 0° and that the telescope moves horizontally about the axis of right ascension in a counterclockwise direction. The motion of the telescope, as viewed from above, is represented in the diagram below. The angle of right ascension α is formed by a ray pointing due east and the telescope. The vertical distance from the east-west line to the outer end of the telescope is $|v|$. The variable v has a positive value when the vertical distance is measured above the east-west line and a negative value when the vertical distance is measured below the east-west line.

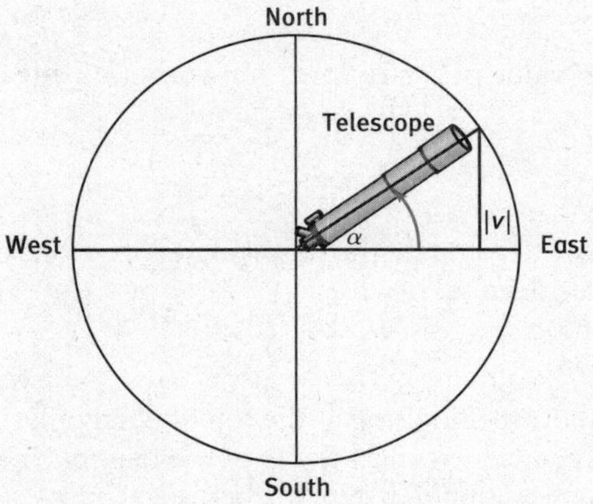

2. Given that the length of the telescope is 200 inches, use a trigonometric ratio to relate the variables α and v.

3. For the 200-inch telescope and each given value of α, find the value of v.
a. 60°

b. 225°

My Notes

c. 110°

d. −75°

e. Explain why some of the values of v in parts a–d are negative.

4. Suppose that v is a positive number.
a. In what general direction(s)—northeast, northwest, southeast, or southwest—would the telescope be directed?

b. What does the answer to part a indicate about the possible values of α when v is a positive number?

5. Describe the direction of the rotation of the telescope for the following values of α.
a. positive values

b. negative values

Suppose that the one-meter telescope at the local astronomy club can rotate clockwise or counterclockwise. Let the angle of right ascension α be measured in radians.

6. Find the value of v for each given value of α.
a. $\frac{\pi}{4}$

b. $\frac{2\pi}{3}$

c. $-\frac{\pi}{2}$

7. Model with mathematics. Sketch a graph below to show the relationship between α and v for one full clockwise rotation and one full counterclockwise rotation of the telescope.

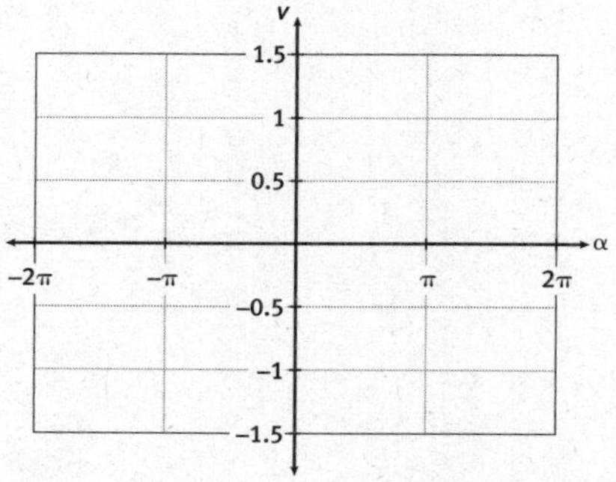

My Notes

8. Refer to the graph in Item 7 to answer parts a–e.

a. Write an equation for the graphed relation and state the domain and range for the problem situation.

b. Is the relation that you graphed a function? Explain why or why not.

c. **Construct viable arguments.** Is the inverse of the relation that you graphed a function? Explain why or why not.

d. Let the movement of the telescope be limited to $\frac{1}{4}$ of a rotation clockwise or counterclockwise from due east. Highlight the portion of the graph that represents this movement. What is the domain of the highlighted portion of the graph?

e. Is the inverse of the relation that you highlighted in part *d* a function? Explain why or why not.

My Notes

9. Complete the values for $y = \sin(x)$ in the table below. When answers are irrational, give both the exact value and an approximation, correct to three decimal places.

x	y
$-\frac{\pi}{2}$	
$-\frac{\pi}{3}$	
$-\frac{\pi}{4}$	
$-\frac{\pi}{6}$	
0	
$\frac{\pi}{6}$	
$\frac{\pi}{4}$	
$\frac{\pi}{3}$	
$\frac{\pi}{2}$	

Because the function $y = \sin(x)$ is one-to-one over the domain $-\frac{\pi}{2} \le x \le \frac{\pi}{2}$, the inverse of the function over this domain is a function. Although there are other domains over which the sine function is one-to-one, this is the function that mathematicians have chosen to use to define the inverse sine function. The notation for the inverse sine function is $y = \sin^{-1}(x)$, where $\sin(y) = x$, and $-\frac{\pi}{2} \le y \le \frac{\pi}{2}$.

MATH TIP

The inverse functions
$y = \sin^{-1}(x)$,
$y = \cos^{-1}(x)$, and
$y = \tan^{-1}(x)$
may also be denoted as
$y = \arcsin(x)$,
$y = \arccos(x)$, and
$y = \arctan(x)$, respectively.

10. Make sense of problems. Explain how you can use the table of values in Item 9 to obtain values for the function $y = \sin^{-1}(x)$.

11. State the domain and range of $y = \sin^{-1}(x)$.

My Notes

12. Attend to precision. Use your responses to Items 9–11 to graph $y = \sin^{-1}(x)$ on the grid below.

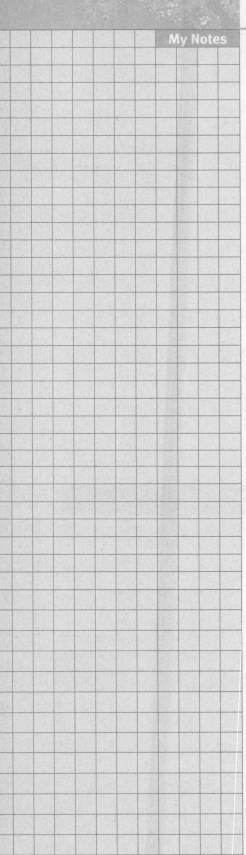

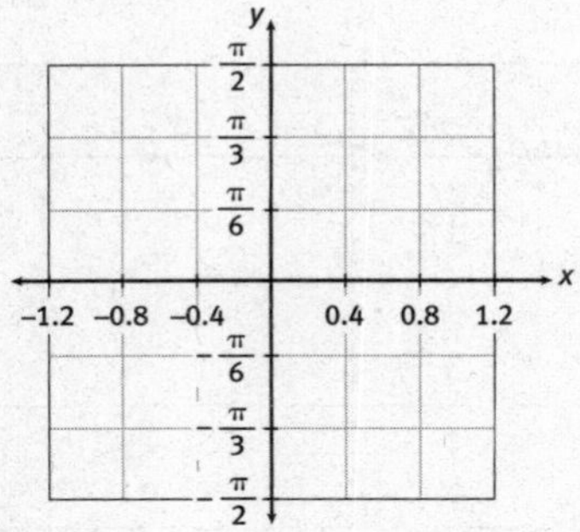

13. Complete the following information for $f(x) = \sin^{-1}(x)$.

Zeros:

Increasing:

Decreasing:

14. Suppose that the Caltech 200-inch telescope completes, at most, one-fourth of a clockwise rotation, or, at most, one-fourth of a counterclockwise rotation. You can find the angle of right ascension α by using the inverse sine function.

a. If $v = 100$ inches, determine α in degrees.

b. If $v = -150$ inches, determine α in degrees.

c. If the radius of any telescope is r and the distance is v, write an expression for angle α.

15. One night, a Caltech astronomer tracks an object moving across the sky.

a. Determine the range of the values of the angle of declination θ if the horizontal distance d changes from 150 inches to 75 inches.

b. Determine the range of the values of the angle of declination α if v changes from -65 to -5.

My Notes

Check Your Understanding

16. Describe the symmetry of the function $f(x) = \sin^{-1}(x)$.

17. Reason quantitatively. Explain why $\sin^{-1}(2)$ displays an error when you use a calculator to find its value.

LESSON 19-2 PRACTICE

18. Find the exact value of each expression without using a calculator.

a. $\sin^{-1}\left(\frac{1}{2}\right)$ **b.** $\sin^{-1}(1)$

c. $\sin^{-1}\left(-\frac{1}{2}\right)$ **d.** $\sin^{-1}\left(\frac{\sqrt{2}}{2}\right)$

19. Use a calculator to evaluate the following expressions in radians, correct to three decimal places.

a. $\sin^{-1}(-0.85)$ **b.** $\sin^{-1}(0.25)$

c. $\sin^{-1}(-0.93)$ **d.** $\sin^{-1}(0.55)$

20. A pole of a badminton net is tethered to the ground with a rope that is 4 feet long. If the length of the pole is 3.5 feet, what is the measure of the angle of elevation θ?

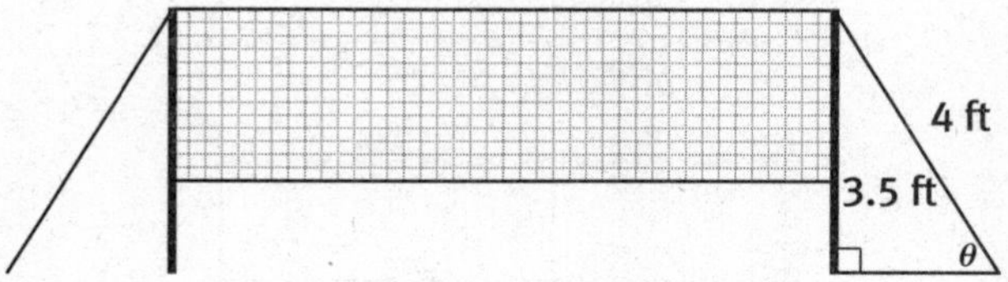

21. Look for and express regularity in repeated reasoning. How would you restrict the domain of the function $f(x) = x^2 - 4x - 5$ so that its inverse exists? Explain how you arrived at this answer.

My Notes

Learning Targets:

- Define and apply the inverse tangent function.
- Find values of inverse trigonometric functions.

SUGGESTED LEARNING STRATEGIES: Create Representations, Quickwrite, Think-Pair-Share

In a similar manner, because the function $y = \tan(x)$ is one-to-one over the domain $-\frac{\pi}{2} < x < \frac{\pi}{2}$, and although there are other domains over which the tangent function is one-to-one, this is the function that mathematicians have chosen to use to define the inverse tangent function. The notation for the inverse tangent function is $y = \tan^{-1}(x)$, where $\tan(y) = x$, and $-\frac{\pi}{2} < y < \frac{\pi}{2}$.

1. Complete the table of values below for the function $y = \tan(x)$. Explain how you can use the table of values to obtain values for the function $y = \tan^{-1}(x)$.

x	y
$-\frac{\pi}{2}$	
$-\frac{\pi}{3}$	
$-\frac{\pi}{4}$	
$-\frac{\pi}{6}$	
0	
$\frac{\pi}{6}$	
$\frac{\pi}{4}$	
$\frac{\pi}{3}$	
$\frac{\pi}{2}$	

My Notes

2. State the domain and range of $y = \tan^{-1}(x)$.

3. Model with mathematics. Graph the function $y = \tan^{-1}(x)$ on the grid below.

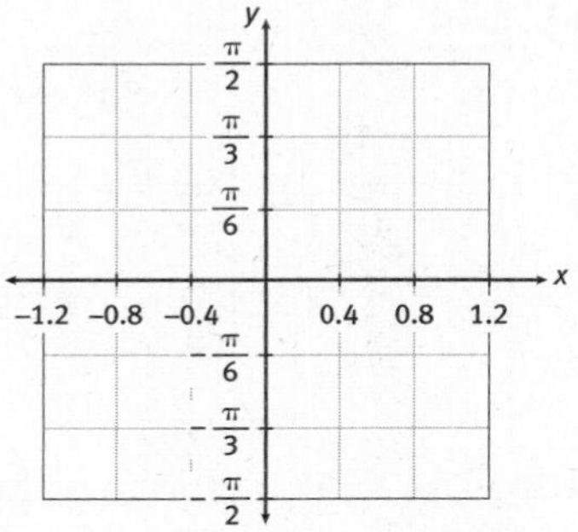

4. Complete the following information for $f(x) = \tan^{-1}(x)$.

Zeros:

Increasing:

Decreasing:

5. Make sense of problems. Write the domain and range of each function.

Function	Domain	Range
$y = \sin^{-1}(x)$		
$y = \cos^{-1}(x)$		
$y = \tan^{-1}(x)$		

6. Determine whether the following angles are in the range for inverse sine. For those angles that are not, find a coterminal angle that lies in the range.

a. $\frac{3\pi}{2}$

b. $\frac{11\pi}{6}$

c. $\frac{7\pi}{4}$

My Notes

7. Use your knowledge of the unit circle and the ranges of the inverse trigonometric functions to find the exact value of each expression without using a calculator.

a. $\sin^{-1}\left(\frac{1}{2}\right)$ **b.** $\tan^{-1}(-1)$ **c.** $\cos^{-1}\left(\frac{\sqrt{3}}{2}\right)$

d. $\cos^{-1}\left(-\frac{1}{2}\right)$ **e.** $\sin^{-1}\left(-\frac{\sqrt{2}}{2}\right)$ **f.** $\tan^{-1}\left(-\sqrt{3}\right)$

8. **Attend to precision.** Use a calculator to evaluate the following expressions in radian measure, correct to three decimal places.

a. $\tan^{-1}(1.5)$ **b.** $\cos^{-1}(0.7)$

c. $\sin^{-1}(0.7)$ **d.** $\tan^{-1}(-0.8)$

CONNECT TO AP

In AP Calculus, the trigonometric ratios as defined using a right triangle can assist you in finding inverse trigonometric functions.

9. Use a calculator to evaluate the following expressions, correct to three decimal places.

a. $\sin(\sin^{-1}(0.3))$ **b.** $\tan(\tan^{-1}(3.2))$

c. $\cos^{-1}(\cos(1.5))$ **d.** $\sin^{-1}(\sin(0.7))$

e. $\cos^{-1}(\cos(-1.4))$ **f.** $\tan^{-1}(\tan(2.1))$

10. **Reason abstractly and quantitatively.** Explain your answers to parts e and f of Item 9.

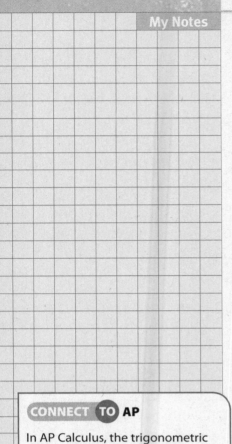

My Notes

In general, for inverse functions f and f^{-1}, $f(f^{-1}(x)) = x$ for all x in the domain of f^{-1}, and $f^{-1}(f(x)) = x$ for all x in the domain of f.

11. Since the domains of the trigonometric functions were restricted in order to define the inverse trigonometric functions, the domains must be similarly restricted for the following inverse properties. State the domain for which each of these inverse properties is true.

a. $\sin(\sin^{-1}(x)) = x$

b. $\sin^{-1}(\sin(x)) = x$

c. $\cos(\cos^{-1}(x)) = x$

d. $\cos^{-1}(\cos(x)) = x$

e. $\tan(\tan^{-1}(x)) = x$

f. $\tan^{-1}(\tan(x)) = x$

12. Without using a calculator, find the exact value of each expression.

a. $\cos^{-1}\left(\cos\left(\frac{\pi}{6}\right)\right)$

b. $\sin(\sin^{-1}(1))$

c. $\tan^{-1}\left(\tan\left(\frac{7\pi}{4}\right)\right)$

d. $\sin^{-1}\left(\sin\left(\frac{2\pi}{3}\right)\right)$

MATH TIP

The *inverses of the reciprocal trigonometric functions* can be defined as follows:

$y = \csc^{-1}(x)$,
where $\csc(y) = x$, and
$-\frac{\pi}{2} \le y \le \frac{\pi}{2}, y \ne 0$.

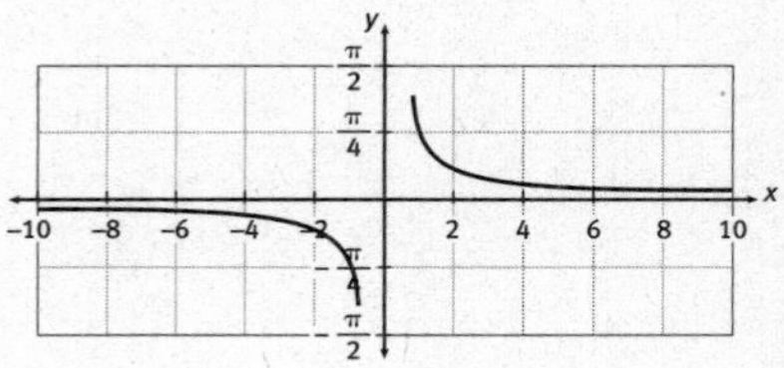

$y = \sec^{-1}(x)$,
where $\sec(y) = x$, and
$0 \le y \le \pi, y \ne \frac{\pi}{2}$.

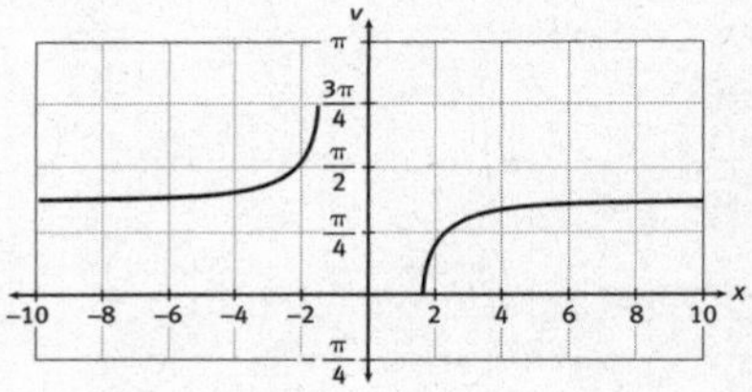

$y = \cot^{-1}(x)$,
where $\cot(y) = x$, and
$0 < y < \pi$.

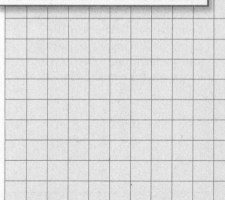

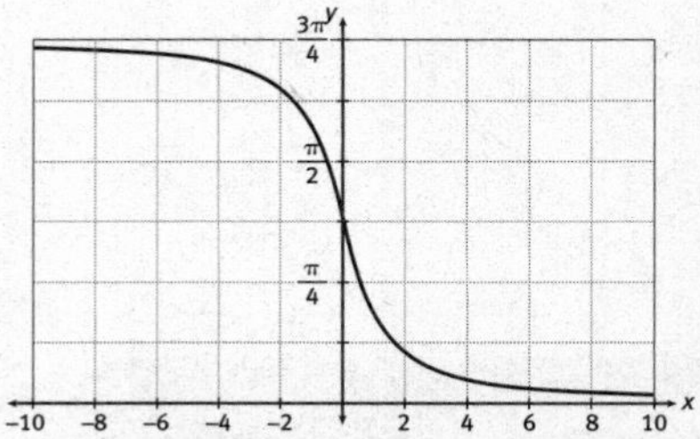

My Notes

Check Your Understanding

13. Describe the symmetry of the function $f(x) = \tan^{-1}(x)$.

14. Use the diagram to write the expression $\tan(\sin^{-1} x)$ as an algebraic expression in terms of x.

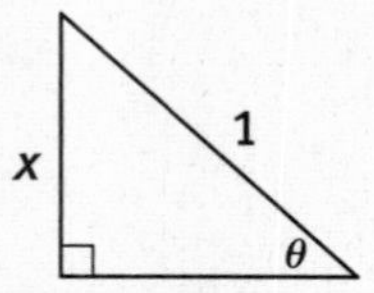

LESSON 19-3 PRACTICE

15. Find the exact value of each expression without using a calculator.

a. $\tan^{-1}(\sqrt{3})$ **b.** $\tan^{-1}(-1)$

16. Use a calculator to evaluate the following expressions in radians, correct to three decimal places.

a. $\tan^{-1}(0.45)$ **b.** $\tan^{-1}(-2.32)$
c. $\tan^{-1}(1.72)$ **d.** $\tan^{-1}(22.45)$

17. Jenna is at the top of a lighthouse looking at a boat that is 400 meters from the lighthouse.

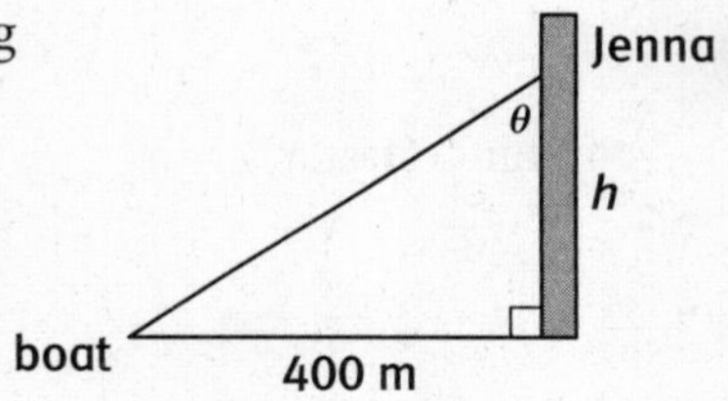

a. Express the height h of the lighthouse as a function of the angle θ.
b. Express angle θ as a function of the height h of the lighthouse.
c. If the height of the lighthouse is 52 meters, what is the angle of elevation?

18. Use a calculator to evaluate the following expressions, correct to three decimal places.

a. $\sin(\sin^{-1}(0.5))$ **b.** $\tan(\tan^{-1}(5.2))$
c. $\cos^{-1}(\cos(-1.2))$ **d.** $\tan^{-1}(\tan(2.5))$

19. **Model with mathematics.** A lighthouse is located 15 miles north and 12 miles east of a ship. What bearing should the ship take to cover the shortest distance to get to the lighthouse? Draw a diagram to help you solve the problem.

MATH TIP

A bearing is an angle measured from the north direction. The bearing from point *A* to point *B* is the angle formed when moving clockwise from the north.

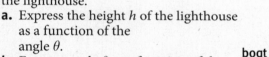

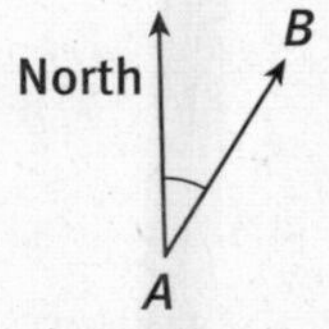

ACTIVITY 19 PRACTICE

Write your answers on a separate sheet of notebook paper.

Lesson 19-1

1. What are the restrictions on the domain of $f(x) = \cos(x)$ when defining $f(x) = \cos^{-1}(x)$?

2. Which of the following domains would also have been suitable for $f(x) = \cos(x)$ when defining $f(x) = \cos^{-1}(x)$? Explain why each is suitable or unsuitable.

a. $-\pi \le x \le 0$
b. $-\pi \le x \le \pi$
c. $\pi < x < 2\pi$

3. Find the exact value of each expression without using a calculator.

a. $\cos^{-1}\left(\frac{1}{2}\right)$ **b.** $\cos^{-1}(-1)$
c. $\cos^{-1}\left(\frac{-\sqrt{2}}{2}\right)$ **d.** $\cos^{-1}\left(\frac{-\sqrt{3}}{2}\right)$

4. Use a calculator to evaluate the following expressions, correct to three decimal places.

a. $\cos^{-1}(-0.6)$ **b.** $\cos^{-1}(-0.28)$
c. $\cos^{-1}(0.89)$ **d.** $\cos^{-1}(0.45)$

5. Without using a calculator, find the exact value of the following expressions.

a. $\cos^{-1}\left(\cos\left(-\frac{\pi}{4}\right)\right)$
b. $\cos\left(\cos^{-1}\left(\frac{2}{3}\right)\right)$
c. $\cos\left(\cos^{-1}(0)\right)$

6. Describe the symmetry of the inverse cosine function.

7. Which graph shows a function that has an inverse defined over its entire domain?

A.
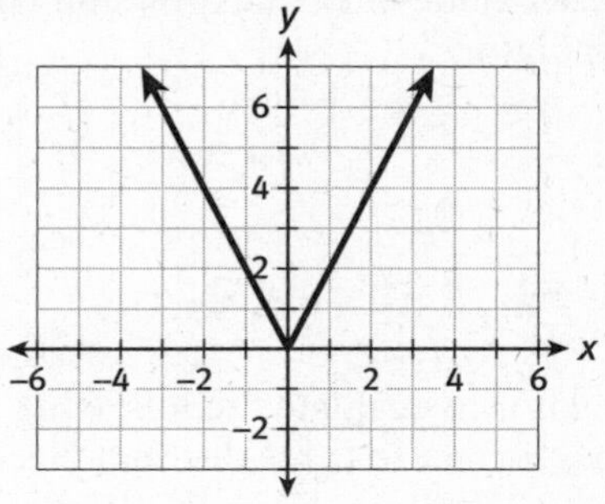

B.
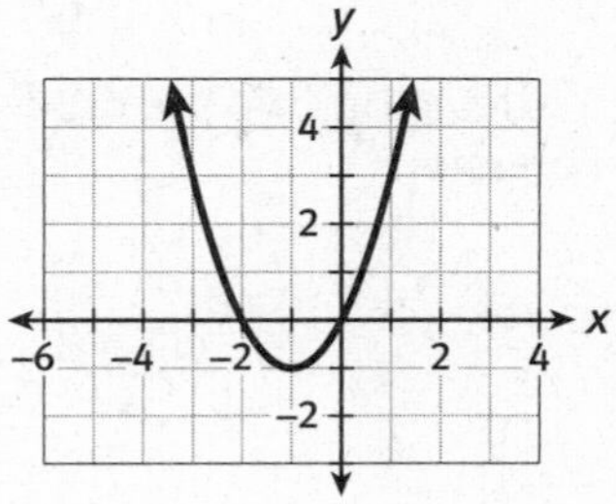

C.
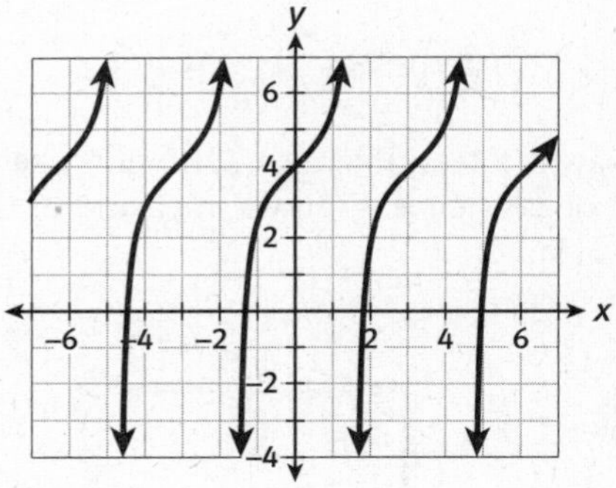

D.
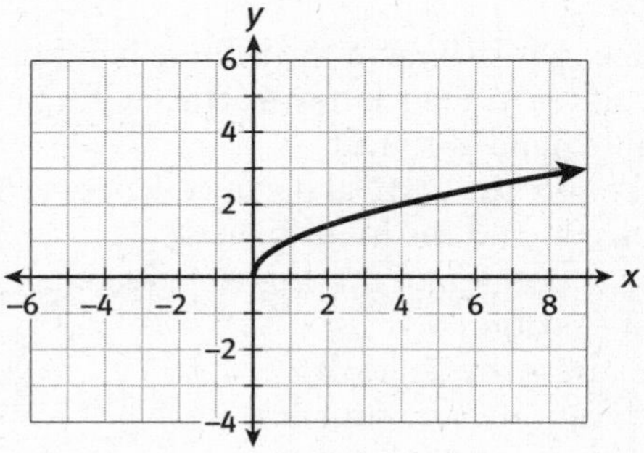

Lesson 19-2

8. Find the exact value of each expression without using a calculator.

a. $\sin^{-1}\left(-\frac{\sqrt{2}}{2}\right)$ **b.** $\sin^{-1}\left(\frac{\sqrt{2}}{2}\right)$

c. $\sin^{-1}\left(-\frac{\sqrt{3}}{2}\right)$ **d.** $\sin^{-1}(0)$

9. Use a calculator to evaluate the following expressions, correct to three decimal places.

a. $\sin^{-1}(-0.12)$ **b.** $\sin^{-1}(0.2)$
c. $\sin^{-1}(0.85)$ **d.** $\sin^{-1}(0.65)$

10. Without using a calculator, find the exact value of the following expressions.

a. $\sin^{-1}(\sin(\pi))$

b. $\sin^{-1}\left(\sin\left(\frac{\pi}{2}\right)\right)$

c. $\sin\left(\sin^{-1}\left(-\frac{\sqrt{3}}{2}\right)\right)$

d. $\sin\left(\sin^{-1}\left(\frac{1}{2}\right)\right)$

11. A seesaw is 6 feet in length. One side rises to a height of 28 inches. Find the measure of the angle of elevation θ.

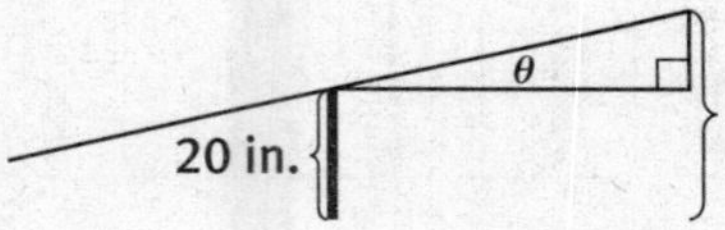

12. A pigeon is sitting on the minute hand of a clock that sits atop a clock tower. The length of the minute hand is 15 feet.

a. Express the vertical distance h between the pigeon and the hour hand as a function of the angle of elevation θ.

b. Express the angle of elevation θ as a function of the vertical distance h between the pigeon and the hour hand.

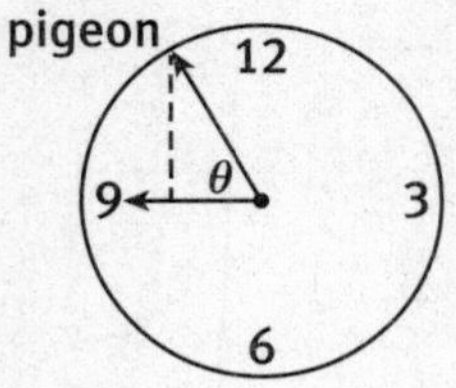

c. If the vertical distance between the pigeon and the 9 on the clock is 8 feet, what is the measure of the angle of elevation?

13. The angle $\frac{5\pi}{3}$ does not lie in the range for inverse sine. Find a coterminal angle that does lie in the range.

Lessons 19-3

14. Find the exact value of each expression without using a calculator.

a. $\tan^{-1}(-1)$ **b.** $\tan^{-1}(1)$
c. $\tan^{-1}(-\sqrt{3})$ **d.** $\tan^{-1}(\sqrt{3})$

15. Use a calculator to evaluate the following expressions in radian measure, correct to three decimal places.

a. $\tan^{-1}(0.42)$ **b.** $\tan^{-1}(1.78)$
c. $\tan^{-1}(-2.3)$ **d.** $\tan^{-1}(0.5)$

16. Without using a calculator, find the exact value of the following expressions.

a. $\tan^{-1}\left(\tan\left(\frac{2\pi}{3}\right)\right)$

b. $\tan\left(\tan^{-1}(0)\right)$

c. $\tan^{-1}\left(\tan\left(\frac{\pi}{3}\right)\right)$

d. $\tan\left(\tan^{-1}(0.5)\right)$

17. Name another domain that would also have been suitable for $f(x) = \tan(x)$ when defining $f(x) = \tan^{-1}(x)$.

18. A plane is located 38 miles south and 18 miles east of an airport. What bearing should the plane use to take the shortest distance to the airport? Draw a diagram to help you solve the problem.

MATHEMATICAL PRACTICES
Make Sense of Problems and Persevere in Solving Them

19. Explain how to find the exact value of $\sin\left(\cos^{-1}\left(\frac{5}{13}\right)\right)$ without using a calculator and without actually finding a value for $\cos^{-1}\left(\frac{5}{13}\right)$.

Solving Simple Trigonometric Equations

Daylight Minutes

Lesson 20-1 Writing and Solving Trigonometric Equations

Learning Targets:

- Apply a trigonometric equation to represent a real-world situation.
- Find the general solution to a trigonometric equation.

SUGGESTED LEARNING STRATEGIES: Create Representations, Think-Pair-Share, Activating Prior Knowledge

Tourists, people involved in outdoor sports, and agriculturists are among those who might need to know the number of minutes of daylight on a given day. As the seasons change during each year, the number of minutes of daylight at a given location changes in a periodic way.

1. The number of minutes of daylight for any location at 60° N latitude is modeled by the function below.

$$m(d) = 390 \sin\left[\frac{2\pi}{365.25}(d - 80)\right] + 738, \text{ for } d = \text{day of the year}$$

a. Model with mathematics. Use a calculator to graph the function m. Then sketch the graph on the axes below.

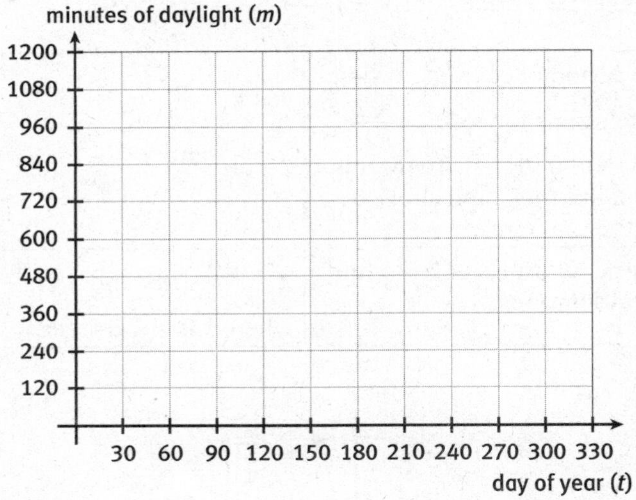

b. Write an equation that you can use to find the days of the year when cities located at 60° N latitude have 14 hours of daylight.

c. Use appropriate tools strategically. Use the graph in part a to estimate the solutions to this equation over the interval [0, 365]. Then use a graphing calculator to find the solutions to the nearest whole number.

d. Use the table to determine the dates on which a city located at 60° N latitude has 14 hours of daylight.

2. The function $m(x) = 170.5 \sin\left[\frac{2\pi}{365.25}(x - 80)\right] + 731$ can be used to model the number of minutes of daylight on day x for any location at 40° N latitude. Find the dates on which cities located at 40° N latitude will have the given amount of daylight.

a. 11 hours **b.** 16 hours

My Notes

The table below shows the date for certain days of a year.

Day of Year	Date
1	Jan 1
15	Jan 15
30	Jan 30
45	Feb 14
60	Mar 1
75	Mar 16
90	Mar 31
105	Apr 15
120	Apr 30
135	May 15
150	May 30
165	Jun 14
180	Jun 29
195	Jul 14
210	Jul 29
225	Aug 13
240	Aug 28
255	Sep 12
270	Sep 27
285	Oct 12
300	Oct 27
315	Nov 11
330	Nov 26
345	Dec 11
360	Dec 26

My Notes

MATH TIP

To find the *general solutions* to a trigonometric equation over the interval $(-\infty, \infty)$, find the solutions over one period of the trigonometric function, and then add integral multiples of the period.

Previous problems in this activity approximated answers to a trigonometric equation over a given interval. Now consider finding the exact solutions to the trigonometric equation $\cos x = \frac{\sqrt{2}}{2}$. The graph shown below suggests that there are infinitely many solutions to this equation. This infinite number of solutions can be expressed as *general solutions* of the equation.

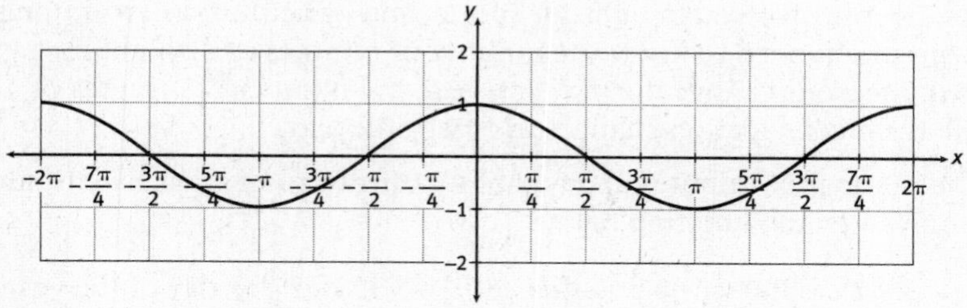

Example A

Find the general solutions of $\cos x = \frac{\sqrt{2}}{2}$.

Since the period of $\cos x$ is 2π, first find the solutions for $\cos x = \frac{\sqrt{2}}{2}$ over the interval $[0, 2\pi)$. To do this, either visualize the graph above or visualize the unit circle.	$\cos x = \frac{\sqrt{2}}{2}$ $x = \frac{\pi}{4}$ and $x = \frac{7\pi}{4}$
Add integral multiples of 2π to find the general solutions.	$x = \frac{\pi}{4} + 2\pi k$ and $x = \frac{7\pi}{4} + 2\pi k$, where k is any integer.

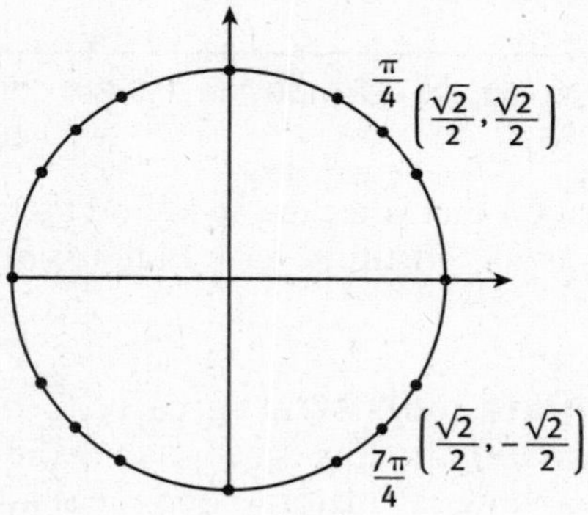

Try These A

Find the general solutions of each equation.

a. $\sin x = -\frac{1}{2}$

b. $\tan x = \sqrt{3}$

My Notes

To solve some trigonometric equations, it is helpful to think of the steps you might take to solve a similar algebraic equation.

Example B

Solve $4 \cos x + 9 = 11$ over the interval $[0, 2\pi)$. Compare this to solving the equation $4x + 9 = 11$.

Trigonometric equation	**Corresponding algebraic equation**
$4 \cos x + 9 = 11$	$4x + 9 = 11$
$4 \cos x = 2$	$4x = 2$
$\cos x = \frac{1}{2}$	$x = \frac{1}{2}$

The solutions to the equation $\cos x = \frac{1}{2}$ over the interval $[0, 2\pi)$ are $x = \frac{\pi}{3}$ and $x = \frac{5\pi}{3}$.

Example C

Solve $\sin^2 x + \sin x = 0$ over the interval $[0, 2\pi)$. Compare this to solving the equation $x^2 + x = 0$.

Trigonometric equation	**Corresponding algebraic equation**
$\sin^2 x + \sin x = 0$	$x^2 + x = 0$
$\sin x(\sin x + 1) = 0$	$x(x + 1) = 0$
$\sin x = 0$ or $\sin x + 1 = 0$	$x = 0$ or $x + 1 = 0$
$\sin x = 0$ or $\sin x = -1$	$x = 0$ or $x = -1$

The solutions to $\sin x = 0$ or $\sin x = -1$ over the interval $[0, 2\pi)$ are $x = 0$, $x = \pi$, $x = \frac{3\pi}{2}$.

Try These B–C

Find the solutions of each equation over the interval $[0, 2\pi)$.

a. $8 \cos(x) + \sqrt{3} = 5\sqrt{3}$

b. $\tan^2 x + 2 \tan x = -1$

My Notes

Solutions to trigonometric equations can also be given in degrees.

Example D

Solve $2 + \sec^2\theta = 6$ over the interval [0°, 360°). Compare this to solving the equation $2 + x^2 = 6$.

Trigonometric equation	**Corresponding algebraic equation**
$2 + \sec^2\theta = 6$	$2 + x^2 = 6$
$\sec^2\theta = 4$	$x^2 = 4$
$\sec\theta = \pm 2$	$x = \pm 2$

If $\sec\theta = \pm 2$, then $\cos\theta = \pm\frac{1}{2}$. The solutions to $\cos\theta = \pm\frac{1}{2}$ over the interval [0°, 360°) are $\theta = 60°, 120°, 240°, 300°$.

MATH TIP

Since secant and cosine are reciprocal functions, the equations $\sec\theta = a$ and $\cos\theta = \frac{1}{a}$ will have the same solutions.

Since cosecant and sine are reciprocal functions, the equations $\csc\theta = b$ and $\sin\theta = \frac{1}{b}$ will have the same solutions.

Try These D

Find the solutions of each equation over the interval [0°, 360°).

a. $2\sin^2\theta - 1 = 0$

b. $-6\csc\theta - 7 = 5$

c. $9\cot^2\theta - 3 = 0$

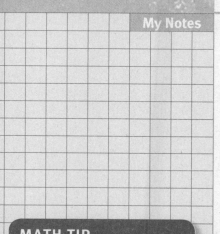

My Notes

Check Your Understanding

3. Explain why there are infinitely many solutions to the equation $\sin x = \frac{1}{2}$.

4. Reason abstractly and quantitatively. Using the information from Item 1, are there any days of the year when there are 20 hours of sunlight? Explain.

LESSON 20-1 PRACTICE

5. Find the general solutions of each equation.

a. $\cos x = \frac{1}{2}$ **b.** $2\sin x = \sqrt{3}$ **c.** $\sin^2 x - \frac{1}{2} = 0$

6. Find the exact solutions of each equation over the interval $[0, 2\pi)$.

a. $2\cos x - 1 = 0$ **b.** $4\sin x - 2 = 0$
c. $\sec^2 x = 2$ **d.** $\tan^2 x = 3$

7. Find the exact solutions of each equation over the interval $[0°, 360°)$.

a. $2\sin\theta - \sqrt{3} = 0$ **b.** $2\cos^2\theta = 2$
c. $4\cos\theta = 2$ **d.** $\tan^3\theta = 3\tan\theta$

8. Attend to precision. Use the table and the information in Item 1a to determine the dates on which a city located at 60° N latitude has 10 hours of daylight.

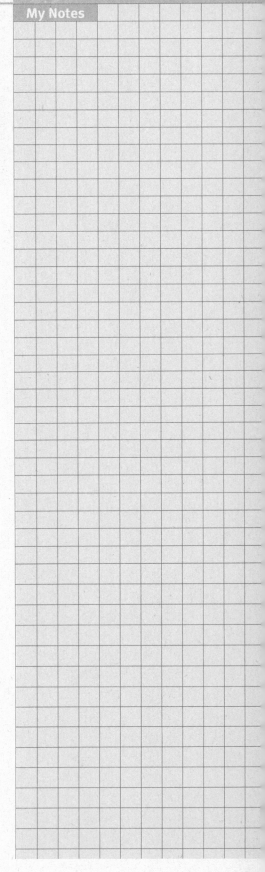

My Notes

Learning Targets:

- Use reference angles to solve trigonometric equations.
- Find the solution to a trigonometric equation over an interval.
- Generate a trigonometric equation for a real-world situation.

SUGGESTED LEARNING STRATEGIES: Close Reading, Think-Pair-Share, Discussion Groups

Reference angles can be useful when solving some trigonometric equations. If θ is an angle in standard position, then its ***reference angle*** α is the acute angle formed by the terminal side of θ and the horizontal axis.

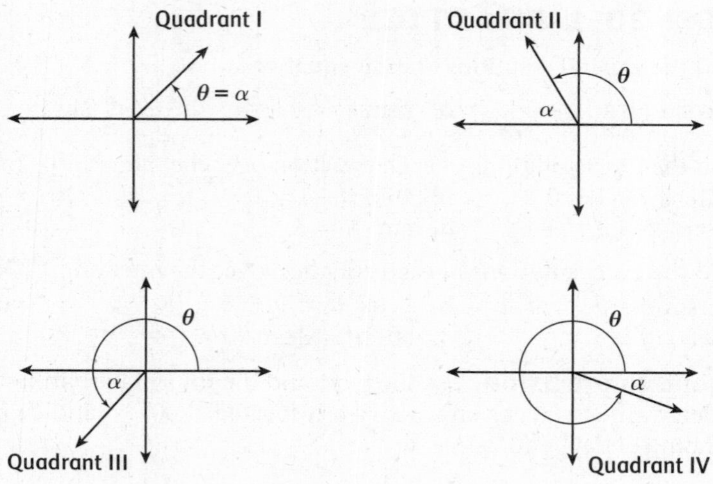

For $0° < \theta < 360°$ or $0 < \theta < 2\pi$:

$\theta = \alpha$	$\theta = 180° - \alpha$	$\theta = 180° + \alpha$	$\theta = 360° - \alpha$
$\theta = \alpha$	$\theta = \pi - \alpha$	$\theta = \pi + \alpha$	$\theta = 2\pi - \alpha$

If $\theta > 360°$ or $\theta < 0°$ ($\theta > 2\pi$ or $\theta < 0$), first find a coterminal angle between $0°$ and $360°$ (between 0 and 2π).

For a reference angle of $\alpha = 20°$,

if θ lies in Quadrant II, then $\theta = 180° - 20° = 160°$,
if θ lies in Quadrant III, then $\theta = 180° + 20° = 200°$, and
if θ lies in Quadrant IV, then $\theta = 360° - 20° = 340°$.

Example A

Solve $3 \cos \theta + 4 = 5$ over the interval $[0°, 360°)$. Give answers to the nearest tenth of a degree.

Solve for $\cos \theta$. Note that since $\cos \theta$ is positive, solutions lie in Quadrants I and IV.	$3 \cos \theta + 4 = 5$ $\cos \theta = \frac{1}{3}$
Find the reference angle for the solutions. Be sure your calculator is in degree mode.	$\alpha = \cos^{-1} \frac{1}{3} \approx 70.5°$
The reference angle is the Quadrant I solution. Find the Quadrant IV solution by using $\theta = 360° - \alpha$.	$\alpha = 70.5°, \theta = 289.5°$

My Notes

Example B

Solve $\sin x + 3.2 = 3$ over the interval $[0, 2\pi)$. Give answers to the nearest thousandth of a radian.

Solve for $\sin x$. Note that since $\sin x$ is negative, solutions lie in Quadrants III and IV.	$\sin x + 3.2 = 3$ $\sin x = -0.2$
When finding the reference angle for the solutions, ignore the negative sign. Be sure that your calculator is in radian mode.	$\alpha = \sin^{-1} 0.2$ ≈ 0.201
Find the Quadrant III solution by using $x = \pi + \alpha$. Find the Quadrant IV solution by using $x = 2\pi - \alpha$.	$x = 3.343$ $x = 6.082$

Try These A–B

Find the solutions of each equation over the interval $[0°, 360°)$. Give answers to the nearest tenth of a degree.

a. $5 \sin \theta + 4 = 7$

b. $\cot (\theta) - 2 = -7$

Find the solutions of each equation over the interval $[0, 2\pi)$. Give answers to the nearest thousandth of a radian.

c. $\cos^2 x = \frac{1}{16}$

d. $6 \csc x + 9 = 0$

My Notes

Day of the Year	Number of Minutes of Daylight
1	
15	
30	
45	
60	
75	
90	
105	
120	
135	
150	
165	
180	
195	
210	
225	
240	
255	
270	
285	
300	
315	
330	
345	
360	

1. Now let's use what we've learned to find out about the number of minutes of daylight in your city. Let's return to the equation from the beginning of the activity.

a. Find the latitude, to the nearest 10 degrees, of the city in which you live.

b. Complete the table at the left for your city.

c. Graph the data from your table for your city.

d. Express regularity in repeated reasoning. Write an equation to model the number of minutes of daylight for the latitude of your city.

e. Use the equation from part d to find the number of minutes of daylight on July 4.

Check Your Understanding

2. Suppose θ lies in Quadrant III and its reference angle $\alpha = 33.8°$. What is the measure of θ?

3. Construct viable arguments. Suppose θ lies in Quadrant IV. Jimmy finds that the reference angle of θ is $\alpha = 120.5°$. What is Jimmy's error? Explain.

LESSON 20-2 PRACTICE

4. Find the solutions of each equation over the interval $[0°, 360°)$. Give answers to the nearest tenth of a degree.

a. $5\sin\theta - 3 = 0$

b. $3\cos\theta + 7 = 9$

c. $-4\cot\theta - 3 = 2$

5. Find the solutions of each equation over the interval $[0, 2\pi)$. Give answers to the nearest thousandth of a radian.

a. $\cos^2 x = \frac{4}{25}$

b. $\frac{\csc x}{2} = -3$

c. $\sin x \tan x - 3\sin x = 0$

6. Reason quantitatively. What are the greatest number and least number of minutes of daylight for your city?

ACTIVITY 20 PRACTICE

Write your answers on notebook paper.

Lesson 20-1

1. Find the general solutions of each equation. Express your answers in radians.
   a. $\sin x = -\frac{\sqrt{3}}{2}$
   b. $\cot x = 1$
   c. $\cos x = \frac{\sqrt{2}}{2}$
   d. $\csc x = 1$
   e. $\tan x = -\frac{\sqrt{3}}{3}$
   f. $\tan x = \sqrt{3}$
2. Find the exact solutions of each equation over the interval $[0, 2\pi)$.
   a. $4 \sin x + 11 = 13$
   b. $\sec^2 x + 3 \sec x + 2 = 0$
   c. $-\sqrt{2} + 2 \sin x = 0$
   d. $6 + 2 \sec x = 4$
   e. $\cot^2 x - \cot x = 0$
   f. $2 \cos^2 x + 3 = 7 \cos x$
3. Find the exact solutions of each equation over the interval $[0°, 360°)$.
   a. $9 \tan^2 \theta - 3 = 0$
   b. $2 \cos^2 \theta - \cos \theta = 1$
   c. $\tan \theta + \sqrt{3} = -2 \tan \theta$
   d. $\sin^3 \theta - \sin \theta = 0$
   e. $-2 \sec \theta = 0$
   f. $\sin x + \sqrt{2} = -\sin x$
4. The number of daylight hours for San Diego can be modeled by the equation
   $h(d) = 2.4 \sin\left[\frac{2\pi}{365.25}(d - 80)\right] + 12,$
   for $d =$ day of the year.
   a. Graph the function.
   b. On what dates does San Diego have 10 hours of daylight?
   c. On what dates does San Diego have more than 15 hours of daylight?
   d. Rounded to the nearest hour, what are the maximum and minimum numbers of hours of daylight in San Diego?
5. The average daily temperature (in °F) for a city is modeled by the function
   $T(m) = 25.2 \sin\left(\frac{2\pi}{12} m + 4.3\right) + 54$, where m is the month.
   a. Graph the function.
   b. Which months have an average temperature greater than 60°?

Lesson 20-2

6. Find the solutions of each equation over the interval $[0°, 360°)$. Give answers to the nearest tenth of a degree.

a. $6 \cos \theta - 4 = 1$

b. $\frac{3 \tan \theta}{5} = -2$

c. $3 \tan x + 3 = 15$

d. $8 \sin x + 6 = 12$

e. $4 \sin \theta - 3 = 0$

f. $3 \cos^2 \theta - 5 \cos \theta - 2 = 0$

7. Find the solutions of each equation over the interval $[0, 2\pi)$. Give answers to the nearest thousandth of a radian.

a. $3 \sin x + 6 = 4$

b. $-2 + 5 \csc x = 7$

c. $3 \sin x = -3 \sin x - 4$

d. $8 \cos x + 5 = 6$

8. Mia solved the equation as shown. Explain why Mia's solution is incorrect.

$$3 \tan x + 1 = 12$$
$$3 \tan x = 11$$
$$\tan x = \frac{11}{3}$$
$$x = 0.579$$

9. Summarize various strategies for solving trigonometric equations.

MATHEMATICAL PRACTICES
Model with Mathematics

10. Choose a city that is at least 300 miles north or south of your city.

a. Complete the table below for the city.

Day of the Year	Number of Minutes of Daylight
1	
15	
30	
45	
60	
75	
90	
105	
120	
135	
150	
165	
180	
195	
210	
225	
240	
255	
270	
285	
300	
315	
330	
345	
360	

b. Graph the data from your table for the city.

c. Write an equation to model the number of minutes of daylight for the latitude of the city.

d. Find the number of minutes of daylight on January 20.

e. Compare and contrast the information for your city with the city that is north or south of your city. Explain why the city you chose has a greater or lesser range for the number of daylight hours than the city in which you live.

Inverse Trigonometric Functions and Trigonometric Equations

HOW DEEP IS THE RIVER?

Carlotta hopes to do some surfing on her vacation this year. She wants to gather information about the tides and temperatures of the city she will be visiting.

1. The depth of a river in the city varies depending on the ocean tides. The depth in feet for a given day can be modeled by the function below, where x is the hour of the day. At midnight $x = 0$, at 1 a.m. $x = 1$, at 2 a.m. $x = 2$, and so on.

$$d(x) = 3\sin\left[\frac{\pi}{6}(x - 4)\right] + 10$$

a. Graph the function.
b. What was the depth of the river at 6 a.m.?
c. What is the minimum depth of the river on the given day?
d. At what time is the river 7 feet deep?

2. The average daily temperature for the city is shown in the graph below.

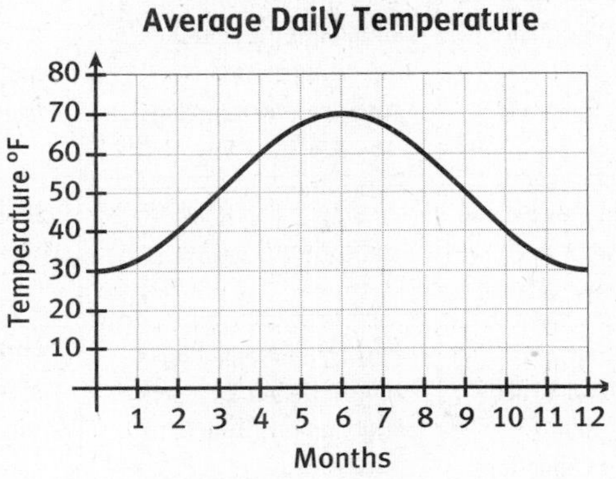

a. Write a function to model the average daily temperature.
b. Use the equation to find the average daily temperature in July.

3. Sketch the graph for each function.

a. $y = \sin^{-1} x$

b. $y = \cos^{-1} x$

4. Find the exact value of each expression without using a calculator.

a. $\sin^{-1}\left(-\frac{\sqrt{2}}{2}\right)$

b. $\cos^{-1}\left(\frac{\sqrt{3}}{2}\right)$

c. $\tan^{-1}(-1)$

d. $\sin^{-1}\left(\frac{1}{2}\right)$

e. $\cos\left[\cos^{-1}\left(\frac{\sqrt{2}}{2}\right)\right]$

f. $\sin(\sin^{-1}(0))$

g. $\cos^{-1}\left(\cos\left(-\frac{\pi}{5}\right)\right)$

h. $\tan^{-1}\left(\tan\left(\frac{4\pi}{3}\right)\right)$

5. Find the general solutions for each equation. Express each answer in radians.

a. $\cos x = \frac{\sqrt{3}}{2}$

b. $\tan x + 1 = 0$

6. Find the solutions for each equation over the interval $(0, 2\pi)$.
   a. $\cos^2 x - \cos x = 0$
   b. $3\tan^2 x - 1 = 0$
7. Find the solutions for each equation over the interval $(0°, 360°)$. Write each answer to the nearest tenth of a degree.
   a. $5\sin\theta - 2 = 0$
   b. $\sec^2\theta + 5\sec\theta + 4 = 0$
8. When defining the inverse sine function, the domain of $y = \sin x$ is restricted to $-\frac{\pi}{2} \le x \le \frac{\pi}{2}$. Why is restricting the domain of $y = \sin x$ to $0 \le x \le \frac{\pi}{2}$ not suitable for defining the inverse sine function?

Scoring Guide	Exemplary	Proficient	Emerging	Incomplete
	The solution demonstrates these characteristics:			
Mathematics Knowledge and Thinking (Items 3, 4, 5, 6, 7, 8)	• Clear and accurate understanding of solving trigonometric equations and using inverse trigonometric functions	• A functional understanding of trigonometric equations and using inverse trigonometric functions	• Partial understanding of trigonometric equations and using inverse trigonometric functions	• Little or no understanding of trigonometric equations and using inverse trigonometric functions
Problem Solving (Items 1, 2, 5, 6, 7)	• An appropriate and efficient strategy that results in a correct answer	• A strategy that may include unnecessary steps but results in a correct answer	• A strategy that results in some incorrect answers	• No clear strategy when solving problems
Mathematical Modeling / Representations (Items 1, 2, 4, 5, 6, 7, 8)	• Clear and accurate understanding of inverse trigonometric functions conceptually, via the unit circle, and with the use of a calculator (to solve equations) • Clear and accurate understanding of creating and using trigonometric graphs to interpret and analyze data	• A functional understanding of inverse trigonometric functions to evaluate expressions and equations • Mostly accurate understanding of creating and using trigonometric graphs to interpret and analyze data	• Partial understanding of representations of inverse trigonometric functions • Partial understanding of creating and using trigonometric graphs to interpret and analyze data	• Little or no understanding of representations of inverse trigonometric functions • Inaccurate or incomplete understanding of creating and using trigonometric graphs
Reasoning and Communication (Items 1, 2)	• Precise use of appropriate math terms and language to describe understanding of trigonometric functions in the context of the problem	• Correct characterization of transformed trigonometric functions but may not be able to interpret completely within the context of the problem	• Misleading or confusing characterization of transformed trigonometric functions	• Incomplete or inaccurate characterization of transformed trigonometric functions

Analytic Trigonometry and Trigonometric Applications

4

Unit Overview

This unit will extend your knowledge of trigonometry as you study trigonometric identities, equations, and formulas. You will explore the Law of Cosines and the Law of Sines, and apply them to solve non-right triangles.

Key Terms

As you study this unit, add these and other terms to your math notebook. Include in your notes your prior knowledge of each word, as well as your experiences in using the word in different mathematical examples. If needed, ask for help in pronouncing new words and add information on pronunciation to your math notebook. It is important that you learn new terms and use them correctly in your class discussions and in your problem solutions.

Academic Vocabulary

- ambiguous

Math Terms

- identity
- Pythagorean identity
- trigonometric identity
- cofunction identity
- sum and difference identities
- Law of Cosines
- oblique triangle
- Law of Sines
- ambiguous case (SSA)

ESSENTIAL QUESTIONS

How are algebraic and geometric concepts related to trigonometric identities and formulas?

How is trigonometry used to solve real-world problems involving measure?

EMBEDDED ASSESSMENTS

These assessments, following Activities 23 and 25, will give you an opportunity to demonstrate what you have learned about trigonometry, in particular the Law of Cosines and the Law of Sines.

Embedded Assessment 1:

Trigonometric Identities and Equations p. 319

Embedded Assessment 2:

Right and Oblique Triangles, Area p. 343

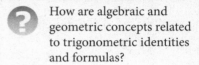

Getting Ready

Write your answers on notebook paper.
Show your work.

1. Factor each of the following completely.
   a. $6x^4 - 12x^3 + 3x^2$
   b. $49x^4 - 36y^2$
   c. $8x^2 - 2x - 15$

2. Simplify each of the following rational expressions.
   a. $\dfrac{2x}{x+3} + \dfrac{12}{2x+6}$
   b. $\dfrac{3}{ab^2} + \dfrac{2}{a^2b} - \dfrac{1}{a^2b^2}$
   c. $\dfrac{\dfrac{x^2}{y} - y}{\dfrac{x}{y} - 1}$
   d. $\dfrac{x^2+5x}{x^2+6x+5} \div \dfrac{x^3}{3x+3}$

3. A 32 ft ladder leans against a building, making a 75° angle with the ground. How high above the ground is the top of the ladder?

4. Tell four measures of $\angle\beta$ such that $\cos\beta = \left|\dfrac{1}{2}\right|$.

5. Sketch two angles α such that $\tan\alpha = -1$.

Use right triangles *ABC* and *DEF* for Items 6 and 7.

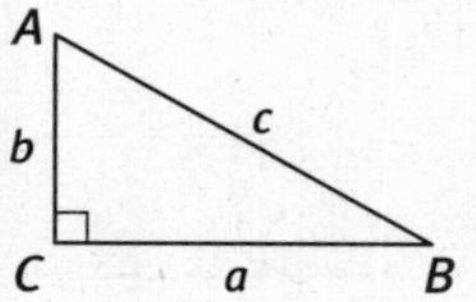

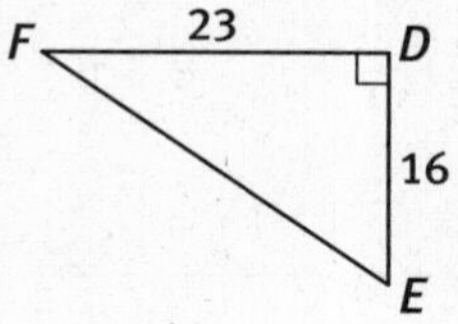

6. State the following ratios.
   a. $\sin A$ **b.** $\cos A$ **c.** $\tan A$
   d. $\cot A$ **e.** $\csc A$ **f.** $\sec A$

7. Find the measure of the following angles to the nearest tenth of a degree.
   a. $\angle E$ **b.** $\angle F$

8. Write an equation of the graph below.

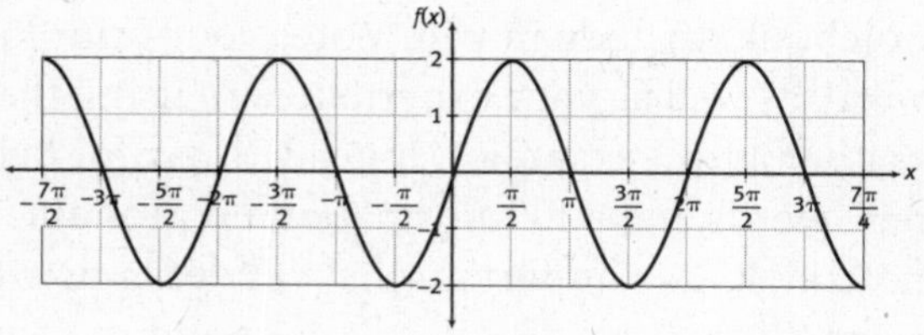

Trigonometric Identities

Imagine That

Lesson 21-1 Trigonometric Identities

My Notes

Learning Targets:

- Define the reciprocal and quotient identities.
- Use and transform the Pythagorean identity.

SUGGESTED LEARNING STRATEGIES: Summarizing, Paraphrasing, Marking the Text, Create Representations, Look for Patterns, Graphic Organizer

The use of computer-generated imagery (CGI) in the movie industry became common with the release of blockbuster films such as *Jurassic Park* (1993) and *Toy Story* (1995). CGI animators use specialized software to render and animate 3-D images, but they also need to understand and apply mathematics, including basic trigonometry and trigonometric identities.

This activity will introduce the basic identities that are fundamental to the advanced computer graphics work done by animators and video game designers every day.

An ***identity*** is a relationship of equality that is true for all values of the variables for which each side of the equation is defined.

1. Reason abstractly. Which of the following statements are identities? Explain your reasoning. Be sure to use correct mathematical terms to support your reasoning and that your sentences are complete and grammatically correct.

a. $2(x + 3) = 2x + 6$

b. $\frac{2}{2x + 4} = \frac{1}{x + 2}$

c. $x^2 + 1 = (x + 1)(x - 1)$

d. $\sec\theta = \frac{1}{\cos\theta}$

DISCUSSION GROUP TIPS

As you listen to the group discussion, take notes to aid comprehension and to help you describe your own ideas to others in your group. Ask questions to clarify ideas and to gain further understanding of key concepts.

A ***trigonometric identity*** is an identity that involves one or more trigonometric functions. Identities like the one in Item 1d are derived from the definitions of sine and cosine as coordinates of a point on a unit circle.

2. What is another identity you may already know based on the definitions of sine and cosine?

My Notes

3. Use the unit circle shown below to express each trigonometric function in terms of x and/or y.

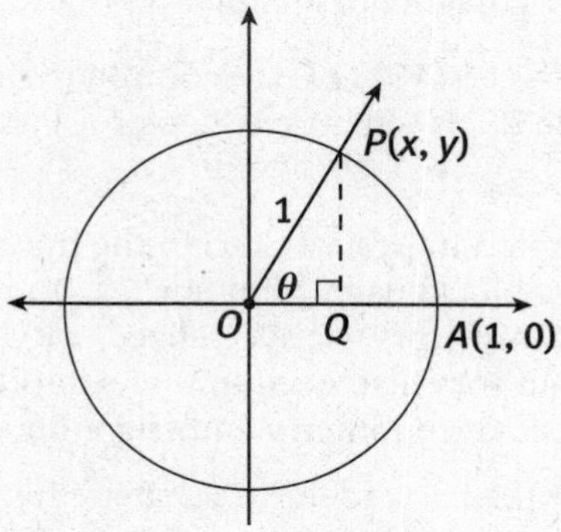

$\sin\theta =$ $\csc\theta =$

$\cos\theta =$ $\sec\theta =$

$\tan\theta =$ $\cot\theta =$

4. Make use of structure. Use the results of Item 3 to write identities that express tangent and cotangent as quotients of the sine and cosine functions.

a. $\tan\theta =$

b. $\cot\theta =$

5. Use appropriate tools strategically. How can you use your graphing calculator to support that the statements you wrote in Item 4 are identities?

6. Are there any values of θ for which the expressions in Item 4 are undefined? Explain your reasoning.

My Notes

7. Use the results of Item 3 to write identities that express each trigonometric function as a *reciprocal* of another trigonometric function.

a. $\sin\theta =$ **b.** $\csc\theta =$

c. $\cos\theta =$ **d.** $\sec\theta =$

e. $\tan\theta =$ **f.** $\cot\theta =$

8. Use your knowledge of special angle ratios to complete the table shown below.

θ	60°	225°	−90°	$-\frac{19\pi}{6}$	π	$\frac{11\pi}{6}$	$\frac{5\pi}{6}$
$\cos^2\theta$							
$\sin^2\theta$							
$\sin^2\theta + \cos^2\theta$							

WRITING MATH

$\cos^2\theta = (\cos\theta)^2$

The exponent is written between the trigonometric function and the angle to avoid confusion with $\cos\theta^2 = \cos(\theta \cdot \theta)$.

9. Express regularity in repeated reasoning. Based on the above table, complete the identity that appears to be true for all values of θ.

10. Use the unit circle and the Pythagorean Theorem to verify that the identity you wrote in Item 9 is true for all values of θ.

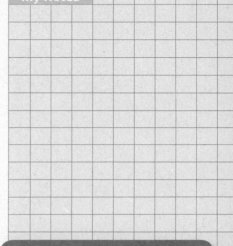

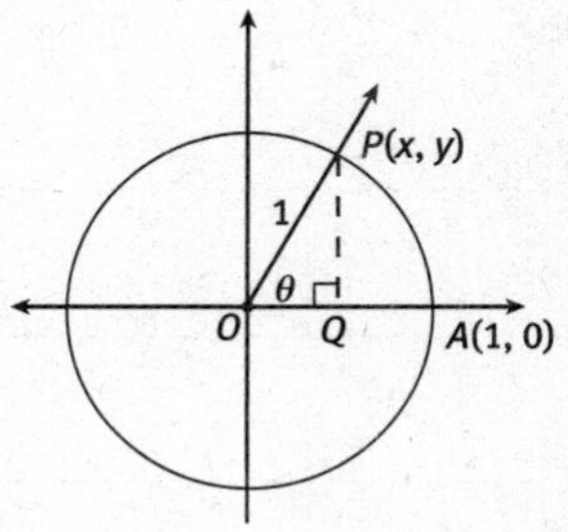

My Notes

The identity in Item 9 is known as the ***Pythagorean identity***. Two other identities can be derived from the results of Item 10.

Example A

Write an identity relating the tangent and secant functions.

$\sin^2\theta + \cos^2\theta = 1$ Given

$\dfrac{\sin^2\theta}{\cos^2\theta} + \dfrac{\cos^2\theta}{\cos^2\theta} = \dfrac{1}{\cos^2\theta}$ Divide by $\cos^2\theta$.

$\tan^2\theta + 1 = \sec^2\theta$ Rewrite using basic identities.

Try These A

Complete the following to write an identity relating the cotangent and cosecant functions.

$\sin^2\theta + \cos^2\theta = 1$ Given

________________ Divide by $\sin^2\theta$.

________________ Rewrite using basic identities.

CONNECT TO AP

Identities are used frequently in AP Calculus to simplify problems and derive differentiation and integration rules.

11. Summarize your work by completing the following graphic organizer.

Quotient and Reciprocal Identities

$\sin\theta =$ __________ $\csc\theta =$ __________

$\cos\theta =$ __________ $\sec\theta =$ __________

$\tan\theta =$ __________ $=$ __________

$\cot\theta =$ __________ $=$ __________

Pythagorean Identities

____

____

____

My Notes

Check Your Understanding

12. Are there any values of θ for which the identity $\sec\theta = \frac{1}{\cos\theta}$ does *not* hold? Explain.

13. Construct viable arguments. Connor had difficulty remembering the three Pythagorean identities. His friend Amani said that she only memorized one of the identities and then quickly derived the others when she needed them. Explain what Amani meant by this statement.

LESSON 21-1 PRACTICE

14. Express each trigonometric function as a reciprocal to write an identity.

a. $\cos(x + 45°) =$ **b.** $\tan\left(\frac{\theta}{3}\right) =$ **c.** $\csc(2\theta) =$

15. Express the tangent or cotangent as a quotient to write an identity.

a. $\cot(4\theta) =$ **b.** $\tan(x - 180°) =$ **c.** $\cot(90° + x) =$

16. Explain why $\cos\theta\sec\theta = 1$.

17. Consider the function $f(x) = \sin^2 x + \cos^2 x$.

a. What is the domain of the function?
b. What is the range of the function?
c. What is $f(\sqrt{7})$?

18. Make use of structure. Suppose you know that $\sin\theta = 0.4$.

a. Using the Pythagorean identity, what can you conclude about $\cos\theta$?
b. How does your answer to part a change if you know that θ lies in Quadrant II?
c. What is the approximate value of θ, in degrees, given that θ lies in Quadrant II?

My Notes

Learning Targets:

- Simplify trigonometric expressions.
- Verify trigonometric identities.

SUGGESTED LEARNING STRATEGIES: Note Taking, Think-Pair-Share, Identify a Subtask, Simplify the Problem, Work Backward

The identities you learned in the previous lesson can be used to simplify expressions and to make certain calculations easier. There are several strategies that are helpful when simplifying trigonometric expressions.

Some key strategies are listed below.

• Substitute using an identity. • Use multiplication or factoring. • Rewrite the expression in terms of sine and cosine.	• Combine a sum or difference into a single expression. • Rewrite division as multiplication.

MATH TIP

Create an organized summary of the trigonometric and Pythagorean identities to use when simplifying trigonometric expressions.

Example A

Simplify $\sin\theta \cot\theta \sec\theta$.

$\sin\theta \cot\theta \sec\theta$

$= \frac{\sin\theta}{1} \cdot \frac{\cos\theta}{\sin\theta} \cdot \frac{1}{\cos\theta}$ Rewrite in terms of sine and cosine.

$= \frac{\cancel{\sin\theta}}{1} \cdot \frac{\cancel{\cos\theta}}{\cancel{\sin\theta}} \cdot \frac{1}{\cancel{\cos\theta}}$ Simplify.

$= 1$

Example B

Simplify $\tan^2\theta - \sec^2\theta + 1$.

$\tan^2\theta - \sec^2\theta + 1$

$= (\tan^2\theta + 1) - \sec^2\theta$ Reorder terms.

$= \sec^2\theta - \sec^2\theta$ Substitute using an identity.

$= 0$ Simplify.

MATH TIP

The Pythagorean identities can be transformed using the properties of equality and used to simplify expressions.

For example, $\sin^2\theta + \cos^2\theta = 1$ is equivalent to $\cos^2\theta = 1 - \sin^2\theta$ and $\sin^2\theta = 1 - \cos^2\theta$.

Try These A–B

Simplify each expression. The simplest form will be a single trigonometric function or a constant.

a. $\cos^2\theta + \sin^2\theta - 1$

b. $\frac{\cos\theta \csc\theta}{\cot\theta}$

c. $\sec\theta\,(1 - \sin^2\theta)$

My Notes

1. **Use appropriate tools strategically.** You can use your calculator to check your work when you simplify a trigonometric expression.
   a. Suppose you enter the expression from Try These A Part b in your calculator as Y1. What would you expect to see when you graph the function? Why?

   b. Enter the expression as Y1 and graph the function. Is your prediction correct?

Not every trigonometric expression simplifies to a single term or constant.

2. Fill in the strategies used to simplify the expression shown below.

$\frac{\sin^2\theta - \cos^2\theta}{\sin\theta + \cos\theta}$ Original expression

$\frac{(\sin\theta - \cos\theta)(\sin\theta + \cos\theta)}{\sin\theta + \cos\theta}$

$\frac{(\sin\theta - \cos\theta)\cancel{(\sin\theta + \cos\theta)}}{\cancel{(\sin\theta + \cos\theta)}}$

$\sin\theta - \cos\theta$

3. **Reason abstractly.** Fill in the strategies used to simplify the expression shown below.

$\tan\theta + \frac{1}{\tan\theta}$ Original expression

$\frac{\tan\theta \cdot \tan\theta}{\tan\theta} + \frac{1}{\tan\theta}$

$\frac{\tan^2\theta + 1}{\tan\theta}$

$\frac{\sec^2\theta}{\tan\theta}$

$\frac{\frac{1}{\cos^2\theta}}{\frac{\sin\theta}{\cos\theta}}$

$\frac{1}{\cos^2\theta} \cdot \frac{\cos\theta}{\sin\theta}$

$\frac{1}{\sin\theta\cos\theta}$

$\csc\theta\sec\theta$

MATH TIP

Factoring patterns like the *difference of two squares* can be applied to trigonometric expressions.
$a^2 - b^2 = (a + b)(a - b)$

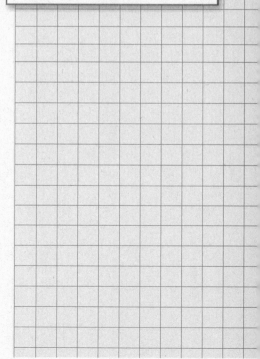

My Notes

4. Simplify each expression.

a. $\cos\theta\left(\frac{1}{\sin\theta}+\csc\theta\right)$

b. $\csc\theta - \tan\theta\cos\theta$

c. $\frac{\sin\theta-\csc\theta}{\cot\theta}$

Earlier in this activity, you used a table and a graphing calculator to explore and informally confirm identities. To formally verify an identity, you must use the known identities and the strategies you learned when simplifying expressions to show that one side of the identity can be transformed into the other side.

> **To Verify an Identity**
>
> Transform one side of the equation into the other side using simplification techniques.

Example C

Verify the identity $\cot\theta\sin\theta=\cos\theta$.

$\cot\theta\sin\theta=\cos\theta$	Original identity
$\frac{\cos\theta}{\sin\theta}\cdot\frac{\sin\theta}{1}=$	Rewrite using sine and cosine.
$\frac{\cos\theta}{\sin\theta}\cdot\frac{\sin\theta}{1}=$	Simplify by canceling common sine factors.
$\cos\theta=\cos\theta$	

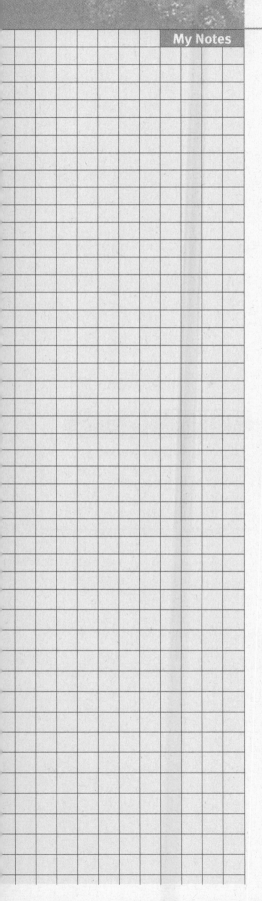

Example D

Verify the identity $\dfrac{1}{1-\cos\theta}+\dfrac{1}{1+\cos\theta}=2\csc^2\theta$

$\dfrac{1}{1-\cos\theta}+\dfrac{1}{1+\cos\theta}=2\csc^2\theta$	Original identity
$\dfrac{1+\cos\theta+1-\cos\theta}{(1-\cos\theta)(1+\cos\theta)}=$	Add two fractions using LCD.
$\dfrac{2}{1-\cos^2\theta}=$	Simplify numerator and multiply denominator.
$\dfrac{2}{\sin^2\theta}=$	Pythagorean identity
$2\csc^2\theta=2\csc^2\theta$	Basic identity

Try These C–D

Verify each identity.

a. $\tan\theta\csc\theta=\sec\theta$

b. $2-\sin^2\theta-\cos^2\theta=1$

c. $\dfrac{\cos x}{\sin x+\cos x}-\dfrac{\sin x}{\sin x-\cos x}=\dfrac{-1}{\sin^2 x-\cos^2 x}$

My Notes

CONNECT TO TECHNOLOGY

Use a graphing calculator to provide a visual confirmation of your work by graphing both sides of the identity.

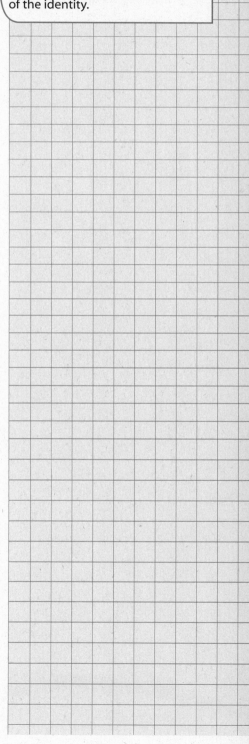

My Notes

When verifying identities, you can start on either side of the equal sign, but it is often advantageous to start on the more complicated side.

Example E

Verify the identity $1 - \sin^2\theta = \dfrac{\sin\theta\cot\theta}{\sec\theta}$.

$1 - \sin^2\theta = \dfrac{\sin\theta\cot\theta}{\sec\theta}$ Original identity

$= \dfrac{\frac{\sin\theta}{1} \cdot \frac{\cos\theta}{\sin\theta}}{\frac{1}{\cos\theta}}$ Rewrite using sine and cosine.

$= \dfrac{\frac{\cancel{\sin\theta}}{1} \cdot \frac{\cos\theta}{\cancel{\sin\theta}}}{\frac{1}{\cos\theta}}$ Simplify.

$= \dfrac{\cos\theta}{1} \cdot \dfrac{\cos\theta}{1}$ Rewrite multiplication as division.

$= \cos^2\theta$

$1 - \sin^2\theta = 1 - \sin^2\theta$ Substitute using an identity.

Try These E

Verify each identity.

a. $\tan x + \cot x = \csc x \sec x$

b. $\cos^2 x(\sec^2 x - 1) = 1 - \cos^2 x$

c. $\sec\theta + 1 = \dfrac{\sin\theta\tan\theta}{1-\cos\theta}$

My Notes

Check Your Understanding

4. Describe two different ways to simplify the expression shown below. Do you get the same result with either method?

$\dfrac{1}{\sin\theta} + \csc\theta\cot^2\theta$

5. Reason abstractly. Rima was asked to verify the identity $\sin x = \dfrac{\cos x}{\sin x \csc x \cot x}$. She handed in the work shown below. When she got her paper back, there was a note from her teacher saying that her method was incorrect. Explain what her teacher meant.

$\sin x = \dfrac{\cos x}{\sin x \csc x \cot x}$	Original identity
$\sin^2 x = \dfrac{\cos x}{\csc x \cot x}$	Multiply both sides by sin x.
$\csc x \cot x \sin^2 x = \cos x$	Multiply both sides by csc x cot x.
$\dfrac{1}{\sin x} \cdot \dfrac{\cos x}{\sin x} \cdot \sin^2 x = \cos x$	Rewrite using sine and cosine.
$\dfrac{1}{\cancel{\sin x}} \cdot \dfrac{\cos x}{\cancel{\sin x}} \cdot \cancel{\sin^2 x} = \cos x$	Simplify.
$\cos x = \cos x$	

My Notes

LESSON 21-2 PRACTICE

6. Simplify each expression.
a. $\tan x \cdot \cot x$
b. $\cos^2 \theta + 1 - \sin^2 \theta$
c. $\csc^2 \theta - \cot^2 \theta$
d. $\cos x \tan x \csc x$

7. Verify each identity.
a. $\sin x = \cos x \tan x$
b. $\dfrac{\cos x \tan x}{\sec x} = \sin x \cos x$
c. $(\sin x + \cos x)^2 = 1 + 2 \sin x \cos x$
d. $\dfrac{\cos^2 \theta}{1 + \sin \theta} = 1 - \sin \theta$
e. $\csc^2 \theta + 2 \cot \theta = (1 + \cot \theta)^2$
f. $\sec^2 x = \dfrac{\cot x \sec x \tan x}{\cos x}$

8. Use trigonometric identities to help you compare the graphs of the functions $f(x)$ and $g(x)$, where $f(x) = \cos^2 x + 1$ and $g(x) = 1 - \sin^2 x$.

9. Describe two different ways you could use a graphing calculator to verify the identity $\sin^2 \theta \csc \theta \sec \theta = \tan \theta$.

10. Critique the reasoning of others. Nick was asked to simplify the expression $\dfrac{\sin^2 \theta}{1 - \cos \theta}$ and justify his steps. His work is shown below. Do you agree with his result? If not, explain his error and provide the correct answer.

Step 1: $\dfrac{\sin^2 \theta}{1 - \cos \theta}$ Original expression

Step 2: $\dfrac{1 - \cos^2 \theta}{1 - \cos \theta}$ Pythagorean identity

Step 3: $\dfrac{(1 - \cos \theta)(1 - \cos \theta)}{1 - \cos \theta}$ Factor.

Step 4: $\dfrac{\cancel{(1 - \cos \theta)}(1 - \cos \theta)}{\cancel{1 - \cos \theta}}$ Simplify.

Step 5: $1 - \cos \theta$

ACTIVITY 21 PRACTICE

Write your answers on notebook paper.
Show your work.

Lesson 21-1

Express each trigonometric function as a reciprocal to write an identity.

1. $\sec(x - 30°) =$
2. $\cot(3\theta) =$
3. $\sin\left(\frac{\theta}{4}\right) =$

Express the tangent or cotangent as a quotient to write an identity.

4. $\tan(2\theta) =$
5. $\cot(\theta - \pi) =$
6. $\tan\left(\frac{\theta}{2}\right) =$
7. Consider the expressions in the table.

Column A	Column B
$\cos^2 x + \sin^2 x$	$1 + \tan^2 x$

Which of the following statements is true for every value of x?
A. The values of the two columns are equal.
B. The value of Column A is greater than the value of Column B.
C. The value of Column B is greater than or equal to the value of Column A.
D. The values of both columns are greater than 1.

8. Diego said that the identity $\sin\theta = \frac{1}{\csc\theta}$ holds for all values of θ. Do you agree? Explain.
9. Which expression is NOT equivalent to the other three?
A. $\frac{\cos\theta}{\sin\theta}$
B. $\cot\theta$
C. $\frac{1}{\tan\theta}$
D. $1 + \cot^2\theta$
10. Consider an angle θ such that $\cos\theta = 0.2$.
a. What do you know about the value of $\sin\theta$? Explain how you know.
b. Find the value of $\sin\theta$ given that $270° \le \theta \le 360°$.
c. What is the approximate value of θ, in degrees, given that $270° \le \theta \le 360°$?
d. Explain how you can check that your answer to part c is reasonable.
11. As θ increases from 0 to $\frac{\pi}{2}$, what happens to the value of $\sin\theta$? Use an identity to describe what happens to the value of $\csc\theta$ as θ increases from 0 to $\frac{\pi}{2}$.
12. Is there an identity that states $\sin^2\theta = \sin(\theta^2)$? If so, explain why. If not, provide a counterexample to show why the identity does not hold.

Determine whether each statement is always, sometimes, or never true.

13. The value of $\tan^2\theta + 1$ is negative.
14. If $\cos\theta = 0.5$, then $\sin\theta = \sqrt{1 - (0.5)^2}$.
15. $\cos^2\theta = 1 - \sin^2\theta$
16. For a constant k, the graph of the function $y = k + \sin^2 x + \cos^2 x$ is a straight line.

Lesson 21-2

Simplify each expression.

17. $\dfrac{\tan^2\theta}{\sec\theta - 1}$

18. $\cos\theta\,(\sec\theta + \tan\theta)$

19. $\dfrac{1+\cot^2\theta}{\sec^2\theta}$

20. $\cos^2 x \sin x + \sin^3 x$

Verify each identity.

21. $\dfrac{1}{1+\cos x} - \dfrac{1}{1-\cos x} = -2\csc x \cot x$

22. $\dfrac{1}{1+\sin\theta} + \dfrac{1}{1-\sin\theta} = 2\sec^2\theta$

23. $\dfrac{-\sin\theta}{\cos\theta - 1} = \cot\theta + \csc\theta$

24. $\tan x \sec^2 x - \tan^3 x = \dfrac{\sec x}{\csc x}$

25. $\dfrac{\sin^2 x + \tan^2 x + \cos^2 x}{\sec^3 x} = \cos x$

26. Which expression is NOT equivalent to $\dfrac{1+\cot^2\theta}{\csc\theta}$?

A. $\dfrac{\sin\theta}{\csc\theta}$ **B.** $\dfrac{1}{\sin\theta}$

C. $\csc\theta$ **D.** $\sin\theta\csc^2\theta$

27. Explain how you can find the minimum value of the function $f(x) = \tan x(\tan x + \cot x)$ without using your graphing calculator.

28. Consider the three expressions shown below.

I. $\cos^2 x \tan^2 x$

II. $\dfrac{\sec^2\theta - 1}{\sec^2\theta}$

III. $\sin^2\theta$

Which of the expressions are equivalent?

A. I and II only **B.** II and III only

C. I and III only **D.** I, II, and III

29. Given that $\dfrac{\cos^2\theta}{\sin\theta - \sin^2\theta} = \csc\theta + p$, find the value of p. Show your work.

30. Mayumi wanted to know if the equation below was a correct identity.

$$\frac{1}{\sec\theta} = \cos\theta - \cos\theta\sin^2\theta$$

She entered the left side of the equation in her calculator as Y1 and the right side as Y2. Then she viewed a table of values, as shown below.

X	Y1	Y2
3.1416	-1	-1
6.2832	1	1
9.4248	-1	-1
12.566	1	1
15.708	-1	-1
18.85	1	1
21.991	-1	-1

X=3.14159265359

Mayumi concluded that the equation was a correct identity. Do you agree? Justify your answer.

MATHEMATICAL PRACTICES
Make Sense of Problems and Persevere in Solving Them

31. It is possible to write any of the six trigonometric functions in terms of any of the other trigonometric functions. For example, $\sin x$ can be written in terms of $\cos x$ as $\sin x = \pm\sqrt{1-\cos^2 x}$. Show how to write $\sin x$ in terms of $\tan x$. (*Hint:* Your expression should involve no trigonometric functions other than $\tan x$.)

Identities and Equations

Triangle Measure

Lesson 22-1 Cofunction Identities

My Notes

Learning Targets:

- Use the unit circle to write equivalent trigonometric expressions.
- Write cofunction identities for sine and cosine.

SUGGESTED LEARNING STRATEGIES: Summarizing, Paraphrasing, Marking the Text, Create Representations, Look for a Pattern, Visualization, Think-Pair-Share

When the German mathematician Bartholomaeus Pitiscus wrote *Trigonometria* in 1595, the word *trigonometry* made its first appearance in print. However, Egyptian and Babylonian mathematicians used aspects of what we now call trigonometry as early as 1800 B.C. The word *trigonometry* comes from two Greek words: *trigon*, meaning triangle, and *metron*, meaning measure. Thus, trigonometry is the study of triangle measures. The definitions of the trigonometric functions on the unit circle are attributed to Swiss mathematician Leonhard Euler.

In this activity, you will derive and use identities based on the measures of triangles found in a unit circle.

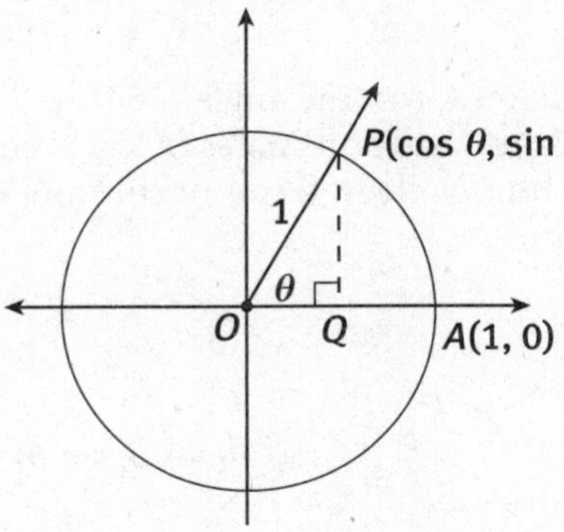

In the diagram above, θ is an angle in standard position whose terminal side passes through the point $P(\cos\theta, \sin\theta)$ located on a unit circle.

1. On the unit circle below, draw the angle $-\theta$ in standard position, label the coordinates of the point where it passes through the unit circle in terms of sine and cosine, and then complete the identities.

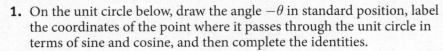

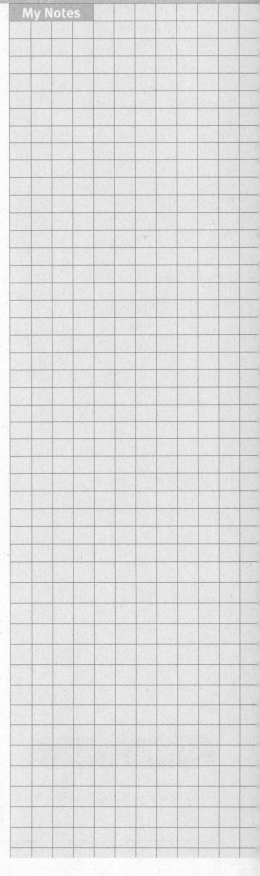

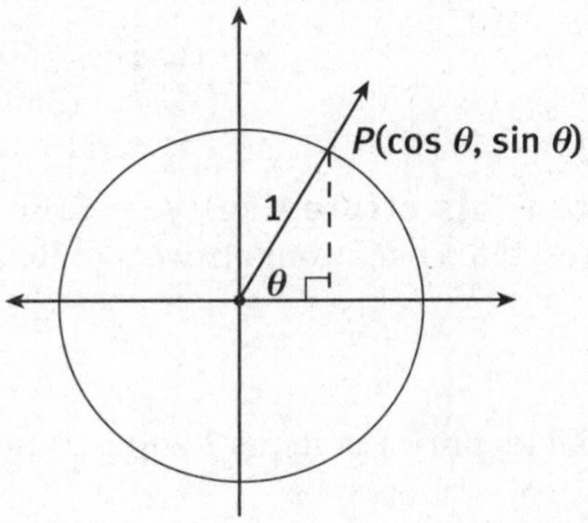

a. $\sin(-\theta) =$

b. $\cos(-\theta) =$

My Notes

2. On the unit circle below, draw the angles $180° + \theta$ and $180° - \theta$ in standard position, label the coordinates of the point where each angle passes through the unit circle in terms of sine θ and cosine θ, and then complete the identities.

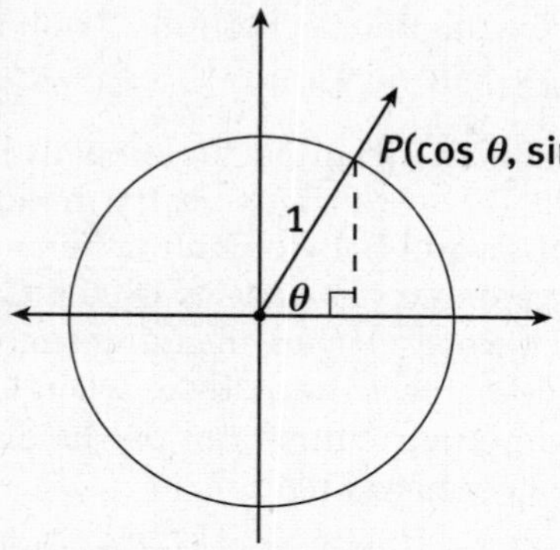

a. $\sin(180° + \theta) =$
b. $\cos(180° + \theta) =$
c. $\tan(180° + \theta) =$
d. $\sin(180° - \theta) =$
e. $\cos(180° - \theta) =$
f. $\tan(180° - \theta) =$

3. On the unit circle below, draw the angles $360° + \theta$ and $360° - \theta$ in standard position, label the coordinates of the point where each angle passes through the unit circle in terms of sine and cosine, and then complete the identities.

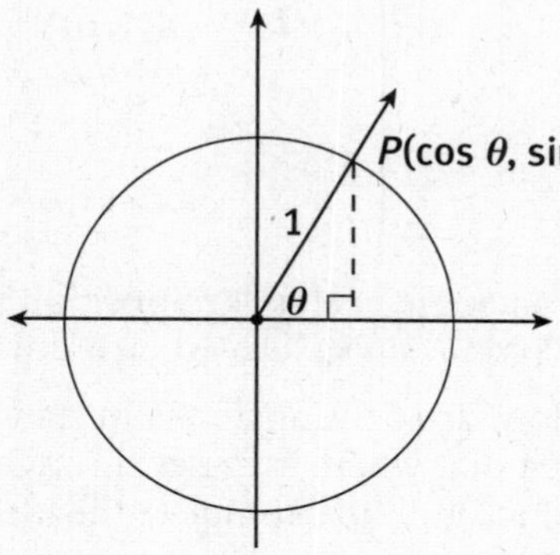

a. $\sin(360° + \theta) =$
b. $\cos(360° + \theta) =$
c. $\tan(360° + \theta) =$
d. $\sin(360° - \theta) =$
e. $\cos(360° - \theta) =$
f. $\tan(360° - \theta) =$

4. Use appropriate tools strategically. Explain how a graphing calculator can be used to check your answers to Items 1 to 3. Then, check your work.

MATH TIP

To convert degrees to radians, multiply the degree measure by $\frac{\pi}{180°}$.

5. Express each of the identities in Items 2 and 3 using radians.

My Notes

6. **Reason abstractly.** If $\cos\theta = a$ and $\sin\theta = b$, complete each statement using a and/or b with the correct sign.
   a. $\sin(-\theta) =$ **b.** $\cos(360° + \theta) =$
   c. $\sin(360° - \theta) =$ **d.** $\sin(180° + \theta) =$
   e. $\cos(180° - \theta) =$ **f.** $\tan(180° + \theta) =$

7. Use the diagram to help you complete each statement below in terms of x, y, and r.

   $\sin\theta =$ $\cos(90° - \theta) =$ $\cos\theta =$ $\sin(90° - \theta) =$

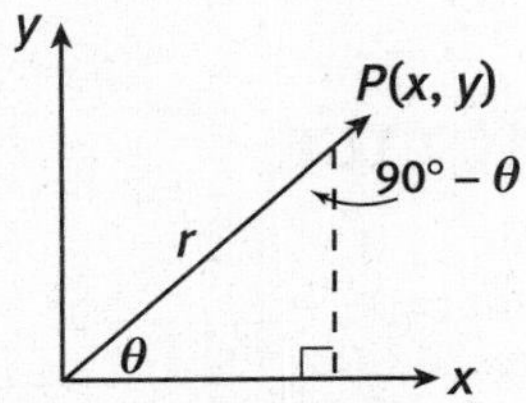

8. What do you notice about the relationship between the sine of an angle and the cosine of its complement? Express this relationship as an identity.

The statement you wrote in Item 8 is called a ***cofunction identity***.

9. Cofunction identities exist for other pairs of trigonometric functions. List these identities below.

10. **Construct viable arguments.** Explain why cofunction is an appropriate description for these identities. Be certain to include an explanation of the relationship between θ and $(90° - \theta)$.

11. Given $\cos\theta = \frac{2}{3}$, what is the value of each expression?
    a. $\sin\left(\frac{\pi}{2} - \theta\right)$ **b.** $\cos(\pi + \theta)$ **c.** $\sin(-\theta)$

12. Given $\sin\frac{\pi}{6} = \frac{1}{2}$, what is the value of each expression?
    a. $\cos\frac{\pi}{3}$ **b.** $\sin\frac{13\pi}{6}$ **c.** $\csc\frac{\pi}{6}$

13. Given $\sin 63° = x$, what is the value of each expression?
    a. $\cos 27°$ **b.** $\cos(-27°)$ **c.** $\sin(243°)$

My Notes

Check Your Understanding

14. Suppose you are told that $\sin 57° \approx 0.8387$. What is another angle between 0° and 360° whose sine is approximately equal to 0.8387? Justify your response with an identity.

15. Make use of structure. Use the relationship between the value of $\cos(2\pi - \theta)$ and $\cos(-\theta)$ to write an identity. Explain your reasoning.

LESSON 22-1 PRACTICE

16. Complete each statement.

a. If $\sin(x) = a$, then $\sin(-x) =$ ______.

b. If $\cos(x) = 0.4$, then $\cos(\pi - x) =$ ______.

c. If $\sin(-x) = -0.13$, then $\sin(x + 2\pi) =$ ______.

d. If $\cos(47°) = y$, then $\sin(43°) =$ ______.

e. If $\sin\left(\frac{\pi}{5}\right) = y$, then $\csc\left(\frac{4\pi}{5}\right) =$ ______.

17. You have seen that $\sin(-\theta) = -\sin\theta$. What does this identity tell you about the relationship between the graphs of $f(x) = \sin(-x)$ and $g(x) = \sin x$? Graph the two functions on your calculator to check that your answer is reasonable.

18. Use the figure of the unit circle to find the value of each of the following.

a. $\tan\theta$

b. $\cos(180° - \theta)$

c. $\sin(\pi + \theta)$

d. $\tan(360° - \theta)$

e. $\csc(-\theta)$

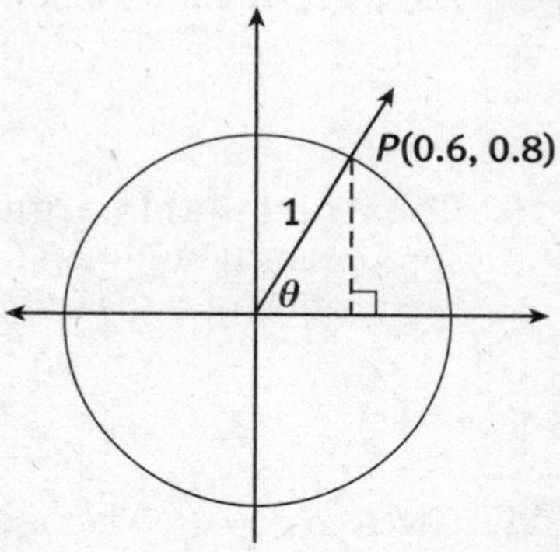

19. Given that $\cos\frac{\pi}{7} \approx 0.9$, name three additional angles whose cosine is approximately equal to 0.9.

20. Construct viable arguments. Verify the identity $\tan\left(\frac{\pi}{2} - \theta\right)\sin\theta = \cos\theta$. Be sure to justify each step of your argument with a valid reason.

My Notes

Learning Targets:

- Use trigonometric identities to solve equations.
- Solve trigonometric equations by graphing.

SUGGESTED LEARNING STRATEGIES: Create Representations, Look for a Pattern, Identify a Subtask, Simplify the Problem

Trigonometric graphs and identities like the ones in Items 1 to 3 of Lesson 22-1 can help you find solutions to trigonometric equations.

1. Consider the equation $2\sin\theta - 1 = 0$
   a. Sketch the graph of the function $f(\theta) = 2\sin\theta - 1$ over the interval $[0°, 360°]$.
   b. Using the graph, explain why there must be two solutions to the equation $2\sin\theta - 1 = 0$ on the interval $[0°, 360°)$.

   c. Determine the solutions to the equation $2\sin\theta - 1 = 0$ over the interval $[0°, 360°)$. Explain how these solutions relate to the identity $\sin\theta = \sin(180° - \theta)$.

   d. Use an algebraic method to solve the equation $2\sin\theta - 1 = 0$. Compare the solutions to the answers in item *c*.

   e. Use an algebraic method to solve $\sqrt{2}\sin\theta + 1 = 0$ over the interval $[0°, 360°)$. Use a graph to confirm your solutions.

For each trigonometric equation shown below, find the angle measures that satisfy the equation.

2. Solve for θ on $[0°, 360°)$.
   a. $1 = \sqrt{3}\tan\theta$
   b. $2\cos\theta + \sqrt{3} = 0$
   c. $\sin\theta - 3 = 0$

3. **Make use of structure.** Solve each equation on the given interval by using factoring.
   a. $4\sin^2 x - 1 = 0,\ [0, 2\pi)$

   b. $2\tan^2\theta - \tan\theta - 3 = 0,\ [0°, 360°)$

   c. $\sin^2 x = 2\sin x,\ [-\pi, \pi]$

   d. $\cos\theta - 2\cos\theta\sin\theta = 0,\ [0°, 180°]$

My Notes

When there is more than one trigonometric function in a particular equation, another solution strategy is using identities to rewrite the equation in terms of a single trigonometric function.

4. Solve the equation $\cos^2 \theta = 1 - \sin \theta$ on the interval [0°, 360°). Start by rewriting the cosine term in terms of sine.

5. Solve the following equations on the interval $[0, 2\pi)$. Use identities to rewrite the equation in terms of a single trigonometric function.

a. $\csc x - \sin x = 0$

b. $\tan^2 \theta = 1 - \sec \theta$

c. $\tan^2 x + \sec^2 x = 3$

6. Use appropriate tools strategically. Trigonometric equations can also be solved by graphing the functions represented by each side of the equation and finding their intersection point(s).

a. Solve the equation $\sin x = \cos x$ on the interval $[0, 2\pi]$ using a graphing calculator.

b. Change the graphing window to $[-2\pi, 2\pi]$. What are the solutions to this equation on this interval?

c. Change the graphing window to $[0, 4\pi]$. What are the solutions to this equation on this interval?

d. How many solutions would this equation have on the interval $(-\infty, \infty)$?

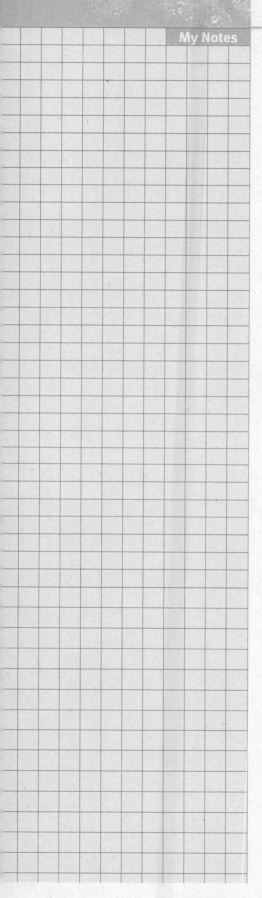

My Notes

When the solution interval is not restricted to a subset of the real numbers, you must find the *general solutions*.

7. Attend to precision. Use your work from Items 1 to 6 to write the general solutions to these equations on the interval $(-\infty, \infty)$.

a. $\sqrt{2}\sin\theta + 1 = 0$

b. $2\tan^2\theta - \tan\theta - 3 = 0$

c. $\cos^2\theta = 1 - \sin\theta$

d. $\sin x = \cos x$

8. The equation $4\sin^2 x - 1 = 0$ has the solutions $\left\{\frac{\pi}{6}, \frac{5\pi}{6}, \frac{7\pi}{6}, \frac{11\pi}{6}\right\}$ on $[0, 2\pi)$.

a. What are the solutions on $(-\infty, \infty)$?

b. Find a way to write your answers to part a in a more concise manner.

9. Attend to precision. Find a way to write your answers to Items 7b and 7d in a more concise manner.

MATH TIP

You can write *general solutions* by adding integral multiples of the period. Use $2\pi k$ or $360°k$ for sine and cosine. Use πk or $180°k$ for tangent.

My Notes

Check Your Understanding

10. Explain how you could rewrite each equation in terms of a single trigonometric function.

a. $\sin^2 x - 1 + \cos x = 0$

b. $1 = \sin\left(\frac{\pi}{2} - x\right)\cos x$

c. $\tan x = 3\cot x$

11. Melinda was asked to solve the equation $\sec^2 x - \tan^2 x = 1$. She looked at the equation and quickly stated that all real numbers are solutions. Explain how Melinda knew this.

12. Make use of structure. How is the process of finding all solutions to the equation $2\cos^2 x + \cos x - 1 = 0$ similar to the process of finding all solutions to the equation $2x^2 + x - 1 = 0$? How is the process different?

LESSON 22-2 PRACTICE

13. Solve each equation over the given interval. You do not need a calculator.

a. $3 \csc x - 6 = 0$, $[0, 2\pi)$

b. $4 \sin^2 \theta - 3 = 0$, $[-180°, 180°]$

c. $\sin x \tan x - \sin x = 0$, $\left[-\frac{\pi}{2}, \frac{\pi}{2}\right]$

d. $\sin^2 \theta - \cos^2 \theta = 1$, $(0°, 360°)$

14. Write the general solutions to Item 13 on the interval $(-\infty, \infty)$.

15. Solve each equation over the given interval. You may use a calculator.

a. $3 \cos \theta - 2 = 0$, $(-\infty, \infty)$

b. $\sin^2 x - 4 = 0$, $[0, 2\pi)$

c. $\sin\theta = \sqrt{3}\cos\theta$, $[0°, 360°)$

d. $\tan^2 \theta + 2 \tan \theta - 3 = 0$, $(-\infty, \infty)$

16. Without using a calculator, determine the number of times the graphs of the functions $f(x) = 4\sin^2 x$ and $g(x) = 5 - 4\cos x$ intersect on the interval $[0°, 360°)$. Explain your method.

17. A student was asked to find all solutions to the equation $\sin x = 0.25x$. The student stated that the equation must have infinitely many solutions on the interval $(-\infty, \infty)$ since the sine function is periodic. Do you agree or disagree with the student's reasoning? Explain.

18. Critique the reasoning of others. Carlos solved the equation $1 - \sin^2 x = 0.5\cos x$ on the interval $\left[0, \frac{\pi}{2}\right]$. His work is shown below. Explain his error and find the correct solution.

Step 1:	$1 - \sin^2 x = 0.5\cos x$	Original equation
Step 2:	$\cos^2 x = 0.5\cos x$	Pythagorean identity
Step 3:	$\cos x = 0.5$	Divide both sides by cos *x*.
Step 4:	$x = \frac{\pi}{3}$	Solve for *x*.

19. Make use of structure. How can identities help you to understand how to find all of the solutions to trigonometric equations?

ACTIVITY 22 PRACTICE

Write your answers on notebook paper. Show your work.

Lesson 22-1

Complete each statement.

1. If $\cos\theta = k$, then $\cos(-\theta) =$ ______.
2. If $\tan(180^\circ - x) = 0.41$, then $\tan x =$ ______.
3. If $\sin 16^\circ = x$, then $\cos(74^\circ) =$ ______.
4. If $\tan x = a$, then $\tan(2\pi - x) =$ ______.
5. If $\cos\left(\frac{\pi}{11}\right) = y$, then $\sec\left(\frac{10\pi}{11}\right) =$ ______.

Given $\sin\theta = \frac{3}{5}$, what is the value of each expression?

6. $\sin(2\pi - \theta)$
7. $\cos\left(\frac{\pi}{2} - \theta\right)$
8. $\tan\theta$
9. Which of the following expressions must have the same value for any angle θ? Choose all that apply.
   A. $\cos\theta$
   B. $\sin\theta$
   C. $\sin\left(\frac{\pi}{2} - \theta\right)$
   D. $\cos(-\theta)$
   E. $\cos(\pi - \theta)$
   F. $\cos(2\pi - \theta)$
10. Verify the identity $\sec^2\theta \sin\left(\frac{\pi}{2} - \theta\right) = \sec\theta$. Be sure to justify each step of your argument with a valid reason.

11. The sentence shown below appears in Jamal's textbook. However, part of the sentence is covered by a drop of ink. Which expression could be covered by the drop of ink?
    If $\cos\theta = \frac{3}{7}$, then $\sin(?) = \frac{3}{7}$.
    A. $-\theta$ **B.** $180^\circ - \theta$
    C. $90^\circ - \theta$ **D.** $90^\circ + \theta$
12. Point P lies on the unit circle, with coordinates (r, s), as shown. Find each of the following in terms of r and s.

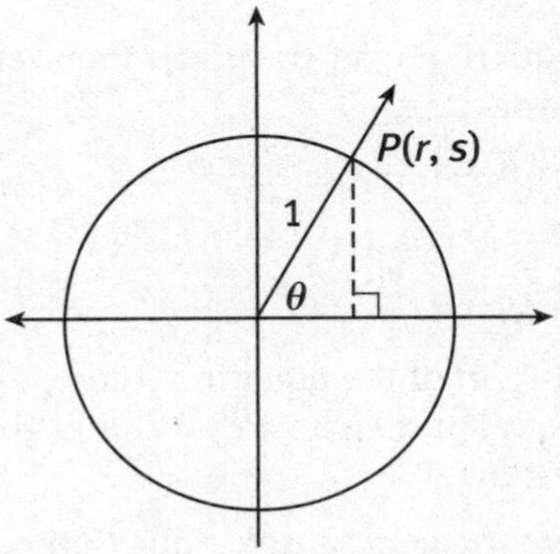

    A. $\sin(\pi - \theta)$ **B.** $\cot\left(\frac{\pi}{2} - \theta\right)$
    C. $\cos\left(\frac{\pi}{2} - \theta\right)$ **D.** $\csc(2\pi - \theta)$
13. What is the range of the function $h(x)$, where $h(x)$ is defined as follows? Explain.
$$h(x) = \frac{\sin x}{\sin\left(\frac{\pi}{2} - x\right)} + 1$$
14. Write an expression involving sine that has the same value as $\cos(\pi - x)$ for all x. Then explain how you can use your calculator to check that your answer is reasonable.
15. If $\sin\theta > 0$, which of the following must be negative?
    A. $\sin(-\theta)$ **B.** $\cos\theta$
    C. $\sin\left(\frac{\pi}{2} - \theta\right)$ **D.** $\cos(-\theta)$

Lesson 22-2

Solve each equation over the given interval. You do not need a calculator.

16. $\sin\theta = \sqrt{3} - \sin\theta, [0°, 360°)$

17. $\sin^2 x + \cos x + 1 = 0, [0, 2\pi)$

18. $\csc x \tan x - \csc x = 0, \left[-\frac{\pi}{2}, \frac{\pi}{2}\right]$

19. $2\cos^2\theta + 3\sin\theta = 3, [0°, 360°)$

20. Write the general solutions to Item 17 on the interval $(-\infty, \infty)$.

Solve each equation over the given interval. You may use a calculator.

21. $7 = 5\csc\theta + 1, (-\infty, \infty)$

22. $9\cos^2\theta - 12\cos\theta + 4 = 0, (-\infty, \infty)$

23. $1 - 2\sec x = 0, [0, 2\pi)$

24. The solution of the equation $3\cos x - p = 0$ on the interval $[0, \pi)$ is $x = \frac{\pi}{3}$. What is the value of the constant p?

25. What are the general solutions to the equation $\cos x \sin\left(\frac{\pi}{2} - x\right) = 1$?

A. $2\pi k$, where k is an integer
B. πk, where k is an integer
C. $\frac{\pi}{2} + 2\pi k$, where k is an integer
D. $\frac{\pi}{2} + \pi k$, where k is an integer

26. Give the general solutions of the equation $\sin(-x)\sin x = 1$. Explain your answer.

27. Which of the following equations has the greatest number of solutions on the interval $[0, 2\pi)$?

A. $4\cos\theta = -3$
B. $4\cos^2\theta = -3$
C. $4\cos\theta = 3$
D. $4\cos^2\theta = 3$

28. Write and solve an equation to find the exact point(s) of intersection of the graphs of $f(x) = 2 - 2\cos^2 x$ and $g(x) = 5\sin x - 2$ on the interval $[0, 2\pi)$.

Determine whether each statement is always, sometimes, or never true.

29. If c is a real number, then the equation $\sin x \sin(\pi - x) = c$ has a solution on the interval $[0, 2\pi)$.

30. The graph of $y = \tan x$ intersects the graph of $y = kx$, where k is a real number.

31. 0 is a solution of $\cos^2 x = p\cos x$ when p is a nonzero real number.

MATHEMATICAL PRACTICES
Model with Mathematics

32. The height of a car on a Ferris wheel, in feet, is modeled by the function $h(t) = 60\cos\left(\frac{\pi}{2} - t\right) + 70$, where t is the time in minutes since the ride began.

a. What is the height of the car when the ride begins? How do you know?
b. What is the maximum height of the car?
c. During the first revolution of the Ferris wheel, when is the car at a height of 100 feet? Write and solve an equation algebraically to find the exact times. Then use a calculator to find the times to the nearest hundredth of a minute.
d. How many solutions did you find for part c? Explain why this number of solutions makes sense in terms of the real-world context.

Multiple Angle Identities

ACTIVITY 23

Sounds Like Trigonometry

Lesson 23-1 Exploring Sums of Trig Functions

My Notes

Learning Targets:

- Model a sound wave with a trigonometric function.
- Derive an expression for the cosine of a difference.

SUGGESTED LEARNING STRATEGIES: Marking the Text, Create Representations, Look for a Pattern, Visualization, Identify a Subtask

The sound of a single musical note can be represented using the function

$$y = a \sin(2\pi ft)$$

where a is the amplitude (volume) of the sound measured in decibels (dB), f is the frequency (pitch) of the note measured in hertz (Hz), and t is time.

1. The frequency of the musical note middle C is about 262 Hz. Write the equation for a sine wave that represents middle C played at a volume of 60 dB.

2. In music, a note one octave higher vibrates twice as fast. Write an equation for a sine wave for the note one octave above middle C played at a volume of 70 dB.

When more than one musical note is played at the same time, the sound is represented by the sum or difference of two or more sine or cosine waves.

3. Use appropriate tools strategically. Use your calculator to graph the functions you wrote in Items 1 and 2. Also graph the sum of the two functions. What do you notice about the graphs?

The sum of another pair of sinusoidal curves whose periods are equal could represent two musical notes with the same frequency played at the same time.

4. Model with mathematics. Let $y_1 = \frac{1}{2}\sin x$ and $y_2 = \frac{\sqrt{3}}{2}\cos x$.

a. Use your calculator to graph the functions Y1, Y2, and Y1 + Y2 on the interval $[-2\pi, 2\pi]$ and then make a sketch in the space below.

CONNECT TO MUSIC

Periodic functions like sine and cosine model physical phenomena that oscillate or vibrate in waves. Sound is one such physical phenomenon.

As a increases, a musical note sounds louder. As f increases, a musical note sounds higher.

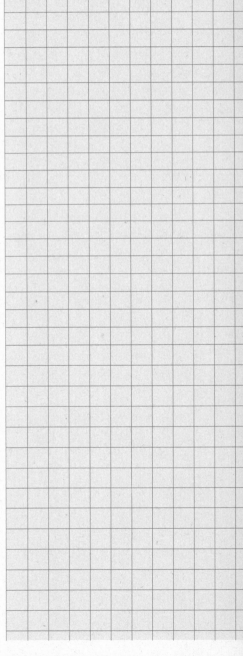

My Notes

b. Describe the graph of $y_1 + y_2$.

c. Express the function $y_1 + y_2$ in the form $y = \sin(x + c)$.

d. You found the value of c so that $\sin(x + c) = \frac{1}{2}\sin x + \frac{\sqrt{3}}{2}\cos x$. Does $\sin(x + c)$ also equal $\sin(x) + \sin(c)$? Explain how you determine your answer.

To further explore the properties of sums and differences of sine and cosine functions, answer the following items.

5. Reason quantitatively. Determine whether or not each statement below is true. Explain your reasoning.

a. $\sin(90° + 60°) = \sin 90° + \sin 60°$

b. $\cos\left(\frac{\pi}{3} - \frac{\pi}{6}\right) = \cos\frac{\pi}{3} - \cos\frac{\pi}{6}$

6. Are the following statements true for all values of x and y? Explain.

a. $\sin(x - y) = \sin x - \sin y$

b. $\cos(x + y) = \cos x + \cos y$

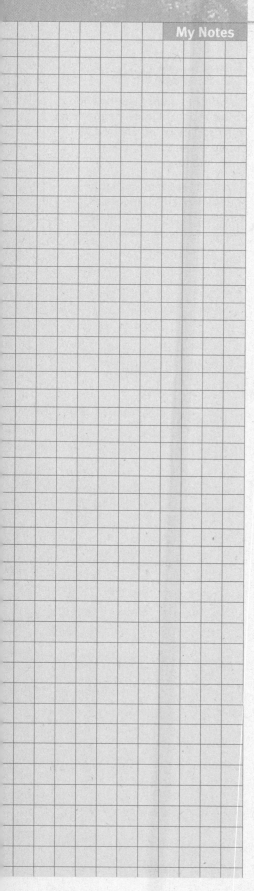

My Notes

The unit circle, the distance formula, and trigonometric identities can be used to determine a formula for the sine or cosine of the sum or difference of two angles. The next items will help you derive an expression equal to $\cos(\alpha - \beta)$, where α, β, and θ are measures of three unit circle angles with $\theta = \alpha - \beta$ as shown in the diagrams.

7. Write the coordinates of points *B*, *C*, and *D* in terms of the sine and cosine.

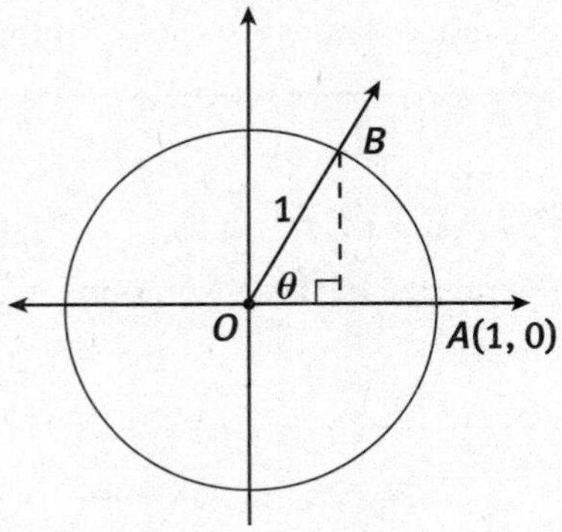

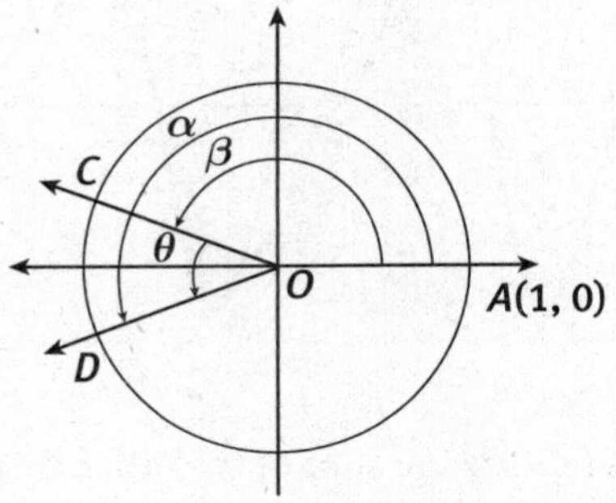

8. Draw segment *AB* and segment *CD*. Explain why their lengths are equal.

9. Use the distance formula to write the lengths of segments *AB* and *CD* in terms of sine and cosine. Then solve the resulting equation for $\cos\theta$. Show your work below.

Length of segment AB = Length of segment CD

10. Express regularity in repeated reasoning. Recall that $\theta = \alpha - \beta$. Use your answer from Item 9 to complete the statement below.

$\cos(\alpha - \beta) =$

My Notes

Check Your Understanding

11. Explain how you wrote the coordinates for point B in terms of the sine and cosine in Item 7.

12. Explain how you used a trigonometric identity in Item 9 to help simplify the expressions on either side of the equation.

13. Reason abstractly. Write the formula you discovered in Item 10 in words. Be sure to use one or more complete sentences.

LESSON 23-1 PRACTICE

14. The figure shows the graphs of three functions, f, g, and h.

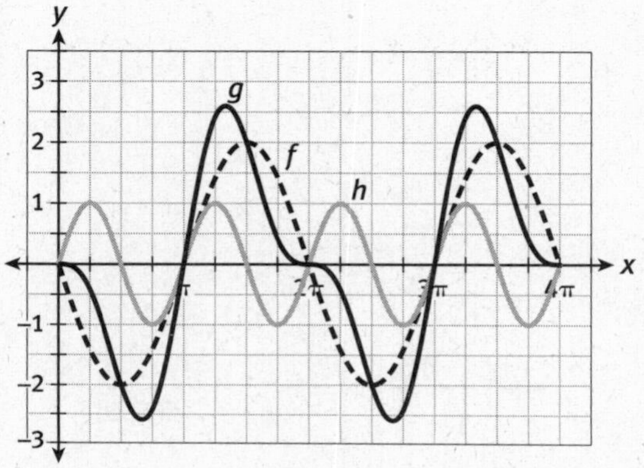

a. One of the functions is the sum of the other two. Which function is it? Justify your answer.
b. Write the other two functions as sine functions.
c. Write the function you identified in part a as a sum of the expressions you wrote in part b.
d. Do you think the function you wrote in part c could be written in the form $y = a\sin(bx + c) + d$? Why or why not?

15. Is the statement $\tan(x + y) = \tan x + \tan y$ true for all values of x and y? Explain.

16. Verify that the formula $\cos(\alpha - \beta) = \cos\alpha\cos\beta + \sin\alpha\sin\beta$ works when $\alpha = 150°$ and $\beta = 90°$.

17. Simplify the formula $\cos(\alpha - \beta) = \cos\alpha\cos\beta + \sin\alpha\sin\beta$ when $\alpha = \frac{\pi}{2}$. Explain what identity this proves.

18. Critique the reasoning of others. Wei said she could use the formula $\cos(\alpha - \beta) = \cos\alpha\cos\beta + \sin\alpha\sin\beta$ to prove that $\cos 90° = 0$. Her work is shown below. Is this a correct way to prove that $\cos 90° = 0$? Why or why not?

$$\begin{aligned}\cos 90° &= \cos(90° - 0°)\\ &= \cos 90°\cos 0° + \sin 90°\sin 0°\\ &= 0 \cdot 1 + 1 \cdot 0\\ &= 0\end{aligned}$$

My Notes

Learning Targets:

- Write the sum and difference identities for sine, cosine, and tangent.
- Use sum and difference identities to find exact values of a trig function.
- Derive the double angle and half angle identities.

SUGGESTED LEARNING STRATEGIES: Predict and Confirm, Simplify the Problem, Look for a Pattern, Identify a Subtask, Think-Pair-Share

Using the identities learned in Activity 22 and the results of Item 10 from the last lesson, you can derive the following ***sum and difference identities***.

$$\cos(\alpha + \beta) = \cos\alpha\cos\beta - \sin\alpha\sin\beta$$
$$\sin(\alpha + \beta) = \sin\alpha\cos\beta + \sin\beta\cos\alpha$$
$$\sin(\alpha - \beta) = \sin\alpha\cos\beta - \sin\beta\cos\alpha$$

These identities are sometimes written in a condensed fashion as shown below for the tangent sum and difference identities.

$$\tan(\alpha \pm \beta) = \frac{\tan\alpha \pm \tan\beta}{1 \mp \tan\alpha\tan\beta}$$

MATH TIP

When reading $\pm$ say "plus or minus." When reading $\mp$ say "minus or plus."

1. Express the tangent identity as two separate identities, one for the sum and one for the difference.

2. Make sense of problems. In Item 4 of the last lesson you discovered that $\sin\left(x + \frac{\pi}{3}\right) = \frac{1}{2}\sin x + \frac{\sqrt{3}}{2}\cos x$. Use the sum identity for sine to algebraically verify this identity.

My Notes

The sum and difference identities are also used to find exact values of nonspecial angle measures.

Example A

Find the exact value of $\sin 15°$.

Step 1: Rewrite $\sin 15°$. $\sin 15° = \sin(60° - 45°)$

Step 2: Substitute using identity. $= \sin 60° \cos 45° - \sin 45° \cos 60°$

Step 3: Evaluate. Use special angle ratios. $= \frac{\sqrt{3}}{2} \cdot \frac{\sqrt{2}}{2} - \frac{\sqrt{2}}{2} \cdot \frac{1}{2}$

Step 4: Simplify. $= \frac{\sqrt{6}}{4} - \frac{\sqrt{2}}{4}$

Solution: $\sin 15° = \frac{\sqrt{6} - \sqrt{2}}{4}$

Try These A

a. $\cos 105°$ **b.** $\sin \frac{7\pi}{12}$ **c.** $\tan 75°$

3. Use appropriate tools strategically. Explain how you could use your calculator to check that your answer to Try These Part A is correct.

MATH TIP

Draw a right triangle to help you quickly determine the other trigonometric ratios for a given angle if you know one ratio.

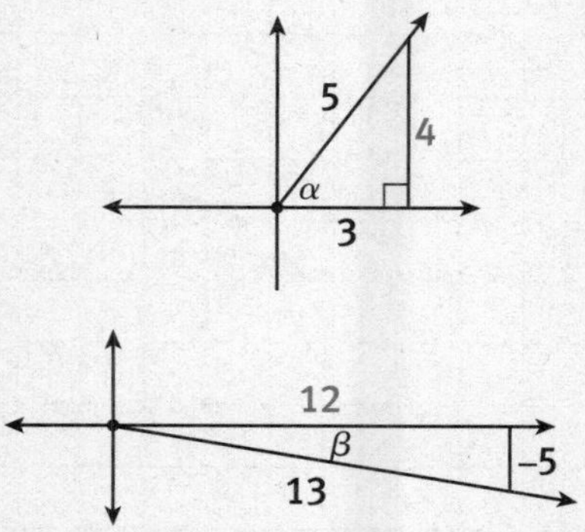

Here is another type of sum-and-difference problem.

Example B

Let α be an angle on the interval $[0°, 90°]$ and β be an angle on the interval $[-90°, 0°]$ with $\cos\alpha = \frac{3}{5}$ and $\sin\beta = -\frac{5}{13}$. Find $\cos(\alpha + \beta)$.

Step 1: Cosine sum identity $\cos(\alpha + \beta) = \cos\alpha\cos\beta - \sin\alpha\sin\beta$

Step 2: Substitute trig ratios from right triangle diagrams. $= \left(\frac{3}{5}\right)\left(\frac{12}{13}\right) - \left(\frac{4}{5}\right)\left(-\frac{5}{13}\right)$

Step 3: Simplify. $= \frac{36}{65} + \frac{20}{65}$

Solution: $\cos(\alpha + \beta) = \frac{56}{65}$

My Notes

Try These B

Reason quantitatively. Let α terminate in Quadrant I and β terminate in Quadrant II.

a. If $\sin\alpha = \frac{3}{5}$ and $\tan\beta = -\frac{8}{15}$, find $\sin(\alpha - \beta)$ and $\tan(\alpha + \beta)$.

b. If $\sin\alpha = \frac{1}{3}$ and $\sin\beta = \frac{3}{4}$, find $\sin(\alpha + \beta)$ and $\cos(\alpha + \beta)$.

From the sum and difference identities, you can derive double angle identities.

4. Use the fact that $2\theta = \theta + \theta$ and the appropriate sum identity to verify each double-angle identity.

a. $\sin 2\theta = 2\sin\theta\cos\theta$

b. $\cos 2\theta = \cos^2\theta - \sin^2\theta$

c. $\tan 2\theta = \dfrac{2\tan\theta}{1 - \tan^2\theta}$

5. Use the identities $\cos 2\theta = \cos^2\theta - \sin^2\theta$ and $\sin^2\theta + \cos^2\theta = 1$ to derive an identity for $\cos 2\theta$ in terms of cosine only.

6. Use the identities $\cos 2\theta = \cos^2\theta - \sin^2\theta$ and $\sin^2\theta + \cos^2\theta = 1$ to derive an identity for $\cos 2\theta$ in terms of sine only.

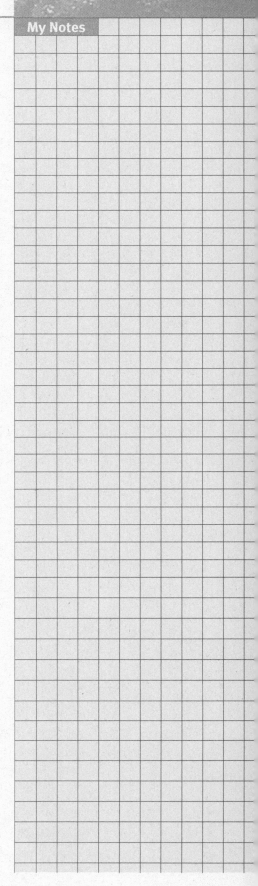

My Notes

Example C

Given $\sin\theta = \frac{1}{4}$ with $\frac{\pi}{2} < \theta < \pi$, what is the exact value of $\cos\theta$, $\sin 2\theta$, and $\cos 2\theta$?

$\cos\theta = -\frac{\sqrt{4^2 - 1^1}}{4} = -\frac{\sqrt{15}}{4}$ Use a triangle, cosine is negative, θ terminates in Quadrant II.

$\sin 2\theta = 2\left(\frac{1}{4}\right)\left(-\frac{\sqrt{15}}{4}\right) = -\frac{\sqrt{15}}{8}$ Use $\sin 2\theta = 2\sin\theta\cos\theta$, substituting sine and cosine values.

$\cos 2\theta = \left(-\frac{\sqrt{15}}{4}\right)^2 - \left(\frac{1}{4}\right)^2 = \frac{14}{16} = \frac{7}{8}$ Use $\cos 2\theta = \cos^2\theta - \sin^2\theta$, substituting sine and cosine values.

Try These C

a. Given $\cos\theta = \frac{3}{5}$ with $0 < \theta < \frac{\pi}{2}$, find $\sin\theta$, $\tan\theta$, $\sin 2\theta$, and $\tan 2\theta$.

b. Given $\tan\theta = -\frac{8}{17}$ with $\frac{3\pi}{2} < \theta < 2\pi$, find $\cos\theta$, $\cos 2\theta$, and $\tan 2\theta$.

c. Given $\sin\theta = \frac{2}{3}$ and $\cos\theta < 0$, find $\cos\theta$, $\sin 2\theta$, and $\cos 2\theta$.

7. Classify each statement as true or false.

a. $\sin 60° = 2\sin 30°\cos 30°$

b. $\cos\pi = \cos^2\left(\frac{\pi}{2}\right) - \sin^2\left(\frac{\pi}{2}\right)$

c. $\tan 48° = \frac{2\tan 24°}{1 + \tan 24°}$

d. $1 - 2\sin^2\left(\frac{\pi}{5}\right) = \sin\left(\frac{\pi}{10}\right)$

My Notes

8. **Reason abstractly.** From the double angle identities for cosine, you can derive the **half-angle identities**.
   a. Solve the identity $\cos 2\theta = 2\cos^2\theta - 1$ for $\cos\theta$.

   b. Let $2\theta = \alpha$; solve for θ.

   c. Write your results from part a in terms of α.

   d. Derive the half-angle identity for $\sin\frac{\alpha}{2}$.

9. How could you use the half-angle identities for sine and cosine to derive this half-angle identity: $\tan\left(\frac{\alpha}{2}\right) = \pm\sqrt{\frac{1-\cos\alpha}{1+\cos\alpha}}$?

Example D

Use a half-angle identity to find the exact value of $\sin(-15°)$.

Substitute $\theta = -30°$ and use the sine half-angle identity. Use the negative square root because the sine of an angle terminating in Quadrant IV is negative. Simplify.

$$\sin(-15°) = \sin\left(\frac{-30°}{2}\right) = -\sqrt{\frac{1-\cos(-30°)}{2}} = -\sqrt{\frac{1-\frac{\sqrt{3}}{2}}{2}} = \frac{\sqrt{2-\sqrt{3}}}{4}$$

$$= -\frac{\sqrt{2-\sqrt{3}}}{2}$$

My Notes

Try These D

Use a half-angle identity to find the exact value of each trigonometric function.

a. $\cos\left(\frac{\pi}{8}\right)$ **b.** $\tan 15°$ **c.** $\sin\left(\frac{13\pi}{12}\right)$

Example E

If $\sin\theta = -\frac{5}{13}$ and $\cos\theta < 0$, find the exact value of $\cos\left(\frac{\theta}{2}\right)$ and $\tan 2\theta$.

a. Find the exact value of $\cos\left(\frac{\theta}{2}\right)$.

Step 1: Half-angle identity. Since θ terminates in Quadrant III, $\frac{\theta}{2}$ terminates in Quadrant II and cosine will be negative. $\cos\left(\frac{\theta}{2}\right) = -\sqrt{\frac{1+\cos\theta}{2}}$

Step 2: Substitute ratio. Use a triangle if needed. $= -\sqrt{\frac{1+\left(-\frac{12}{13}\right)}{2}}$

Step 3: Simplify. $= -\sqrt{\left(\frac{1}{13}\right)\left(\frac{1}{2}\right)}$

Solution: $\cos\left(\frac{\theta}{2}\right) = -\sqrt{\frac{1}{26}}$ or $-\frac{\sqrt{26}}{26}$

b. Find the exact value of $\tan 2\theta$.

Step 1: Double angle identity $\tan 2\theta = \frac{2\tan\theta}{1-\tan^2\theta}$

Step 2: Substitute ratios. Use a triangle if needed. $= \frac{2\left(\frac{5}{12}\right)}{1-\left(\frac{5}{12}\right)^2}$

Step 3: Simplify. $= 2\left(\frac{5}{12}\right) \div \left(\frac{119}{144}\right)$

$= 2\left(\frac{5}{12}\right)\left(\frac{144}{119}\right)$

Solution: $\tan 2\theta = \frac{120}{119}$

Try These E

If $\tan\theta = \frac{3}{4}$ and θ terminates in Quadrant III, find $\cos\left(\frac{\theta}{2}\right)$, $\tan\left(\frac{\theta}{2}\right)$, and $\sin 2\theta$.

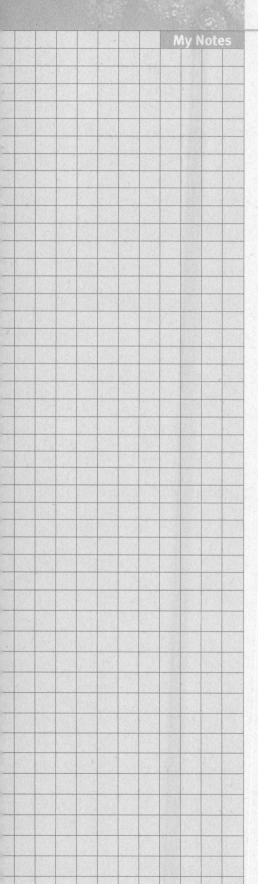

My Notes

10. Calculate the exact value of sin (105°) two different ways, once using a sum or difference identity and once using a half-angle identity.

Check Your Understanding

11. In Example 5, how do you use the information that $\cos\theta < 0$ to solve the problem? Explain why this is important.

12. **Make use of structure.** Is it possible to use the identities you learned in this lesson to find the exact value of $\sin 65°$? If so, explain how. If not, explain why not.

LESSON 23-2 PRACTICE

13. Find the exact value.

a. $\cos(165°)$ **b.** $\tan\left(\frac{17\pi}{12}\right)$

14. Given $\sin a = -\frac{8}{17}$ and $\tan b = -\frac{3}{4}$ with a terminating in Quadrant II and b terminating in Quadrant IV. Find the exact value of each ratio.

a. $\sin(a - b)$ **b.** $\tan(a + b)$

c. $\cos(2a)$ **d.** $\sin\left(\frac{b}{2}\right)$

15. Find the exact value.
$\tan(-67.5°)$

16. Use the sum identities for the sine and cosine to derive the sum identity for tangent: $\tan(\alpha+\beta) = \frac{\tan\alpha + \tan\beta}{1 - \tan\alpha\tan\beta}$.

17. **Reason quantitatively.** The function $y = 2.5\cos\left(\frac{\pi}{2}t + \frac{\pi}{2}\right)$ gives the displacement y, in centimeters, of a mass on a spring, where t is the time in seconds. As shown in the figure, when the mass is at rest, the displacement is 0 centimeters.

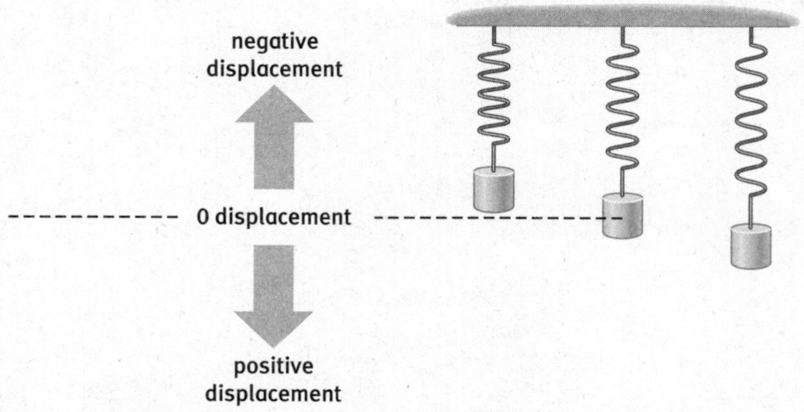

a. Write the displacement function using only the sine function.

b. What is the displacement after 4 seconds? 5 seconds? What do these values tell you about the position of the mass at these times?

My Notes

Learning Targets:

- Use trigonometric identities to solve equations.
- Verify trigonometric identities.

SUGGESTED LEARNING STRATEGIES: Think-Pair-Share, Identify a Subtask, Simplify the Problem, Note Taking

The identities introduced in this activity can be used to verify identities.

Example A

Verify the identity $\sin(\theta + 180) = -\sin\theta$.

$\sin(\theta + 180^\circ) = -\sin\theta$	
$\sin\theta\cos 180^\circ + \sin 180^\circ\cos\theta =$	Sum identity for sine
$(\sin\theta)(1) + (0)(\cos\theta) =$	Evaluate special angle ratios.
$-\sin\theta + 0 =$	
$-\sin\theta = -\sin\theta$	Simplify.

Try These A

Make use of structure. Verify each identity.

a. $\cos\left(x + \frac{\pi}{2}\right) = -\sin x$

b. $\frac{\sin 2x}{\tan x} = 2\cos^2 x$

c. $\cos^4\theta - \sin^4\theta = \cos 2\theta$

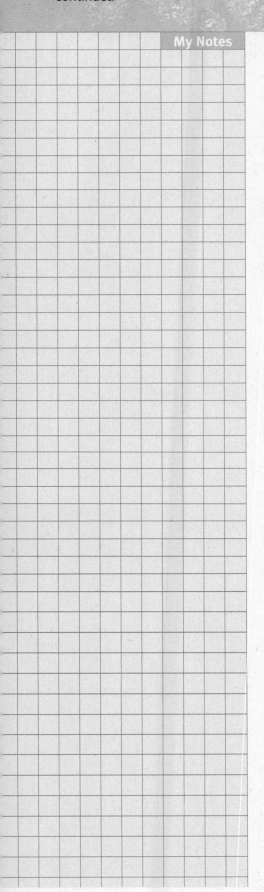

The identities introduced in this activity can also be used to solve equations.

Example B

Solve $\sin 2\theta - \sin \theta = 0$ on the interval $[0°, 360°)$.

Step 1: Double-angle formula $\quad \sin 2\theta - \sin \theta = 0$

Step 2: Factor. $\quad 2 \sin \theta \cos \theta - \sin \theta = 0$

Step 3: Set each factor equal to 0 and solve for θ on the given interval.

$\sin \theta(2 \cos \theta - 1) = 0$

$\sin \theta = 0$ or $2 \cos \theta - 1 = 0$

$\sin \theta = 0$ or $\cos \theta = \frac{1}{2}$

Solution: $\theta = 0°, 60°, 180°, 300°$

Try These B

Solve each equation on the interval $[0°, 360°)$.

a. $\cos 2\theta - \sin \theta = 0$

b. $\cos 2\theta = \cos^2 \theta$

Another way to solve trigonometric equations with multiple angles is shown below.

Example C

Solve $\sin \sin 3x = \frac{1}{2}$ on the interval $[0, 2\pi)$.

Step 1: Let $3x$ equal the solutions to $\sin \theta = \frac{1}{2}$ on the interval $[0, 6\pi)$. Multiply the interval by the x-coefficient.

$\sin 3x = \frac{1}{2}$

$3x = \frac{\pi}{6}, \frac{5\pi}{6}, \frac{13\pi}{6}, \frac{17\pi}{6}, \frac{25\pi}{6}, \frac{29\pi}{6}$

Step 2: Divide these solutions by 3 to isolate x.

$x = \frac{\pi}{18}, \frac{5\pi}{18}, \frac{13\pi}{18}, \frac{17\pi}{18}, \frac{25\pi}{18}, \frac{29\pi}{18}$

Try These C

Solve each equation on the interval $[0, 2\pi)$.

a. $\tan 4x = 1$

b. $4 \sin^2 (2x) - 3 = 0$

c. $2 \sin 3x \cos 3x = 0$

My Notes

Check Your Understanding

1. Describe two different ways to verify the identity $\cos(180° - x) = -\cos x$.
2. In Example B, you saw that the solutions of the equation $\sin 2x - \sin x = 0$ on the interval $[0°, 360°)$ are $0°$, $60°$, $180°$, and $300°$. What does this tell you about the graphs of $f(x) = \sin 2x$ and $g(x) = \sin x$?
3. **Critique the reasoning of others.** As the first step in solving the equation $\cos 2x + \sin x = 0$, Miguel used a double-angle identity to substitute $2\cos^2 x - 1$ for $\cos 2x$. Critique Miguel's method.

LESSON 23-3 PRACTICE

4. Verify the identity.

$$\sin\left(x - \frac{\pi}{6}\right) = \frac{\sqrt{3}\sin x - \cos x}{2}$$

5. Verify the identity.
   a. $\cos(\pi - x) = -\cos x$
   b. $\cot 2x = \frac{1}{2}(\cot x - \tan x)$
6. Solve each equation on the interval $[0°, 360°)$.
   a. $2\tan\theta\sin 2\theta = 1$
   b. $2\sin 3\theta = \sin^2\theta + \cos^2\theta$
7. Rewrite the expression $\sin 4\theta$ in terms of trigonometric functions of θ. Simplify and then write your result as a new identity.
8. **Express regularity in repeated reasoning.** Determine the number of solutions on the interval $[0, 2\pi)$ for each of the equations shown below.
   a. $\sin 2x = \frac{\sqrt{3}}{2}$ **b.** $\sin 3x = \frac{\sqrt{3}}{2}$ **c.** $\sin 4x = \frac{\sqrt{3}}{2}$
   d. Make a conjecture about the number of solutions on the interval $[0, 2\pi)$ for the equation $\sin nx = \frac{\sqrt{3}}{2}$, where n is a positive integer.

ACTIVITY 23 PRACTICE

Write your answers on notebook paper.
Show your work.

Lesson 23-1

Determine whether or not each statement is true. Explain your reasoning.

1. $\tan(45^\circ + 45^\circ) = \tan 45^\circ + \tan 45^\circ$
2. $\cos\left(\frac{\pi}{2} - \frac{\pi}{6}\right) = \cos\left(\frac{\pi}{2}\right)\cos\left(\frac{\pi}{6}\right) + \sin\left(\frac{\pi}{2}\right)\sin\left(\frac{\pi}{6}\right)$
3. $\sin(x + y) = \sin x + \sin y$ for all values of x and y.
4. Consider the function $f(x) = \cos\left(x - \frac{3\pi}{2}\right)$.
   a. Use the formula $\cos(\alpha - \beta) = \cos\alpha\cos\beta + \sin\alpha\sin\beta$ to write the function $f(x)$ in terms of the sine function only.
   b. How does the graph of $f(x)$ compare to the graph of $y = \sin x$? Explain.
5. Let $y_1 = \frac{\sqrt{2}}{2}\cos x$ and $y_2 = \frac{\sqrt{2}}{2}\sin x$.
   a. Graph y_1, y_2, and $y_1 + y_2$ on the interval $[-2\pi, 2\pi]$.
   b. Use the graph to help you express the function $y_1 + y_2$ in the form $y = a\cos(x - b)$.
   c. How can you apply the formula $\cos(\alpha - \beta) = \cos\alpha\cos\beta + \sin\alpha\sin\beta$ to show that your answer to part c is correct?
6. The expression $\cos\frac{2\pi}{3}\cos\frac{\pi}{2} + \sin\frac{2\pi}{3}\sin\frac{\pi}{2}$ can be used to calculate the value of which of the following?
   A. $\cos\frac{\pi}{6}$
   B. $\sin\frac{\pi}{6}$
   C. $\cos\frac{7\pi}{6}$
   D. $\cos\frac{\pi}{3}$
7. True or false? $\cos(2\theta) = 2\cos\theta$ for all θ. Justify your answer.

Lesson 23-2

Find the exact value of each of the following.

8. $\sin\left(\frac{11\pi}{12}\right)$
9. $\cos(-75^\circ)$
10. $\tan\left(\frac{5\pi}{12}\right)$
11. $\sin\left(\frac{\pi}{8}\right)$
12. $\cos(112.5^\circ)$
13. $\tan\left(\frac{3\pi}{8}\right)$
14. Let α be an angle on the interval $[180^\circ, 270^\circ]$ and β be an angle on the interval $[0^\circ, 90^\circ]$ with $\sin\alpha = -\frac{7}{25}$ and $\cos\beta = \frac{12}{13}$.
    a. Find $\cos(\alpha + \beta)$.
    b. Find $\tan(\alpha + \beta)$.
15. Which of the following is a true statement?
    A. $\tan 56^\circ = \frac{\tan 28^\circ}{1 - \tan^2 28^\circ}$
    B. $\cos\left(\frac{\pi}{8}\right) = \cos^2\left(\frac{\pi}{16}\right) - \sin^2\left(\frac{\pi}{16}\right)$
    C. $\sin 31^\circ = 2\sin 62^\circ\cos 62^\circ$
    D. $1 + 2\sin^2\left(\frac{\pi}{10}\right) = \cos\left(\frac{\pi}{5}\right)$
16. If $\sin\theta = -\frac{24}{25}$ and θ lies in Quadrant III, which of the following has a value of $\frac{4}{5}$?
    A. $\sin\left(\frac{\theta}{2}\right)$
    B. $\cos\left(\frac{\theta}{2}\right)$
    C. $\tan\left(\frac{\theta}{2}\right)$
    D. $\cot\left(\frac{\theta}{2}\right)$
17. Given that $\sin\theta = \frac{4}{5}$ with $0 < \theta < \frac{\pi}{2}$, what is the exact value of $\tan 2\theta$?
18. Jenna solved the following problem: Given that $\cos\alpha = -\frac{4}{5}$ with $\pi < \alpha < \frac{3\pi}{2}$ and $\sin\beta = \frac{5}{13}$ with $0 < \beta < \frac{\pi}{2}$, find the value of $\cos(\alpha - \beta)$.

    Jenna's work is shown below. Do you agree with her solution? If not, explain her error and find the correct solution.

$$\begin{aligned}\cos(\alpha - \beta) &= \cos\alpha\cos\beta + \sin\alpha\sin\beta \\ &= \frac{-4}{5}\left(\frac{12}{13}\right) + \frac{3}{5}\left(\frac{5}{13}\right) \\ &= -\frac{33}{65}\end{aligned}$$

Lesson 23-3

Verify the identity.

19. $\cos\left(\frac{3\pi}{2}+x\right)=\sin x$

20. $\tan(\pi+x)=\tan x$

21. $(\cos\theta+\sin\theta)^2=1+\sin 2\theta$

22. Which of the following is NOT a correct way to complete the equation $\cos 80° = \ldots$?

A. $2\cos^2 40°-1$
B. $1-2\sin^2 40°$
C. $\sqrt{\frac{1+\cos 160°}{2}}$
D. $\cos^2 160°-\sin^2 160°$

23. Tyrell was asked to simplify the expression $\frac{1-\cos 2\theta}{\sin 2\theta}$. His work is shown below. Find the error and provide the correct simplified expression.

$$\frac{1-\cos 2\theta}{\sin 2\theta}=\frac{1-(1+2\sin^2\theta)}{\sin 2\theta}$$
$$=\frac{-2\sin^2\theta}{2\sin\theta\cos\theta}$$
$$=\frac{-\sin\theta}{\cos\theta}$$
$$=-\tan\theta$$

Solve each equation on the interval $[0°, 360°)$.

24. $\cos 2\theta+3\cos\theta+2=0$

25. $2\sin^2\theta=\cos 2\theta$

26. $\sin 2\theta=-\cos\theta$

27. $\tan 3x=1$

28. $2\sin x\cos x-1=0$

29. Let $g(x)=\cos 2x$ and $h(x)=-1-\cos x$. Which of the following is a true statement about the functions?

A. The graphs of the functions intersect at 4 points on the interval $[0°, 360°)$.
B. $g(x)=h(x)$
C. Both graphs have the same x-intercepts.
D. $g(x)+h(x)=1$

30. Olivia simplified the expression $\frac{\cos 2\theta-1}{\sin^2\theta}$. Assuming each step of her work was correct, which of the following could have been her simplified expression?

A. -2
B. 2
C. $-\tan\theta$
D. $\tan\theta$

MATHEMATICAL PRACTICES
Use Appropriate Tools Strategically

31. Let $f(x)=\frac{\cos x\sin 2x}{1+\cos 2x}$.

a. Use your calculator to graph $f(x)$. Then use the graph to help you discover and write an identity.
b. Verify the identity you wrote in part a.
c. Use the identity to help you evaluate $f\left(\frac{\pi}{6}\right)$.

Trigonometric Identities and Equations
A QUICK-START GUIDE FOR TRIGONOMETRY

Many user's manuals include a quick-start guide as a handy reference. The guide includes examples of the most common tasks or procedures. Create a quick-start guide that a precalculus student could use as a trigonometry reference. The items below describe the elements your guide must include. Be sure each of your completed examples and explanations is clear so that another student can easily understand it.

1. Explain how to use the unit circle to derive each of the following trigonometric relationships.
   a. $\cos(2\pi - \theta) = \_\_\_$ **b.** $\sin(2\pi - \theta) = \_\_\_$ **c.** $\tan(2\pi - \theta) = \_\_\_$
   d. If you know that $\tan 38° = 0.7813$, what can you conclude about $\tan 322°$?
2. Simplify each expression.
   a. $\dfrac{\cos\theta}{\sin^2\theta - 1}$ **b.** $\dfrac{1 + \tan\theta}{1 + \cot\theta}$ **c.** $\dfrac{\cos 2\theta}{\cos\theta - \sin\theta}$
3. Develop and use sum and difference identities, as follows.
   a. Is the statement $\tan(x - y) = \tan x - \tan y$ true for all values of x and y? Justify your answer.
   b. Given the sum and difference identities for sine and cosine, explain how to derive an identity for $\tan(\alpha - \beta)$.
   c. Show how you can use your result to derive an identity for $\tan(\pi - \theta)$.
4. Evaluate each expression without using a calculator.
   a. $\sin(75°)$
   b. $\cos 2x$, given $\sin x = \dfrac{1}{5}$ and $\cos x < 0$
5. Verify each identity.
   a. $\cos x \cot x + \sin x = \csc x$
   b. $\sin(2\pi - \theta) = -\sin\theta$
   c. $\dfrac{2\cot 2x}{\cos x - \sin x} = \csc x + \sec x$
6. Solve each equation over the given interval.
   a. $\tan^2 x + 2 = 3$, $[0, 2\pi)$
   b. $2\cos^2\theta - 3\sin\theta = 0$, $[0°, 360°)$
   c. $\sin 2x = \cos x$ for all values of x
7. How does solving an equation over an interval like $[0, 2\pi)$ differ from solving the same equation for all real values of the variable?

Trigonometric Identities and Equations

A QUICK-START GUIDE FOR TRIGONOMETRY

Scoring Guide	Exemplary	Proficient	Emerging	Incomplete
	The solution demonstrates these characteristics:			
Mathematics Knowledge and Thinking (Items 2, 3, 4, 5, 6)	• Clear and accurate understanding of trigonometric identities, particularly double angle formulae, sum and difference formulae, Pythagorean identities, and $\tan x = \frac{\sin x}{\cos x}$	• A functional understanding of trigonometric identities, applying them generally in a correct way, but with some errors	• Partial understanding of trigonometric identities	• Little or no understanding of any trigonometric identities
Problem Solving (Items 1, 6)	• An appropriate and efficient strategy that results in a correct answer when solving trigonometric equations	• A strategy that may include unnecessary steps but results in a correct answer	• A strategy that results in some incorrect answers	• No clear strategy when solving problems
Mathematical Modeling / Representations (Items 1, 7)	• Clear and accurate understanding of representations of the unit circle and how it is used to find the ratios of sine, cosine, and tangent	• A functional understanding of representations of the unit circle and how it is used to find the ratios of sine, cosine, and tangent	• Partial understanding of representations of the trigonometric ratios and how they exist as functions and on the unit circle	• Little or no understanding of representations of the trigonometric ratios and how they exist as functions and on the unit circle
Reasoning and Communication (Items 1d, 3b, 7)	• Precise use of appropriate math terms and language to describe behavior of trigonometric ratios on the unit circle, explain how to derive identities, and state solutions to trigonometric equations	• Correct characterization of the behavior of trigonometric ratios on the unit circle, explanation of how to derive identities, and statement of differing solutions to trigonometric equations	• Misleading or confusing characterization of behavior of trigonometric ratios on the unit circle, explanation of how to derive identities, and statement of differing solutions to trigonometric equations	• Incomplete or inaccurate characterization of behavior of trigonometric ratios on the unit circle, explanation of how to derive identities, and statement of differing solutions to trigonometric equations

Law of Cosines
The Chocolate Factory
Lesson 24-1 Modeling with Trigonometric Functions

Learning Targets:
- Use trigonometry to draw and interpret diagrams for a model.
- Write a trigonometric function for a real-world situation.

SUGGESTED LEARNING STRATEGIES: Create Representations, Group Presentation, Guess and Check, Identify a Subtask, Look for a Pattern, Marking the Text, Quickwrite, Simplify the Problem, Visualization, Work Backward

At the Ghirardelli Chocolate Factory in San Francisco, California, the original equipment that stirred the milk chocolate mixture was driven by a wheel that pushed a stirrer blade back and forth across the bottom of the vat, as illustrated below. The wheel has a radius of 2 feet, and the rod connecting the wheel and the blade, represented below by segment PT, has length of 5 feet. Point T is on the same level as the center of the wheel C as shown by the dotted line.

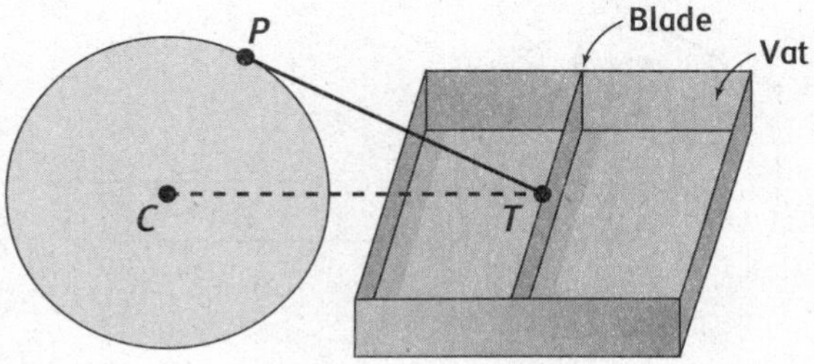

My Notes

CONNECT TO ENGINEERING

In many mechanical devices, circular motion is converted to linear motion or linear motion is converted to circular motion in order to apply energy as required.

1. **Model with mathematics.** Sketch the position of the rod and blade at each angle of rotation. Assume angles are in the standard position. Then, find the distance from the center of the wheel to the stirrer blade for each angle.
   a. angle of rotation = 0°

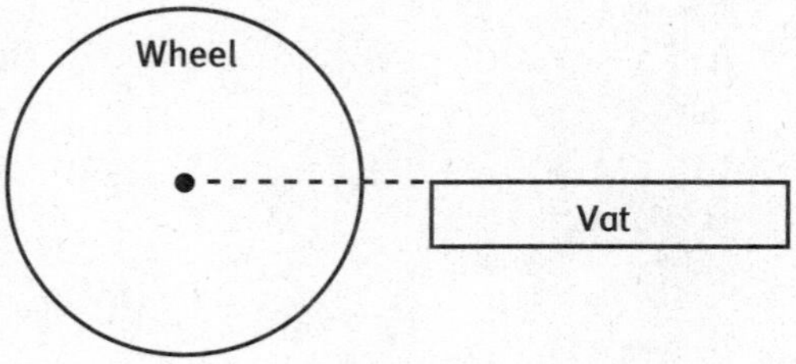

   b. angle of rotation = 180°

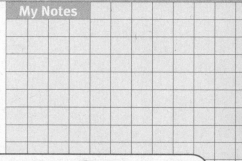

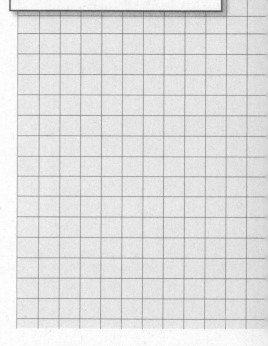

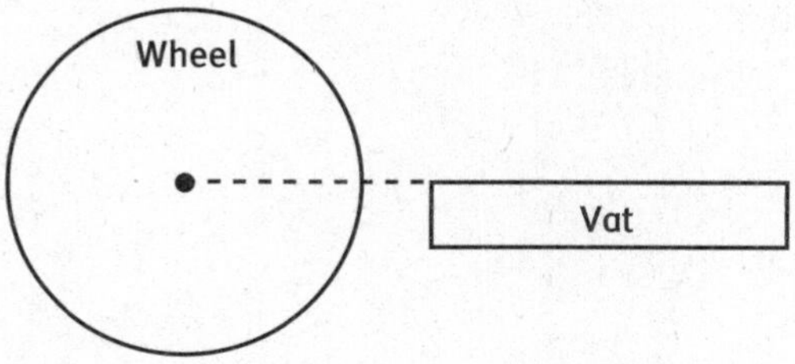

DISCUSSION GROUP TIP

As you share ideas in your group, ask your group members or your teacher for clarification of any language, terms, or concepts that you do not understand.

My Notes

c. angle of rotation = 30°

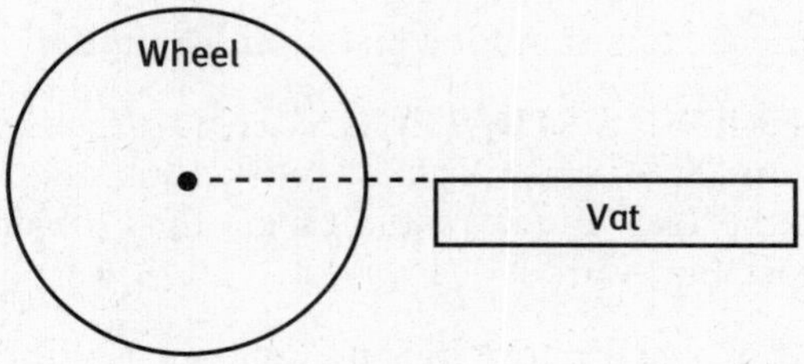

d. angle of rotation = 225°

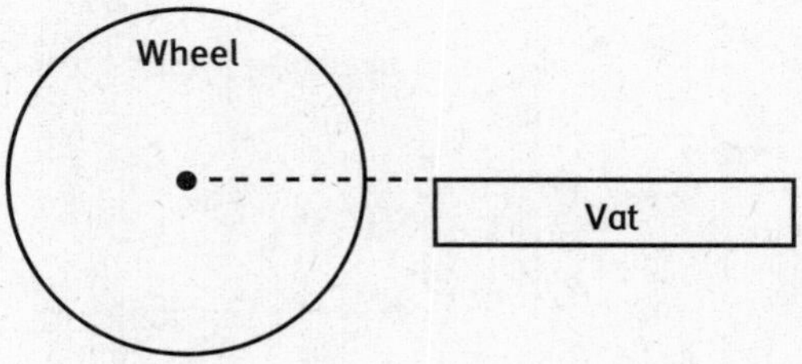

2. Make sense of problems. What is the length of the vat? Explain your reasoning.

3. How far away from the center of the wheel is the closest edge of the vat? Explain your reasoning.

The stirring mechanism is shown below. Suppose point C is at the origin. The wheel turns counterclockwise and θ is the angle in standard position whose terminal side contains point $P(x, y)$.

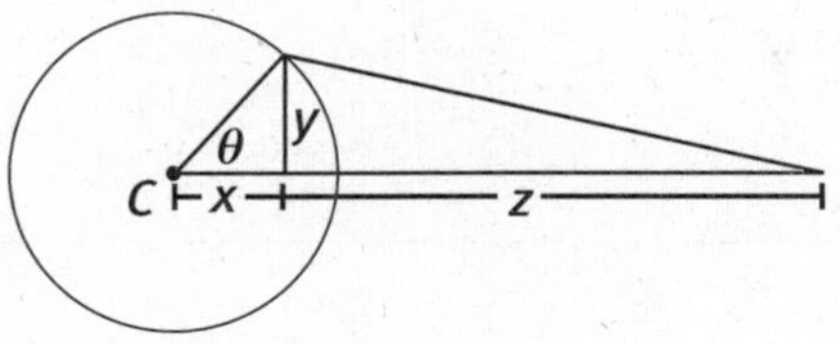

4. Express x as function of θ.

5. Express z as a function of θ.

6. How far is the stirrer blade from the center of the wheel for each angle of rotation? Write a function d for the distance in terms of the angle θ.

Check Your Understanding

7. Your answer to Item 6 should be a sum of two terms to represent $d(\theta)$.
   a. Using the diagram above Item 4, describe what the two terms represent.
   b. Explain the steps you took to obtain an expression for each of those two terms.

8. **Reason quantitatively.** Verify that your function is correct by evaluating $d(0°)$, $d(180°)$, $d(30°)$, and $d(225°)$ and then comparing the results with your answers to Item 1.

Use the radius of 2 feet and a rod length of 5 feet to answer the following.

9. If the stirrer blade is at the midpoint of the vat, what is the measure of the angle from the horizontal ray to the attachment point P? Explain how you arrived at your answer.

10. If the stirrer blade is three-fourths of the distance from the end nearest the wheel to the far end of the vat, use algebraic methods to find the measure of the angle from the horizontal ray to the attachment point P.

My Notes

CONNECT TO AP

In this activity, you are exploring a problem using multiple representations. In AP Calculus, you will be expected to:

- Work with functions represented in a variety of ways: graphical, numerical, analytical, or verbal;
- Model a written description of a physical situation with a function, a differential equation, or an integral; and
- Use technology to help solve problems, experiment, interpret results, and support conclusions.

My Notes

11. Write the function for the distance of the stirrer blade from the center of the wheel in terms of the angle of rotation θ, radius r, and rod length s.

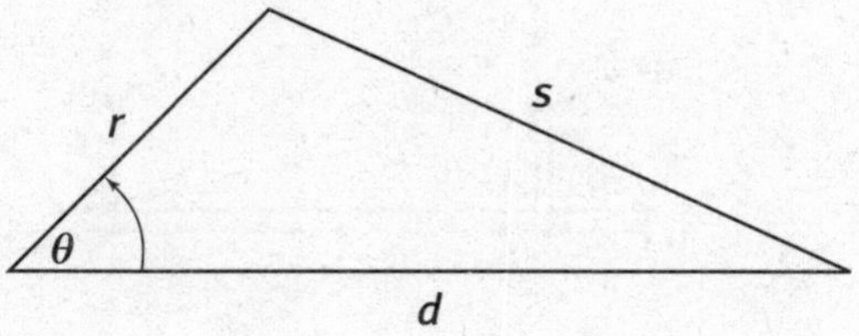

12. There are several ways to think about the relationship between s and r.

a. What expression contains s and r in your answer to Item 11? What relationship must exist between s and r?

b. In the diagram for Item 11, draw the ***altitude*** to the side whose length is d. Write an expression for the length of the altitude using what you know about right triangles.

MATH TERMS

The **altitude** of a triangle is the perpendicular line from the base to the opposite vertex.

c. Compare your relationships from part a and part b.

Check Your Understanding

13. For the chocolate stirrer, the situation with the wheel and stirrer blade represents a conversion between linear motion and circular motion.

a. Do both motions represent constant velocity? Explain.

b. Do both the wheel and the blade represent motions in a constant direction? Explain.

14. How is trigonometry used to translate motion along the point of a wheel into a different kind of motion?

15. **Reason quantitatively.** The equation from Item 11 relates three sides, r, d, and s, and the included angle between r and d. Rewrite this equation below and solve it for s^2, the side opposite the given angle. Use the Pythagorean identity to simplify your result.

My Notes

LESSON 24-1 PRACTICE

Refer to the diagram from Item 4.

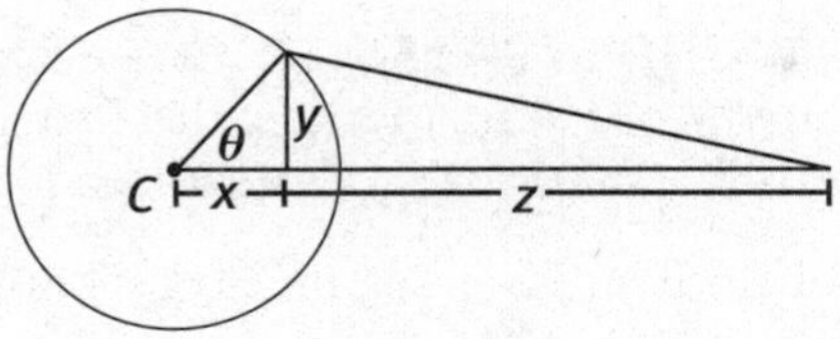

16. Find the distance from the center of the wheel to the stirrer blade for each angle.
a. 45° **b.** 270°

17. a. At what value(s) of θ is the speed of the stirrer blade at 0 ft/sec?
b. At what value(s) of θ does the speed of the stirrer blade reach its maximum?
c. During what range for θ is the velocity of the stirrer blade increasing? During what range for θ is the velocity of the stirrer blade decreasing?

18. Suppose the stirrer blade starts at the far end of the vat and the wheel makes one revolution in 30 seconds. After how many seconds does the stirrer blade reach the middle of the vat for the *first time*? After how many seconds does it reach the middle of the vat for the *second time*?

19. Express y as a function of θ.

20. Construct viable arguments. Express $x^2 + y^2$ in terms of θ and simplify your expression. Relate your result to the ordered pair (x, y).

My Notes

Learning Targets:

- Write equations for the Law of Cosines using a standard angle.
- Apply the Law of Cosines in real-world and mathematical situations.

SUGGESTED LEARNING STRATEGIES: Create Representations, Debriefing, Interactive Word Wall, Marking the Text, Simplify the Problem, Think-Pair-Share, Vocabulary Organizer

The equation you wrote in Item 15 of Lesson 24-1 is known as the ***Law of Cosines***.

1. **Express regularity in repeated reasoning.** Using the standard triangle, complete the Law of Cosines for each set of given information.

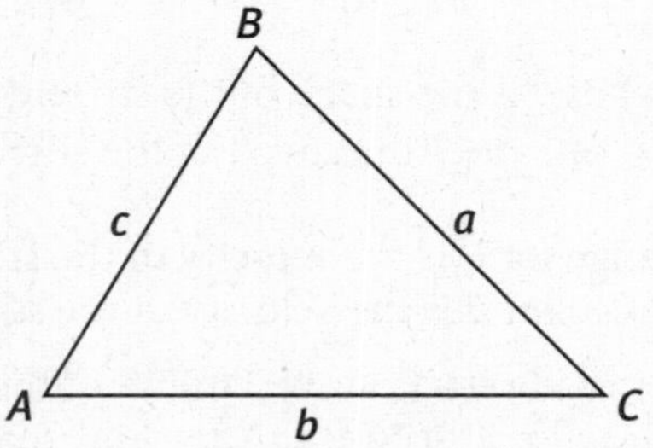

   a. Given sides a and b and included angle C.

   b. Given sides b and c and included angle A.

   c. Given sides a and c and included angle B.

Check Your Understanding

2. Here is an expression for the Law of Cosines:
   $[\ ]^2 = (\ )^2 + \{\ \}^2 - 2(\ )\{\ \}\cos[\ ]$
   a. The expressions inside the square brackets are related to each other. What is that relationship?
   b. The expressions inside the other grouping symbols are also related. What are those relationships?
   c. **Reason abstractly.** Write out the Law of Cosines using your own words.
3. In order to use the Law of Cosines, what is the minimum information needed about the sides and/or the angles of the triangle?

My Notes

The Law of Cosines is useful in many applications involving non-right triangles, also known as ***oblique triangles***.

4. A new courtyard at Ghirardelli Square in San Francisco will be triangular. Find the length of the retaining wall given the diagram shown below.

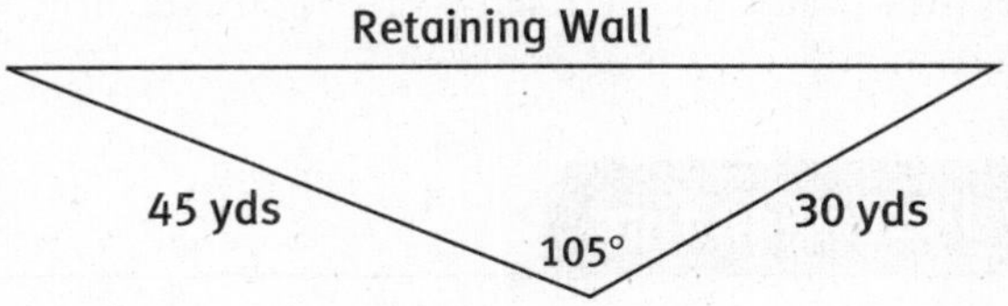

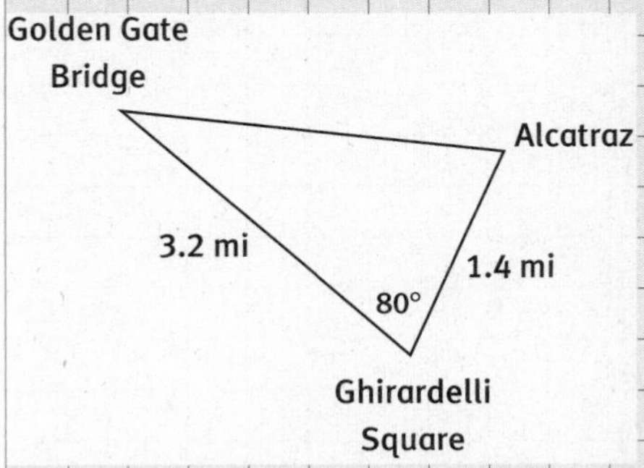

5. From Ghirardelli Square in San Francisco, you can see the Golden Gate Bridge and Alcatraz Island. The angle between the sight lines to these landmarks is approximately 80°. If the approximate distance from Ghirardelli Square to the Golden Gate Bridge is 3.2 miles and to Alcatraz is 1.4 miles, how far is Alcatraz Island from the Golden Gate Bridge?

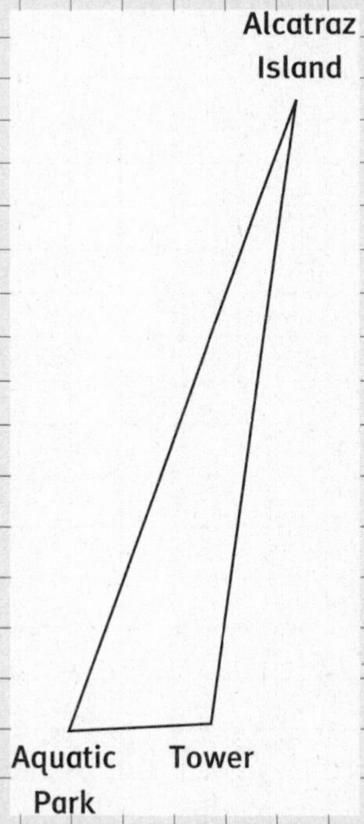

6. Model with mathematics. The annual Escape from Alcatraz Triathlon includes a 1.5-mile open-water swim from the island to Aquatic Park. Due to the strong currents, swimmers aim for a tower located 0.3 miles up the shore from Aquatic Park and 1.25 miles from Alcatraz Island. What is the angle between the course the swimmers set and the actual course they swim in the race?

7. Two sides of an isosceles triangle have lengths 8.5 and 10.5.

a. What are the angles of the triangle if the two congruent sides are 10.5?

b. What are the angles of the triangle if the two congruent sides are 8.5?

8. Two sides of an isosceles triangle have lengths 12.2 and 5.8.

a. Why is there only one possible triangle in this situation?

b. What are the angles of the triangle?

My Notes

9. Two ships leave a dock at the same time. They travel in straight lines so the angle between them is 52.1°. One ship travels at a rate of 15.8 miles per hour and the other travels at a rate of 12.16 miles per hour.
a. How far apart are they after four hours?

b. After four hours, they change direction and sail directly toward each other. If they maintain their same rates of travel, how long will it be until they meet?

Check Your Understanding

10. Model with mathematics. In Item 6, suppose you want to calculate the measure of the angle whose vertex is the Tower. Write a specific form of the Law of Cosines that will let you find that angle. Explain why you chose that form, and then find the angle.

LESSON 24-2 PRACTICE

11. Find the three angles of triangle *ABC*.

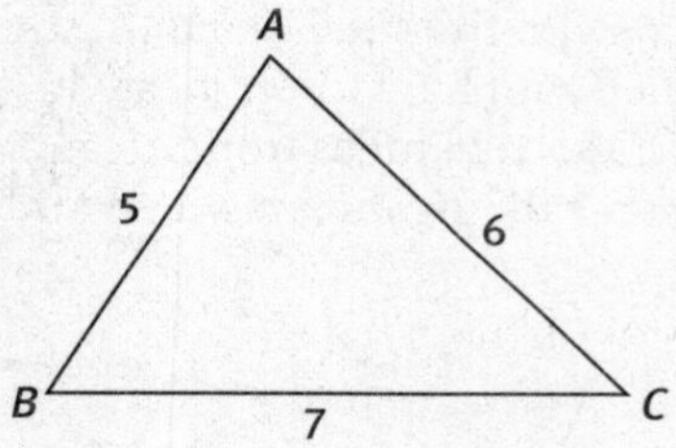

12. Find the missing sides and angles.

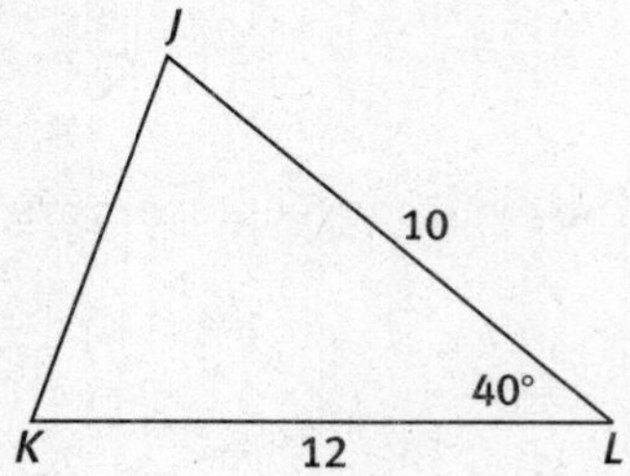

13.

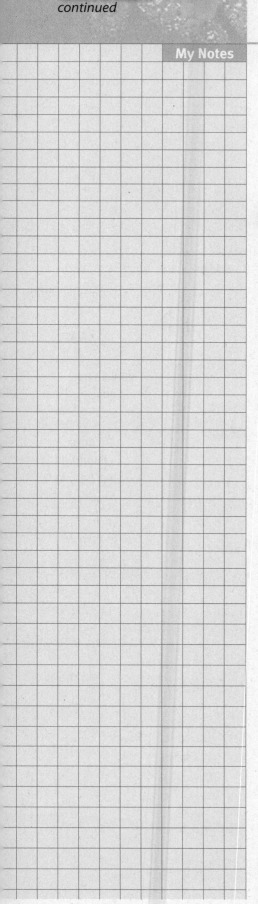

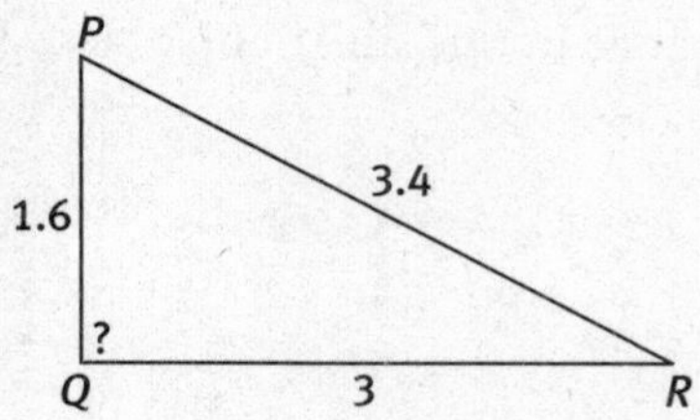

a. Use the Law of Cosines to find angle *Q*.
b. What kind of triangle is $\triangle PQR$? Verify your result.

14. When you use the Law of Cosines $c^2 = a^2 + b^2 - 2ab\cos C$, under what circumstances is a positive number subtracted from $a^2 + b^2$? Under what circumstances is a negative number subtracted from $a^2 + b^2$?

15. Make use of structure. The equation for the Law of Cosines is similar to the equation for the Pythagorean Theorem.

Law of Cosines

$c^2 = a^2 + b^2 - 2ab \cos C$

Pythagorean Theorem

$c^2 = a^2 + b^2$

Compare the two equations. Then explain how the Law of Cosines changes based on whether the triangle is acute, right, or obtuse.

ACTIVITY 24 PRACTICE

Write your answers on notebook paper. Show your work.

Lesson 24-1

1. Kyle is riding on a merry-go-round in a counterclockwise direction. Suppose point K represents his location on the ride as the merry-go-round turns. Kyle's mom Tammy is watching her son at point T. The radius of the merry-go-round is 5 meters and Tammy is 7 meters from the edge of the ride. Kyle's distance d from his mom can be expressed as a function of the angle of rotation θ.

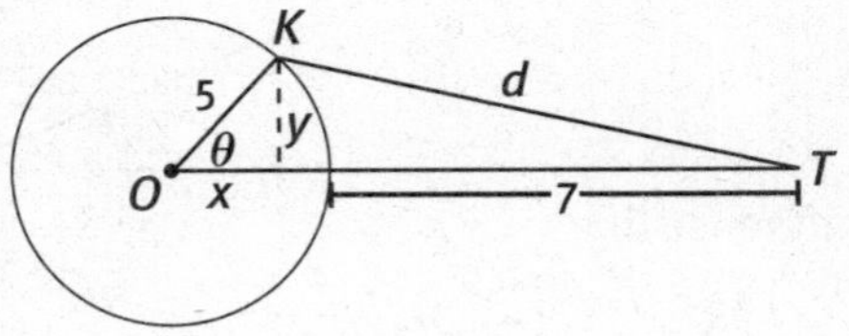

   a. What is d when $\theta = 0°$?
   b. What is d when $\theta = 150°$?
   c. What is d when $\theta = 180°$?
   d. What is the range of d?

2. Write the distance d between Kyle and Tammy as a function of angle θ.

3. For one rotation of the wheel, find all values of θ such that d is equal to 10.

4. For one rotation of the wheel, find all values of θ such that d is less than 9.

5. The wheel spins so that θ changes at a constant rate. Which statement about the rate at which d changes is true?
   A. d changes at a constant rate.
   B. d changes most rapidly when θ is near 90° or near 270°.
   C. d changes most rapidly when θ is near 0° or near 180°.
   D. The value of d does not change.

6. An 8-foot rod is attached to a wheel with a 3-foot radius to produce a vertical motion used to crush cocoa shells. The crusher plate moves up and down in a cylinder containing the shells as point P rotates counterclockwise around the wheel.

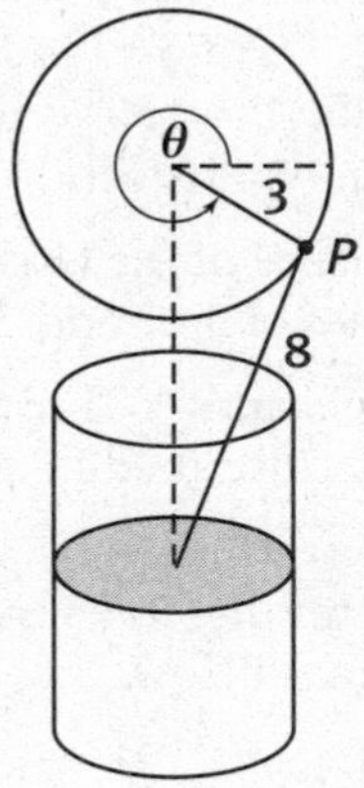

   a. Write a function in terms of the angle of rotation to give the distance of the crusher plate from the center of the wheel.
   b. Find the minimum and maximum distances that the crusher plate will extend below the center of the wheel. Illustrate your answer with a diagram.
   c. Graph the function on your calculator, sketch the graph on your paper, and identify the period and the range of the function.
   d. Find the distance of the crusher plate from the center of the wheel for $\theta = 0°$, 30°, 90°, 180°, and 225°.
   e. For what angles of rotation will the crusher plate be 10 feet from the center of the wheel?

7. In Item 6, suppose the radius of the wheel is c, the length of the rod is r, and the distance between the center of the wheel and the crusher plate is g. Write a function for g in terms of θ, c, and r.

Lessons 24-2

8. Use the Law of Cosines to solve for the indicated side or angle measure.
a. $a = 10$, $b = 11$, $C = 45°$. Find c.
b. $b = 9$, $c = 22$, $A = 150°$. Find a.
c. $a = 15$, $b = 62$, $c = 65$. Find B.
d. $a = 4$, $b = 10$, $C = 75°$. Find c.
e. $b = 50$, $c = 25$, $A = 150°$. Find a.
f. $a = 10$, $b = 6$, $c = 13$. Find C.

9. What is the measure of the largest angle in a triangle with sides of 3, 5, and 7?

10. Use the Law of Cosines to find the perimeter of a regular pentagon inscribed in a circle with a radius of 6.

11. Find the perimeter of Terry's triangular garden plot in the diagram below.

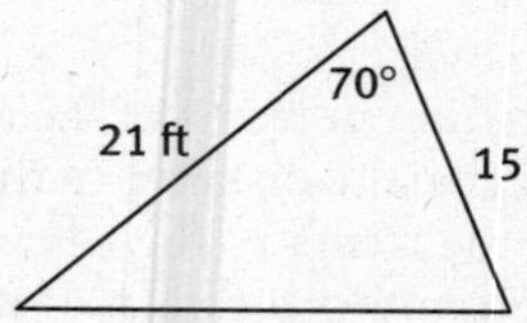

12. Two fishing boats leave the harbor at 6 a.m., each traveling in a straight line. The angle between their paths is 65°. The first boat averages 15 mph and the second boat averages 25 mph.
a. How far apart are the two boats after 1 hour? After 2 hours?
b. Without using the Law of Cosines, predict how far apart the boats would be after n hours if they maintain their respective speeds and directions. Explain your reasoning.

13. You CANNOT use the Law of Cosines if you know:
A. the three sides of a triangle
B. two sides and the included angle
C. two angles and the included side
D. two sides and the nonincluded angle

14. A surveyor establishes a reference point R and a reference line. Then the surveyor measures the distance from the reference point to two other points P and Q and measures the angles from P and Q to the reference line. Find the distance QR for each diagram below.

a.

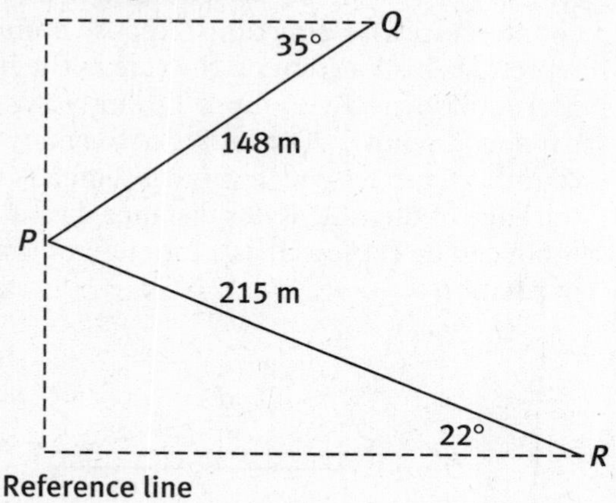

b.

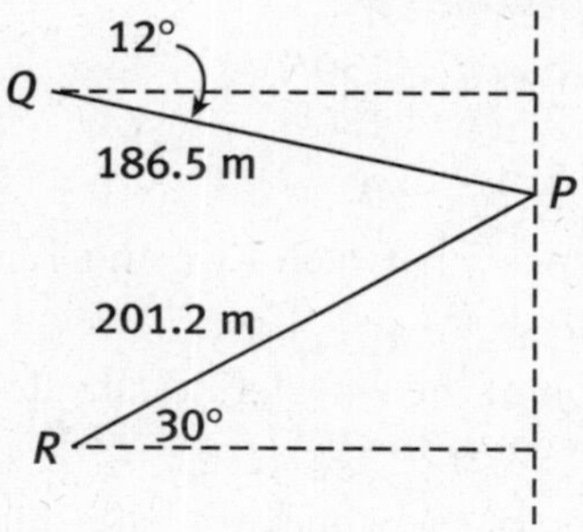

c.

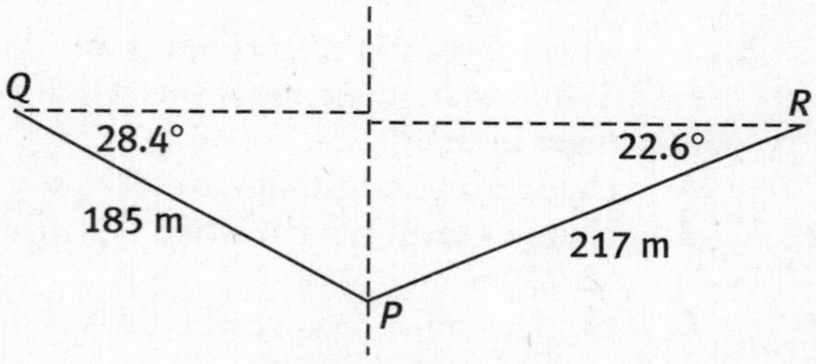

MATHEMATICAL PRACTICES
Construct Viable Arguments and Critique the Reasoning of Others

15. A student claims that all four choices in Item 13 are correct. How would you respond?

The Law of Sines

Got Lost?

Lesson 25-1 Modeling and Applying the Law of Sines

My Notes

Learning Targets:

- Calculate the bearing of a flight.
- Derive and use the Law of Sines.
- Find unknown sides or angles in oblique triangles.

SUGGESTED LEARNING STRATEGIES: Marking the Text, Visualization, Identify a Subtask, Simplify the Problem, Create Representations, Summarizing, Paraphrasing, Work Backward, Look for a Pattern, Quickwrite, Graphic Organizer, Think-Pair-Share, Group Presentation, Guess and Check

CONNECT TO AVIATION

This activity measures speed in miles per hour. However, the speed of commercial jets is typically represented as a Mach number, a percentage of the speed of sound. Mach speed varies as temperature and altitude change.

CONNECT TO NAVIGATION

Bearing is the direction an aircraft is pointing, but the course is the actual direction in which the plane is moving when wind is taken into account. The heading is the clockwise angle in degrees between an aircraft's destination and north.

In navigation, an object's heading indicates the direction of movement as measured by an angle rotated clockwise from north. A heading of 90° means an object is heading due east. A heading of 225° means an object is heading southwest. The *directional bearing* of a point is stated as the number of degrees east or west of the north-south line. To state the directional bearing of a point, write:

- N or S which is determined by the angle being measured
- the angle between the north or south line and the point, measured in degrees
- E or W which is determined by the location of the point relative to the north-south line

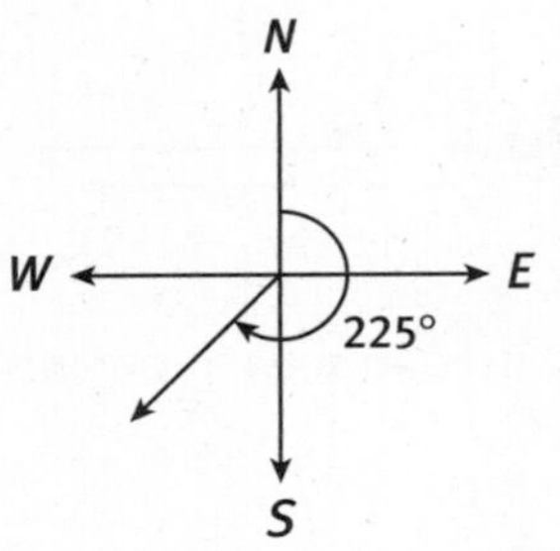

Heading

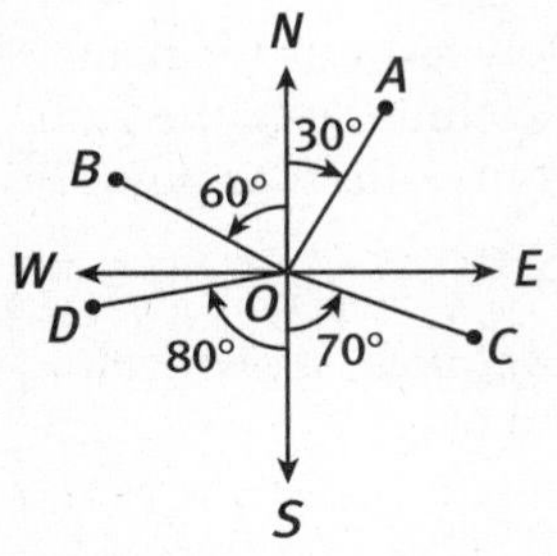

Directional Bearing

In the figure, *A* from *O* is N30°E, *B* from *O* is N60°W, *C* from *O* is S70°E, and *D* from *O* is S80°W.

International Flight 22 was on a course due north from Auckland, New Zealand, to Honolulu, Hawaii. Two thousand miles south of Honolulu, the plane encountered unexpected weather and the pilot changed bearing by 20°, as shown in the figure. The plane traveled on this new course for 1.5 hours, averaging 500 miles per hour.

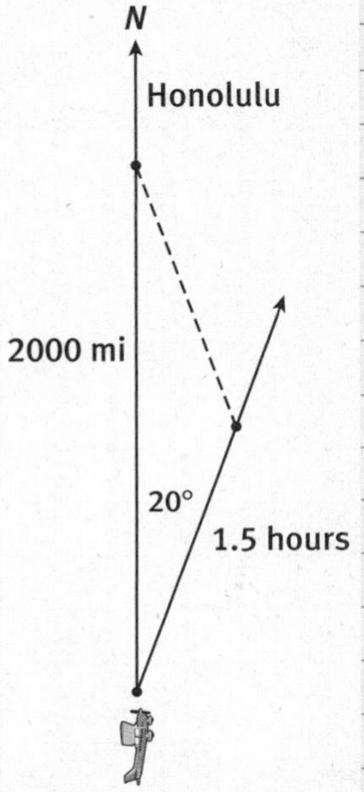

1. How far did the plane travel during the 1.5 hours it was flying on its new flight path?

2. How far was the plane from Honolulu after 1.5 hours?

My Notes

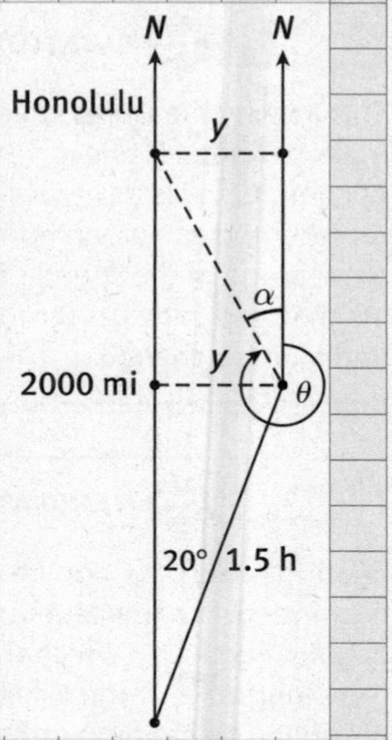

3. To adjust the flight path, the pilot changed the course by α degrees, as shown in the figure.
   a. Find the length y of the horizontal dotted lines in the diagram. Then use that length and your answer to Item 2 to find the value of α. What is the directional bearing of the plane?

   b. Use the value of α to determine the bearing θ of the plane.

Another flight, Flight 33, was 1100 miles southwest of Honolulu when the plane sped up and headed due east. Radio contact with Flight 33 occurred 2.5 hours later, and air traffic controllers placed it somewhere over the Cook Islands at point B.

4. Draw the altitude of the triangle from the point representing Honolulu to the horizontal flight path.
   a. What is length of the altitude?

   b. How far did the plane travel in 2.5 hours?

   c. How fast was the plane traveling along the path from point A to point B?

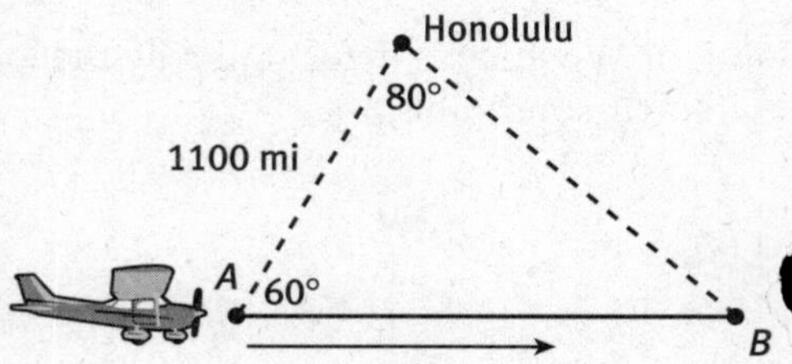

The ***Law of Sines***, shown below, could also be used to solve problems like Items 3 and 4.

$$\frac{a}{\sin A} = \frac{b}{\sin B} = \frac{c}{\sin C}$$

The next series of items will show you how your work from the previous items can be generalized to derive the Law of Sines.

5. **Model with mathematics.** Use the triangle shown below to answer the questions.

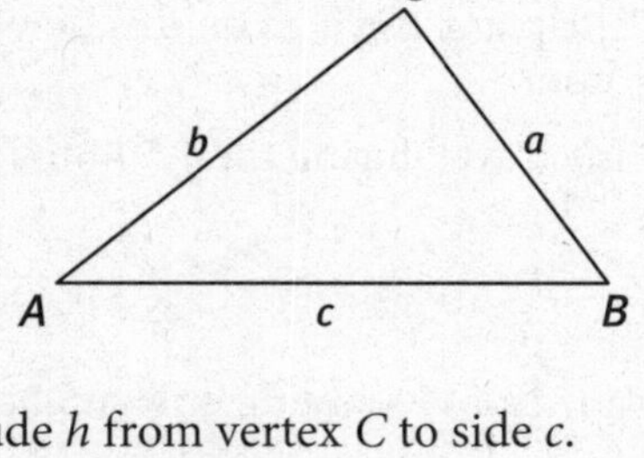

   a. Draw the altitude h from vertex C to side c.

   b. What is the measure of h in terms of A and b?

   c. What is the measure of h in terms of B and a?

   d. Use your work from parts b and c to write an equation relating A, B, a, and b.

My Notes

6. **Express regularity in repeated reasoning.** Repeat the process used in Item 5, but draw the altitude from vertex B to side b.

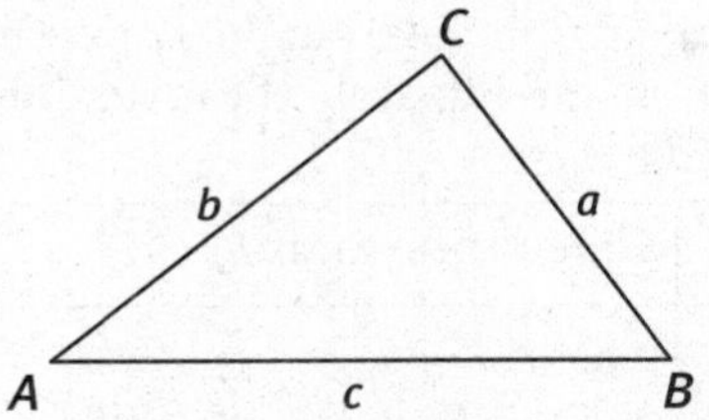

7. How do the equations you wrote in Items 5 and 6 compare to the Law of Sines written before Item 5?

Example A

Use the Law of Cosines and the Law of Sines to find the missing parts of this triangle. Explain which law you used.

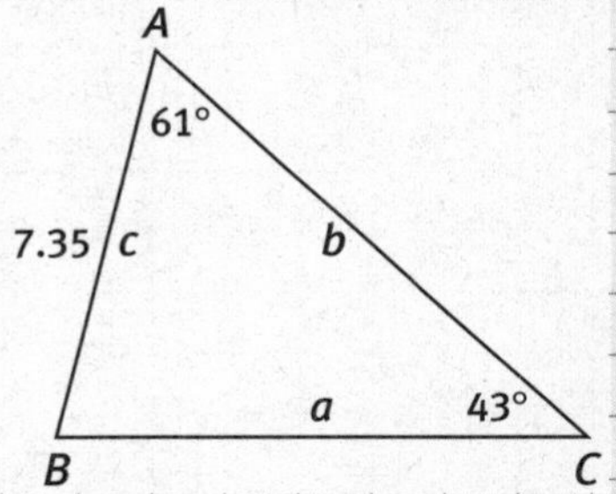

Step 1: There are two known angles and one known side. We know c and C, and we know A, so we can use the Law of Sines to find a.

$$\frac{c}{\sin C} = \frac{a}{\sin A};\ a = \frac{(7.35)(\sin 61^\circ)}{\sin 43^\circ} = 9.43$$

Step 2: Find angle B: $B = 180^\circ - (61^\circ + 43^\circ) = 76^\circ$

Step 3: To find the third side, we can use the Law of Cosines. We can check the answer using the Law of Sines.

$b^2 = a^2 + c^2 - 2ac\cos B = 9.43^2 + 7.35^2 - 2(9.43)(7.35)\cos 76^\circ = 109.41$

$b = 10.46$

Check: $\frac{b}{\sin B} = \frac{c}{\sin C};\ b = \frac{(7.35)(\sin 76^\circ)}{\sin 43^\circ} = 10.46$

Try These A

a. Use the Law of Sines to find q.

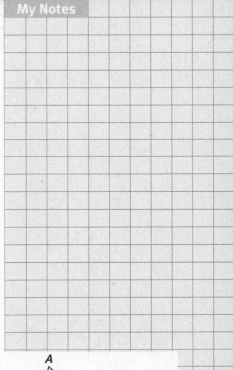

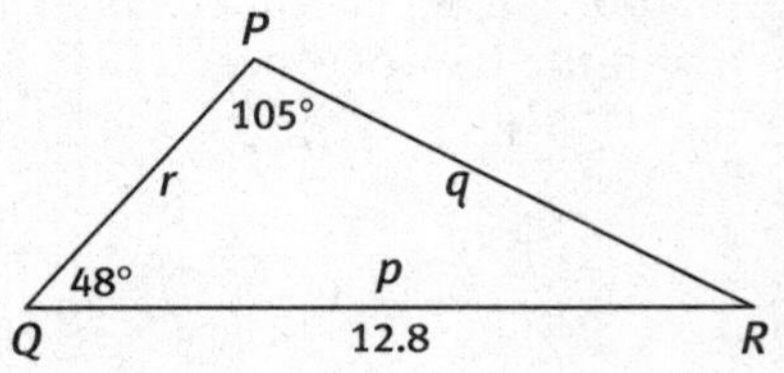

b. Use the Law of Cosines to find r. Check your value for r using the Law of Sines.

My Notes

Like the Law of Cosines, the Law of Sines relates the sides and angles in an ***oblique triangle***, and these can be used to find unknown sides or angles given at least three known measures that are not all angle measures.

8. The following table summarizes when each rule should be used to find missing measures in an oblique triangle. For each abbreviation, complete the given information and illustrate the given information by drawing and marking a triangle.

Rule	Given information	Illustration
Law of Cosines	SAS side, included angle, side SSS	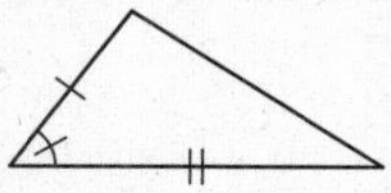
Law of Sines	ASA AAS	

Check Your Understanding

9. What is the minimum information needed in order to use the Law of Sines?

10. Make use of structure. What information about a triangle is enough to apply the Law of Sines but not the Law of Cosines? What information about a triangle is enough to apply the Law of Cosines but not the Law of Sines?

11. In a board game, a plane is flying from the origin of a coordinate plane toward the point (3, 4). What is the directional bearing of the plane? (Assume that north is the direction of the positive *y*-axis.)

My Notes

Use the Law of Sines to solve the following problems.

12. The pilots of Flight 33 spotted a deserted island 300 miles from their current location but continued on their course knowing there was another island 500 miles ahead on their current course. After a while they experienced engine trouble and turned to head for the deserted island, hoping to land safely. After making the turn, they estimated the plane could travel another 200 miles. They landed the plane knowing they were very lucky. How many additional miles could they have flown? Explain your reasoning.

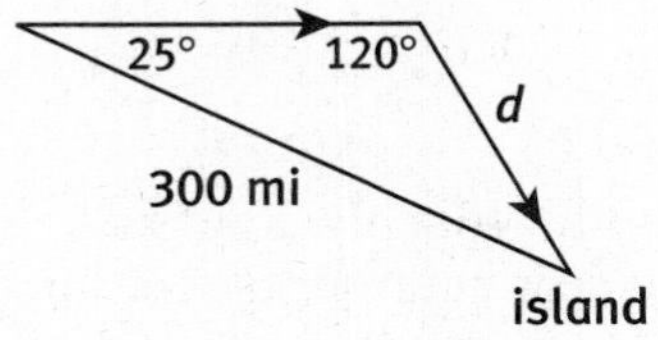

13. Survivors Taylor and Hank are on the beach of the deserted island, 500 yards apart. They spot a boat out at sea and estimate the angles between their positions and the boat as shown below. How far is the boat from Hank? How far is the boat from Taylor?

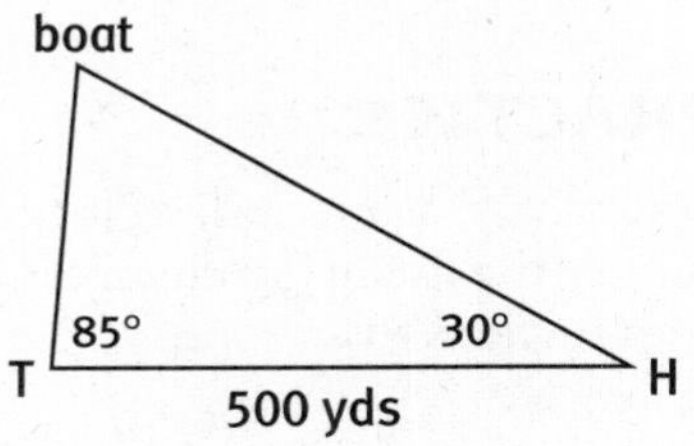

14. Reason quantitatively. Survivors Tariq and Jess were trying to estimate the distance to the top of a mountain they hoped to hike up to get a better view of the landscape. They measured the angles of elevation at points P_1 and P_2 located 100 yards apart. If the two survivors started at point P_2, how far would they have to walk to get to the top of the mountain?

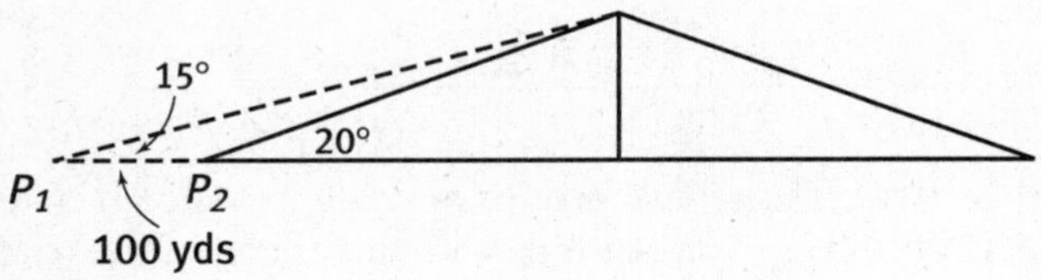

My Notes

Check Your Understanding

The last known location of Transcontinental Flight 22 was 1000 miles from a tracking station located at point *C*. The plane was flying due east at a 55° angle with the tracking station.

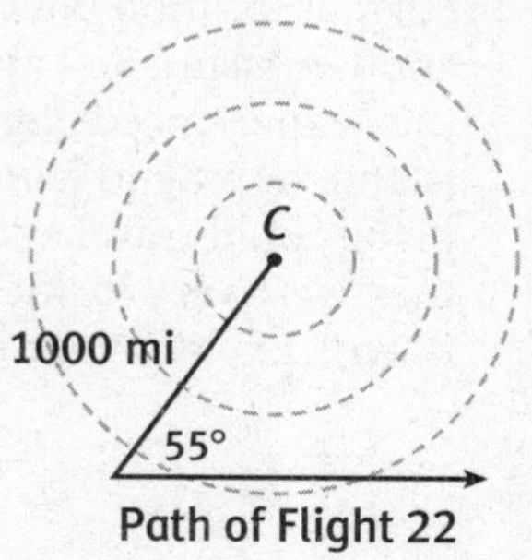

15. Suppose Flight 22 continued to fly due east.

a. If a search plane is sent out from the tracking station and searches a 600-mile radius, will the search plane intercept the flight path? Show your work to explain your reasoning.

b. Would the search plane intercept the flight path if the search radius were 1000 miles? Explain.

c. Would the search plane intercept the flight path if the search radius were 900 miles? Explain.

16. What are some other possible search radii that would intercept the flight path in exactly one point?

LESSON 25-1 PRACTICE

17. A flight has a heading of 32°, as measured clockwise from north. What is its new heading under the following changes?

a. a quarter turn counterclockwise

b. a quarter turn clockwise

c. a rotation of 55° counterclockwise

18. In triangle *ABC*, angle *A* is 54°, angle *C* is 96°, and $AC = 275$. Find angle *B*, *AB*, and *BC*.

19. In triangle *PQR*, $PR = 14$, $QR = 15$, and $PQ = 13$. Find the three angles of the triangle.

20. In the diagram below, two sightings of the top of a flagpole are taken 75 meters apart on level ground. The two sightings are 21° and 32°. What is the height of the flagpole?

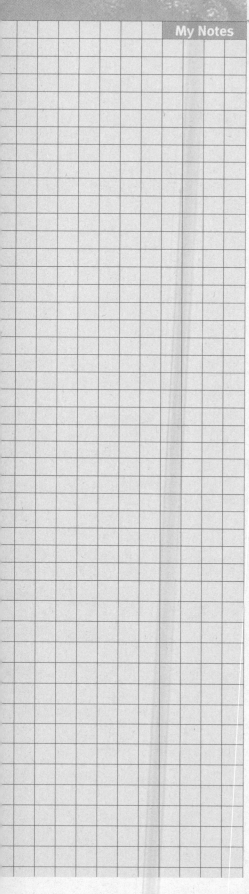

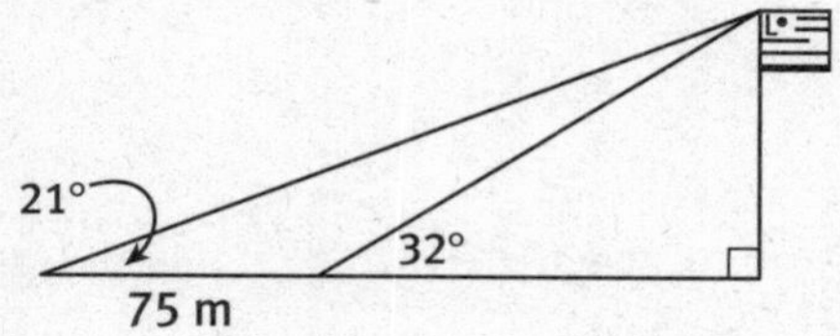

21. Attend to precision. Two groups of students were given a copy of triangle *MNP*. Group 1 measured sides and angles of the triangle and found that $MN = 21$ cm, angle $N = 47°$, and $MP = 37$ cm. Group 2 found that $MN = 20.8$ cm, angle $N = 47.42°$, and $MP = 37.4$ cm. Using the Law of Sines, what values will Group 1 and Group 2 get for angle *P*, for angle *M*, and for *NP*?

Learning Targets:

- Determine the number of distinct triangles given certain criteria.
- Use the Law of Sines to solve triangles with unknown sides or angles.

SUGGESTED LEARNING STRATEGIES: Note Taking, Interactive Word Wall, Graphic Organizer, Quick Write, Look for a Pattern, Think-Pair-Share, Create Representations, Guess and Check, Role Play, Identify a Subtask, Simplify the Problem, Group Presentation

When you are given two sides and the opposite angle, it is possible to have zero, one, or two distinct triangles depending on the given information. This situation is known as the ***ambiguous case (SSA)*** and is summarized below.

The Ambiguous Case (SSA)

Given a, b, and A with $h = b \sin A$, where b is adjacent to and a is opposite angle A, and h is the altitude of the potential triangle.

A is obtuse, $a \leq b$ 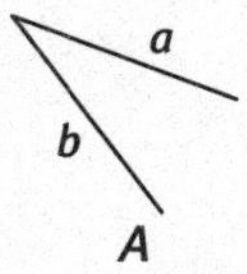 no triangle	A is obtuse, $a > b$ 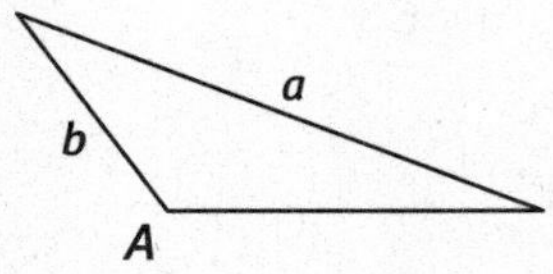 one triangle
A is acute, $a < h$ 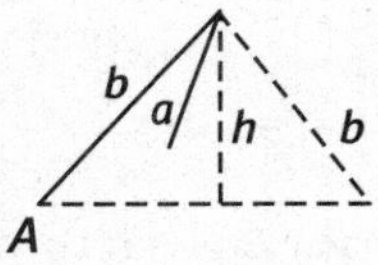 no triangle	A is acute, $a \geq b$ 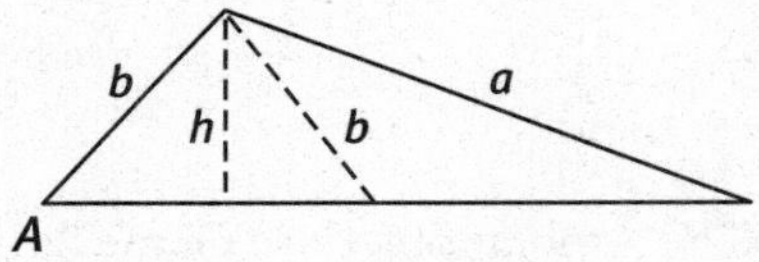 one triangle
A is acute, $a = h$ 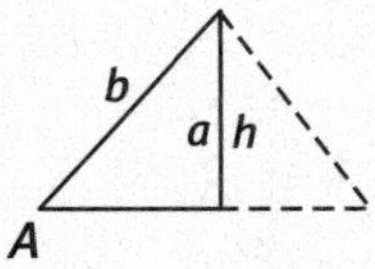 one triangle	A is acute, $h < a < b$ 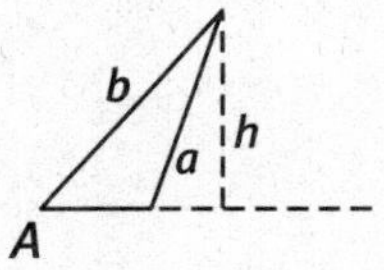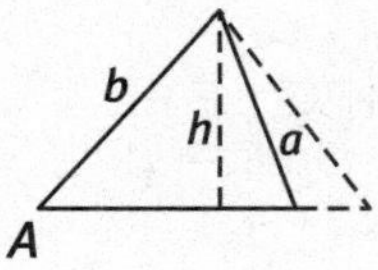 two triangles

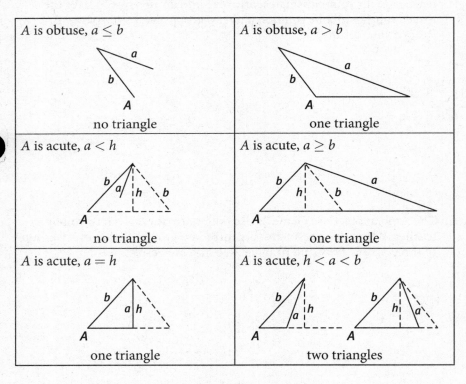

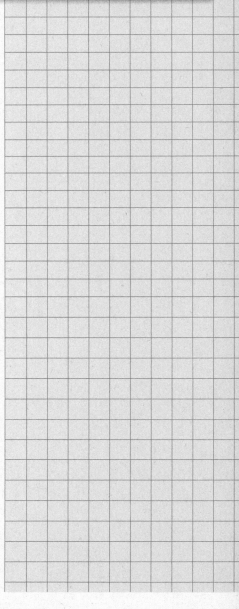

1. How can the value of $b \sin A$ help you determine the number of solutions given the ambiguous case?

2. How would you use this table to interpret the number of possible triangles for the ambiguous case if you were given angle C, side b, and side c?

My Notes

ACADEMIC VOCABULARY

The word ***ambiguous*** is used for things that are open to interpretation, or can have two meanings.

My Notes

3. Construct viable arguments. Determine how many triangles are possible with the given information. Draw a sketch and show any calculations you used.

a. $A = 30°, b = 10, a = 5$

b. $C = 75°, c = 18, a = 7$

c. $B = 100°, b = 50, c = 75$

d. $C = 40°, b = 25, c = 21$

e. $A = 63°, a = 10, c = 45$

4. The Ambiguous Case Game 1: Use the information given to you by your teacher. With your classmates, organize into groups so you have the three groups with one solution and two groups with two solutions. Record your results.

5. The Ambiguous Case Game 2: Use the information given to you by your teacher. With your classmates, organize into groups so that every group of three people forms no triangle. Record your results.

My Notes

Example A

Solving the two-solution SSA situation: Use the Law of Sines to solve a triangle given $A = 42°$, $a = 18$, $b = 22$.

Step 1: Determine the number of solutions. There are two solutions since the measure of side a is between $b \sin A$ and b.

$$b \sin A = 22 \sin 42° \approx 14.720 < 18$$

Step 2: Solve the first acute triangle using the Law of Sines.

$$\frac{18}{\sin 42°} = \frac{22}{\sin B_1}$$

$$\sin B_1 = \frac{22 \sin 42°}{18} \approx 0.8178$$

Find B_1.

$$B_1 = \sin^{-1}\left(\frac{22 \sin 42°}{18}\right) \approx 54.9°$$

Find C_1.

$$C_1 = 180° - (42° + 54.9°) = 83.1°$$

Find c_1.

$$c_1 = \frac{18 \sin(83.1°)}{\sin 42°} \approx 26.7$$

Step 3: Solve the second obtuse triangle. The angles B_1 and B_2 opposite the given adjacent side are supplementary.

$$B_2 = 180 - B = 180 - 54.9 = 125.1$$

$$C_2 = 180 - (42 + 125.1) = 12.9$$

$$c_2 = \frac{18 \sin 12.9}{\sin 42} \approx 6.0$$

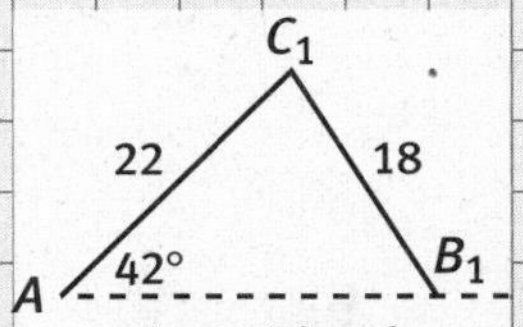

Acute triangle

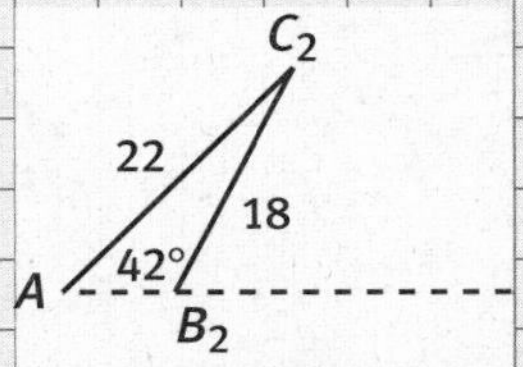

Obtuse triangle

Try These A

Each of these triangles has two possible solutions. Find them both.

a. $A = 55°$, $b = 40$, $a = 35$

b. $C = 20°$, $c = 6$, $b = 12$

Check Your Understanding

6. Solve each triangle using the Law of Sines.

a. $A = 52°$, $B = 85°$, $c = 16.8$

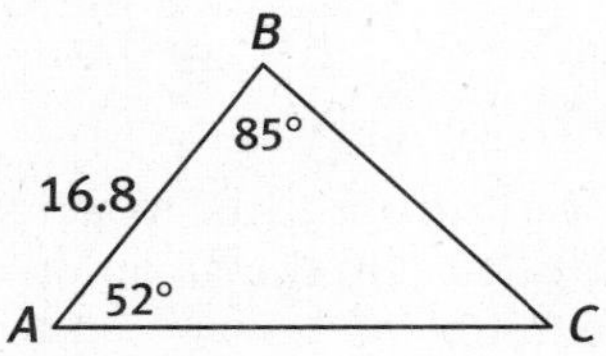

b. $A = 100°$, $B = 40°$, $a = 75$

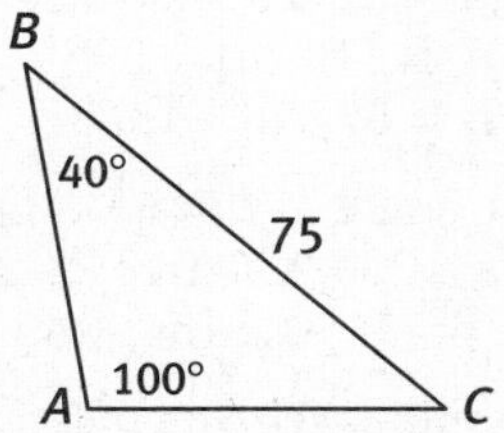

c. $B = 77°$, $a = 23$, $b = 36$

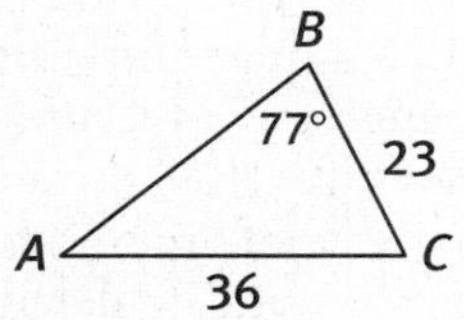

My Notes

7. A lookout tower, firefighters located 25 miles from the tower, and a forest fire form three vertices of a triangle. At the lookout tower, the angle between the forest fire and the firefighters is 35°. At the firefighters' location, the angle between the lookout tower and the fire is 100°. How far are the firefighters from the fire?

8. **Make sense of problems.** Determine the number of possible triangles for each given situation.
   a. $A = 45°$, $c = 100$, $a = 25$
   b. $B = 70°$, $c = 90$, $b = 85$
   c. $C = 100°$, $c = 6$, $a = 7.5$
   d. $A = 60°$, $b = 4$, $a = 2\sqrt{3}$

9. Why is the term *ambiguous case* used in this lesson? Explain how you know the situation is ambiguous. Describe how to solve an "ambiguous case" situation without using a formula.

LESSON 25-2 PRACTICE

10. Two marine biologists spotted some sea lions in the bay. The biologists were located on a beach about 100 feet apart. The angle between the shore and the sea lions for each biologist is shown below. How far were the sea lions from each biologist?

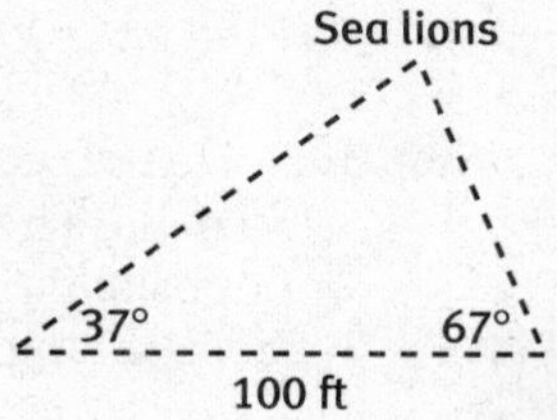

11. A billboard is 40 feet tall. At a horizontal distance x feet from the billboard, the angle of elevation to the bottom of the sign is 20° and the angle of elevation to the top of the sign is 40°. How far away is the billboard?

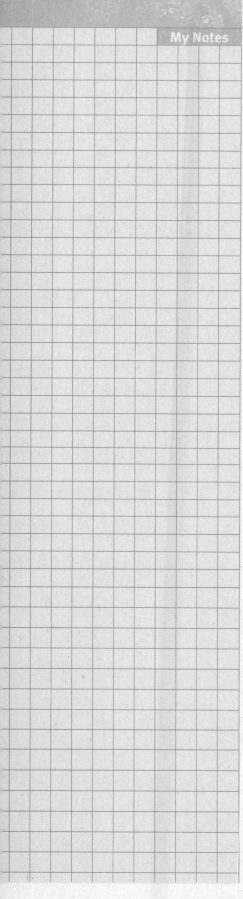

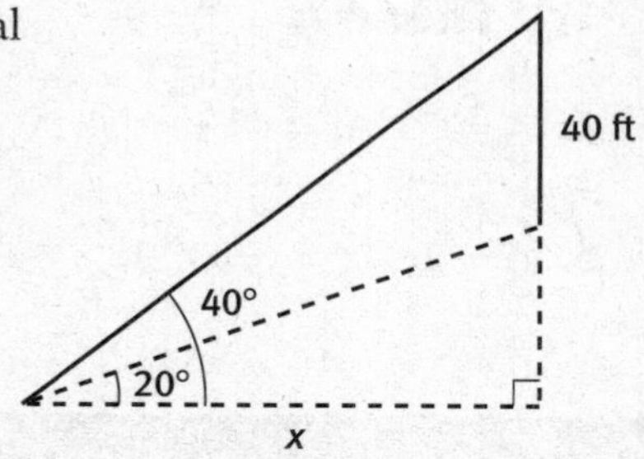

12. Solve the two-solution ambiguous case situation given $C = 50°$, $b = 120$, $c = 100$.

13. Solve each triangle using the Law of Sines.
    a. $A = 22°$, $B = 35°$, $c = 43$
    b. $A = 110°$, $B = 30°$, $a = 8$
    c. $B = 57°$, $a = 13$, $b = 30$

14. The angle of elevation from a point 50 yards from a tree to the top of the tree is 23°. The tree leans 4° away from vertical in the direction opposite the point 50 yards away. How tall is the tree?

15. Joaquin is fencing in a triangular pasture. Two posts are located 300 yards apart, and the angles from the posts to the third one are 75° and 68°, respectively. About how much fencing does Joaquin need?

16. **Use appropriate tools strategically.** Use a ruler and protractor to construct triangle ABC with $AB = 12.5$ cm, angle $A = 42°$, and angle $B = 40°$. Use your ruler and protractor to measure AC, CB, and angle C. Then calculate the size of angle C and use the Law of Sines to find AC and CB. How close were your measurements to your calculated values?

ACTIVITY 25 PRACTICE

Write your answers on notebook paper.
Show your work.

Lesson 25-1

1. Use the Law of Sines to solve triangle ABC with the following measures.

   angle $A = 150°$, angle $C = 20°$, $a = 200$

2. Two points, A and B, are 6 miles apart on level ground. An airplane is flying between A and B. The angle of elevation to the plane from point A is 51° and from point B is 68°. What is the altitude of the airplane?

3. A rescue boat and a pirate ship located 5 nautical miles apart both spotted a stranded sailboat at the same time. The rescue boat had a maximum speed of 18 knots (nautical miles per hour), and the pirate ship was capable of 22 knots. The angle between boats is shown below. If both ships set off at their top speed, which one will get to the stranded sailboat first, and how long will it take?

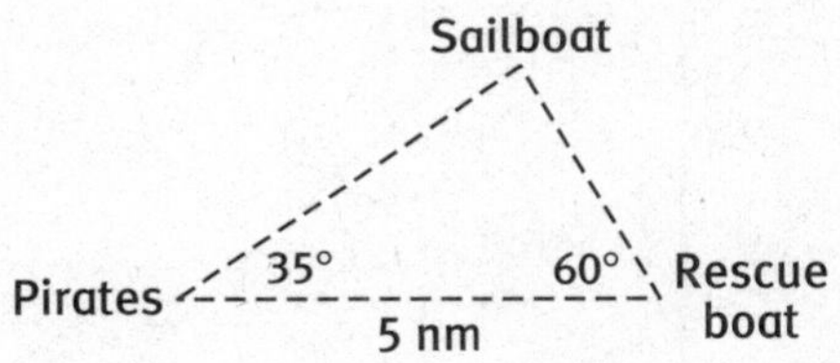

4. The angle of elevation from a point P 65 yards from a tree to the top of the tree is 31°. The tree leans 7 degrees away from P. How tall is the tree?

5. In triangle DEF below, angle DEF is divided into three angles, each of 15°, and angle F is 50°. If $XZ = 210$, find the values of x, y, z, a, b, and c.

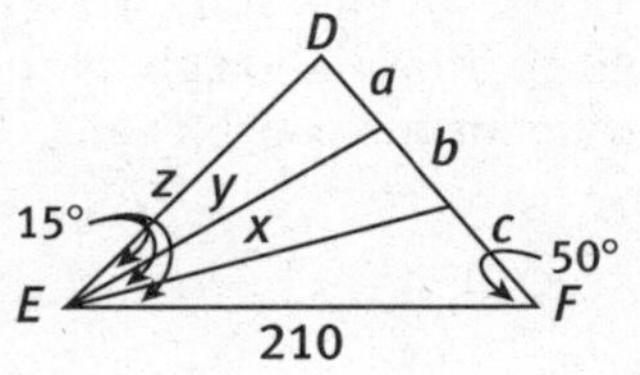

6. Joanna is interested in determining the height of a tree. She is at a point A, 80 feet from the base of the tree, and she notices that the angle of elevation to the top of the tree is 52°. The tree is leaning toward her and is growing at an angle of 85° with respect to the ground. What is the height of the tree?

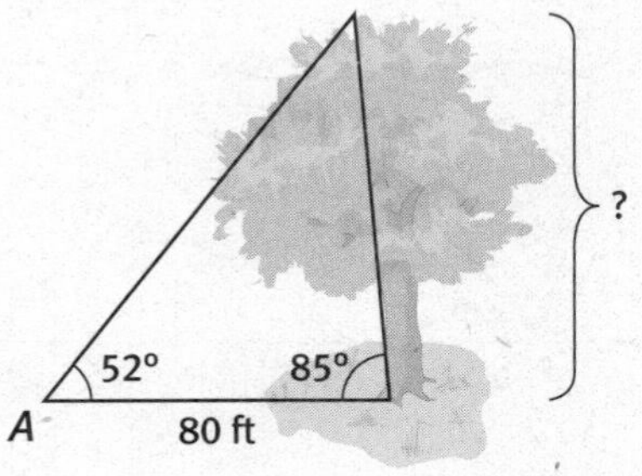

7. From a point B on the ground that is level with the base of a building and is 160 meters from the building, the angle of elevation to the top of the building is 41°. From point B, the angle of elevation to a ledge on the side of the building is 19°. What is the distance between the ledge and the top of the building?

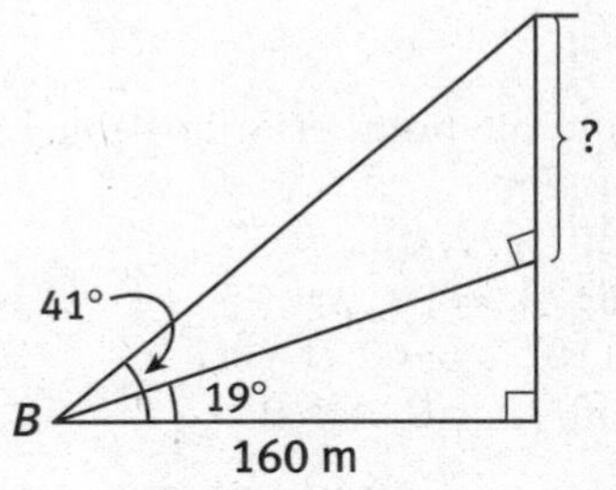

8. An explorer wants to know the width of a river. She starts by establishing two points, *P* and *Q*, on one side of the river that are 280 feet apart. She notices that a particular tree on the far side of the river forms an angle of 48° with side *PQ* when sighted from point *P*, and forms an angle of 52° with side *PQ* when sighted from point *Q*. How wide is the river? Show your work.

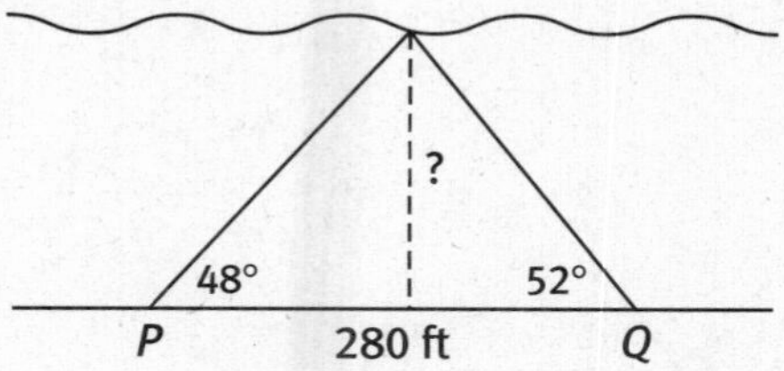

9. Which of the following statements is NOT true?
A. You can use the Law of Sines if you know any two angles and any one side of a triangle.
B. You can use the Law of Sines if you know the three sides of a triangle.
C. You can use the Law of Cosines if you know any two sides and any one angle of a triangle.
D. You can use the Law of Cosines if you know the three sides of a triangle.

Lesson 25-2

10. Determine the number of possible triangles for each situation:
a. $A = 30°, c = 10, a = 5$
b. $B = 63°, c = 90, b = 75$
c. $C = 110°, c = 60, a = 47$
d. $A = 60°, b = 9, a = 9$

11. Solve the two-solution ambiguous case situation.
a. $B = 52°, a = 9, b = 8$
b. $C = 30°, b = 20, c = 12$

12. Explain why only one triangle *ABC* is possible if $a = 20$, $b = 16$, and angle $A = 30°$.

13. Explain why no triangle *MNP* is possible if $m = 7, p = 16$, and angle $M = 30°$.

14. Explain why two triangles are possible if $x = 10$, $y = 16$, and angle $X = 30°$.

15. For the figure below, find angles 1, 2, 3, 4, and 5, and find *QR*, *RS*, and *QS*.

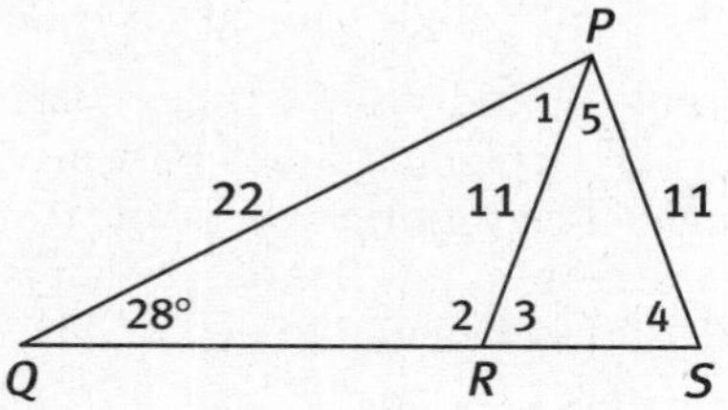

16. For the figure below, find angles *Z*, 1, 2, 3, and 4, and find *XW*, *WX*, *YZ*, and *XZ*. If necessary, round values to the nearest tenth.

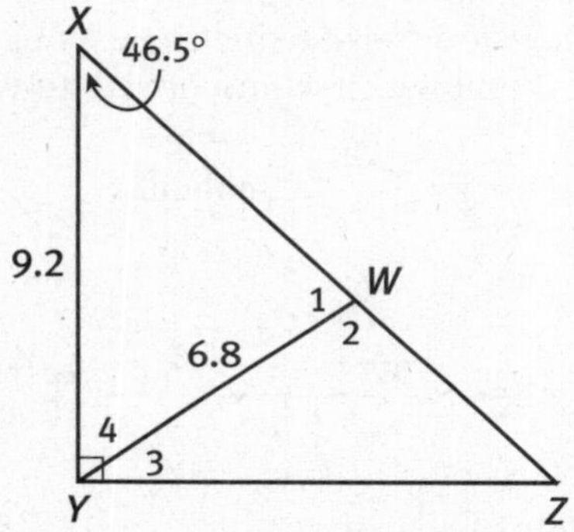

MATHEMATICAL PRACTICES
Construct Viable Arguments and Critique the Reasoning of Others

17. A student claims that the ambiguous case means you cannot tell whether 0, 1, or 2 triangles are possible given information about the triangle. Is that statement correct? Explain.

The bell tower of the cathedral in Pisa, Italy, is known to most of the world as the Leaning Tower of Pisa. The tower began leaning during construction around 1275. In 1990, Italian officials feared it would topple over and closed the site to the public. Engineers used steel cables attached to a counterweight to stabilize the structure during repairs. At the time the 130-meter cables were attached, the tower leaned about 5.5° past vertical.

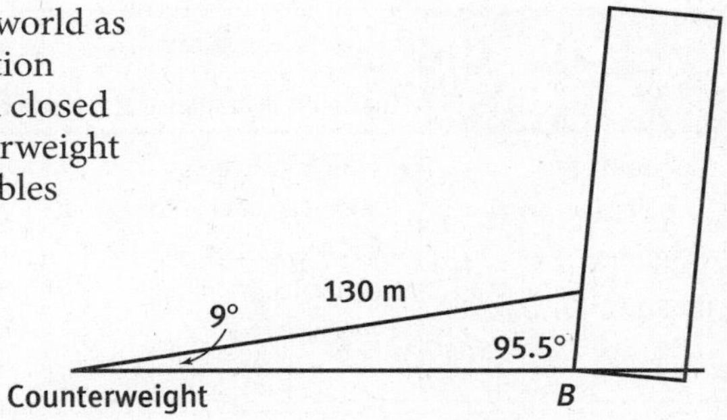

1. Why is the measure of angle B equal to 95.5°?

2. How far from the base of the tower were the counterweights?

The Leaning Tower of Pisa is not the only leaning bell tower in Europe. In 2008, a newspaper reported that since the repair of the Leaning Tower of Pisa, the 120 ft Tower of Walfridus in Bedum, Netherlands, was now the most tilted tower in Europe. It leaned 8.5 feet off center while the postrepair Tower of Pisa, at 180 ft tall, leaned only 13 feet off center.

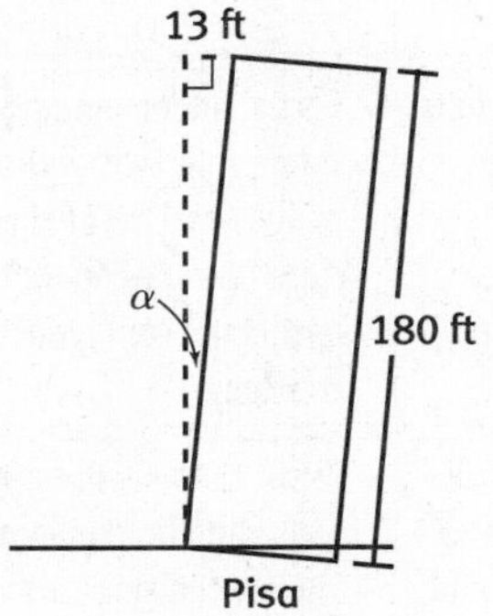

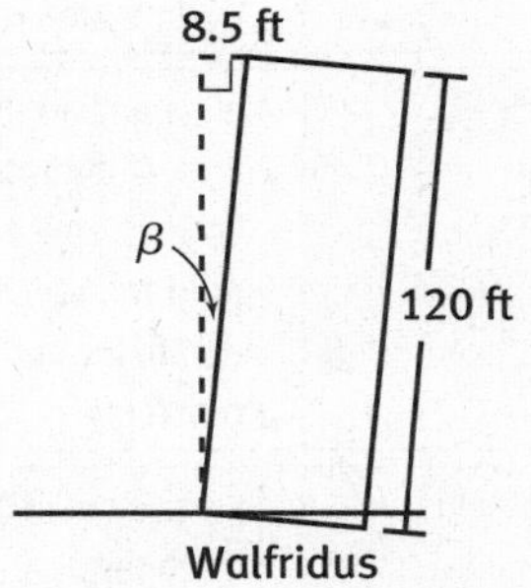

3. What are the angles α and β at which each tower is leaning?

4. Is the newspaper's report valid? Explain your reasoning.

5. The Leaning Tower of Pisa is a *cylindrical* building. Architects design buildings in all shapes to fit various sites. The Flatiron Building in New York City is probably the most famous *triangular* building. The sides of the building are 173 feet along 5th Ave, 190 feet along Broadway, and 87 feet along 22nd St. Follow the steps below to find the area of the roof.

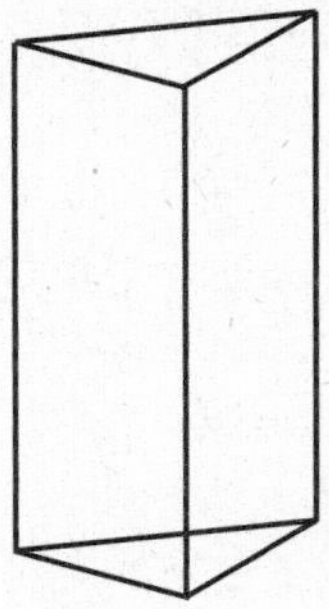

a. Draw triangle ABC for the roof, with $AB = 173$, $BC = 87$, and $AC = 190$. Use the Law of Cosines to find angle A.

b. Draw the altitude h from vertex B to side AC. Find an expression for h in terms of angle A and side c.

c. A formula for the area of a triangle is Area $= \frac{1}{2}bh$, where b is a side of the triangle and h is the altitude to that side. Restate that formula using your results from part b. Then use your restated formula to find the area of triangle ABC.

d. For any triangle XYZ, use the ideas in parts b and c to write three formulas for the area of the triangle in terms of two sides and one angle.

6. Two airplanes leave an airport at the same time. One flies with a bearing of 24° at an average speed of 475 mph, and the other flies with a bearing of 285° at an average speed of 450 mph. How far apart are the two planes after two hours?

Right and Oblique Triangles, Area

TILTING TOWERS AND TRIANGLES

Scoring Guide	Exemplary	Proficient	Emerging	Incomplete
	The solution demonstrates these characteristics:			
Mathematics Knowledge and Thinking (Items 2, 3, 4, 5, 6)	• Clear and accurate understanding of the Law of Cosines, Law of Sines, and general right triangle trigonometry	• A functional understanding of the Law of Cosines, Law of Sines, and general right triangle trigonometry in a mostly correct way, but with some errors	• Partial understanding of some of the following: Law of Cosines, Law of Sines, and general right triangle trigonometry	• Little or no understanding of the Law of Cosines, Law of Sines, and general right triangle trigonometry
Problem Solving (Items 1, 2, 3, 4, 5, 6)	• An appropriate and efficient strategy that results in a correct answer when solving triangles using Law of Cosines, Law of Sines or Heron's Area Theorem	• A strategy that may include unnecessary steps but results in a correct answer	• A strategy that results in some incorrect answers	• No clear strategy when solving problems
Mathematical Modeling / Representations (Items 2, 3, 4, 5)	• Clear and accurate understanding of the Law of Cosines, Law of Sines, and right triangle trigonometry within the context of the problem	• A functional understanding of representations of the Law of Cosines, Law of Sines, and right triangle trigonometry within the context of the problem	• Partial understanding of representations of the Law of Cosines, Law of Sines, and right triangle trigonometry within the context of the problem	• Little or no understanding of representations of the Law of Cosines, Law of Sines, and right triangle trigonometry within the context of the problem
Reasoning and Communication (Items 1, 4)	• Precise use of appropriate math terms and language to explain the application and resulting solutions of the Law of Cosines, Law of Sines, and right triangle trigonometry	• Correct characterization of the terms and language to explain the application and resulting solutions of the Law of Cosines, Law of Sines, and right triangle trigonometry	• Misleading or confusing terms and language to explain the application and resulting solutions of the Law of Cosines, Law of Sines, and right triangle trigonometry	• Incomplete or inaccurate characterization and language to explain the application and resulting solutions of the Law of Cosines, Law of Sines, and right triangle trigonometry

Conics, Parametric Equations, and Vectors

5

Unit Overview

In this unit, you will study symbolic and graphic representations of conic sections and apply them to real-world situations. You will also represent points and curves in polar form and relate these to their rectangular form. In addition, you will represent, investigate, and solve problems using parametric equations, vectors, and complex numbers.

Key Terms

As you study this unit, add these and other terms to your math notebook. Include in your notes your prior knowledge of each word, as well as your experiences in using the word in different mathematical examples. If needed, ask for help in pronouncing new words and add information on pronunciation to your math notebook. It is important that you learn new terms and use them correctly in your class discussions and in your problem solutions.

Academic Vocabulary

- denote

Math Terms

- conic section
- ellipse
- foci of a conic section
- minor axis
- major axis
- hyperbola
- transverse axis
- polar grid
- polar axis
- initial ray
- terminal ray
- polar coordinates
- polar equation
- rose curve
- cardioid
- limaçon
- parametric equations
- angular velocity
- linear velocity
- vector
- magnitude of a vector
- absolute value of a complex number
- argument of a complex number
- polar form of a complex number
- rectilinear motion
- planar motion
- position vector

ESSENTIAL QUESTIONS

? How are multiple representations of conic sections related and used to model real-world situations?

? How are parametric equations and vectors used to solve real-world problems involving motion?

EMBEDDED ASSESSMENTS

These assessments, following Activities 29, 31, and 33, will allow you to demonstrate your ability to write the equations of conic sections from descriptive information and your understanding of the relationship between polar and rectangular graphs. You will also have an opportunity to demonstrate your understanding of parametric equations, vectors, and complex numbers.

Getting Ready

Write your answers on notebook paper.
Show your work.

1. Solve the following by completing the square. Show the steps of the process.

$$x^2 - 6x - 16 = 0$$

2. Solve the following using the Quadratic Formula.
a. $2x^2 - 5x + 7 = 0$
b. $x^2 + 3x - 5 = 0$

3. Graph $y = \tan^{-1} x$ and give the domain and range of the function.

4. If $\tan\theta = 1$, give the values of θ for $0° < \theta < 360°$.

5. Give the exact value of the following.
a. $\cos 32° \cos 2° + \sin 32° \sin 2°$
b. $\sin 193° \cos 43° - \cos 193° \sin 43°$

6. The point $(-3, 4)$ is a point on the terminal side of an angle θ. Find each value.
a. $\cos\theta =$
b. $\sin\theta =$
c. $\tan\theta =$
d. $\theta =$

7. Write the equation of the line that passes through $(4, -3)$ and $(7, 3)$.

8. Find the point of intersection of each of the following.
a. lines $x - y - 7 = 0$ and $3x - 11y + 11 = 0$
b. a line passing through $(2, 1)$ and $(-4, -3)$ and a line through $(-3, 2)$ and $(1, -4)$

9. Tell the measure of θ, for $0° < \theta < 90°$, if
a. $\cos\theta = \frac{1}{2}$.
b. $\cos\theta = \frac{\sqrt{2}}{2}$.
c. $\cos\theta = 0.5592$.

10. Use the right triangle below.
a. Find β if $c = 15$ and $a = 8$.
b. Find a and b, given $\beta = 53.4°$ and $c = 34.8$.

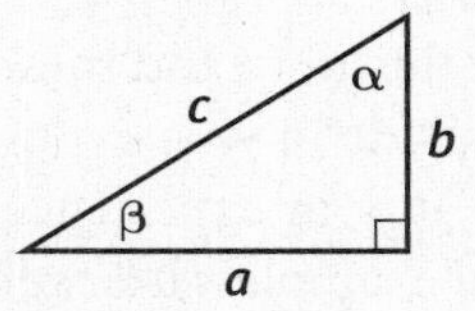

Parabola Equations and Graphs

The Human Cannonball

Lesson 26-1 Parabolas and Conic Sections

My Notes

Learning Targets:

- Define conic sections as intersections of a double-napped cone.
- Relate the locus definition of a parabola to its equation.
- Find the inverse relation for a parabola.

SUGGESTED LEARNING STRATEGIES: Visualization, Think-Pair-Share, Interactive Word Wall, Create Representations, Quickwrite

As a human cannonball, Rossa is shot from a special cannon. She is launched into the air by a spring. Rossa lands in a horizontal net 150 ft from the cannon.

The equation $h = -0.0112x^2 + 1.84x + 5$ represents Rossa's height h above the ground in feet, when she has traveled a horizontal distance of x feet. Rossa's launch will be filmed in 3-D with two cameras. Camera 1 is stationary and positioned under the vertex of her flight path. Camera 2 moves along a horizontal cable above Rossa's flight path. The cameras must always be the same distance from Rossa while filming. Camera 1 is mounted on a 58.250 ft high stand, at a horizontal distance of 82.143 ft from the launch point.

1. Describe the graph of $h = -0.0112x^2 + 1.84x + 5$.

2. Make sense of problems. Suppose that point P corresponds to the point where Rossa is directly above Camera 1. Find the coordinates of point P, and explain the meaning of each coordinate of the point.

3. When Rossa is at point P, how high must the cable be secured so the cameras will be the same distance apart?

4. Model with mathematics. Write an equation for the horizontal line representing the height of the cable for Camera 2.

5. Sketch a graph of the human cannonball situation. Graph the line representing Camera 2's movement, and label the point at which Camera 1 is located.

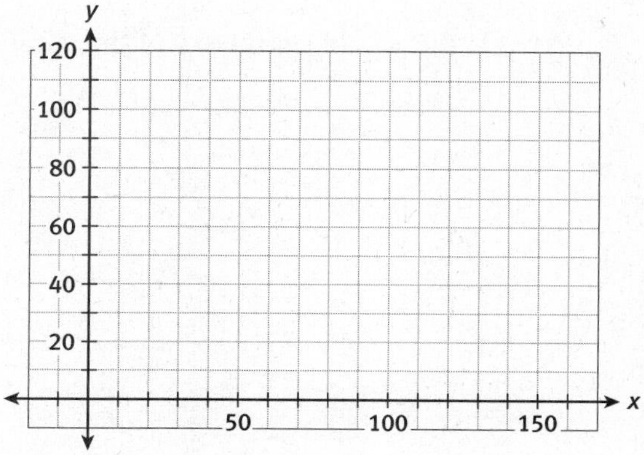

My Notes

MATH TIP

The distance formula is $d = \sqrt{(x_2 - x_1)^2 + (y_2 - y_1)^2}$.

Conic Sections

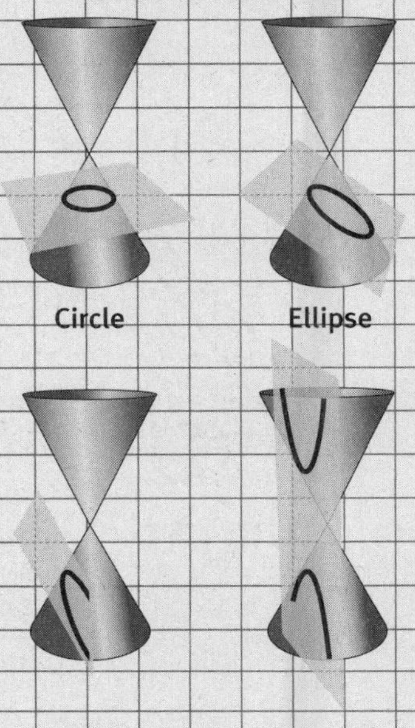

MATH TERMS

A **conic section** is a figure formed by the intersection of a double-napped right cone and a plane. A *parabola* is one conic section. A parabola is the set of points in a plane that are equidistant from a fixed point called the *focus* and a fixed line called the *directrix*.

A *double-napped right cone* is a pair of identical right cones that share a vertex but have bases on opposite sides of the vertex. A right cone is a cone with an axis of symmetry perpendicular to the base.

6. When Rossa has traveled a horizontal distance of 20 feet, how far is each camera from her?

7. Show how this is true for two other horizontal distances that Rossa must travel.

You have previously worked with quadratic functions. The graph of a quadratic function is a parabola. A parabola is one of the four conic sections studied by Apollonius, a third century BCE Greek mathematician. ***Conic sections*** are formed by the intersection of a plane and a double-napped right cone. The other conic sections—circles, ellipses, and hyperbolas—will be studied in later activities in this unit.

A *parabola* is the locus of points in a plane that are equidistant from a fixed point and a fixed line. The fixed point is called the *focus* and the fixed line is called the *directrix*.

8. In the human cannonball context, what represents the parabola, the focus, and the directrix?

The parabola shown below has its vertex at the origin. Its focus is the point $(0, d)$, and its directrix is the line $y = -d$. The point (x, y) is a point on the parabola. You can use this information to derive an equation for the parabola.

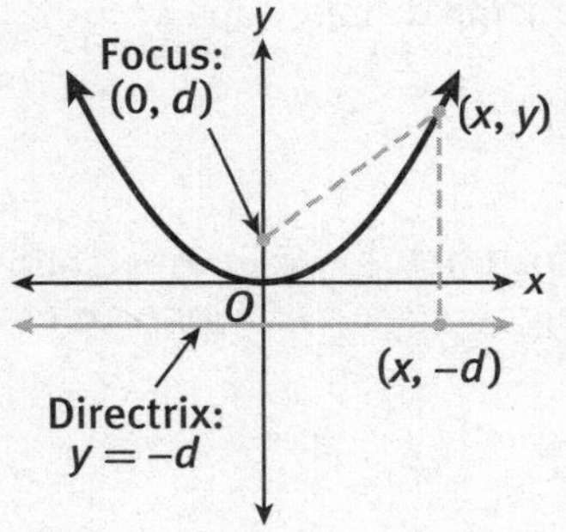

9. What is the axis of symmetry of the parabola? How do you know?

My Notes

10. Write and simplify an expression for the distance between the focus and any point (x, y).

11. Write and simplify an expression for the distance between the directrix and any point (x, y).

MATH TIP

The distance from a point (x, y) to a line is the length of the segment perpendicular to the line that has one endpoint at (x, y) and one endpoint on the line.

12. Explain how you know that the expressions you wrote in Items 10 and 11 are equal to each other.

13. Set the expressions from Items 10 and 11 equal to each other, and solve for y. The result represents the equation of a parabola with its vertex at the origin and a vertical axis of symmetry.

MATH TIP

To solve the equation in Item 13 for y, start by squaring both sides of the equation.

14. Consider the constant d from the equation of the parabola. What does $|d|$ represent?

What if the vertex of a parabola with a vertical axis of symmetry is not at the origin? Suppose the parabola shown on the previous page is translated h units horizontally and k units vertically.

15. What is the vertex of the translated parabola in terms of h and k?

16. Construct viable arguments. Use what you know about translations to write the equation of the translated parabola. Explain how you determined your answer.

My Notes

17. Sketch a graph of $y = x^2$.

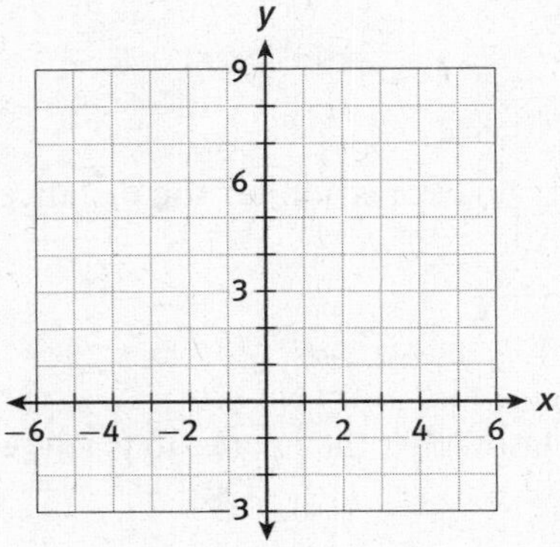

18. Form the inverse relation by exchanging x and y, and use your knowledge of the properties of inverses to sketch a graph of this relation on the coordinate grid in Item 17.

MATH TIP

You can use key points and transformations when graphing vertical or horizontal parabolas.

19. For each parabola, write the inverse relation, and then sketch the original parabola and its inverse.

a. $y = x^2 + 2$

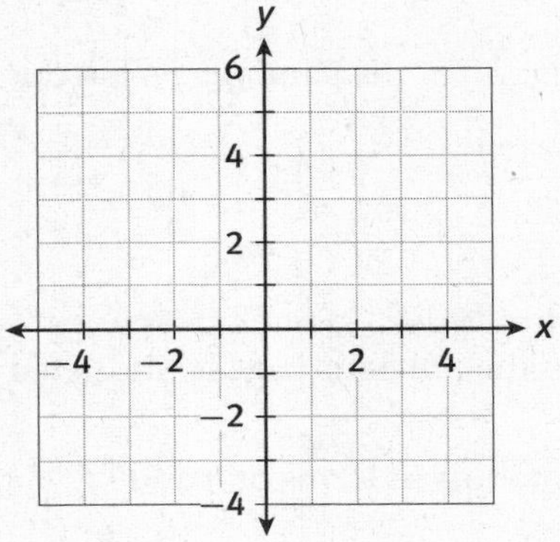

b. $y = (x + 1)^2$

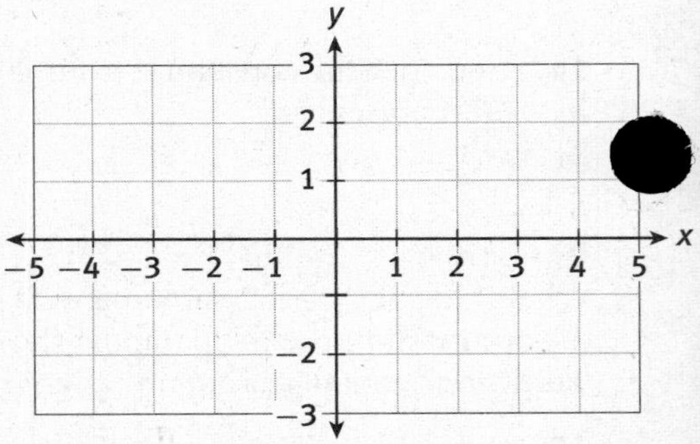

c. $y = \frac{1}{2}(x - 1)^2 + 3$

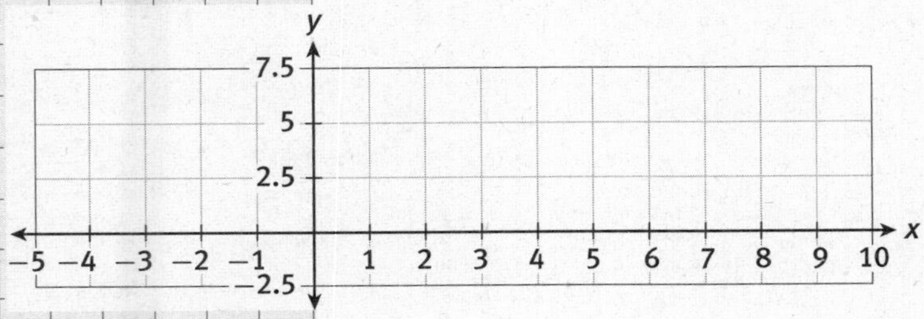

d. $y = -2(x - 3)^2$

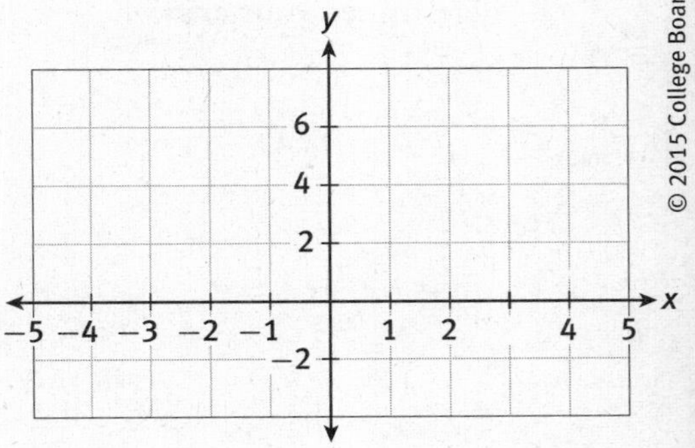

My Notes

The inverse relations you graphed in Item 19 are parabolas with a horizontal axis of symmetry.

20. Sketch and label the axis of symmetry for each parabola you graphed in Item 19.

21. Label the coordinates of the vertex of each parabola you graphed in Item 19.

22. Use your answers to Item 19 to answer the following.

a. Does the equation of a parabola with a vertical axis of symmetry represent a function? Explain.

b. Does the equation of a parabola with a horizontal axis of symmetry represent a function? Explain.

23. Describe how you could restrict the domain of a parabola with a vertical axis of symmetry so that its inverse will be a function.

24. For each equation given in Item 19, tell how you can restrict its domain so that its inverse will be a function.

25. Sketch the graph of each parabola. For each parabola, also label the vertex coordinates and the axis of symmetry.

a. $y = x^2 - 5$

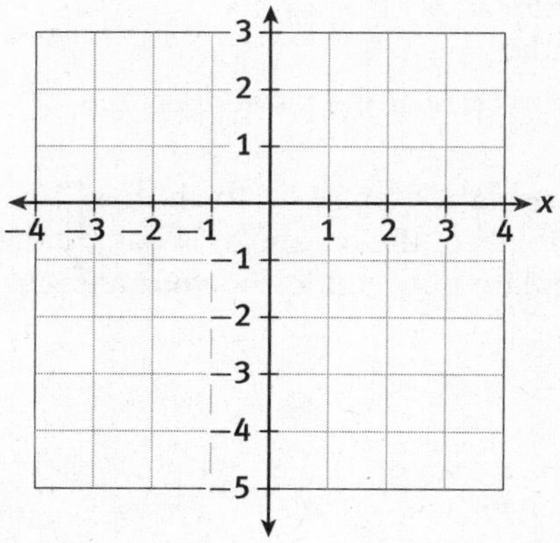

b. $x = 2y^2 + 3$

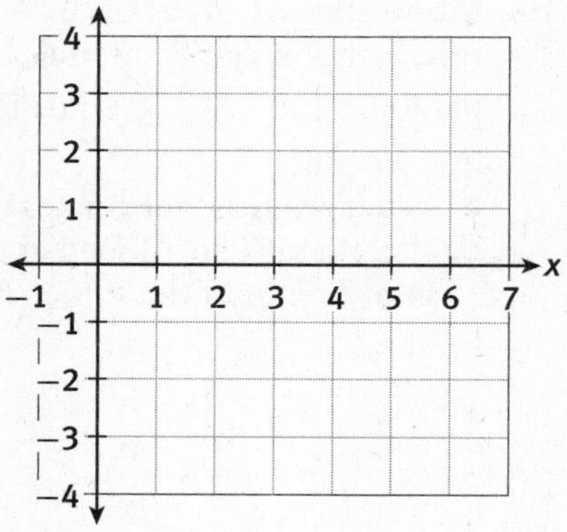

c. $y - 1 = 2(x + 1)^2$

c.

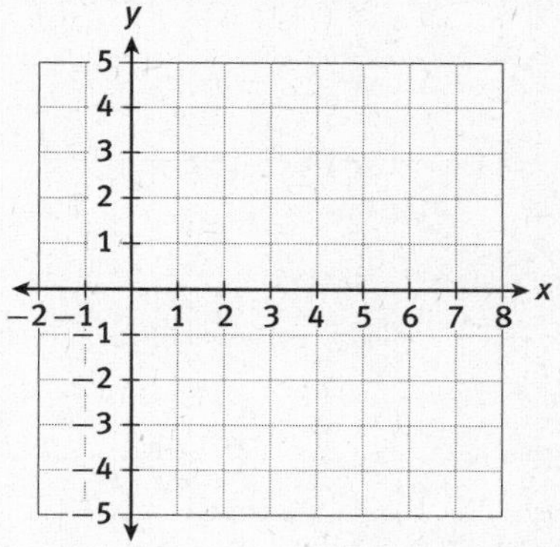

d. $x + 4 = -(y - 3)^2$

d.

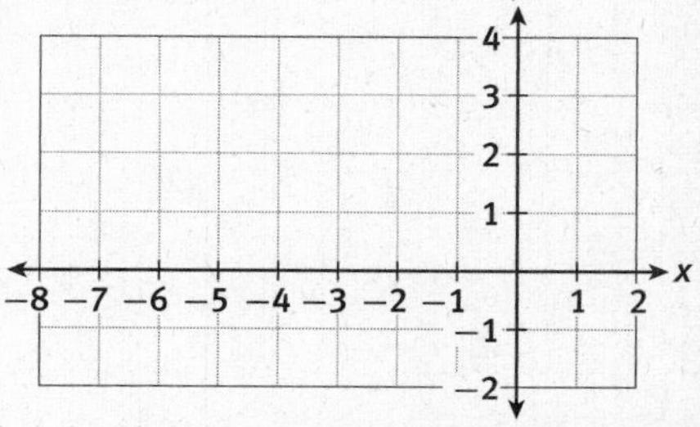

My Notes

26. How can you determine whether or not a parabola has a vertical or horizontal axis of symmetry?

Check Your Understanding

27. The parabola shown has its vertex at the origin. Derive an equation for the parabola. Solve the equation for x.

28. What is the relationship between the axis of symmetry of a parabola and its directrix?

29. A parabola opens upward. Its vertex is (3, 4), and its focus is (3, 6). What is the equation of its directrix? Explain your reasoning.

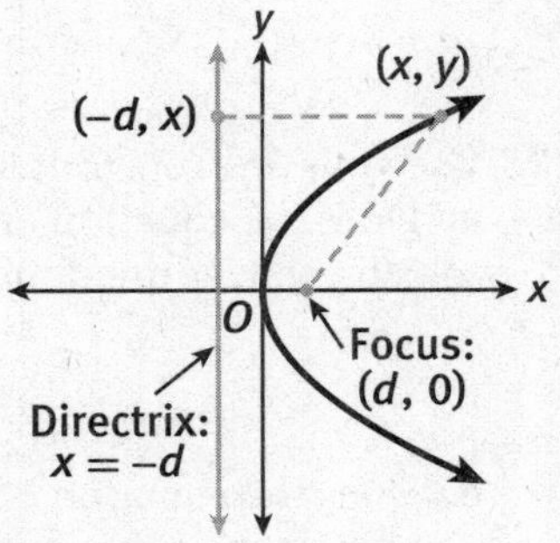

LESSON 26-1 PRACTICE

Graph each parabola. State the vertex and axis of symmetry.

30. $x = y^2 + 7$

31. $y = (x - 4)^2 + 2$

32. $y = \frac{1}{2}(x + 3)^2$

33. $x + 5y^2 = 1$

34. The graph shows a parabola with a focus of (3, 3) and a directrix of $y = 1$.

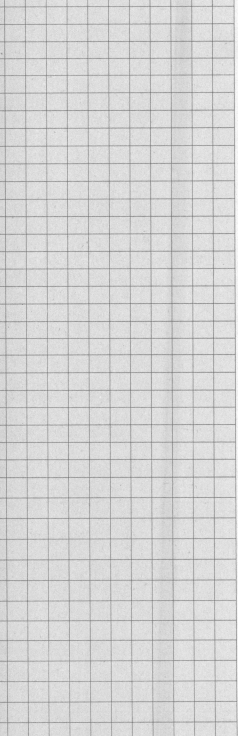

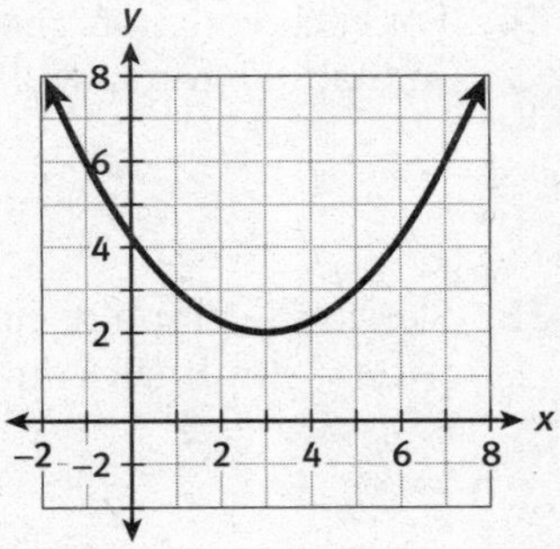

a. Graph the inverse relation.

b. What are the vertex and axis of symmetry of the parabola that represents the inverse relation?

c. What are the focus and directrix of the parabola that represents the inverse relation? How do you know?

35. Make use of structure. A hill on a roller coaster can be modeled by the parabola $y = -\frac{1}{32}x^2 + 50$. The directrix of the parabola is the line $y = 58$.

a. What are the coordinates of the highest point on the hill?

b. A camera is positioned at the focus of the parabola. What are the coordinates of the camera? Explain how you found your answer.

My Notes

Learning Targets:

- Find the standard form of a parabola.
- Graph parabolas in the coordinate plane.
- Find the focus, directrix, and axis of symmetry of a parabola.
- Find the equation of a parabola with certain characteristics.

SUGGESTED LEARNING STRATEGIES: Close Reading, Note Taking, Think-Pair-Share, Create Representations, Construct an Argument

Standard Form of a Parabola

- Vertical Axis of Symmetry: $y - k = \frac{1}{4d}(x - h)^2$
- Horizontal Axis of Symmetry: $x - h = \frac{1}{4d}(y - k)^2$

where (h, k) is the vertex and $|d|$ is the distance from the vertex to the focus.

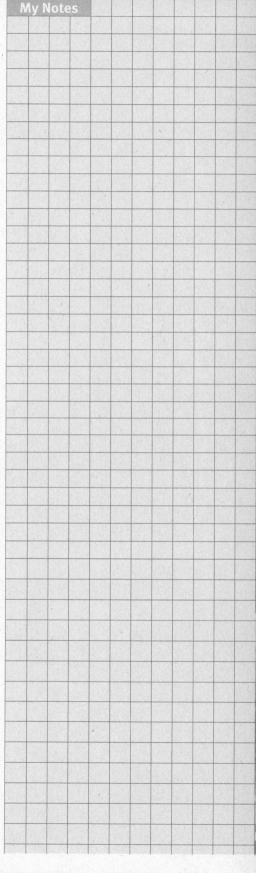

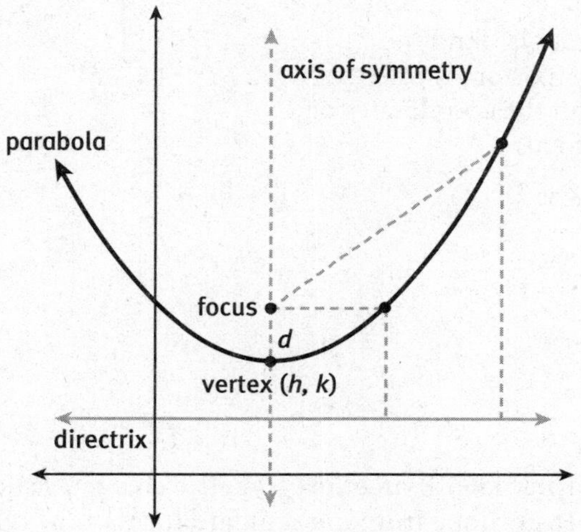

To find the coordinates of the focus, you add d to either h or k depending on the orientation of the parabola.

1. For the vertical parabola shown above, what are the coordinates of the focus?

Recall that all points on a parabola are equidistant from the focus and the directrix, including the vertex. To find the equation of the directrix, you subtract d from either h or k depending on the orientation of the parabola.

2. For the vertical parabola shown above, what is the equation of the directrix?

My Notes

Example A

Graph the parabola $x - 1 = \frac{1}{2}(y + 2)^2$. Find the equations of the axis of symmetry and directrix and the coordinates of the vertex and focus.

- Horizontal orientation, vertex is (1, −2), axis of symmetry is $y = -2$.
- Solve $\frac{1}{4d} = \frac{1}{2}$ to find d. $d = \frac{1}{2}$
- Add d to the x-coordinate of the vertex. Focus is (1.5, −2).
- Subtract d from the x-coordinate of the vertex. Directrix is $x = \frac{1}{2}$.

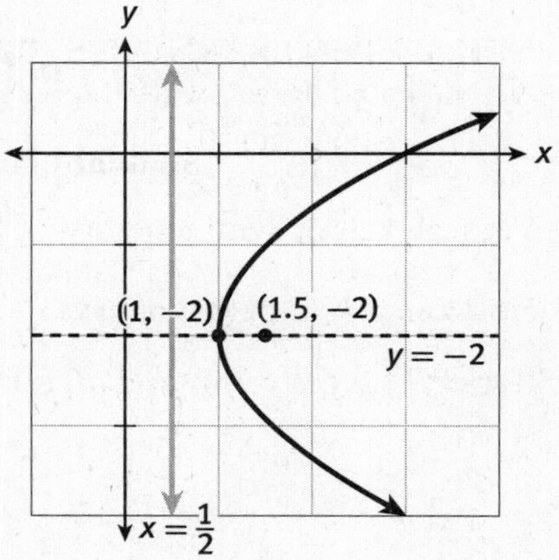

Try These A

Graph each parabola. Find the equations of the axis of symmetry and directrix and the coordinates of the vertex and focus.

a. $y - 2 = \frac{1}{4}(x - 3)^2$

b. $x + 1 = \frac{1}{8}(y + 3)^2$

Because graphing and identifying the geometric characteristics of a conic section are most easily done from the standard form of the relation, it is important to be able to rewrite the equation of a conic section in the standard form.

To find the vertex, focus, and directrix of a parabola given its equation, you can complete the square to write the equation in standard form.

Example B

Find the standard form, vertex, focus, directrix, and axis of symmetry of the parabola $x = -y^2 + 2y - 6$.

Step 1:	Write the original equation.	$x = -y^2 + 2y - 6$
Step 2:	Multiply each side by −1.	$-x = y^2 - 2y + 6$
Step 3:	Group terms.	$-x - 6 = y^2 - 2y$
Step 4:	Complete the square.	$-x - 6 + 1 = y^2 - 2y + 1$
Step 5:	Combine like terms.	$-x - 5 = y^2 - 2y + 1$
Step 6:	Write in standard form.	**Solution:** $x + 5 = -(y - 1)^2$
Step 7:	Compare the equation with the general form.	$x - h = \frac{1}{4d}(y - k)^2$
Step 8:	Find the vertex.	**Solution:** (−5, 1)

Step 9: Find d. $d = -\frac{1}{4}$

Step 10: Note that d is negative and y is squared. The parabola has a horizontal orientation and opens left.

Step 11: Find the focus. **Solution:** $\left(-5\frac{1}{4}, 1\right)$

Step 12: Find the equation of the directrix. **Solution:** $x = -4\frac{3}{4}$

Step 13: Find the axis of symmetry. **Solution:** $y = 1$

Try These B

Find the standard form, vertex, focus, directrix, and axis of symmetry for the following parabolas.

a. $x^2 - 2x = -8y - 9$

b. $y^2 - 6x + 2y + 13 = 0$

Example C

Find the standard form of the equation of the parabola with a focus of (4, 2) and a vertex of (2, 2).

Step 1: Determine the orientation of the axis. The axis is horizontal, so use the form for a horizontal axis. $x - h = \frac{1}{4d}(y - k)^2$

Step 2: Identify h and k. The vertex is (2, 2). $h = 2, k = 2$

Step 3: Identify d, the distance from the vertex to the focus. $d = |2 - 4| = 2$

Step 4: Substitute the values for h, k, and d in the standard form of the equation. $x - 2 = \frac{1}{4(2)}(y - 2)^2$

Step 5: Multiply. **Solution:** $x - 2 = \frac{1}{8}(y - 2)^2$

Try These C

Find the standard form of the equation of the parabola with the given focus and vertex.

a. focus: (7, −1), vertex: (2, −1)

b. focus: (3, 0), vertex: (3, 2)

c. focus: (1, 2), vertex: (3, 2)

d. focus: (2, 2), vertex: (2, −1)

My Notes

Check Your Understanding

3. **Critique the reasoning of others.** A student claims that the vertex of a parabola is the midpoint of a segment on the axis of symmetry with one endpoint at the focus and one endpoint on the directrix. Is the student correct? Explain.
4. **Make use of structure.** The equation of a parabola is $x - 3 = -\frac{1}{8}(y + 4)^2$. Explain how you can determine which direction the parabola opens without graphing the parabola.
5. **Construct viable arguments.** Explain how to determine the coordinates of the focus of a parabola with a vertical axis of symmetry if you are given the equation of the parabola in standard form.
6. Given a horizontal parabola of the form $x - h = \frac{1}{4d}(y - k)^2$, what is the equation of the directrix? What are the coordinates of the focus?

LESSON 26-2 PRACTICE

Graph the parabola. State the vertex, axis of symmetry, focus, and directrix.

7. $x - 4 = (y + 2)^2$
8. $y + 3 = \frac{1}{3}(x - 3)^2$

Find the standard form, vertex, focus, directrix, and axis of symmetry for the following parabolas.

9. $24y = x^2$
10. $(y - 7)^2 = 12x$

Find the standard form of the equation of the parabola with the given focus and vertex.

11. focus: $(2, -1)$, vertex: $(2, 5)$
12. focus: $(-1, 2)$, vertex: $(-4, 2)$

13. **Construct viable arguments.** Write the equation of the parabola shown in the graph. Explain how you determined your answer.

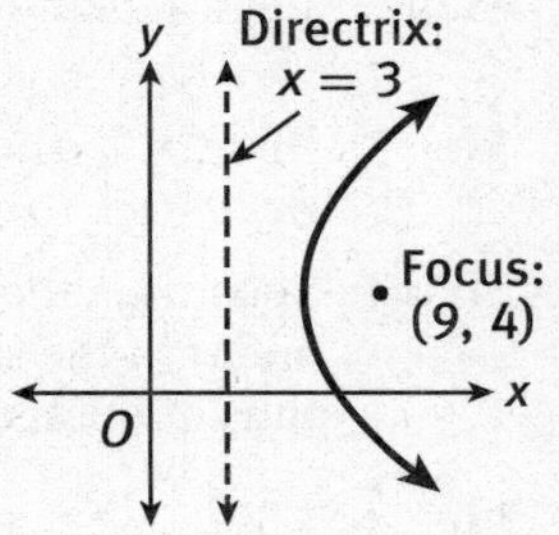

14. A cross-section through the center of a television satellite antenna is a parabola. The parabola can be modeled by the equation $y = \frac{1}{156}x^2$ on a coordinate plane where 1 unit represents 1 cm. What is the distance in centimeters between the vertex of the parabola and its focus?

ACTIVITY 26 PRACTICE

Write your answers on notebook paper.
Show your work.

Lesson 26-1

A landscape architect is designing a new path in a park. Each point along the path will be the same distance from a statue at the center of the park as from a riverbank to the south of the statue. The equation $y = 0.0125x^2 - 20$ represents the path on a map where 1 unit represents 1 ft. The statue is at (0, 0) on the map. The y-axis is the north-south axis of the map, with north at the top of the map. Use this information for Items 1–5.

1. Point P corresponds to the point on the path directly south of the statue. Find the coordinates of point P.

2. Write an equation for the horizontal line representing the riverbank on the map. Explain how you determined the equation of this line.

3. Sketch the new path on a coordinate plane. Graph the line representing the riverbank, and label the point at which the statue is located.

4. A water fountain on the path will be 10 ft east of the statue and 18.75 ft south of the statue. How far will the water fountain be from the riverbank? Explain your answer.

5. In this context, what represents the parabola, the focus, and the directrix?

Graph the parabola. State the vertex and axis of symmetry.

6. $x = -3y^2 + 5$

7. $y - 3 = -(x + 2)^2$

8. $y = x^2 - 4$

9. The vertex of a parabola is the point (3, 5), and the focus of the parabola is the point (6, 5). What is the axis of symmetry of the parabola?

A. $x = 0$ **B.** $x = 5$
C. $y = 0$ **D.** $y = 5$

10. Explain why a parabola is a conic section.

11. The focus of a parabola is the point (0, 4), and the directrix is the line $y = -4$. The point (x, y) lies on the parabola.

a. Write and simplify an expression for the distance between the focus and the point (x, y).

b. Write and simplify an expression for the distance between the directrix and the point (x, y).

c. Explain how you can use the expressions from parts a and b to write the equation of the parabola. Then write the equation and solve it for y.

12. The points (5, 6) and (−13, 15) both lie on the parabola graphed below. Show that each point is the same distance from the focus as from the directrix.

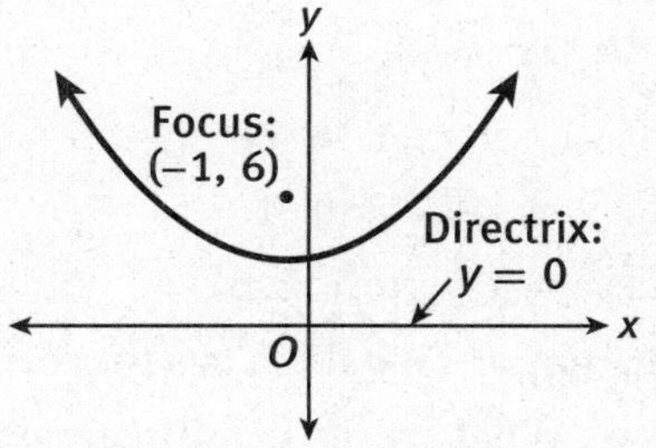

13. For each parabola, write the inverse relation, and then sketch the original parabola and its inverse.

a. $y = \frac{1}{4}(x - 1)^2$

b. $y = (x + 2)^2 - 3$

14. What are the vertex and axis of symmetry of the parabola that represents each inverse relation in Item 13?

15. For each equation given in Item 13, tell how you can restrict its domain so that its inverse will be a function.

Lesson 26-2

Graph each parabola. Find the equations of the axis of symmetry and directrix and the coordinates of the vertex and focus.

16. $x = \frac{1}{8}y^2 - 4$

17. $y + 4 = \frac{1}{20}(x - 1)^2$

18. $x - 3 = -8(y - 6)^2$

Find the standard form, vertex, focus, directrix, and axis of symmetry for the following parabolas.

19. $x^2 + 6y = 0$

20. $4x = y^2 + 2y + 33$

21. $y - 4 = \frac{1}{8}x^2 - x$

Find the standard form of the equation for each parabola.

22. focus: $(-1, 2)$, vertex: $(-1, 0)$

23. focus: $(0, 2)$, vertex: $(-5, 2)$

24. directrix: $y = 3$, focus: $(-1, -5)$

25. directrix: $x = 4$, vertex: $(2, 6)$

26. The equation of a parabola has the form $x = \frac{1}{4d}y^2$. What are the coordinates of the focus of the parabola? What is the equation of the directrix?

27. Explain how to find the directrix of a parabola with a horizontal axis of symmetry when you are given the equation of the parabola in standard form.

28. What is the focus of the parabola given by the equation $y - 3 = -\frac{1}{24}(x + 1)^2$?

A. $(-7, 3)$ **B.** $(-1, -3)$
C. $(-1, 9)$ **D.** $(5, 3)$

29. What is the standard form of the equation of the parabola shown in the graph?

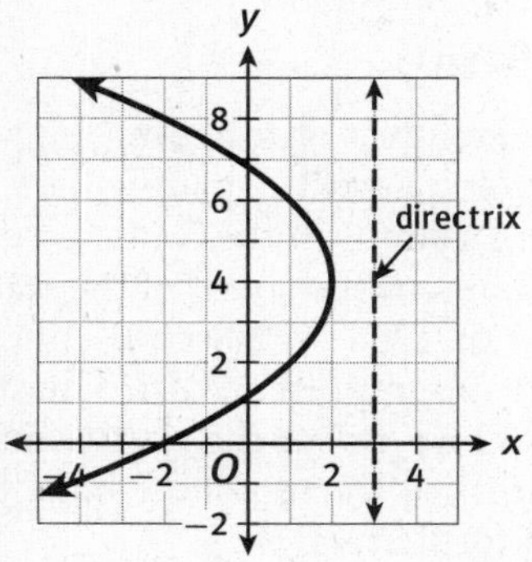

30. What is the directrix of the parabola given by the equation $x - 2 = \frac{1}{12}(y + 4)^2$?

A. $x = -7$ **B.** $x = -1$
C. $y = -4$ **D.** $y = 5$

For Items 31 and 32, consider the following. A flashlight contains a parabolic mirror. The bulb is positioned at the focus of the mirror. A cross-section of the mirror can be modeled on a coordinate plane where 1 unit represents 1 cm, as shown below.

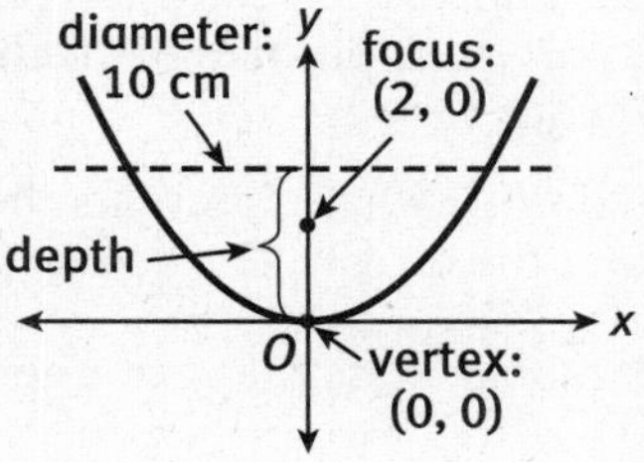

31. Write the equation of the parabola.

32. The diameter of the mirror at its widest part is 10 cm. What is the depth of the mirror to the nearest tenth of a centimeter? Explain how you determined your answer.

MATHEMATICAL PRACTICES
Look For and Make Use of Structure

33. The equation of a parabola is $x = 5 - 2(y + 1)^2$. Explain how you can determine the direction the parabola opens without graphing the parabola.

Ellipses and Hyperbolas

Radio Navigation
Lesson 27-1 Ellipses

My Notes

Learning Targets:

- Define and sketch an ellipse.
- Determine the equation of an ellipse.
- Graph an ellipse using its characteristics.

SUGGESTED LEARNING STRATEGIES: Close Reading, Use Manipulatives, Vocabulary Organizer, Think-Pair-Share, Create Representations

As you work in groups, read the problem scenario carefully and explore together the information provided. Discuss your understanding of the problem and ask peers or your teacher to clarify any areas that are not clear.

LORAN is a long-range radio navigation system that uses land-based radio transmitters to aid ships, aircraft, and terrestrial navigators. The LORAN (Long Range Aid [to] Navigation) system transmits radio signals at precise time intervals from each of its transmitting stations. LORAN is able to locate objects using these radio signals through the use of geometry and conics. This activity will investigate two types of conics.

1. Use appropriate tools strategically. Two points, F_1 and F_2, with coordinates at $(-4, 0)$ and $(4, 0)$, are shown on the coordinate grid. Thumbtack the coordinate grid to a thick piece of cardboard at each of the points, F_1 and F_2. Take a piece of string longer than the length between the two thumbtacks and loop the ends of the string around each thumbtack. Push a pencil against the string until the string forms a triangle with vertices at the pencil point and the points F_1 and F_2. Finally, holding the pencil firmly against the string, move the pencil point such that a curve is drawn. This method will draw the first half of the desired curve. Move the string to the other side of the points F_1 and F_2 and draw the second half of the curve.

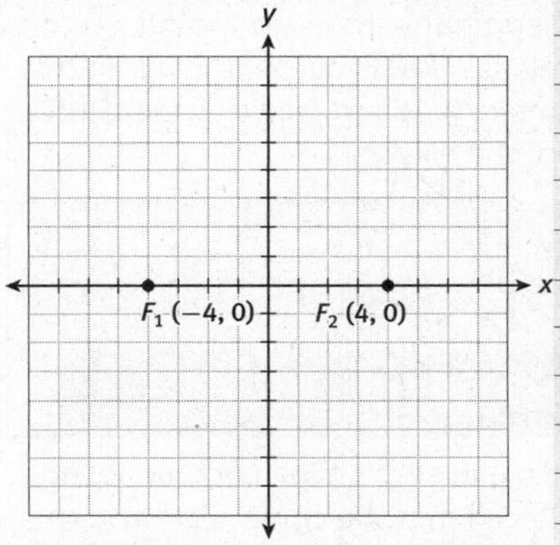

2. Choose three points on the curve that you sketched in Item 1.

a. Label the chosen points A, B, and C. Measure the distances from these three points to the points F_1 and F_2 to the nearest tenth of a centimeter. Use the table below to record the distances and the sum of these distances.

	Distance to F_1	Distance to F_2	Sum of the Distances
Point A			
Point B			
Point C			

b. In the table in part a, the sums of the distances for the three points A, B, and C should be the same. Explain why this is so.

My Notes

MATH TERMS

An **ellipse** is the set of all points (*x*, *y*) in a plane such that the sum of the distances from the point (*x*, *y*) to each of two fixed points is constant. Each of the fixed points is called a **focus of the ellipse**. The plural of *focus* is *foci*.

The **major axis** of an ellipse is the segment with its endpoints on the ellipse that passes through the foci. The endpoints of the major axis are the *vertices of the ellipse*.

The **minor axis** of an ellipse is the segment with its endpoints on the ellipse that is perpendicular to the major axis and contains the center of the ellipse.

MATH TIP

An ellipse is a type of conic section. Recall that the conic sections are formed by the intersection of a plane and a double-napped cone.

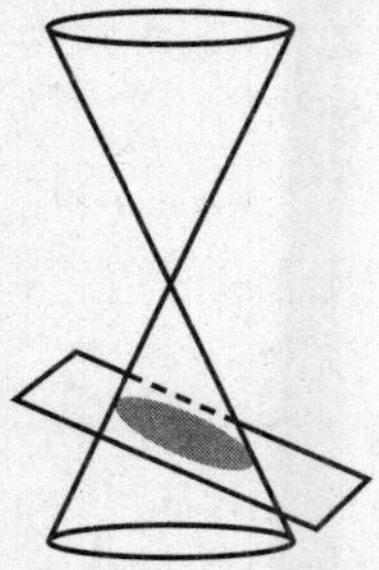

The curve that is drawn in Item 1 is called an *ellipse*. An ellipse, like a parabola, is an example of a conic section.

3. Reason abstractly. Describe the ways that a plane might intersect a double-napped cone to form a conic section.

An ***ellipse*** is the set of all points (x, y) in a plane such that the sum of the distances from (x, y) to each of two fixed points, called ***foci***, is a constant.

4. Suppose that 10 is the constant sum of the distances from a point (x, y) on an ellipse to the foci located at $(-4, 0)$ and $(4, 0)$.

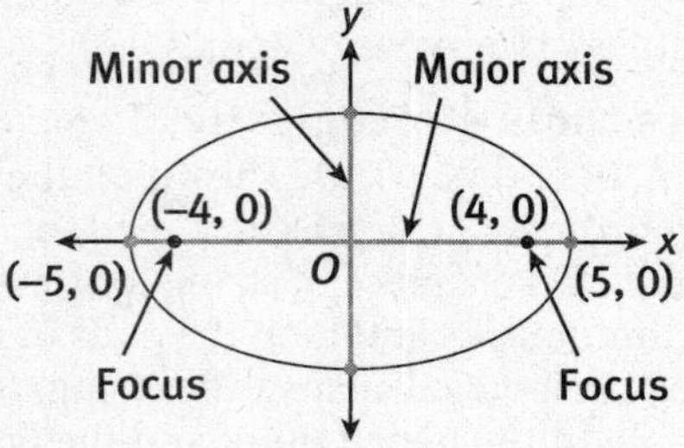

a. For each endpoint of the ***minor axis***, what are the distances to each focus? Explain how you found these distances.

b. Give the coordinates of the endpoints of the minor axis. Justify your answer.

c. For each *vertex of the ellipse* (the endpoints of the ***major axis***), what are the distances to each focus? Explain how you found these distances.

d. Give the coordinates of the vertices. Justify your answer.

My Notes

5. Look at the cross section formed by the plane and the double-napped cone in the Math Tip box on the previous page. Describe the position of the plane if the cross section were a circle.

6. Is a circle also an ellipse? Explain.

MATH TIP

In Item 6, consider what would happen if the distance between the foci of an ellipse were 0 units.

7. Suppose again that 10 is the constant sum of the distances from a point (x, y) on an ellipse to the foci located at $(-4, 0)$ and $(4, 0)$. The following items will lead to an algebraic equation in x and y that represents all points (x, y) on this ellipse.

a. Use the distance formula to write the distance from a point (x, y) on the ellipse to the focus $(-4, 0)$. Call this distance d_1.

b. Use the distance formula to write the distance from a point (x, y) on the ellipse to the focus $(4, 0)$. Call this distance d_2.

c. Write an equation below that relates d_1 and d_2.

d. Eliminate both radicals from the equation written in Part c. Show your work below.

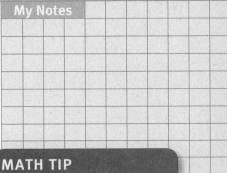

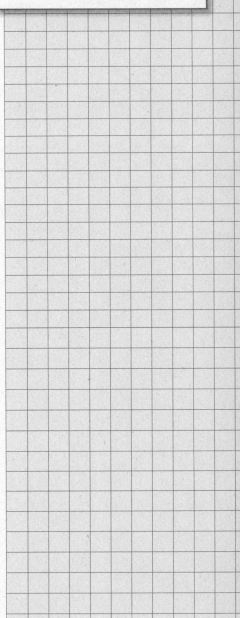

My Notes

e. Collect terms to simplify the equation in Part d into the form $\frac{x^2}{a^2} + \frac{y^2}{b^2} = 1$.

f. What are the values of a and b for the ellipse in this item, and how are these values related to the graph of the ellipse?

g. How is a related to the constant sum of the distances between the foci and a point on the ellipse?

8. Suppose that 6 is the constant sum of the distances from a point (x, y) on an ellipse to the foci located at $(0, -1)$ and $(0, 1)$.

a. Use the procedure from Item 7 to write the equation of this ellipse.

My Notes

b. Sketch a graph of the ellipse.

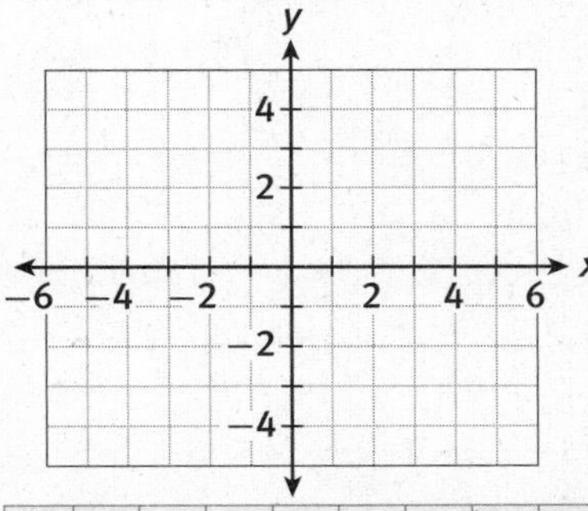

c. Explain any similarities or differences between this ellipse and the one in Item 7.

9. Construct viable arguments. The equation $\frac{x^2}{a^2} + \frac{y^2}{b^2} = 1$ represents an ellipse with its center at the origin, a major axis of length $2a$, and a minor axis of length $2b$.

a. What is the relationship between the parameters a and b if the equation represents a circle?

b. What is the equation of a circle with its center at the origin and radius r? Explain your reasoning.

The standard form of the equation of an ellipse with center (h, k), major axis of length $2a$, and minor axis of length $2b$, where $0 < b < a$, is given by

$$\frac{(x-h)^2}{a^2} + \frac{(y-k)^2}{b^2} = 1 \text{ (horizontal major axis)}$$

$$\frac{(x-h)^2}{b^2} + \frac{(y-k)^2}{a^2} = 1 \text{ (vertical major axis).}$$

The distance between the foci is $2c$, where $c^2 = a^2 - b^2$.

10. Complete the square for x and for y in order to write the equation of each ellipse in standard form. Sketch a graph of the ellipse, and identify the coordinates of the center, the foci, and the endpoints of the major and minor axes.

a. $9x^2 + 4y^2 + 36x - 24y + 36 = 0$

b. $x^2 + 4y^2 - 4x - 16y + 16 = 0$

MATH TIP

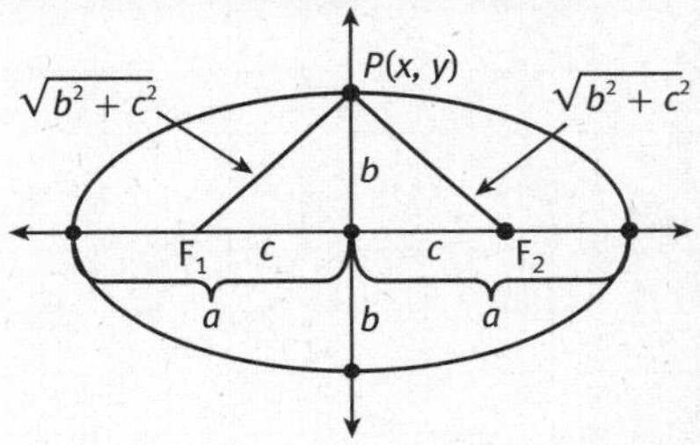

The major axis of the ellipse has length $2a$, the minor axis has length $2b$, and the distance between the two foci is $2c$.

Since the point $P(x, y)$ is a point on the ellipse,

$$F_1P + F_2P = 2a$$
$$\sqrt{b^2 + c^2} + \sqrt{b^2 + c^2} = 2a$$
$$2\sqrt{b^2 + c^2} = 2a$$
$$\sqrt{b^2 + c^2} = a$$
$$b^2 + c^2 = a^2.$$

Therefore, $c^2 = a^2 - b^2$.

My Notes

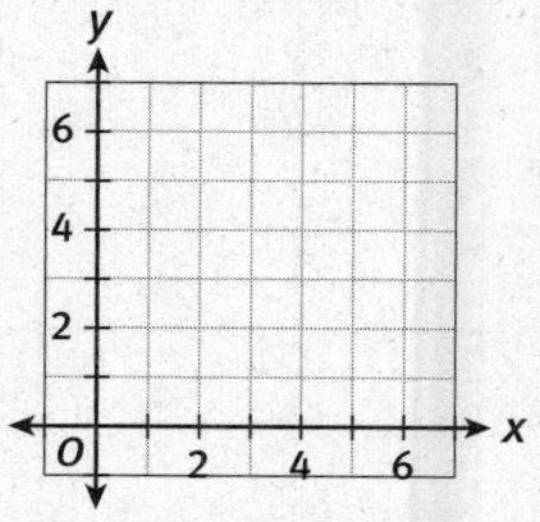

11. Write the equation of a circle with its center at (3, 4) and a radius of 2 units. Then sketch a graph of the circle.

Check Your Understanding

12. Write the equation of the circle shown in the graph.

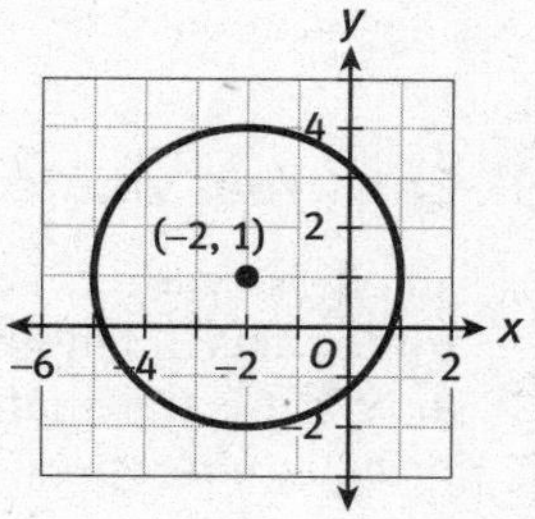

13. The center of an ellipse is the point (5, 2). One focus of the ellipse is at (8, 2), and one vertex of the ellipse is at (10, 2).

a. What are the coordinates of the other focus and the other vertex? Explain your answer.

b. What is the equation of the ellipse? Explain how you determined the equation.

LESSON 27-1 PRACTICE

14. Suppose that 8 is the constant sum of the distances from a point (x, y) on an ellipse to the foci located at (3, 0) and (−3, 0). Use the definition of *ellipse* and the distance formula to derive the equation of the ellipse in standard form. Then sketch the graph of the ellipse. Label the coordinates of the endpoints of the major and minor axes.

Sketch the graph of each ellipse. Label the coordinates of the center, the foci, and the endpoints of the major and minor axes.

15. $\frac{x^2}{144} + \frac{y^2}{169} = 1$

16. $\frac{(x-4)^2}{4} + \frac{(y+2)^2}{9} = 1$

17. $4x^2 + 3y^2 + 8x - 6y - 5 = 0$

18. $9x^2 + 16y^2 - 18x + 64y - 71 = 0$

19. **Model with mathematics.** The "Whispering Gallery" in St. Paul's Cathedral in London has an elliptical ceiling. A sound made at one focus of the ellipse is reflected to the other focus, allowing people on opposite sides of the room to clearly hear each other's whispers. Suppose that a whispering gallery is to be constructed so the foci are 25 feet from the center of the room and that the height of the room at its center is 13 feet. Find an equation that models the elliptical curve of the ceiling, and find the length of the room.

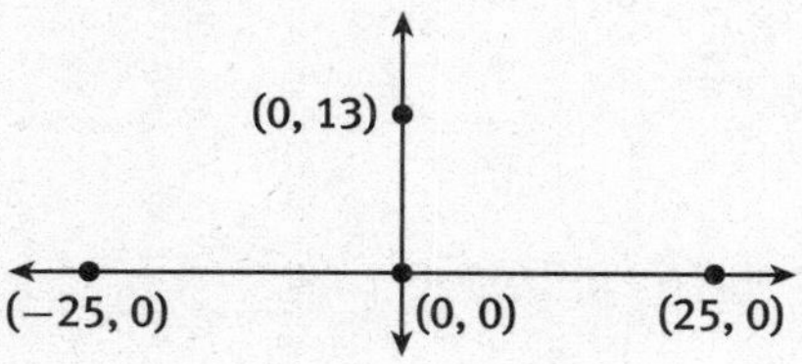

My Notes

Learning Targets:

- Define and sketch a hyperbola.
- Determine the equation of a hyperbola.
- Graph a hyperbola using its characteristics.

SUGGESTED LEARNING STRATEGIES: Close Reading, Vocabulary Organizer, Think-Pair-Share, Create Representations, Quickwrite

Another conic section, the ***hyperbola***, is defined as the set of points (x, y) such that the difference of the distances from (x, y) to each of the foci is a constant.

1. Reason abstractly. Consider a plane that intersects a double-napped cone.

a. Describe the position of the plane if it intersects both cones of the double-napped cone to form a hyperbola.

b. Describe the position of the plane if it intersects only one cone of a double-napped cone to form a parabola.

MATH TERMS

A **hyperbola** is the set of points (x, y) in a plane such that the difference of the distances from (x, y) to each of two fixed points, called foci, is constant.

The figure below shows a plane intersecting a double-napped cone in a hyperbola.

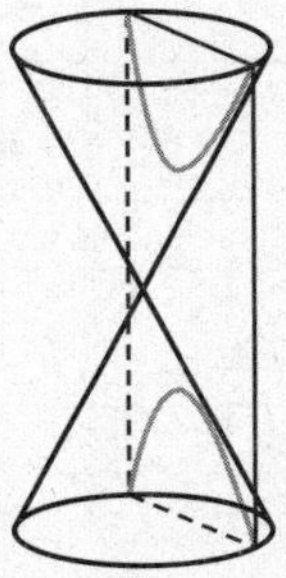

In the figure below, the points $F_1(-4, 0)$ and $F_2(4, 0)$ are foci of a hyperbola, and (x, y) is a point on the hyperbola. Let d_1 be the distance from a point (x, y) to the focus $(-4, 0)$, and let d_2 be the distance from a point (x, y) to the focus $(4, 0)$. Suppose that 6 is the constant difference of the distances from a point (x, y) on the hyperbola to each of the foci.

2. Write an equation that relates d_1 and d_2.

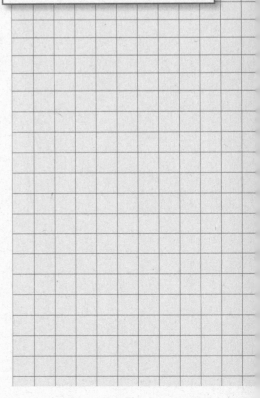

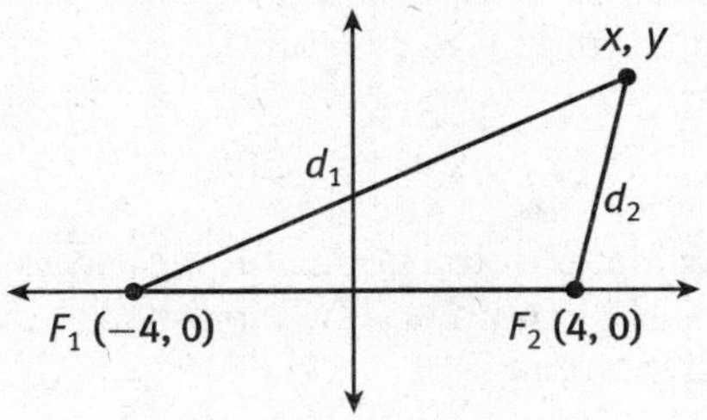

My Notes

3. In order to locate points that satisfy the equation in Item 2, concentric circles are drawn at F_1 and F_2. Use the grid below to answer the following.

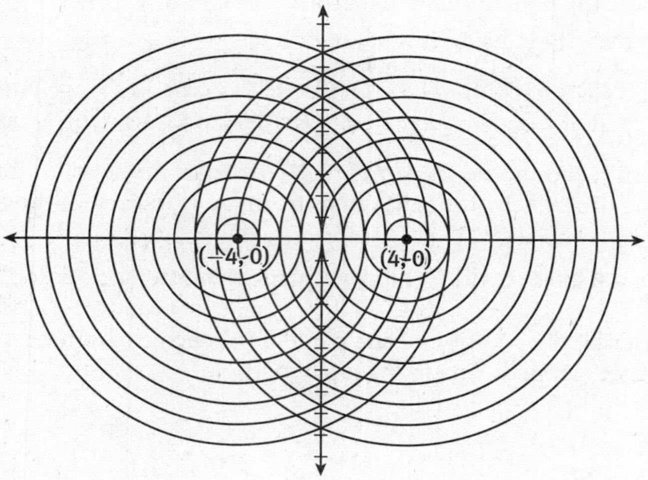

a. To locate points that are 3 units from F_1 and 9 units from F_2, find all intersection points of the circle whose center is F_1 and radius is 3 and the circle whose center is F_2 and radius is 9. Plot these points on the grid above.

b. Explain below why the points you located in Item 3a lie on the hyperbola.

c. Use the concentric circles as a guide to plot at least seven points that satisfy the equation $d_2 - d_1 = 6$ units.

d. Use the concentric circles as a guide to plot at least seven points that satisfy the equation $d_1 - d_2 = 6$ units.

e. Give the coordinates of the points on the *x*-axis that satisfy the equation $|d_2 - d_1| = 6$ units. These points are the vertices of the graph of the hyperbola.

f. Describe the shape of the collection of points that satisfy the property of $|d_2 - d_1| = 6$ units.

My Notes

4. The following items will lead to an algebraic equation in x and y that represents all points (x, y) on the hyperbola with foci located at $(-4, 0)$ and $(4, 0)$ and with 6 as the constant difference between the distances from the foci.

a. Use the distance formula to write the distance d_1 from a point (x, y) on the hyperbola to the focus $(-4, 0)$.

b. Use the distance formula to write the distance d_2 from a point (x, y) on the hyperbola to the focus $(4, 0)$.

c. Write an equation below that relates d_1 and d_2.

d. Eliminate both radicals from the equation written in Part c. Show your work below.

e. Collect terms to simplify the equation in part d into the form $\frac{x^2}{a^2} - \frac{y^2}{b^2} = 1$.

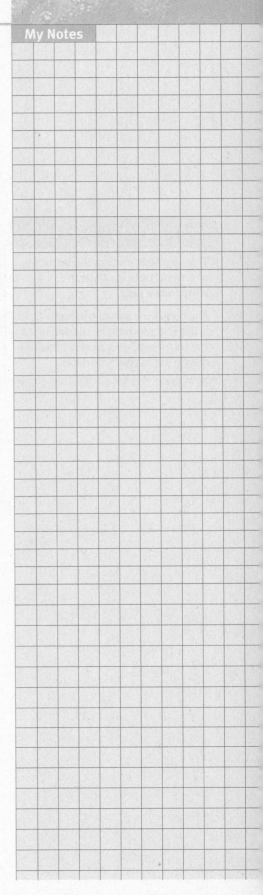

My Notes

f. **Make use of structure.** What is the value of a for the hyperbola in this item, and how is the value related to the graph of the hyperbola?

g. How is a related to the constant difference of the distances?

MATH TERMS

The segment joining the vertices of a hyperbola is called the **transverse axis.**

The *conjugate axis* of the hyperbola is the line segment perpendicular to the transverse axis, passing through the center of the hyperbola.

In a hyperbola with equation $\frac{x^2}{a^2} - \frac{y^2}{b^2} = 1$, the *center of the hyperbola* is at (0, 0), and the hyperbola has a horizontal ***transverse axis***. The constant a represents the distance from the center to each vertex. Let the constant c represent the distance from the center to each focus. The relationship between a, b, and c is $a^2 + b^2 = c^2$.

5. Verify that the relationship between a, b, and c holds true for the hyperbola in Item 3.

The standard form of the equation of a hyperbola with center (h, k) and transverse axis of length $2a$ is given by

$$\frac{(x-h)^2}{a^2} - \frac{(y-k)^2}{b^2} = 1 \text{ (horizontal transverse axis)}$$

$$\frac{(y-k)^2}{a^2} - \frac{(x-h)^2}{b^2} = 1 \text{ (vertical transverse axis).}$$

The distance between the foci is $2c$, where $c^2 = a^2 + b^2$.

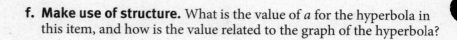

My Notes

6. Complete the square for x and for y in order to write the equation of each hyperbola in standard form. Sketch a graph of the hyperbola and identify the coordinates of the center, the foci, the vertices, and equations of the asymptotes.

a. $4x^2 - y^2 - 16x - 4y - 4 = 0$

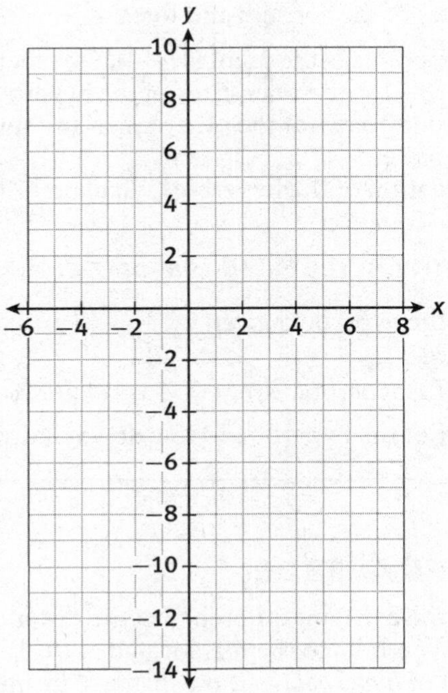

b. $-4x^2 + y^2 + 32x - 12y - 32 = 0$

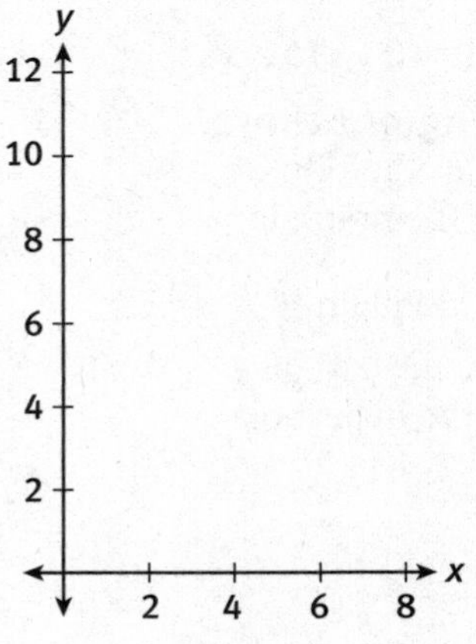

MATH TIP

The asymptotes of a hyperbola contain the center of the hyperbola and contain the vertices of a rectangle with dimensions $2a$ and $2b$.

The equations of the asymptotes of a hyperbola with a horizontal transverse axis are

$$y - k = \pm\frac{a}{b}(x - h).$$

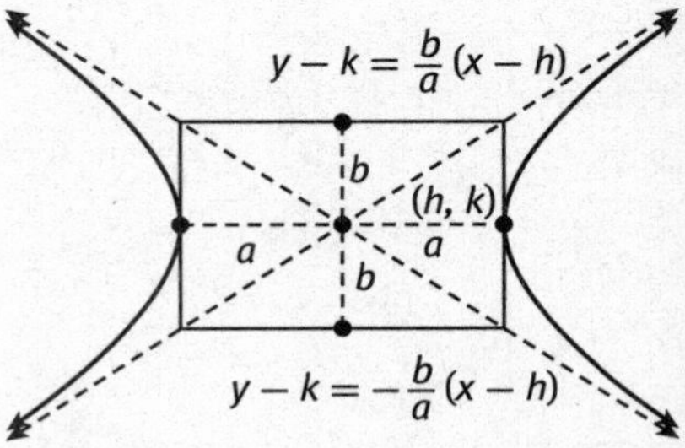

The equations of the asymptotes of a hyperbola with a vertical transverse axis are

$$y - k = \pm\frac{a}{b}(x - h).$$

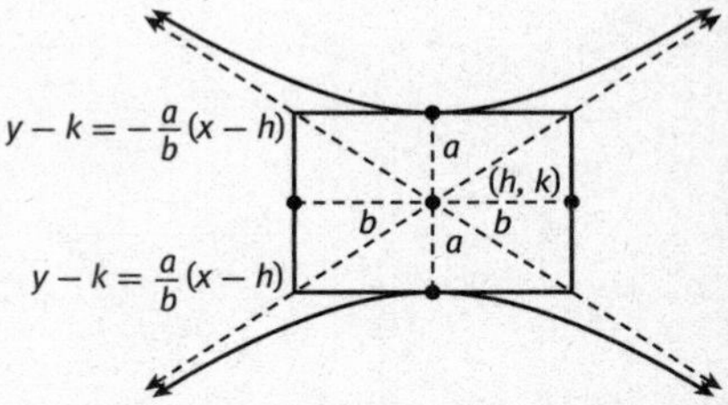

My Notes

Check Your Understanding

7. Compare and contrast a hyperbola centered at the origin with a horizontal transverse axis with an ellipse centered at the origin with a horizontal major axis. Consider the standard forms of the equations and the coordinates of the vertices and foci.

8. The center of a hyperbola is the point $(1, -3)$. One focus of the hyperbola is at $(-3, -3)$, and one vertex of the hyperbola is at $(-2, -3)$.

a. What are the coordinates of the other focus and the other vertex? Explain your answer.

b. What is the equation of the hyperbola? Explain how you determined the equation.

9. **Express regularity in repeated reasoning.** How does increasing the value of a for the hyperbola given by $\frac{x^2}{a^2} - \frac{y^2}{b^2} = 1$ affect its graph?

10. The asymptotes of a hyperbola are $y = \frac{4}{3}x + 4$ and $y = -\frac{4}{3}x + 4$. What is the center of the hyperbola? How do you know?

LESSON 27-2 PRACTICE

11. Suppose that 4 is the constant difference of the distances from a point (x, y) on a hyperbola to the foci located at $(0, 3)$ and $(0, -3)$. Use the definition of *hyperbola* and the distance formula to derive the equation of the hyperbola in standard form. Then sketch the graph of the hyperbola. Identify the coordinates of the foci and the vertices and equations of the asymptotes.

Sketch the graph of each hyperbola. Identify the coordinates of the center, the foci, and the vertices, and the equations of the asymptotes.

12. $\frac{x^2}{25} - \frac{y^2}{16} = 1$

13. $\frac{(y-2)^2}{16} - \frac{(x+3)^2}{9} = 1$

14. $-x^2 + y^2 + 4x - 4y - 1 = 0$

15. $x^2 - y^2 + 6y - 18 = 0$

16. **Critique the reasoning of others.** A student claims that the equation of the hyperbola shown in the graph is $\frac{(x-2)^2}{12} - \frac{(y-3)^2}{4} = 1$. Explain the error that the student made, and give the correct equation of the hyperbola.

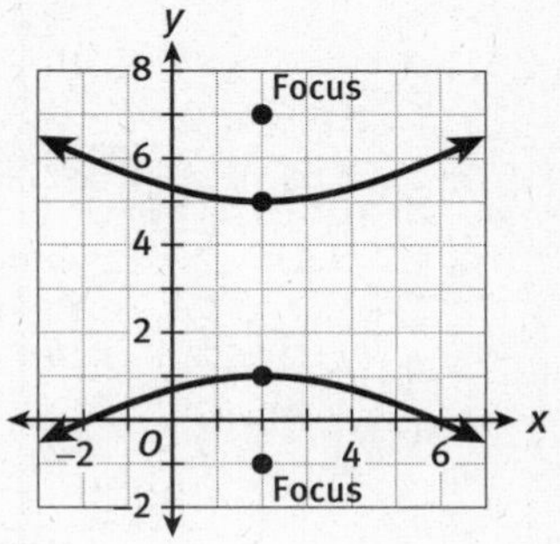

My Notes

Learning Targets:

- Graph hyperbolas to represent a real-world problem.
- Use equations of hyperbolas to find intersection points.

SUGGESTED LEARNING STRATEGIES: Paraphrasing, Sharing and Responding, Create a Plan, Quickwrite, Create Representations

Recall that the LORAN system transmits radio signals at precise time intervals from each of its transmitting stations. The LORAN system is able to compute the difference in the arrival times of the signals for any two stations. This information is used to locate the position of objects.

1. **Reason quantitatively.** Based on the definitions of *ellipse* and *hyperbola*, which conic section do you believe the LORAN system uses for locating objects? Explain your reasoning below.

2. The LORAN system computes time-difference information at two stations, *not* distance-difference information. How can time differences be converted to distance differences? Explain below.

CONNECT TO PHYSICS

Radio signals travel at the speed of light, approximately 186,000 miles per second or 300,000,000 meters per second.

Suppose that a distress signal is received from a ship at sea. The ship reports that it is within 100 miles of the coastline. Three LORAN stations receive the call. The three LORAN stations are located at the land-based points $E(-50, 0)$, $F(50, 0)$, and $G(50, 40)$, as shown in the illustration. The coordinate locations for each of these points are given in miles. The time difference for the radio signals transmitted by stations E and F is 860.22 microseconds. The time difference for the radio signals transmitted by stations F and G is 263.386 microseconds. A microsecond is 10^{-6} seconds.

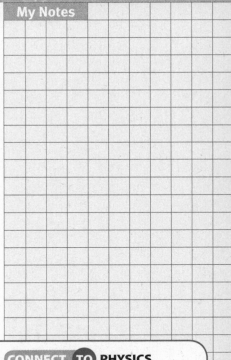

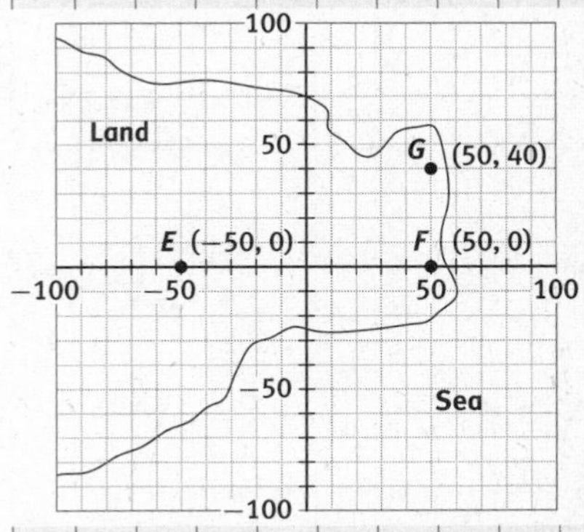

Since a radio signal travels a round trip from the LORAN station to the object and back to the LORAN station, the time difference represents the time difference for double the distance. Thus, the time differences that must be used to determine the distance differences are one-half the time differences that are given. Therefore, the time differences that determine the distance differences are 430.11 microseconds for stations E and F and 131.693 microseconds for stations F and G.

My Notes

3. Radio signals travel with the speed of light at 186,000 miles per second.
   a. Use the speed of light to convert the time difference of the signals for stations E and F into a distance that denotes the difference in distance that the two stations are from the distressed ship.

   b. Use the speed of light to convert the time difference of the signals for stations F and G into a distance that denotes the difference in distance that the two stations are from the distressed ship.

4. **Model with mathematics.** The distressed ship lies on a hyperbola that has foci located at stations E and F.
   a. Give the center and the values for a and c for this hyperbola.

   b. Find the value of b.

   c. Write the equation for the hyperbola having foci at stations E and F that contains the distressed ship.

5. **Model with mathematics.** The distressed ship also lies on a hyperbola that has foci located at stations F and G.
   a. Give the center and the values for a and c for this hyperbola.

   b. Find the value of b.

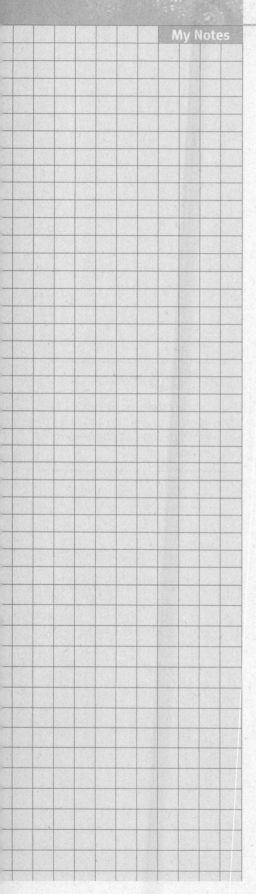

c. Write the equation for the hyperbola having foci at stations F and G that contains the distressed ship.

My Notes

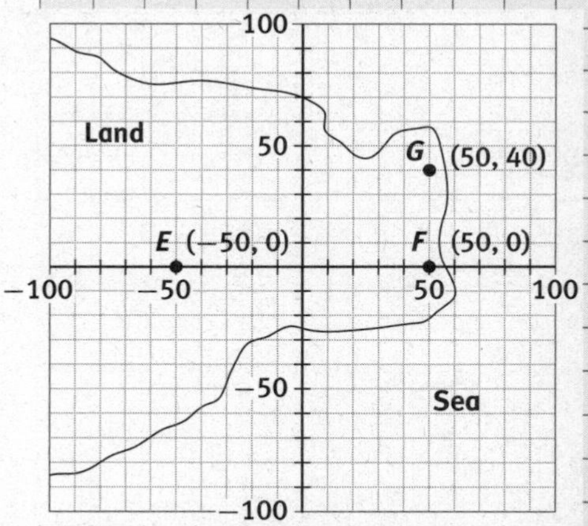

6. Make sense of problems. The equations of the hyperbolas found in Items 4 and 5 form a system of equations that can be solved to locate the distressed ship. Use a graphing calculator to solve this system of equations for the location of the ship. Recall that the distressed ship reported that it was within 100 miles of the coastline. Explain or describe the methods you used to determine the ship's location.

Check Your Understanding

7. Explain why hyperbolas are good models for the ship's location in this situation. As you prepare your explanation, remember to use words that will help your classmates understand the situation. Be careful to communicate mathematical terms correctly.

8. Could you have determined the location of the ship by using time-difference data from only two of the stations? Explain.

9. From which station, E, F, or G, should a helicopter be sent to rescue the crew members from the ship? Use mathematics to justify your answer.

10. Suppose station H has coordinates (0, 0).

a. If you found the location of the ship correctly in Item 6, what should be the difference in distance from the ship to station E and from the ship to station H?

b. Write the equation for the hyperbola having foci at stations E and H. Round the values of a^2 and b^2 to the nearest whole number.

c. Show that the ship's location lies on the hyperbola you found in part b.

My Notes

CONNECT TO METEOROLOGY

You can hear thunder from about 12 miles from the starting point.

LESSON 27-3 PRACTICE

Make sense of problems. Reid is standing 3 miles to the east of Theresa when they both see the same strike of lightning. Theresa hears the thunder 3.89 seconds sooner than Reid does.

11. The speed of sound in air when the lightning strikes is 767.7 mi/h. How many miles farther from the lightning strike is Reid than Theresa? Round to the nearest hundredth.

12. The location of the lightning strike lies on a hyperbola with foci at Theresa's location and Reid's location. Let the point (0, 0) represent Theresa's location and the point (3, 0) represent Reid's location on a coordinate plane in units of miles. Write the equation of the hyperbola and explain how you determined your answer. Round numerical values in the equation to the nearest tenth.

13. If the lightning strike was due south of Theresa's location, what were the coordinates of the strike's location? Round coordinates to the nearest integer.

14. To the nearest mile, what is Theresa's distance from the lightning strike, and what is Reid's distance from the lightning strike?

ACTIVITY 27 PRACTICE

Write your answers on notebook paper. Show your work.

Lesson 27-1

1. Suppose that 12 is the constant sum of the distances from a point (x, y) on an ellipse to the foci located at $(0, 4)$ and $(0, -4)$. Use the definition of *ellipse* and the distance formula to derive the equation of the ellipse in standard form. Then sketch the graph of the ellipse. Label the coordinates of the endpoints of the major and minor axes.
2. What is the equation of a circle with its center at $(-2, 6)$ and a radius of 4?
3. The foci of an ellipse are at $(0, -4)$ and $(0, 4)$. The point $\left(\frac{9}{5}, 4\right)$ lies on the ellipse. Use this information to show that the point $(-3, 0)$ also lies on the ellipse.

For Items 4–7, sketch the graph of each ellipse. Label the coordinates of the center, foci, and the endpoints of the major and minor axes.

4. $\frac{x^2}{64} + \frac{y^2}{100} = 1$
5. $\frac{(x+3)^2}{36} + \frac{(y-4)^2}{16} = 1$
6. $4x^2 + y^2 - 8x + 6y + 9 = 0$
7. $25x^2 + y^2 - 100x - 2y + 76 = 0$
8. What is the equation of an ellipse with its center at $(-1, 4)$, a focus at $(-1, 7)$, and a vertex at $(-1, 8)$?
   A. $\frac{(x-1)^2}{7} + \frac{(y+4)^2}{16} = 1$
   B. $\frac{(x-1)^2}{16} + \frac{(y+4)^2}{7} = 1$
   C. $\frac{(x+1)^2}{7} + \frac{(y-4)^2}{16} = 1$
   D. $\frac{(x+1)^2}{16} + \frac{(y-4)^2}{7} = 1$
9. What is the standard form of the conic section given by $9x^2 + 4y^2 + 54x - 16y + 61 = 0$? State the name of this conic section.
10. A pond shaped like an ellipse has a major axis that is 15 m long and a minor axis that is 6 m long. Two fountains are positioned at the foci of the ellipse. To the nearest tenth of a meter, how far apart are the fountains? Explain how you determined your answer.

Lesson 27-2

11. Suppose that 6 is the constant difference of the distances from a point (x, y) on a hyperbola to the foci located at $(-7, 0)$ and $(7, 0)$. Use the definition of *hyperbola* and the distance formula to derive the equation of the hyperbola in standard form. Then sketch the graph of the hyperbola. Identify the coordinates of the center, the foci, and the vertices, and the equations of the asymptotes.

For Items 12–16, sketch the graph of each hyperbola. Identify the coordinates of the center, the foci, and the vertices, and the equations of the asymptotes.

12. $\frac{y^2}{4} - \frac{x^2}{9} = 1$
13. $\frac{(x-4)^2}{9} - \frac{y^2}{4} = 1$
14. $4x^2 - y^2 - 8x + 4y - 9 = 0$
15. $x^2 - 36y^2 - 16x - 72y + 64 = 0$
16. Some telescopes use hyperbolic mirrors. A light ray directed at one focus is reflected to the other focus. Suppose that a hyperbolic mirror has a focus at $(14, 0)$ and a vertex at $(12, 0)$. When light is reflected from $(14, 0)$, it is reflected to $(-14, 0)$. Find an equation that models that shape of the mirror. Find the width of the mirror at the focus.

17. Compare and contrast a hyperbola centered at (h, k) that has a vertical transverse axis with an ellipse centered at (h, k) that has a vertical major axis. Consider the standard forms of the equations and the coordinates of the vertices and foci.

18. What is the equation of the hyperbola shown in the graph?

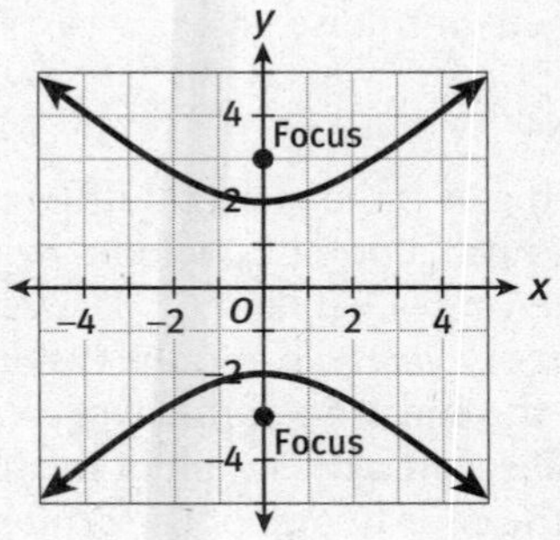

19. What is the equation of a hyperbola with its center at $(-2, 4)$, a vertex at $(-2, -2)$, and a focus at $(-2, -4)$?

A. $\frac{(x+2)^2}{28} - \frac{(y-4)^2}{36} = 1$

B. $\frac{(x+2)^2}{36} - \frac{(y-4)^2}{28} = 1$

C. $\frac{(y-4)^2}{28} - \frac{(x+2)^2}{36} = 1$

D. $\frac{(y-4)^2}{36} - \frac{(x+2)^2}{28} = 1$

Lesson 27-3

The bottom surface of a bridge forms a semi-elliptical arch over a river. The width of the arch is 30 ft, and the height is 10 ft.

20. Write the equation of the ellipse that models the arch. Let (0, 0) on a coordinate plane in units of feet represent the center of the ellipse and the x-axis represent the water line.

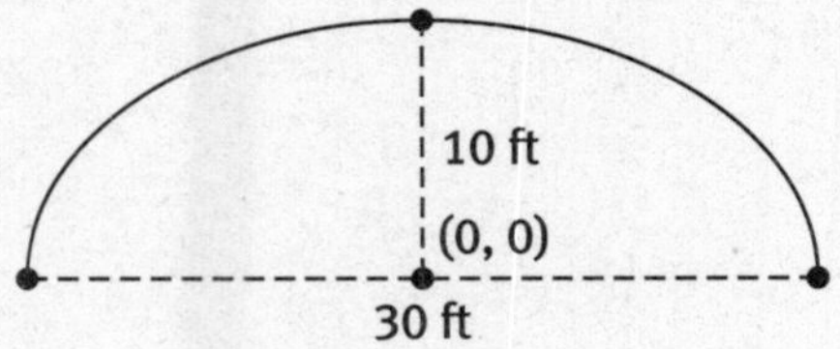

21. A barge shaped approximately like a rectangular prism has a width of 22 ft and a height above water of 8 ft. Will the barge be able to fit under the bridge? Use mathematics to support your answer.

For Items 22–24, consider the following. Sensor A is 2 km north of sensor B. Sensor A detects the sound of an explosion 1.375 s after sensor B.

22. The speed of sound in air at the time of the explosion is 343.2 m/s. To the nearest meter, how much closer to the explosion is sensor B than sensor A?

23. The location of the explosion lies on a hyperbola with foci at sensor A and sensor B. Let the point (0, 0) represent the center of the hyperbola on a coordinate plane in units of kilometers. Write the equation of the hyperbola. Round numerical values in the equation to the nearest hundredth.

24. If the explosion was due east of sensor B, what were the coordinates of the explosion? Round coordinates to the integer.

MATHEMATICAL PRACTICES
Model with Mathematics

25. Cell phone signals show that a driver reported an accident when he was 1.5 mi from a cell phone tower located at (3, 4) on a coordinate plane in units of miles. The driver was also 1.2 mi from a second cell phone tower located at (4, 2).

a. Write the equation of a circle that models the possible locations of the driver compared to the cell phone tower at (3, 4).

b. Write the equation of a circle that models the possible locations of the driver compared to the cell phone tower at (4, 2).

c. Based on the equations from parts a and b, the possible locations of the driver can be narrowed down to two ordered pairs. What two ordered pairs represent the driver's possible locations? Explain how you determined your answer

Polar Graphs

ACTIVITY 28

Air Traffic Controller

Lesson 28-1 The Polar Grid

My Notes

Learning Targets:

- Understand and use the polar grid.
- Define polar coordinates.
- Plot and label points in the polar grid.

SUGGESTED LEARNING STRATEGIES: Marking the Text, Interactive Word Wall, Think-Pair-Share, Quickwrite, Self Revision/Peer Revision

Air traffic controllers play an important role in keeping the aviation skies safe. Their job is to monitor airspace around an airport, typically within a 50-mile radius, in order to manage the traffic of airplanes flying in this airspace. They monitor air traffic by keeping track of the location and movement of planes on a radar screen. A radar screen, similar to the one used by air traffic controllers, is shown below.

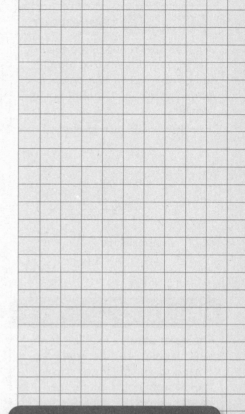

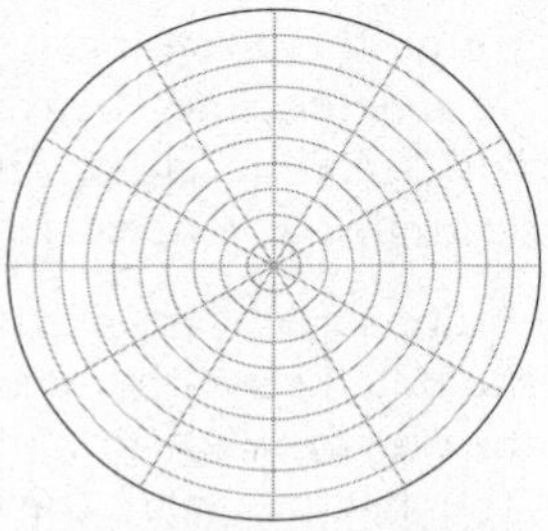

Air Traffic Controller
Radar Screen

The grid on the radar screen is called a ***polar grid***. The grid is made up of concentric circles and rays from the common center of these circles. Suppose that the common center of these circles is point *O*. Point *O* is called the *pole* of the polar grid. Point *O* gives the location of the air traffic control tower, which is where the air traffic controllers work. Thus, all air traffic is referenced with respect to pole *O*, the position of the control tower.

MATH TERMS

A **polar grid** is a grid made up of concentric circles and rays from a common center.

1. In the polar grid on the radar screen, each concentric circle has a radius equal to a multiple of 5 miles, with the smallest circle having a 5-mile radius and the largest circle having a 50-mile radius. The rays from the center of the polar grid form angles that are multiples of $30°$. Describe a method that can be used to verify that the angles formed by the rays are multiples of $30°$.

DISCUSSION GROUP TIPS

As you work in groups, read the problem scenario carefully and explore together the information provided and how to use it to create a potential solution. Discuss your understanding of the problem and ask peers or your teacher to clarify any areas that are not clear.

My Notes

CONNECT TO TECHNOLOGY

A *screen pixel* is one of the small electronic elements that form an image on a screen or monitor. A screen pixel can be thought of as a point.

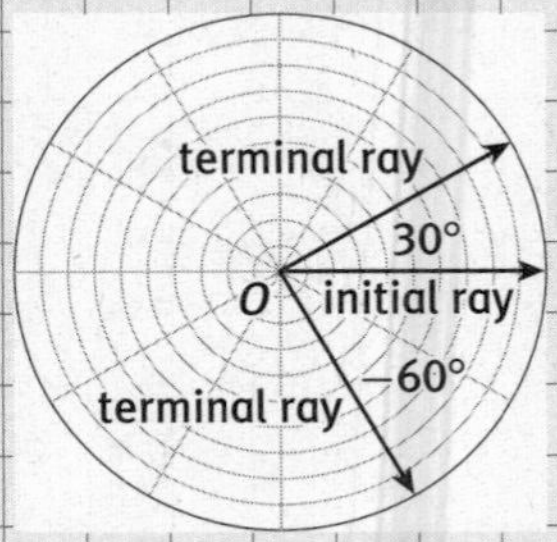

MATH TERMS

The **polar axis** is a fixed ray from which angles are measured on a polar grid. The polar axis is usually the ray from pole *O* along the positive *x*-axis.

The **initial ray** for an angle on a polar grid is the polar axis.

The **terminal ray** of an angle on a polar grid is the ray from pole *O* that passes through a point of interest.

The **polar coordinates** for a point on the polar grid are (r, θ), where *r* is the distance from the pole *O* and θ is the angle from the polar axis.

An air traffic controller must be familiar with the polar grid. When airplanes enter the control tower's airspace, they are identified by radar and their location is displayed on the radar screen by a brightened point on the polar grid. This point is a *screen pixel*. Air traffic controllers often identify the screen pixel by referring to it as "the aircraft being tracked."

2. An airplane is located 30 miles from the air traffic control tower. Indicate on the polar grid, and describe in words, the set of points (pixels) where the airplane could be located.

As aircraft move through the airspace, radar tracks their movement by periodically updating their locations. In addition to a distance to locate an airplane, an angle is needed. The ***initial ray*** for this angle is the ***polar axis***, which is from the pole *O* along the positive *x*-axis and is indicated by the dark ray in the polar grid shown at left. The ***terminal ray*** for this angle is the ray from the pole passing through the point locating the airplane's position on the radar screen. The angle is determined by rotating the initial ray into the terminal ray. If this rotation is counterclockwise, the angle has a positive measure. If it is clockwise, the angle has a negative measure.

To locate an airplane on the radar screen, an ordered pair is used—the first value gives a distance from the pole *O* and the second value gives an angle from the polar axis. The ***polar coordinates*** for a point on the polar grid are given as (r, θ), where *r* gives the distance from the pole *O* and θ gives the angle from the polar axis. A point that is 50 miles from *O* at an angle of 90° from the polar axis could be written as the ordered pair (50, 90°).

Example A

Plot and label point *A* that represents an aircraft 40 miles from *O*, at an angle of 120° from the polar axis. Then write the polar ordered pair (r, θ) for the point described.

The radii of the concentric circles on the radar screen increase in increments of 5, so points on the 8th circle out from *O* are 40 miles from *O*.

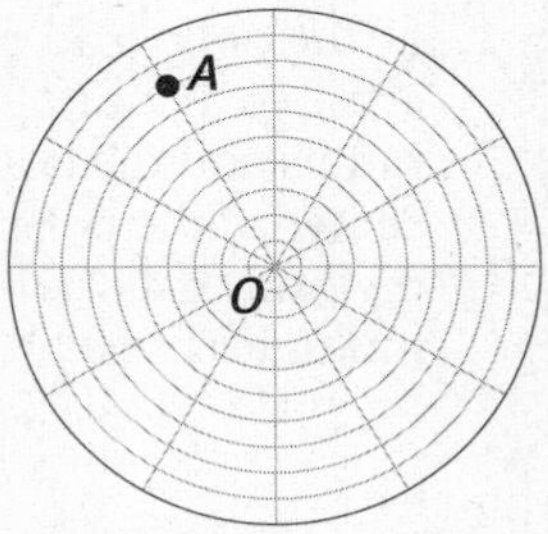

The rays from the center of the grid are separated by 30°. Start at the polar axis and move 4 rays counterclockwise to find the terminal ray of the angle 120° from the polar axis.

Draw point *A* where the terminal ray intersects the circle you identified earlier. Point *A* has the polar pair (40, 120°).

My Notes

Try These A

On the grid below, each concentric circle increases in radius by 5 miles. Plot the following points, then write the polar pairs (r, θ) for the points.

a. Point A, 20 miles from O, at an angle of $60°$ from the polar axis

b. Point B, 20 miles from O, at an angle of $-120°$ from the polar axis

c. Point C, 15 miles from O, at an angle of $150°$ from the polar axis

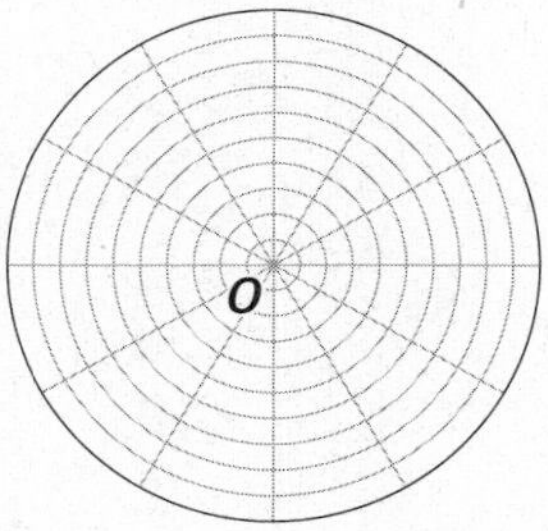

3. Consider the points $(40, 240°)$ and $(40, -120°)$.

a. Describe, in words, what occurs when you plot these points.

b. A rectangular xy-coordinate grid uses ordered pairs of the form (x, y) to indicate points in the plane. Do the rectangular pairs of the form (x, y) have the same property that you observed for the polar pairs $(40, 240°)$ and $(40, -120°)$? Justify your explanation.

c. Express regularity in repeated reasoning. Name some other polar pairs that identify the points $(40, 240°)$ and $(40, -120°)$. Explain how such other polar pairs can be constructed.

My Notes

The r-values in the examples in Items 1–3 were given as positive values marking the distance of the point from the pole. In general, the r-value in a polar ordered pair (r, θ) is a directed (positive or negative) distance from the pole. The value r can be given as a negative number. If θ is a directed angle, and if $r > 0$, the location of the point on the polar grid is found by moving along the terminal ray, making the angle θ. If $r < 0$, the location of the point on the polar grid is found by extending the terminal ray in the opposite (negative) direction, and moving along this opposite extension of the ray, a distance of $|r|$ units from pole O. The point $(-50, 30°)$ is shown on the graph below.

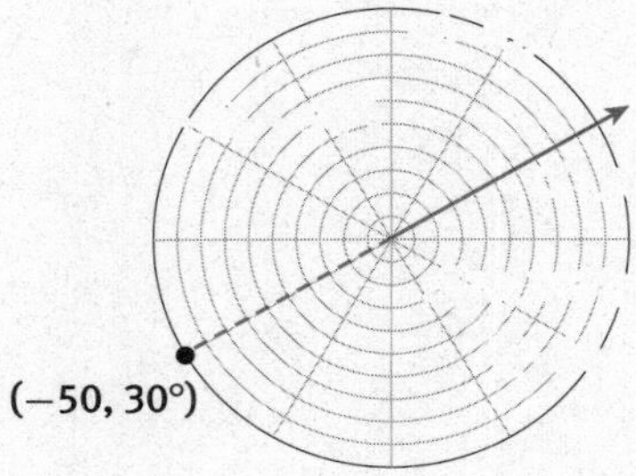

Check Your Understanding

Plot and label the following polar ordered pairs on the polar grid shown above. Each concentric circle increases in radius by 5 units.

4. Point A: $(-30, 120°)$

5. Point B: $(-45, 270°)$

6. Point C: $(-30, -210°)$

7. Point D: $(-25, -90°)$

8. Locate the point given by the polar pair for point E: $(20, 300°)$ on the polar grid above. Next, list three different polar ordered pairs (r, θ) that describe the same point on this grid.

LESSON 28-1 PRACTICE

Plot and label the points given by the polar coordinates. Each concentric circle on the given polar grid increases by 1 unit.

9. $A(2, -30°)$

10. $B(-3, 120°)$

11. $C(2, 195°)$

12. $D(-2, -150°)$

13. $E(0, 270°)$

14. Critique the reasoning of others. A student says that the point $(5, 120°)$ does not have the same graph as the point $(-5, -120°)$. Is the student correct? Explain.

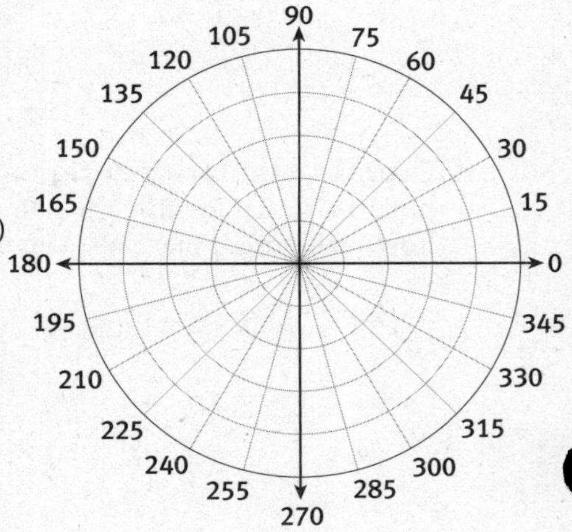

My Notes

Learning Targets:
- Convert rectangular coordinates to a polar point (r, θ).
- Convert polar coordinates to a rectangular point (x, y).

SUGGESTED LEARNING STRATEGIES: Role Play, Summarizing, Think-Pair-Share, Discussion Groups, Group Presentation

1. Reason abstractly. Points on the polar grid can have multiple polar pairs ***denoting*** their location.

a. Suppose $|r_1| = |r_2|$. Must polar pairs (r_1, θ_1) and (r_2, θ_1) denote the same point on the polar grid? Explain why or why not.

ACADEMIC VOCABULARY

If two polar pairs ***denote*** the same point, then the polar pairs name the same point.

b. Suppose $r_1 = -r_2$, and the polar pairs (r_1, θ_1) and (r_2, θ_2) denote the same point on the polar grid. What can you conclude about the angles θ_1 and θ_2?

c. Suppose the polar pairs (r, θ_1) and (r, θ_2) denote the same point on the polar grid. What can you conclude about the angles θ_1 and θ_2?

Although air traffic controllers work with radar screens that require using polar coordinates to locate aircraft, it is important for controllers to translate a location, shown in polar coordinates (r, θ) on their radar screens, into rectangular coordinates. The rectangular coordinates will be referenced to the standard directions of north-south (y-axis directions) and east-west (x-axis directions).

One afternoon, a hot air balloon suddenly appeared as a blip on the air traffic controller's radar screen. To air traffic controllers, hot air balloons can mean trouble. Hot air balloons are prohibited from flying within a 20-mile radius of the airport.

2. The polar grid shows the blip for the hot air balloon at time $t = 0$ minutes and at a time 100 minutes later.

a. Express the two locations of the hot air balloon in polar coordinates.

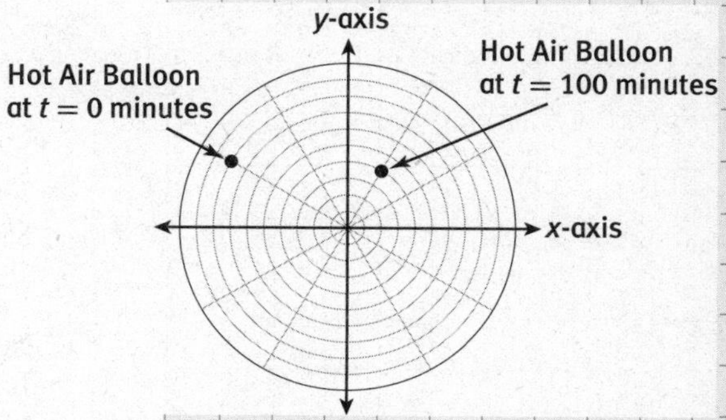

My Notes

b. Is the hot air balloon in violation of the airport airspace at either of these locations? Explain below.

The air traffic controller must warn the hot air balloon pilot of its possible encroachment into the airport airspace. A police car is sent to establish visual contact with the pilot using the police car's warning lights. The police officers will then use their amplified speakers to convey the warning to the balloonist. Rectangular north-south-east-west directions, referenced from the control tower with the origin placed at the pole, can be used to convey the exact location of the hot air balloon to the police.

The origin of the rectangular xy-coordinate system corresponds to the pole of the polar grid, and the positive x-axis lies along the polar axis. Right triangle trigonometry can be used to determine the rectangular coordinates for a polar point.

Example A

Determine the rectangular coordinates for $(40, 30°)$.

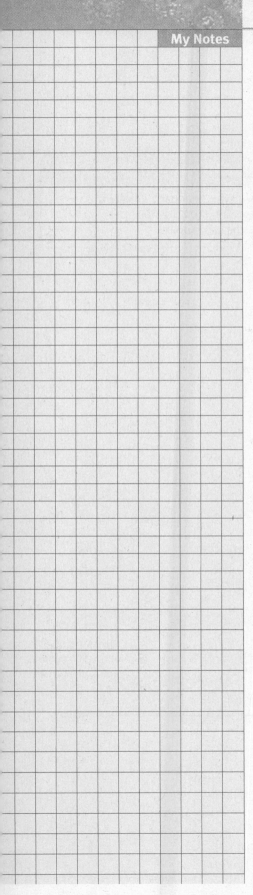

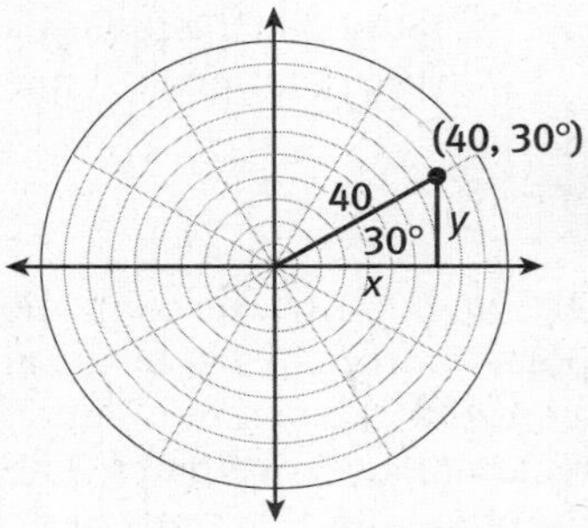

Step 1: Find the x-coordinate.

$$\cos 30° = \frac{x}{40}$$

$$x = 40 \cos 30°$$

$$x = 20\sqrt{3} \approx 34.64$$

Step 2: Find the y-coordinate.

$$\sin 30° = \frac{y}{40}$$

$$y = 40 \sin 30°$$

$$y = 20$$

Solution: $(x, y) = (20\sqrt{3}, 20)$

Try These A

a. Use right triangle trigonometry to determine the rectangular coordinates for the hot air balloon's location when $t = 100$ minutes.

b. How many miles east and how many miles north of the air traffic control tower is the hot air balloon at $t = 100$ minutes?

c. What are the rectangular coordinates for the location of the hot air balloon at $t = 0$ minutes?

My Notes

Air traffic controllers must be prepared for emergencies that require working with area police and fire services. Since fire and police agencies work with rectangular coordinates, generalized expressions translating (r, θ) coordinates into (x, y) coordinates are needed.

3. Given a point described by the polar pair (r, θ), use the diagram below and trigonometry to express the rectangular coordinates of x and y in terms of r and θ. Show work to support your answer.

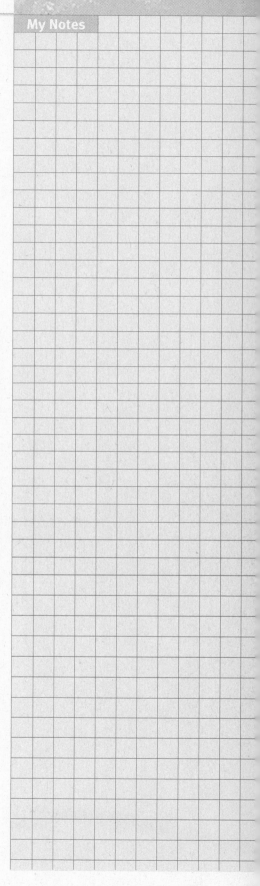

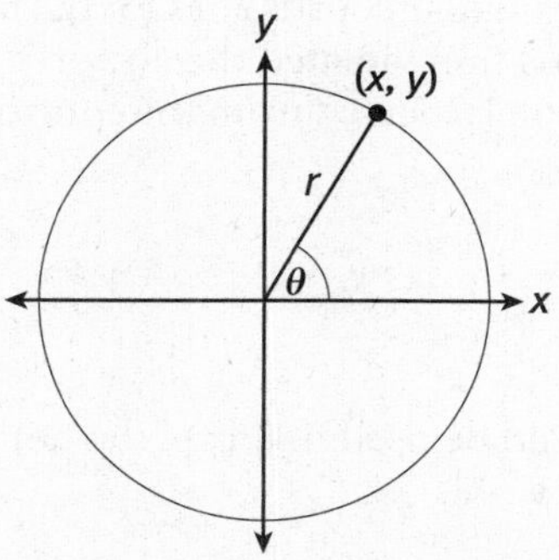

4. Apply the results in Item 3 to write the rectangular coordinates (x, y) for the following polar coordinates (r, θ).

a. $(20, 150°)$

b. $(12, 225°)$

c. $(10, -30°)$

d. $(-30, -315°)$

e. $(17, 128°)$

My Notes

By the time the police are able to catch up to the hot air balloon, it is located 3 miles east and $3\sqrt{3}$ miles south of the control tower. The balloon is on the ground, but not yet secured. The police report this location to the control tower and the air traffic controller records it in rectangular form as $(3, -3\sqrt{3})$. Because the balloon is on the ground, radar is unable to detect the balloon. Until the balloon is secured, it continues to pose a danger to air traffic in the area, especially if a gust of wind should suddenly send it airborne once again.

5. The air traffic controller must mark the balloon's location on the radar screen.

a. Based on the rectangular coordinates for the hot air balloon, determine if the balloon's position violated the airport's 20-mile limit by finding how far the balloon is located from the control tower. Show your work.

b. What angle θ could be used to locate the hot air balloon on the polar grid? Show your work.

c. Give a list of four polar coordinate pairs (r, θ) that could be used to locate the hot air balloon's position.

6. Suppose that before the hot air balloon could be secured, a strong gust of wind pushed the balloon to a new location. When the balloon was finally secured, its new position in relation to the control tower was $(-2\sqrt{3}, -2)$.

a. How far from the control tower is the hot air balloon at this new position? Show your work.

b. Give two possible angles for θ that could be used for the hot air balloon's polar coordinates (r, θ). Show your work.

You can use a graphing calculator to convert between polar and rectangular coordinates. To do so, press [2nd] [ANGLE] to access the angle menu.

To find the value of x for a point (r, θ), select **7: P▶Rx**. Then enter the ordered pair. Likewise, to find the value of y for a point (r, θ), select **8: P▶Ry**, and then enter the ordered pair.

7. Use appropriate tools strategically. Use a graphing calculator to convert each ordered pair from rectangular coordinates to polar coordinates. Round each coordinate to the nearest tenth.

a. (7, 124°) **b.** (20, −50°)

c. (3.5, 29°) **d.** (8.7, −105°)

My Notes

TECHNOLOGY TIP

For this lesson, make sure your calculator is set to degree mode rather than radian mode. To check, press [MODE] and make sure **Degree** is highlighted instead of **Radian**.

Check Your Understanding

8. Describe an advantage and a disadvantage of using a graphing calculator rather than pencil and paper to convert between polar coordinates and rectangular coordinates.

9. Describe a method using the unit circle to convert the polar coordinates (4, 225°) to rectangular coordinates.

10. If a point on a polar grid has a θ coordinate of 90°, what can you conclude about the location of the point on a rectangular coordinate grid? Explain your reasoning.

LESSON 28-2 PRACTICE

Determine the rectangular coordinates of each point.

11. (4, 250°) **12.** (−6, −120°) **13.** (7, 180°)

14. A surveyor sights a fence post marking a property boundary at a distance of 64 m from his location in the direction 30° north of east.

a. Determine the polar coordinates of the fence post on a polar grid in units of meters, with the surveyor's position at the pole O.

b. Express the fence post's location in rectangular coordinates, rounded to the nearest tenth.

15. Make sense of problems. A rover on Mars detects an interesting rock formation 0.8 km from its location in the direction 78° south of east. The operators of the rover plan to direct it to the formation by driving it due east and then due south to avoid a gully. Explain how you can use rectangular coordinates to determine how far the rover will travel to reach the rock formation.

My Notes

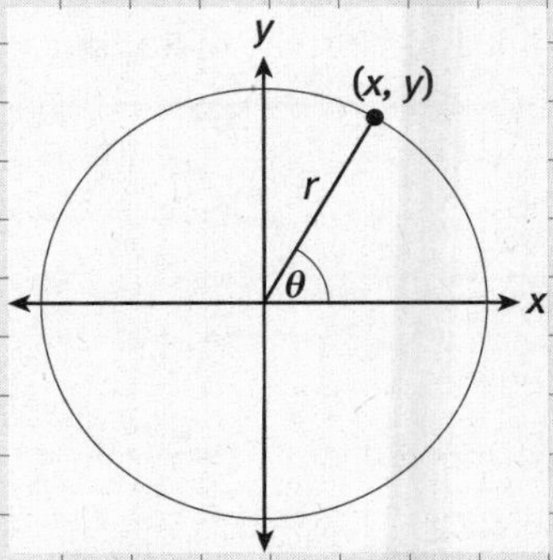

Learning Targets:

- Express x and y in terms of r and θ.
- Sketch polar curves on the polar grid.
- Use polar functions to represent real-world situations.

SUGGESTED LEARNING STRATEGIES: Visualization, Note Taking, Discussion Groups, Create Representations, Quickwrite

1. **Reason abstractly.** Given a point described by the rectangular pair (x, y), use the diagram and trigonometry to express the polar coordinates of r and θ in terms of x and y. Explain your answer.

Example A

An approaching aircraft is 9 miles west and $9\sqrt{3}$ miles north of the air traffic control tower. Determine the polar coordinates of the aircraft.

Step 1: Write the rectangular coordinates.

West is the negative direction along the x-axis, and north is the positive direction along the y-axis, so the rectangular coordinates are $\left(-9, 9\sqrt{3}\right)$.

Step 2: Find the r-coordinate.

$$r = \sqrt{(-9)^2 + \left(9\sqrt{3}\right)^2}$$
$$r = \sqrt{81 + 243}$$
$$r = \sqrt{324} = 18$$

Step 3: Find the θ-coordinate. Because the aircraft is in Quadrant II, the terminal side of θ must also be in Quadrant II.

$$\tan\theta = \frac{9\sqrt{3}}{-9},\ 90° < \theta < 180°$$
$$\tan\theta = -\sqrt{3},\ 90° < \theta < 180°$$
$$\theta = 120°$$

Solution: The polar coordinates of the aircraft are (18, 120°).

My Notes

Try These A

Convert the rectangular coordinates to polar coordinates.

a. $(-12, -9)$ **b.** $(6, -8)$ **c.** $(-12, 5)$

2. Use appropriate tools strategically. Use the inverse tangent function on your calculator to compute the angle for the aircraft at location $(-9, 9\sqrt{3})$, and explain why the calculator gives the angle for the aircraft as located at $(9, -9\sqrt{3})$.

To convert between rectangular and polar coordinates on a graphing calculator, start by pressing [2nd] [ANGLE] to access the angle menu. To find the value of r for a point (x, y), select **5: R▶Pr**. Then enter the ordered pair. Likewise, to find the value of θ for a point (x, y), select **6: R▶Pθ**, and then enter the ordered pair.

3. Use appropriate tools strategically. Use a graphing calculator to convert each ordered pair from rectangular coordinates to polar coordinates. Round each coordinate to the nearest tenth if needed.

a. $(-3, 3)$ **b.** $(10, -14)$ **c.** $(5.8, 1.6)$

Pilots have a radar screen in the cockpit of their airplane. When landing in overcast weather conditions, the radar screen becomes their "eyes," guiding them to the runway for landing their aircraft. This radar screen is also a polar grid, with the pole on the screen giving the location of the instrument landing system (ILS) transmitting tower and the polar axis denoting due east from the ILS. The brightened point on the screen shows the location of the aircraft relative to the ILS transmitting system.

Typically, the ILS transmitting system is positioned at the ends of a runway. This positioning shows the pilot exactly where the beginning and end of the runway are located. From the ILS transmission, the pilot uses the cockpit radar screen to maneuver the airplane toward the pole, which locates the beginning of the runway.

Polar curves of the form $r = f(\theta)$ can be used to describe landing approaches for aircraft pilots.

CONNECT TO AVIATION

The maneuvers performed by pilots to land a plane are referred to as landing approaches. Airports have strict landing approach procedures that must be followed to keep air traffic orderly and safe. These landing approach procedures are similar to traffic lanes usage for cars.

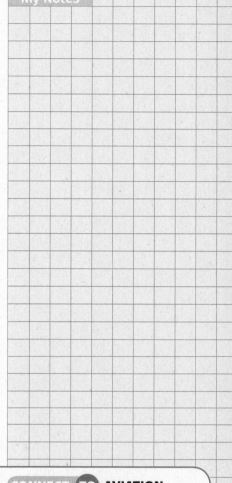

My Notes

4. The ILS signal indicates that the landing approach is toward the south. The scope on the airplane uses concentric circles with radii in steps of 1 mile from the ILS runway signal.
   a. Use the polar grid below to sketch the landing approach that is described by the polar function $r = 6 \cos \theta$ for $0° \leq \theta \leq 90°$. Begin by plotting the location of the plane when $\theta = 0°, 30°, 60°$, and $90°$, and then connect the points.

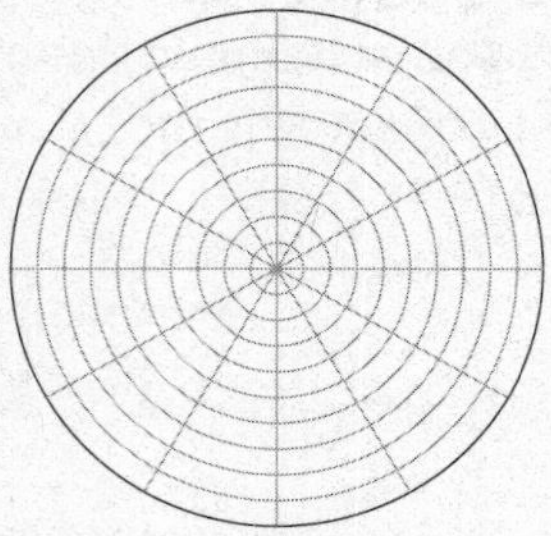

   b. Describe the type of landing approach that is sketched in Part a.

   c. Your graph represents the landing approach for aircraft. However, the graph of this landing approach is only part of the complete graph of the polar curve. Use the polar grid shown below to give a complete graph of $r = 6 \cos \theta$. Indicate the interval of values for θ that gives the complete graph.

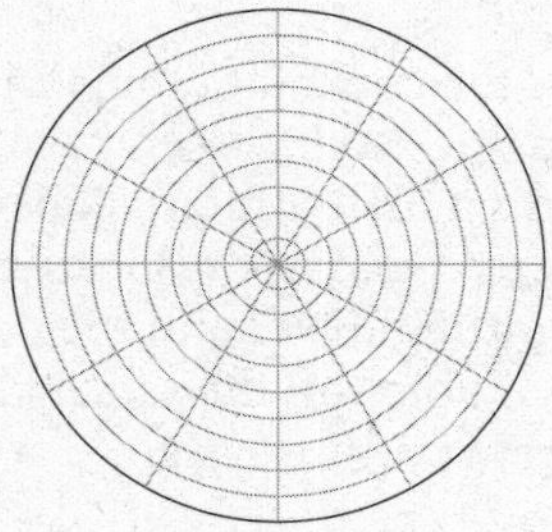

The equation of a polar curve of the form $r = f(\theta)$ can be transformed into an equation using the rectangular variables x and y.

Example B

Transform the equation of the polar curve given by $r = 6\cos\theta$ by writing it as an equation using the rectangular variables x and y.

Step 1: Express r and $\cos\theta$ by using x and y.

$$r = \sqrt{x^2 + y^2} \qquad \cos\theta = \frac{x}{r} = \frac{x}{\sqrt{x^2 + y^2}}$$

Step 2: Substitute the expressions for r and $\cos\theta$ into the equation of the polar curve and simplify.

$r = 6\cos\theta$	Original equation
$\sqrt{x^2 + y^2} = 6\left(\frac{x}{\sqrt{x^2 + y^2}}\right)$	Substitute for r and $\cos\theta$.
$x^2 + y^2 = 6x$	Multiply both sides by $\sqrt{x^2 + y^2}$.

Step 3: If possible, write the equation in the standard form of a conic section.

$x^2 - 6x = -y^2$	Group the terms containing x.
$x^2 - 6x + 9 = -y^2 + 9$	Complete the square for x.
$(x - 3)^2 = -y^2 + 9$	Factor the left side.
$(x - 3)^2 + y^2 = 9$	Add y^2 to both sides. The equation is in the standard form of a circle.

Solution: The equation $r = 6\cos\theta$ is equivalent to $(x - 3)^2 + y^2 = 9$.

Try These B

a. Does the transformation in Example B confirm your answer to Item 4b? Explain.

b. Sketch the complete graph of $r = 4\sin\theta$.

c. Transform the equation of the polar curve $r = 4\sin\theta$ by writing it as an equation using the rectangular variables x and y.

My Notes

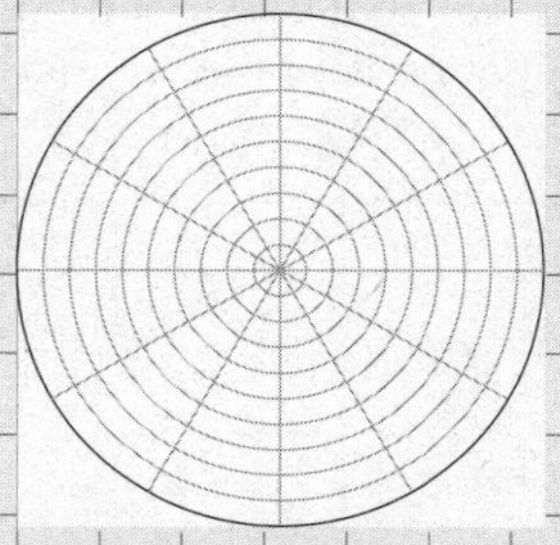

My Notes

Check Your Understanding

5. Write an ordered pair using polar coordinates that is equivalent to (0, 0) in rectangular coordinates. Does it matter what value you use for r? Does it matter what value you use for θ? Explain.

6. Why might it be useful to represent points on the unit circle by using polar coordinates?

7. Graph and describe the polar curves given by the equations $r = 3$ and $\theta = 45°$.

8. Describe a real-world situation that does not involve airplanes where polar coordinates would be useful.

LESSON 28-3 PRACTICE

Determine the polar coordinates of each point.

9. $(-8, 8)$ **10.** $(0, -3)$ **11.** $(-9, -12)$

12. Graph and convert the equation $r = -2 \sin \theta$ to rectangular form.

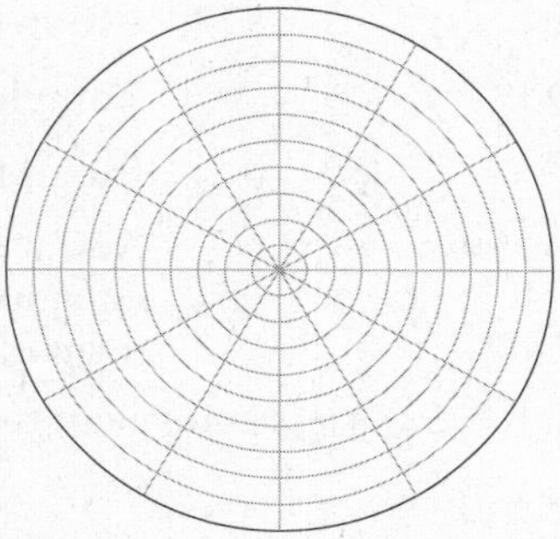

13. A ship is 16 nautical miles east and 12 nautical miles north of a lighthouse. Given that the lighthouse is at the origin, express the ship's position in rectangular coordinates and in polar coordinates, rounded to the nearest tenth.

14. **Make sense of problems.** A campground is 2 miles west and 3 miles south of a park entrance. Tayla and Bridget plan to hike along a straight line from the entrance to the campground. Explain how you can use polar coordinates to determine the direction they should head and how many miles they will hike.

CONNECT TO NAVIGATION

A nautical mile is a unit often used for measuring distance at sea. A nautical mile is equivalent to 6076 feet, so it is longer than a customary mile, which is only 5280 feet.

ACTIVITY 28 PRACTICE

Write your answers on notebook paper.
Show your work.

Lessons 28-1

For Items 1–5, plot and label the points given by the polar coordinates.

1. $A(3, -105°)$ **2.** $B(-2, 15°)$

3. $C(1, 75°)$ **4.** $D(-4, -30°)$

5. $E(0, 300°)$

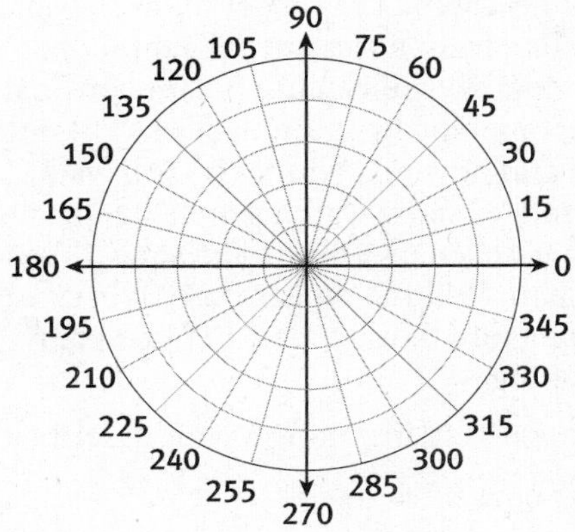

6. Which are possible coordinates of the point graphed below?

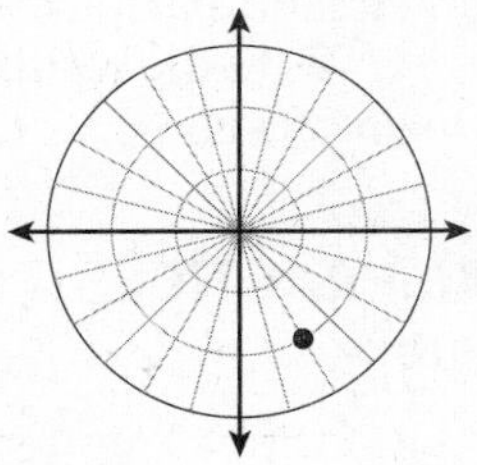

A. $(-2, 120°)$ **B.** $(-2, 60°)$
C. $(2, -120°)$ **D.** $(2, 60°)$

7. Which of the following polar points would *not* have the same graph as $(6, 100°)$?
A. $(6, 460°)$ **B.** $(6, -260°)$
C. $(-6, -100°)$ **D.** $(-6, -80°)$

8. Describe the relationship between the locations of the points $(8, 30°)$ and $(-8, 30°)$ on a polar grid.

9. The ship *Blue Sky*'s radar screen shows the positions of three ships at points *R*, *S*, and *T*. The pole *O* represents the location of *Blue Sky*. The units of the polar grid are in nautical miles. Give the polar coordinates of each ship, and describe its location in words compared to the location of the *Blue Sky*.

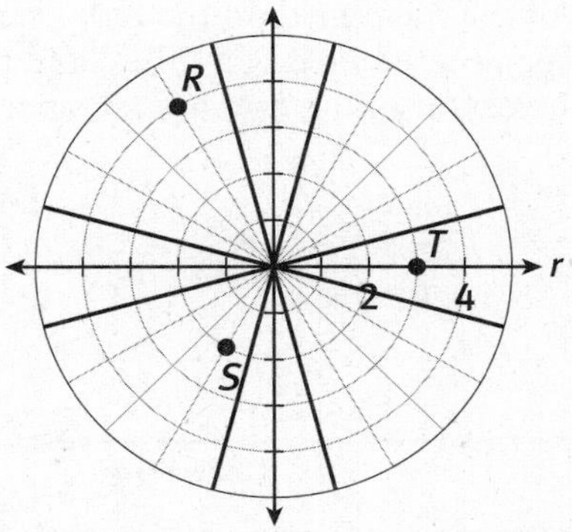

10. Write three other polar pairs that represent the same location as $(9, 20°)$.

Lessons 28-2

For Items 11–16, determine the rectangular coordinates of each polar point.

11. $(7, 162°)$ **12.** $(-4, -30°)$

13. $(5, 270°)$ **14.** $(-6, 45°)$

15. $(24, 16°)$ **16.** $(9.2, -104°)$

17. A rider on horseback leaves a stable and heads 60° north of west for 6 miles.
   a. Determine the polar coordinates of the rider on a polar grid in units of miles, where the pole *O* represents the stable and the polar axis points due east.
   b. Explain how you can use rectangular coordinates to describe the location of the rider in relation to the stable.

18. If a point on a polar grid has a θ-coordinate of 180°, what can you conclude about the location of the point on a rectangular coordinate grid? Explain your reasoning.

19. Point P on a polar grid has coordinates (8, 150°). What is the slope of the ray with its endpoint at the pole O that passes through point P? Explain how you determined your answer.

20. The diagram shows the location of a small plane on a radar screen at time $t = 0$ minutes and at time $t = 15$ minutes. The radii of the concentric circles of the polar grid on the radar screen increase in increments of 5 miles, and the rays from the center of the grid are 15° apart.

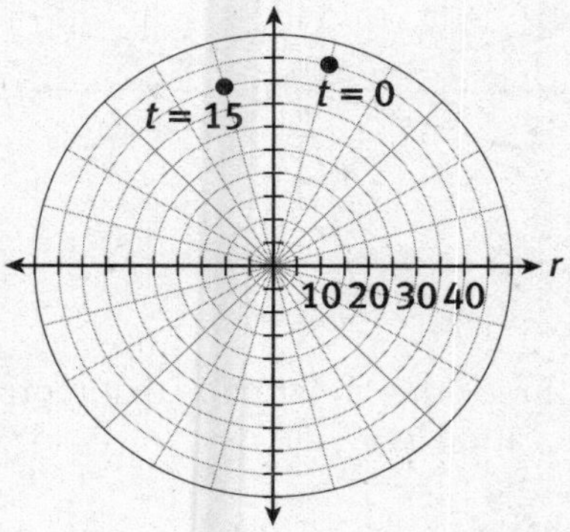

a. Determine the rectangular coordinates of the plane at $t = 0$ and at $t = 15$. Round coordinates to the nearest hundredth.

b. Reason abstractly. If the plane is following a straight path at a constant altitude, what is its average speed in miles per hour? Explain your reasoning.

Lesson 28-3

For Items 21–26, determine the polar coordinates of each rectangular point.

21. $(-6, -6)$ **22.** $(-3, 0)$

23. $(8, -15)$ **24.** $(12, 14)$

25. $(-4, -7)$ **26.** $\left(-3, 3\sqrt{3}\right)$

For Items 27–30, graph each equation, and convert it to rectangular form.

27. $r = -10 \cos\theta$ **28.** $r = 5 \cos\theta$

29. $r = -8 \sin\theta$ **30.** $r = 6 \sin\theta$

31. Consider a polar curve of the form given by $r = a \sin\theta$, where $a \neq 0$, and whose graph is a circle.

a. How does the sign of a affect the graph of the circle?

b. What is the relationship between $|a|$ and the radius of the circle?

c. What are the rectangular coordinates of the center of the circle in terms of a? Explain your reasoning.

32. A park ranger's car has broken down in a forest. A map shows that he is 2.5 miles east and 2 miles north of his cabin. The ranger plans to walk in a straight line from his car to the cabin.

a. Explain how you can use polar coordinates to determine the direction the ranger should head and how many miles he will walk.

b. The ranger starts walking at 3:20 p.m. at an average speed of 3 mi/h. The sun will set at 5:35 p.m. Will the ranger make it back to his cabin before the sun sets? Explain your reasoning.

33. A helicopter is flying along a path described by the polar curve $r = \dfrac{3}{1 - 0.5\cos\theta}$.

a. Sketch a graph of the curve on a polar grid. Then describe the shape of the helicopter's path.

b. Transform the equation of the polar curve by writing it as an equation using the rectangular variables x and y. Write the resulting equation in the standard form of a conic section.

MATHEMATICAL PRACTICES
Attend to Precision

34. Explain the relationships among these terms: polar coordinates, initial side, terminal side, and polar axis.

Polar Curves and Polar Conics

Roses, Rings, and Hearts

Lesson 29-1 Polar Equations

My Notes

Learning Targets:

- Sketch graphs represented by polar equations.
- Compare and contrast polar graphs.
- Write equivalent rectangular and polar equations.

SUGGESTED LEARNING STRATEGIES: Create Representations, Look for a Pattern, Quickwrite, Self Revision/Peer Revision, Predict and Confirm

Many companies, brands, or organizations have a symbol or logo that instantly identifies them to the world. Graphic designers and advertising firms often create designs like the ones shown below to represent their client's image without words.

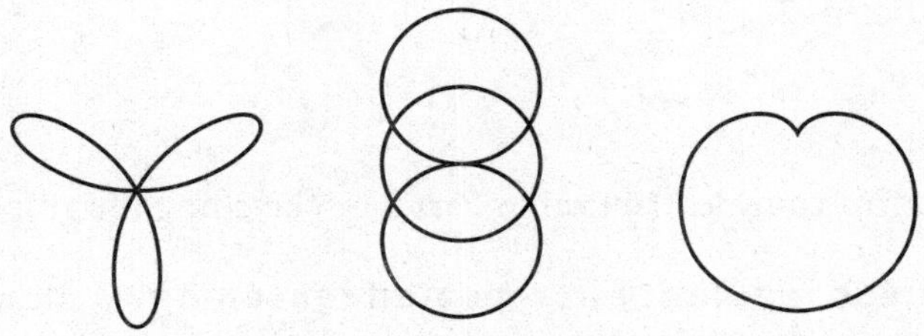

The symbols shown above can be represented by ***polar equations***. In this activity you will investigate graphs such as these and their equations in both polar and rectangular form.

MATH TERMS

A **polar equation** is an equation that defines a curve in terms of polar coordinates r and θ.

1. Consider the polar equation $r = 3$.

a. Describe the characteristics of the graph of the equation.

b. Sketch a graph of the equation.

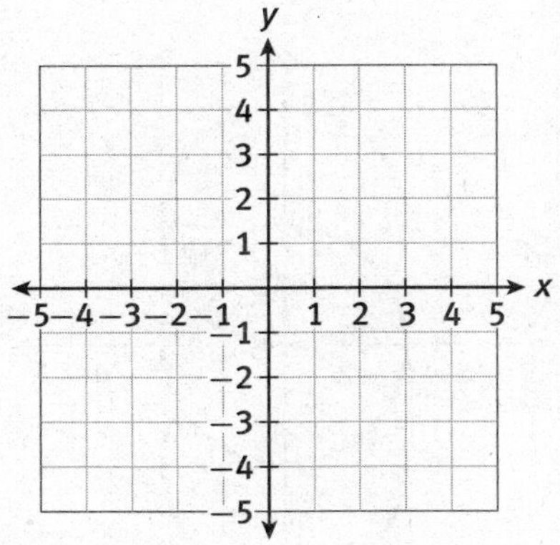

c. Write the rectangular equation for the graph.

d. Show how to convert the equation $r = 3$ from polar to rectangular form in order to confirm your answer to part c.

MATH TIP

If the polar coordinates of (r, θ) represent the point with rectangular coordinate (x, y), then $r^2 = x^2 + y^2$.

My Notes

2. Write the rectangular equation for a polar equation in the form $r = a$.

3. Consider the polar equation of the form $r = a \cos \theta$.

a. Compare and contrast the characteristics of the graphs of $r = 3 \cos \theta$, $r = -4 \cos \theta$, and $r = \frac{1}{2} \cos \theta$.

b. Describe, without graphing, the characteristics of $r = 2 \cos \theta$. Be sure to include a description of the symmetry and the effect of the coefficient 2.

c. Confirm your description in Part b by sketching the graph.

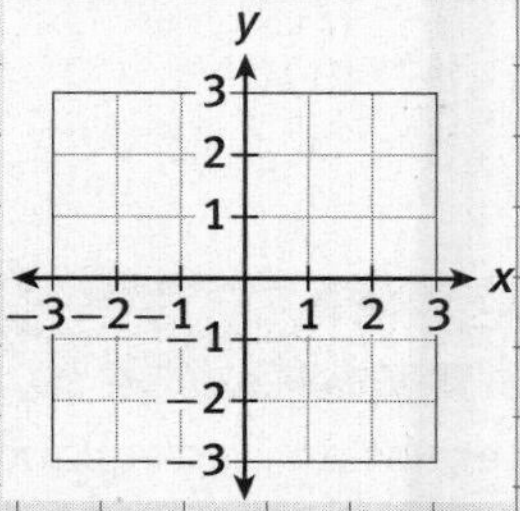

d. Express regularity in repeated reasoning. Write a general statement describing the effect of the coefficient a on the graph of a polar equation in the form $r = a \cos \theta$.

4. Describe the symmetry of and effect of the coefficient a on the graph of a polar equation in the form $r = a \sin \theta$.

CONNECT TO AP

In calculus, you will need to recognize polar equations and be able to sketch their graphs quickly, with and without a calculator.

5. Consider the design below.

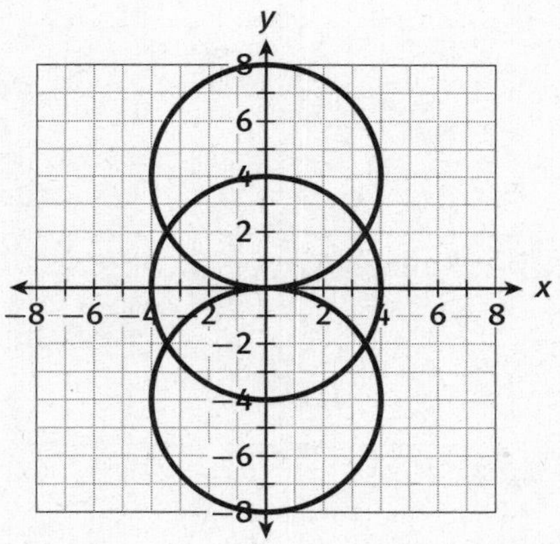

a. Write the polar equation for each of the circles shown in the design.

b. Write the rectangular equation for each of the circles shown in the design.

My Notes

In the previous items, polar equations were used to represent circles. The next item will examine the polar form of another geometric figure.

6. Consider the polar equation $\theta = 45°$.

a. Complete the table and graph the equation.

r	θ
-3	
-1	
1	
2	

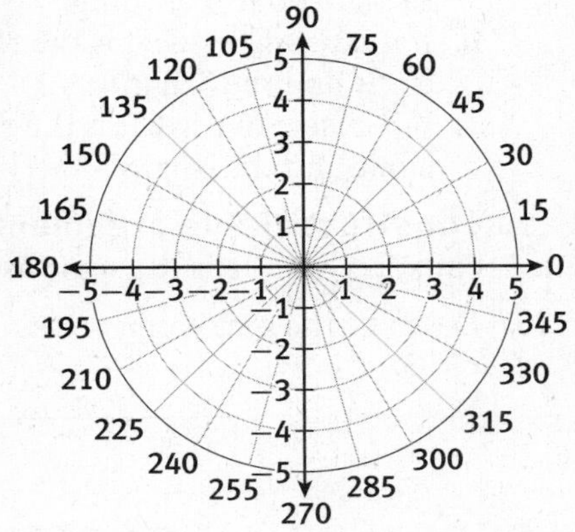

b. Based on the characteristics of the graph, write the rectangular form of the equation $\theta = 45°$.

c. Show how to convert the equation $\theta = 45°$ from polar to rectangular form in order to confirm your answer to Part b.

MATH TIP

If the polar coordinates of (r, θ) represent the point with rectangular coordinates (x, y), then $\tan\theta = \frac{y}{x}$.

7. Write the rectangular equation that is equivalent to the polar equation $\theta = 60°$. Confirm your work by graphing.

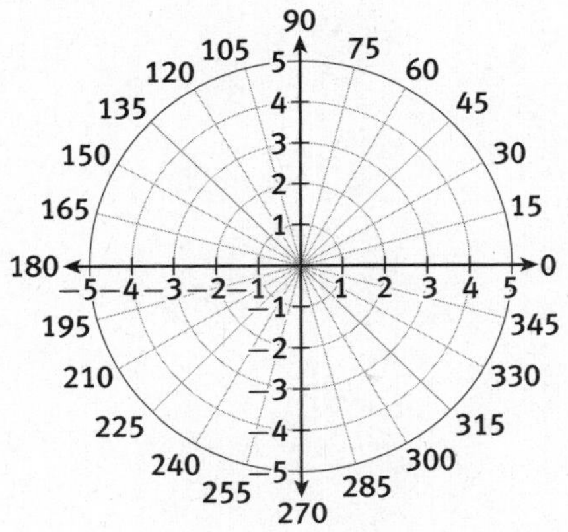

My Notes

Check Your Understanding

8. Consider the polar equation of the form $r = a \cos \theta$.
   a. What are the rectangular coordinates of the center of the circle? Explain your reasoning.
   b. If a is positive, what is the relationship between the center of the circle and the origin?
   c. If a is negative, what is the relationship between the center of the circle and the origin?

9. Construct viable arguments. Explain why the graph of the polar equation $r = -4$ is the same as the graph of the polar equation $r = 4$.

10. Describe the graph of $r = 6 \sin \theta$ as a transformation of the graph of $r = 3$.

LESSON 29-1 PRACTICE

List the characteristics of the graph and write the rectangular form for each polar equation.

11. $r = 5$

12. $\theta = 150°$

13. $r = 14$

14. $\theta = -60°$

Sketch the graph of each equation on a rectangular coordinate plane.

15. $r = -6 \cos \theta$

16. $r = 10 \sin \theta$

17. Write the polar equation of the circle shown on the graph. Then write the rectangular equation of the circle.

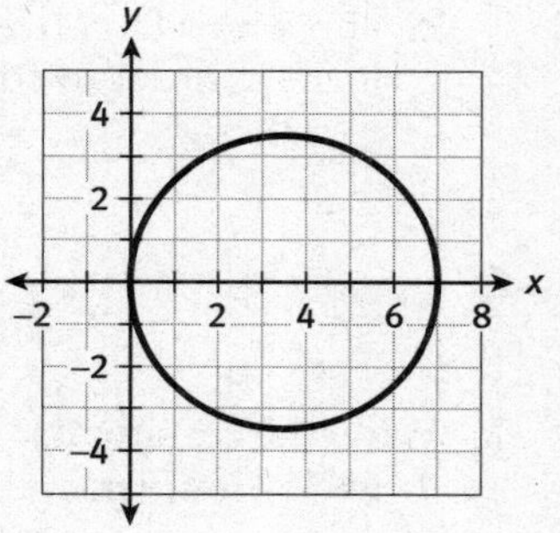

18. Critique the reasoning of others. A student claims that the circle given by the polar equation $r = -12 \cos \theta$ has an area of 36π square units. Is the student's claim correct? Support your answer.

My Notes

Learning Targets:

- Convert a polar equation to rectangular form.
- Convert a rectangular equation to polar form.
- Describe and sketch graphs of polar equations.

SUGGESTED LEARNING STRATEGIES: Note Taking, Discussion Groups, Create Representations, Quickwrite, RAFT

Converting polar equations to rectangular form may require algebraic manipulation.

Example A

Convert $r = 4 \sec \theta$ to rectangular form.

Step 1: Replace $\sec \theta$ by $\frac{1}{\cos \theta}$.

$r = 4 \sec \theta$

$r = \frac{4}{\cos \theta}$

Step 2: Multiply both sides of the equation by $\cos \theta$.

$r \cos \theta = 4$

Step 3: Use the conversion equation $x = r \cos \theta$ to substitute x for $r \cos \theta$.

$x = 4$

Try These A

Convert each of the polar equations to rectangular form.

a. $r = 10$ **b.** $\theta = 135°$ **c.** $r = 8 \csc \theta$

1. Consider the polar equation $r = \frac{2}{3\cos\theta - 6\sin\theta}$.

a. Make use of structure. Predict, without graphing, the characteristics of the graph of $r = \frac{2}{3\cos\theta - 6\sin\theta}$. Explain your reasoning.

b. Convert the polar equation $r = \frac{2}{3\cos\theta - 6\sin\theta}$ to rectangular form. How does this confirm your prediction from part a?

My Notes

Sometimes when converting a polar equation to rectangular form you will want to multiply both sides of the polar equation by r.

Example B

Convert $r = 6 \cos \theta - 8 \sin \theta$ to rectangular form.

Step 1: Multiply both sides of the equation by r.
$r = 6 \cos \theta - 8 \sin \theta$
$r^2 = 6r \cos \theta - 8r \sin \theta$

Step 2: Write r^2, $r \cos \theta$, and $r \sin \theta$ in terms of x and y.
$x^2 + y^2 = 6x - 8y$

Step 3: Complete the square to write the equation in standard rectangular form.
$x^2 + y^2 - 6x + 8y = 0$
$(x - 3)^2 + (y + 4)^2 = 25$

Try These B

Convert each polar equation to rectangular form.

a. $r = -24 \cos \theta + 10 \sin \theta$

b. $r = 16 \cos \theta - 30 \sin \theta$

2. Make use of structure. Use the rectangular form $(x - 3)^2 + (y + 4)^2 = 25$ to describe the graph of the polar equation $r = 6 \cos \theta - 8 \sin \theta$.

3. Convert the polar equation $r = 4 \cos \theta + 10 \sin \theta$ to rectangular form and describe the characteristics of the graph.

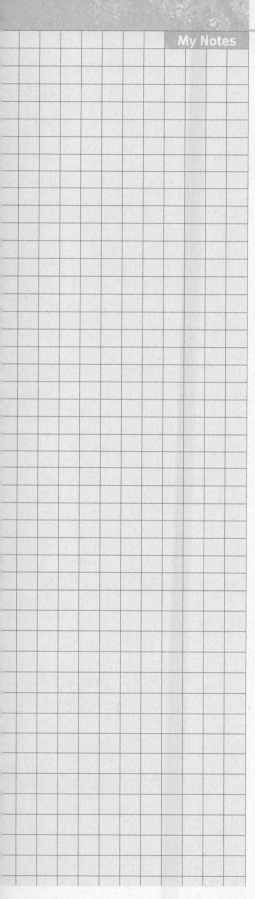

My Notes

It is possible to convert from the rectangular form of an equation to the polar form as well.

Example C

Convert $y = x^2$ to polar form.

Step 1: Substitute $y = r\sin\theta$ and $x = r\cos\theta$.

$$y = x^2$$
$$r\sin\theta = (r\cos\theta)^2$$
$$r\sin\theta = r^2\cos^2\theta$$

Step 2: Divide both sides of the equation by r.

$$\sin\theta = r\cos^2\theta$$

Step 3: Divide both sides of the equation by $\cos^2\theta$.

$$\frac{\sin\theta}{\cos^2\theta} = r$$

Step 4: Simplify.

$$\sec\theta\tan\theta = r$$

Example D

Convert $x^2 + 2y^2 - 8x = 0$ to polar form.

Step 1: Rewrite the equation.

$$x^2 + 2y^2 - 8x = 0$$
$$x^2 + y^2 + y^2 = 8x$$

Step 2: Substitute $r^2 = x^2 + y^2$, $y = r\sin\theta$ and $x = r\cos\theta$.

$$r^2 + r^2\sin^2\theta = 8r\cos\theta$$

Step 3: Factor.

$$r^2(1 + \sin^2\theta) = 8r\cos\theta$$

Step 4: Divide both sides of the equation by r.

$$r(1 + \sin^2\theta) = 8\cos\theta$$

Step 5: Solve for r.

$$r = \frac{8\cos\theta}{(1 + \sin^2\theta)}$$

Try These C–D

Convert each rectangular equation to polar form.

a. $y^2 = 2x$

b. $4x + 5y = 3$

c. $2x^2 + y^2 + 3y = 0$

My Notes

Several types of relations have equations that are simpler to express in polar form than in rectangular form. We will investigate the graphs of some of these.

4. Consider the curve given by the equation $r = 4 \sin 3\theta$.

a. Complete the table by substituting the values of θ into the equation.

θ	0°	15°	30°	45°	60°	75°	90°	105°	120°	135°	150°	165°	180°
r													

b. Plot the points and graph the equation on the polar grid.

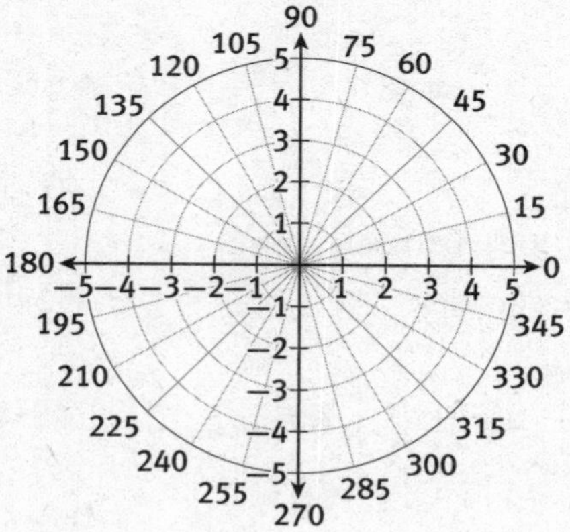

Check Your Understanding

5. Reason abstractly. The slope-intercept form of a linear equation is $y = mx + b$.

a. Write the polar form of the linear equation $y = mx + b$, and solve the polar form for r.

b. Explain how the slope and y-intercept can be determined from a polar equation.

6. Write the polar form of the equation of the ellipse shown on the graph. Explain your answer.

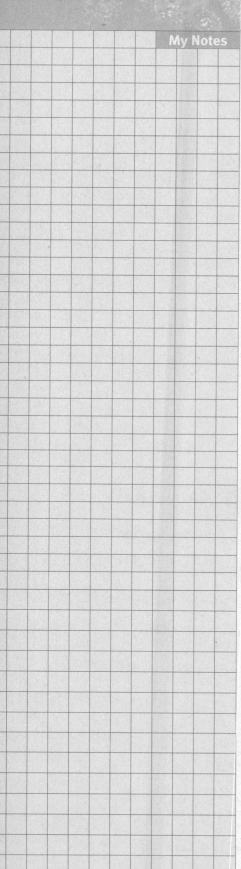

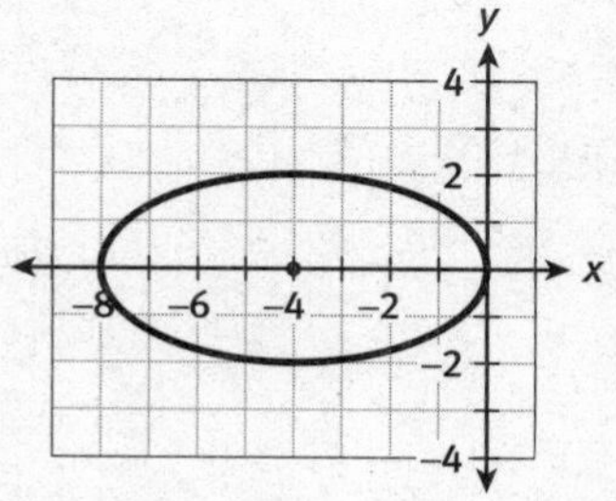

7. Write a set of detailed instructions that explains how to convert the polar equation $r = -4 \cos \theta$ to a rectangular equation in standard form.

My Notes

LESSON 29-2 PRACTICE

List the characteristics of the graph and write the rectangular form for each polar equation.

8. $r = -2 \csc \theta$

9. $r = \dfrac{1}{2\cos\theta + 5\sin\theta}$

10. $r = 2 \cos \theta + 3 \sin \theta$

Convert each rectangular equation to polar form.

11. $x^2 + y^2 = 10$

12. $x = 6$

13. $5x + 7y = 2$

14. $y^2 = 8x$

15. $x^2 + 4x + y^2 - 9y = 0$

16. Make a table of values for the polar equation $r = 4 \cos 3\theta$. Then graph the equation on a polar grid.

17. **Make sense of problems.** The polar equation $r^2 - 268r \sin \theta = -532$ represents the path of a car on a Ferris wheel, where r is measured in feet. To the nearest foot, how far does the car move along the path during one complete rotation of the Ferris wheel? Explain how you determined your answer.

My Notes

Learning Targets:

- Classify different types of polar equations.
- Explore patterns in the graphs of polar curves.
- Predict the resulting graph for a polar equation.

SUGGESTED LEARNING STRATEGIES: Interactive Word Wall, Create Representations, Look for a Pattern, Group Presentation, Self Revision/Peer Revision

1. **Use appropriate tools strategically.** Use your calculator to graph each of the polar equations in the table below, sketch the curve, and complete the table.

Polar Equation	Sketch	Number of Petals	Length of Each Petal
$r = 2\sin 4\theta$			
$r = 2\sin 5\theta$			
$r = -3\sin 2\theta$			
$r = -4\sin 3\theta$			
$r = 2\cos 4\theta$			
$r = 2\cos 5\theta$			

My Notes

Polar Equation	Sketch	Number of Petals	Length of Each Petal
$r = -3\cos 2\theta$			
$r = -4\cos 3\theta$			

The graph of a polar equation in the form $r = a\cos(n\theta)$ or $r = a\sin(n\theta)$ is called a ***rose curve***.

MATH TERMS

A **rose curve** is the graph of a polar equation that can be written in the form $r = a\cos(n\theta)$ or $r = a\sin(n\theta)$. The curve resembles the petals of a flower.

2. **Express regularity in repeated reasoning.** Look for patterns in the table you completed in Item 1 to determine the following.
   a. How does changing the value of a influence the characteristics of the graph of a rose curve?

   b. How does changing the value of n influence the characteristics of the graph of a rose curve?

   c. Describe the differences in the symmetry of the graph of $r = a\cos(n\theta)$ versus $r = a\sin(n\theta)$.

3. Consider the equation $r = 4\sin(n\theta)$.
   a. Use your calculator to explore the graph of the equation for any even number n. Find the interval for θ for which the graph is traced only once.

   b. Use your calculator to explore the graph of the equation for any odd number n. Find the interval for θ for which the graph is traced only once.

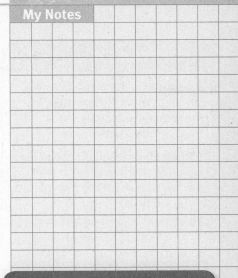

My Notes

MATH TERMS

A **cardioid** is the graph of a polar equation that can be written in the form $r = a \pm b \cos\theta$ or $r = a \pm b \sin\theta$ with $a = b$.

A **limaçon** is the graph of a polar equation that can be written in the form $r = a \pm b \cos\theta$ or $r = a \pm b \sin\theta$ with $a \neq b$.

READING MATH

The mark under the letter *c* in the word *limaçon* [LIM uh son] is called a cedilla [si DIL uh]. It alerts the reader that the letter *c* should be pronounced like the letter *s*.

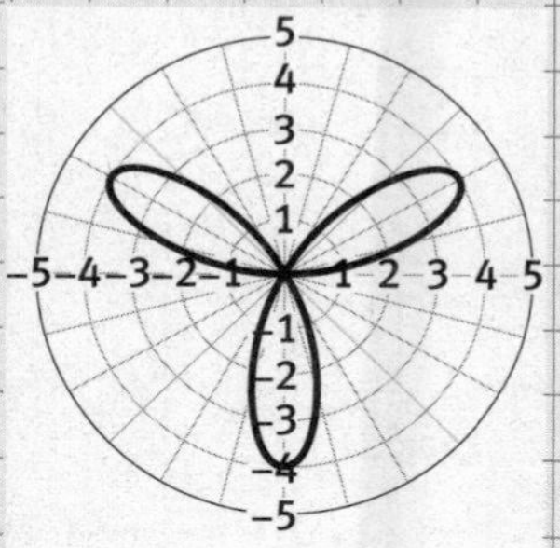

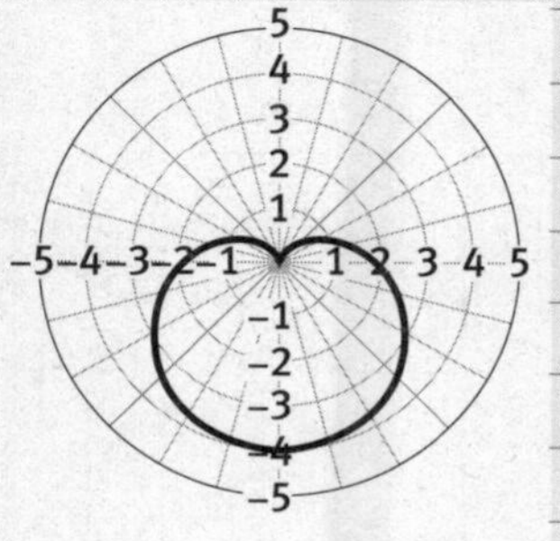

The graph of the polar equation in the form $r = a \pm b \sin\theta$ or $r = a \pm b \cos\theta$ with $a = b$ is called a ***cardioid***. If $a \neq b$, the graph is called a ***limaçon***.

4. Use appropriate tools strategically. Consider the graph of a polar equation in the form $r = a \pm b \sin\theta$ or $r = a \pm b \cos\theta$. Select values of a and b that meet each condition. Use your calculator to graph the equations and then record a sketch labeling key points on the graph.

Form of Polar Equation	Condition	Your Equation	Sketch of Your Graph
$r = a \pm b \sin\theta$	$a = b$		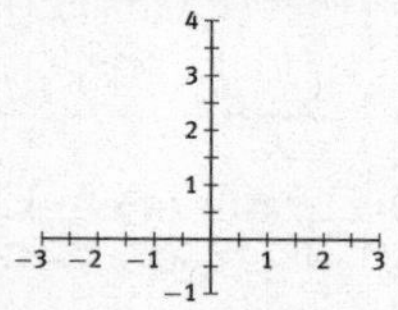
$r = a \pm b \cos\theta$			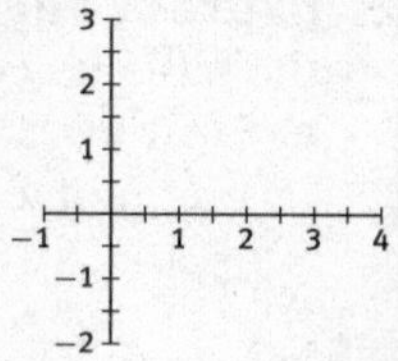
$r = a \pm b \sin\theta$	$a < b$		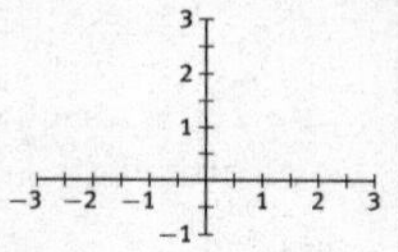
$r = a \pm b \cos\theta$			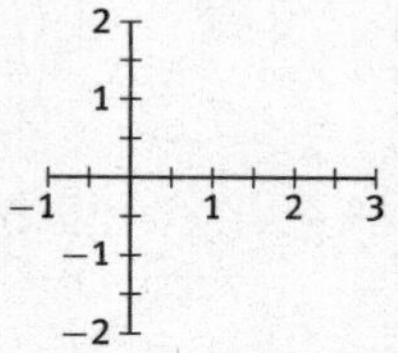
$r = a \pm b \sin\theta$	$a > b$		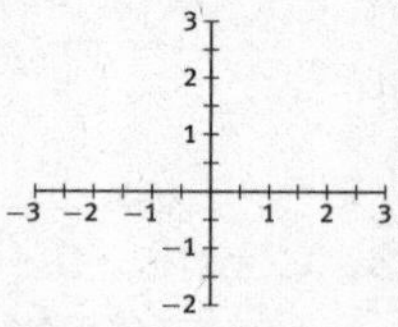
$r = a \pm b \cos\theta$			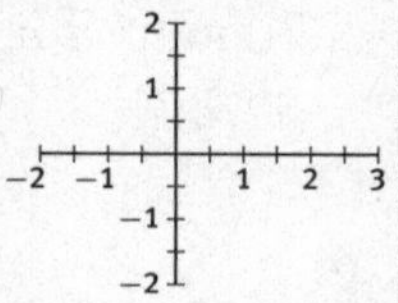

5. For each design shown, write a polar equation.

My Notes

You have studied the standard rectangular form of the equations of conic sections. When one focus of a conic section is located at the pole, conic sections can be written in a standard polar form.

6. Express regularity in repeated reasoning. Conic sections having one focus located at the pole can be expressed in the form $r = \frac{b}{a \pm c\sin\theta}$ or $r = \frac{b}{a \pm c\cos\theta}$.

a. The values of a and c determine whether the graph of the conic section will be a parabola, ellipse, or hyperbola. Make a conjecture about the values of a and c that will determine whether the conic section graphed will be a parabola, ellipse, or hyperbola. Defend your conjecture with examples.

b. What effect does the parameter b have on the graph of the conic section?

c. What effect does changing the sine to cosine have on the graph of the conic section?

7. Make use of structure. Without using your calculator, determine whether the equation gives the graph of a parabola, ellipse, or hyperbola, and describe the symmetry of the graph. Explain.

a. $r = \frac{4}{3 - 2\sin\theta}$

b. $r = \frac{4}{2 - 3\cos\theta}$

c. $r = \frac{4}{3 + 3\sin\theta}$

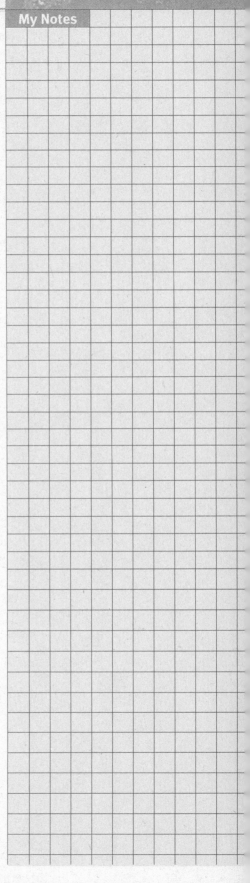

My Notes

Check Your Understanding

8. **Construct viable arguments.** Determine the validity of this statement: A rose curve will always have symmetry with respect to the x-axis.
9. How is the graph of the polar equation $r = 3 \sin (n\theta)$ affected when n represents a rational number such as 1.5 rather than a natural number?
10. What is the relationship between the values of a and b when a limaçon has an inner loop?

LESSON 29-3 PRACTICE

Describe the symmetry of the graph of the polar equation.

11. $r = 9 + 4 \cos \theta$
12. $r = 1 - 4 \sin \theta$
13. $r = \sin (3\theta)$
14. $r = -2 \cos (4\theta)$
15. Write a polar equation for a rose curve that is symmetric to the x-axis and has 5 petals, each with length 3 units.

Use a graphing calculator to graph the polar equation. Find an interval for θ for which the graph is traced only once.

16. $r = 3 - 2 \cos \theta$
17. $r = 10 \sin (7\theta)$
18. $r = 4 + 6 \sin \theta$
19. **Make use of structure.** Without using a graphing calculator, sketch the graph of the polar equation $r = 3 \cos (2\theta)$.

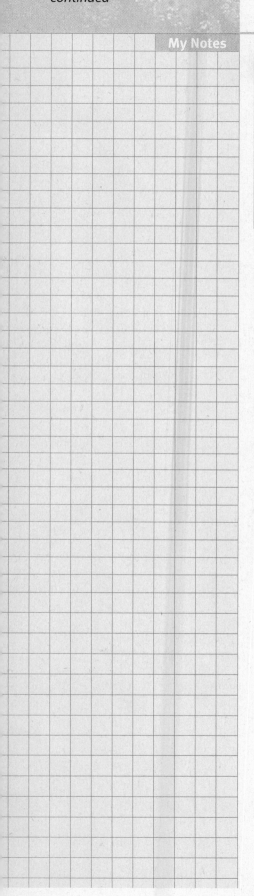

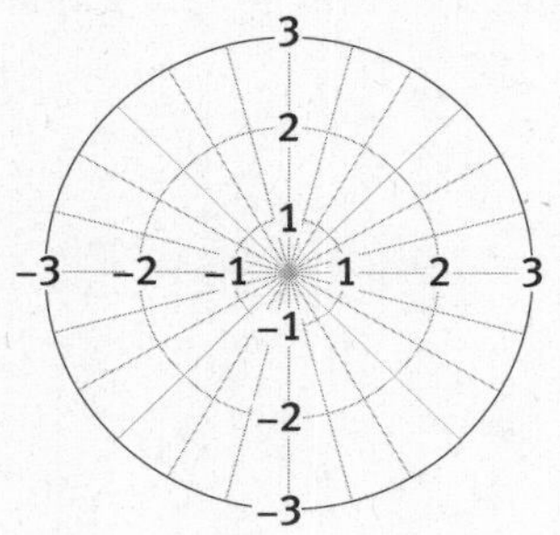

ACTIVITY 29 PRACTICE

Write your answers on notebook paper. Show your work.

Lesson 29-1

For Items 1–3, sketch the graph of each equation on a rectangular coordinate plane.

1. $r = 5 \cos \theta$
2. $r = -4 \sin \theta$
3. Compare and contrast the characteristics of the graphs of $r = 12 \sin \theta$, $r = 0.5 \sin \theta$, and $r = -7 \sin \theta$.

For Items 4–7, describe, without graphing, the characteristics of the graph of each polar equation. Then write the rectangular form of the polar equation.

4. $r = 9$
5. $\theta = 135°$
6. $r = 9 \cos \theta$
7. $r = -6 \sin \theta$

Use the graph of the circle below for Items 8–10.

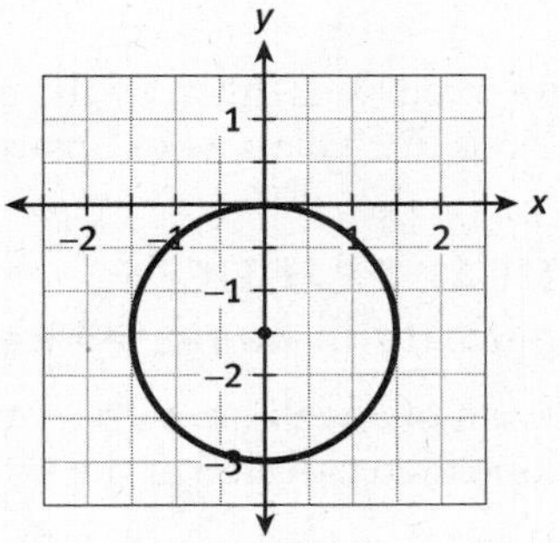

8. What is the polar form of the equation of the circle?
   A. $r = -3 \sin \theta$ **B.** $r = -3 \cos \theta$
   C. $r = -1.5 \sin \theta$ **D.** $r = -1.5 \cos \theta$
9. What is the rectangular form of the equation of the circle?
10. Describe the circle as a transformation of the graph of $r = 1.5$.
11. What is the slope of the line given by $\theta = 120°$? Explain your answer.

Lessons 29-2

List the characteristics of the graph and write the rectangular form of each polar equation below.

12. $r = -8 \sec \theta$
13. $r = \dfrac{1}{9 \cos \theta - 3 \sin \theta}$
14. $r = 7 \cos \theta + 4 \sin \theta$

Convert each rectangular equation to polar form.

15. $x^2 + y^2 = 144$
16. $x = 11$
17. $2x - 9y = 5$
18. $x^2 - 5x + y^2 + y = 0$
19. $x^2 = 10y$

Make a table of values for each polar equation. Then graph the equation on a polar grid.

20. $r = 5 \cos (2\theta)$
21. $r = 3 \sin (3\theta)$
22. The focus of the parabola shown in the graph is $(4, -3)$.

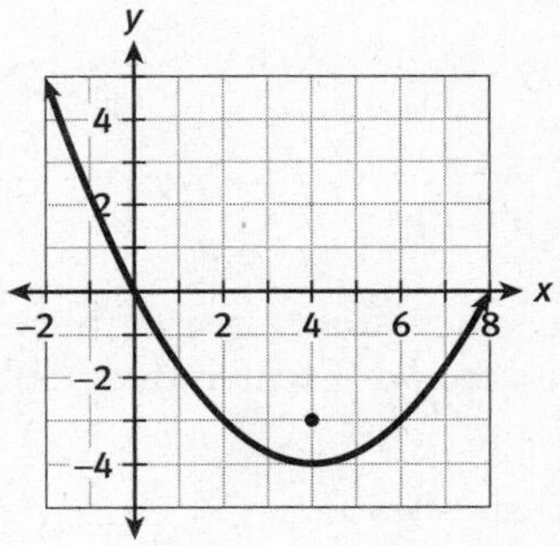

   a. What is the rectangular form of the equation of the parabola? How do you know?
   b. What is the polar form of the equation of the parabola? Explain your reasoning.
   c. How could you check that your answer to Part b is reasonable?

Lesson 29-3

23. Determine the validity of this statement: It is possible for a rose curve to be symmetrical with respect to both the x-axis and the y-axis. Explain your reasoning.

24. Without using a graphing calculator, sketch the graph of the polar equation $r = 6 \sin (4\theta)$. State the number of petals and the length of each petal.

25. What is the equation of the rose curve shown in the graph? Explain your answer.

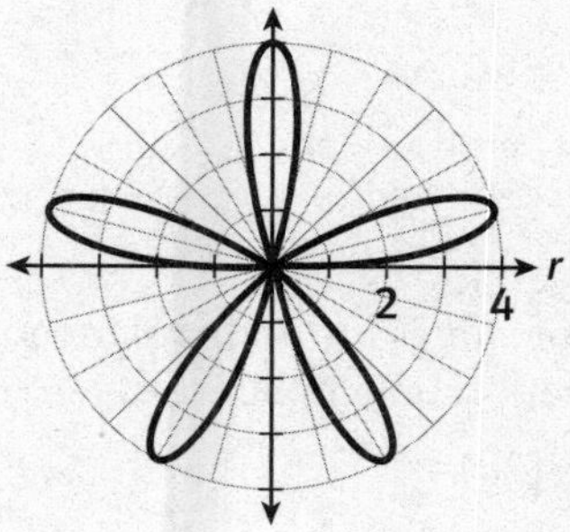

Describe the symmetry of the graph of each polar equation.

26. $r = 7 - 2 \sin \theta$

27. $r = 3 + 10 \cos \theta$

28. $r = \cos (5\theta)$

29. $r = -4 \sin (3\theta)$

Use a graphing calculator to graph the polar equation. Find an interval for θ for which the graph is traced only once.

30. $r = 1 + 3 \sin \theta$

31. $r = 3 \cos (10\theta)$

32. $r = 2 - 2 \cos \theta$

33. Write a polar equation for a rose curve that is symmetric to the y-axis and has 7 petals, each 4 units long.

34. What type of curve is described by the polar equation $r = 4 - 5 \cos \theta$?

A. cardioid **B.** circle
C. limaçon **D.** rose curve

35. What is the equation of the curve shown in the graph?

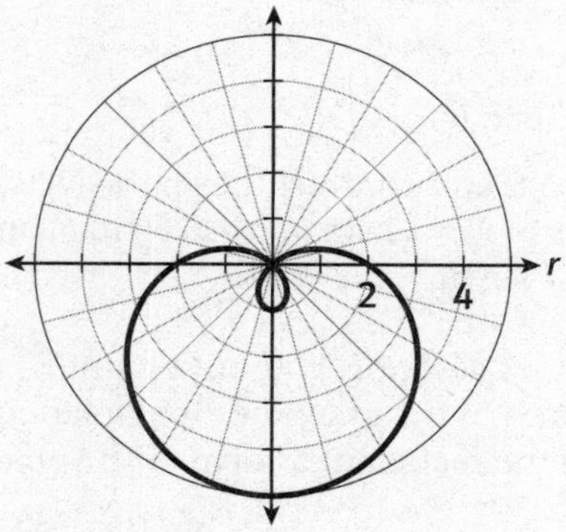

A. $r = 2 - 3 \sin \theta$ **B.** $r = 2 - 3 \cos \theta$
C. $r = -2 \sin (3\theta)$ **D.** $r = -2 \cos (3\theta)$

36. Explain how you determined your answer to Item 35.

37. What type of curve is given by the equation $r = 2 + 2 \cos \theta$? Explain your answer.

MATHEMATICAL PRACTICES
Express Regularity in Repeated Reasoning

38. The equation of an ellipse with a vertical major axis and one focus located at the pole can be expressed as $r = \dfrac{b}{a \pm c \sin \theta}$, where $a > c$.

a. What effect does the sign of b have on the ellipse?

b. What effect does the sign of a have on the ellipse?

Conic Sections and Polar Graphs

MAKE A BEELINE (OR A BEE CURVE)

Honeybees communicate information about food sources using angles and distances. When a worker bee discovers a food source, she flies back to the hive to give the location of this source using one of two dances. When the food source is farther than 80 m from the hive, the bees fly in a path known as a "waggle dance."

1. Suppose a bee's "waggle dance" indicates that a food source is 600 m from the hive with a direction corresponding to a 30° angle in standard position.
   a. What are the polar coordinates of the location of the food? Graph the location of the food on a polar grid.
   b. Determine the rectangular coordinates for the location of the food.
2. The path of one bee's dance is given by the equation $r = 30 \sin \theta$, where r is measured in millimeters.
   a. Describe this path, and graph it on a polar grid.
   b. Convert the equation to rectangular form.
3. Another food source has rectangular coordinates $(-150, -96)$ in units of meters in relation to a bee's hive. What angle and distance would the bee signal for this food?
4. A bee flies around the hive in a pattern that can be described by the rectangular equation $2x^2 + y^2 - 6y = 0$. Convert the equation of this path to polar form, and then graph the path on a polar grid.
5. Two beehives are located at (0, 0) and (0, 100) on a coordinate grid in units of meters. A food source is located 30 m farther from the hive at (0, 0) than from the hive at (0, 100). The food source lies on a hyperbola that has foci located at the two hives.
   a. Write the equation of the hyperbola that contains the food source. Explain how you determined your answer.
   b. If the food source is located due east of the hive at (0, 100), what are the coordinates of the food source to the nearest integer?

A graphic artist is designing a label for a honey company, as shown.

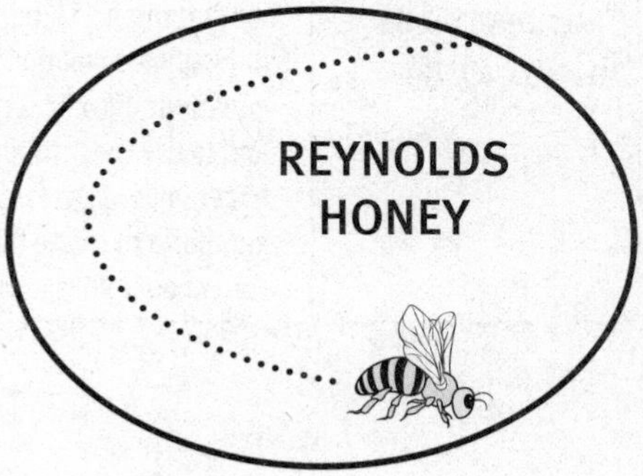

6. The label itself is in the shape of an ellipse. The artist will draw the ellipse so that the major axis has a length of 8 units and the minor axis has a length of 6 units. The leftmost vertex will be at the origin on a coordinate plane.
   a. Give the coordinates of the vertices, the center of the ellipse, and endpoints of the minor axis.
   b. Determine the coordinates of the foci, and explain how you determined your answers.
   c. What is the equation of the ellipse that the artist will draw?
7. The path of the bee on the label is a parabola, with its vertex at (1, 0) and its focus at $\left(\frac{9}{7}, 0\right)$.
   a. What is the equation of the directrix of the parabola? How do you know?
   b. What is the equation of the parabola that the artist will draw? Explain how you determined the equation of the parabola.

Scoring Guide	Exemplary	Proficient	Emerging	Incomplete
	The solution demonstrates these characteristics:			
Mathematics Knowledge and Thinking (Items 1, 2, 3, 4)	• Clear and accurate understanding of polar coordinates, and polar graphs, including their conversion into rectangular coordinates and functions on the rectangular plane	• A functional understanding of polar coordinates and polar graphs and their connection to rectangular coordinates	• Partial understanding of polar coordinates and graphs; may not know how to translate to rectangular form	• Little or no understanding of polar coordinates or graphs in the polar plane
Problem Solving (Items 5, 6, 7)	• An appropriate and efficient strategy that results in a correct answer	• A strategy that may include unnecessary steps but results in a correct answer	• A strategy that results in some incorrect answers	• No clear strategy when solving problems
Mathematical Modeling / Representations (Items 5, 6, 7)	• Clear and accurate understanding of representations of hyperbolas, their foci, and the relationship between vertices and foci, and the general form of a hyperbolic equation; also knows the general form of an ellipse and that of a parabola (including how to find a directrix) • Clear and accurate understanding of conic sections	• A functional understanding of representations of the conic sections; may not be able to find the full equation of a hyperbola or know the vertex, but knows the majority of the important characteristics of conics • Mostly accurate creations of conic equations	• Partial understanding of representations of conic sections	• Little or no understanding of representations of conics
Reasoning and Communication (Items 5a, 6b, 7b)	• Precise use of appropriate math terms and language to justify the creation of the equations of conic sections, and to use the attributes of hyperbolas, ellipses, and parabolas to create the correct equations	• Correct characterization of conic sections, but may have some errors	• Misleading or confusing characterization of conics	• Incomplete or inaccurate characterization of conics

Parametric Equations

ACTIVITY 30

Ships in the Fog

Lesson 30-1 Interpreting Graphical Data

My Notes

Learning Targets:

- Use data points on a grid to write linear equations.
- Interpret the parameters of an equation in a real-world context.
- Write rules to describe the position of an object at time *t*.

SUGGESTED LEARNING STRATEGIES: Paraphrasing, Think-Pair-Share, Create Representations, Look for a Pattern, Quickwrite

The Register Page 6

A Collision in the Fog

TRACK CHARLIE

It was nearing midnight on July 25, 1956 when passengers aboard the Italian liner *Andrea Doria* caught sight of the Swedish-American liner, the *Stockholm*. The *Andrea Doria* was in her eighth and final day of her 101st transatlantic crossing and the *Stockholm* was on its first day of a voyage from Manhattan to Copenhagen. Both liners were passing through the busy, often rough water locale known as "the Times Square of the North Atlantic" — just south of Nantucket. On a clear night, Track Charlie, as this shipping lane was known, presented no serious hazard. However, on this night, an intense fog had settled in and visibility was poor at best. Reports were that the view from the bridge of most ships was not much farther than the bow.

CHAOS REIGNS

When partying passengers aboard the *Andrea Doria* caught sight of the *Stockholm*, they were horrified. They saw eerie lights coming at them out of the fog. Moments later the 12,644-ton *Stockholm's* knife-sharp prow (reinforced for sailing in icy waters) tore into the starboard quarter of the 44,356-ton *Andrea Doria's* bow — ripping apart the first-class cabins and leaving a 30-foot deep gash as it rebounded. Aboard the *Andrea Doria*, passengers were slammed against bulkheads, thrown from beds, or hurled into tangled masses of other bodies. The passageways were lined with luggage of the soon-to-disembark passengers, and chaos reigned as some passengers fought their way upstairs to make their way to lifeboats while others fought their way downstairs to find family or friends.

FOG SURVIVORS

Most passengers were ultimately saved, thanks to several factors. First, the *Stockholm's* damage was able to be repaired enough to keep the ship afloat and even afford to rescue 500 of the *Andrea Doria's* passengers. The *Andrea Doria's* damage — much more severe — would have caused most ships to go down quickly. However, a new compartmented construction that was supposed to keep her afloat in such an accident, slowed the speed at which she sank. This bought time for rescue ships in the area to reach her. The fact that 1,670 passengers survived the crash was seen as nothing short of a miracle.

WHAT HAPPENED?

Electronic failure or human failure was the debate in the weeks that followed. Down with the *Andrea Doria* went a $100,000 sports car prototype built in Turin by Chrysler, 1,764 bags of mail, plus crates of antiques and vintage wines. However, everyone agreed that the loss of human life —25 dead and 17 missing —was clearly the true tragedy.

DISCUSSION GROUP TIPS

As you work in groups, read the problem scenario carefully and explore together the information provided and how to use it to create a potential solution. Discuss your understanding of the problem and ask peers or your teacher to clarify any areas that are not clear.

The preceding article gives an account of the tragic collision in the fog between two ocean liners, the *Andrea Doria* and the *Stockholm*, in 1956. Some blamed the collision on human error. In this activity, we will look at two fictional ships in the fog and develop a mathematical model that could be used to determine the locations of two objects and the distance between them on a tracking screen to determine how such a tragedy might have been avoided.

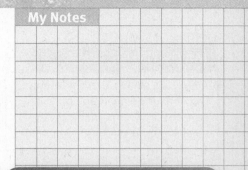

My Notes

MATH TIP

A *pixel* is a small electronic element that makes up an image on a monitor or electronic display. A pixel can be thought of as a point.

Two ships are sailing in the fog. Both ships are being monitored by the same tracking equipment. As the ships enter the area being monitored, their positions are displayed on the observer's rectangular screen by a brightened point called a *pixel*. The lighted pixel representing the first ship, the *Andor*, is at a point 900 mm from the bottom left corner of the screen along the lower edge of the screen. The lighted pixel representing the second ship, the *Helsinki*, is located 100 mm directly above the lower left-hand corner. One minute later the positions have changed. The *Andor* has moved to a location on the screen that is 3 mm west and 2 mm north of its previous location. The *Helsinki* has moved to a position 4 mm east and 1 mm north of where it had been. Assume that the two ships will continue to sail at a constant speed on their respective linear paths.

1. The grid below represents the area being monitored on the tracking screen. Graph and label a point to represent the starting location for each fictional ship, *Andor* (A) and *Helsinki* (H), and sketch the path of each of the ships.

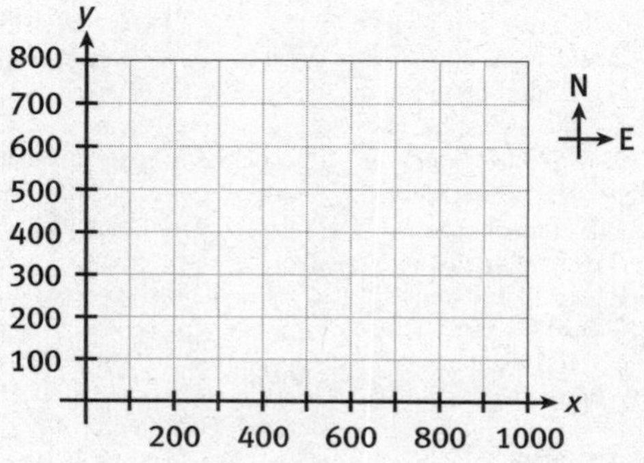

2. To find the coordinates of the point on the grid where the paths cross, you can write functions for the paths of the two ships.
   a. What is there about the ships' motion that tells you the paths are linear?

   b. **Attend to precision.** What speeds are represented by the two ships on the tracking screen?

My Notes

c. **Model with mathematics.** Give the linear equation for each ship's path.

3. How many millimeters east and north of the lower left-hand corner of the screen do the paths of the ships cross?

4. Do you think the ships will collide? Clearly explain the reasoning you used to arrive at the answer.

One question remains. How close did the ships actually come to each other? To answer this item, you can analyze the positions of the ships in terms of the time elapsed since they first appeared on the grid, *t*.

5. **Express regularity in repeated reasoning.** Fill in the tables below to indicate the positions of the ships relative to the lower left corner of the screen at any given time.

Andor

t (in minutes)	Horizontal (x)	Vertical (y)
0		
1		
2		
3		
10		
t		

Helsinki

t (in minutes)	Horizontal (x)	Vertical (y)
0		
1		
2		
3		
10		
t		

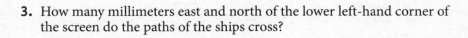

My Notes

6. Model with mathematics. Write the rules for $x(t)$ and $y(t)$ for each ship.

a. For the *Andor*:

$x(t) =$

$y(t) =$

b. For the *Helsinki*:

$x(t) =$

$y(t) =$

Check Your Understanding

7. Make sense of problems. Explain how you determined the speed of the *Andor* in Item 2b.

8. Why might it be useful to know the ships' horizontal and vertical positions as functions of time?

9. Reason quantitatively. Determine the position of the *Andor* at $t = 20$ min. Explain how you determined your answer, and how you know that your answer is reasonable.

LESSON 30-1 PRACTICE

In a video game, a player earns bonus points for each spider his or her character catches. A player moves from (30, 24) to (65, 59) on the screen in 1 second. At the same time, a spider moves from (20, 315) to (100, 255). Assume that the player and the spider will continue to move at constant speeds along linear paths.

10. Model with mathematics. Sketch the paths of the player and the spider. Write the linear equations that model the paths.

11. What are the coordinates of the point of intersection of the paths of the player and the spider?

12. Attend to precision. Determine the speed of both the player and the spider in units per second. Round to the nearest whole number.

13. Make tables of values that show the horizontal position (x) and vertical position (y) of the player and the spider at time $t = 0, 1, 2, 3, 4,$ and 5 seconds.

14. Write rules for $x(t)$ and $y(t)$ to model the horizontal and vertical positions of the player and the spider as functions of time.

My Notes

Learning Targets:

- Define and write parametric equations.
- Use parametric equations to solve real-world problems.

SUGGESTED LEARNING STRATEGIES: Visualization, Look for a Pattern, Create Representations, Quickwrite, Create a Plan

The rules you wrote in Item 6 in the previous lesson have time as the independent variable. Each $x(t)$ and $y(t)$ pair determine the location (x, y) of the ship at time t. When an independent variable is used to define two (or more) dependent variables, the rules that relate the variables are known as ***parametric equations***.

MATH TERMS

Parametric equations are a set of equations that relate two or more dependent variables to the same independent variable.

1. Show algebraically that the parametric equations for the *Andor* are equivalent to the linear function that you found in Item 2c in the previous lesson.

2. **Reason quantitatively.** Explain what the coefficient of the variable and the constant mean in the parametric equations $x(t) = at + b$ and $y(t) = ct + d$ and how they relate to the linear function $y(x)$.

3. Determine the grid location of both the *Andor* and the *Helsinki* at time $t = 3$ min, and then find the distance between the ships at that time.

My Notes

4. Determine the location of each ship one hour after they first appeared on the screen and find the distance between the ships at that time.

5. **Model with mathematics.** Develop a function $f(t)$ that gives the distance between the ships on the grid at any time t since the ships entered the tracking screen.

6. Use the function created in Item 5 and your graphing calculator to answer the following:
   a. Find the minimum distance between the two ships on the tracking screen in millimeters.

   b. Find the time at which the two ships are closest to each other.

   c. At the time the ships are closest, what are the coordinates of each ship's image on the grid?

   Andor (__________, __________)

   Helsinki (__________, __________)

   d. At the time the ships are closest, is either ship at the crossing point of the ships' paths?

TECHNOLOGY TIP

To graph parametric equations on a graphing calculator, first put your calculator in parametric mode. Press MODE, and then highlight **Par** (for parametric) in the fourth line. Then press ENTER.

7. **Use appropriate tools strategically.** You can also determine whether the ships collide by graphing the parametric equations that describe the positions of each ship. Enter the parametric equations for the *Andor* as X_{1T} and Y_{1T}. Enter the parametric equations for the *Helsinki* as X_{2T} and Y_{2T}.
   a. Use the TRACE feature to estimate the time that the *Andor* reaches the intersection point of the ships' paths.

   b. Use the TRACE feature to estimate the time that the *Helsinki* reaches the intersection point of the ships' paths.

My Notes

c. How can you use your answers to parts a and b to determine whether the ships collide?

8. Due to the fog, the visibility in the area in which the ships are sailing is $\frac{1}{4}$ nautical mile. The scale of the observer's grid is 1 mm = 0.05 nautical mile.

a. Determine whether it would have been possible for the two captains to see the other ship through the fog and thus know how close they had come. Explain the methods you can use to arrive at your answer.

DISCUSSION GROUP TIPS

As your share your ideas, be sure to use mathematical terms and academic vocabulary precisely. Ask your teacher if you need help to express your ideas to the group or class.

b. How fast was each ship traveling in knots? (1 knot = 1 nautical mile per hour)

Remember that the *Stockholm* actually crashed into the *Andrea Doria* in the fog on the night of July 25, 1956. Suppose that the *Stockholm* was traveling on the same path and at the same rate as the fictional ship, the *Helsinki*, and that the *Andrea Doria* was traveling at the same rate, but on a parallel path and starting on the same horizontal line as the fictional ship, the *Andor*.

9. Make sense of problems. At what point on the tracking grid would the pixel representing the *Andrea Doria* have first appeared in order to put the two ships on a collision course under the given conditions? Show your work or write an explanation to support your answer.

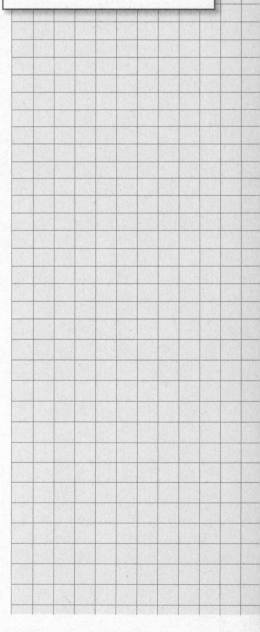

My Notes

Check Your Understanding

10. If you are given parametric equations $x(t)$ and $y(t)$ that give the x- and y-coordinates of a tornado at time t, how can you write an equation that models the path of the tornado in terms of x and y?

11. If you are given parametric equations $x(t)$ and $y(t)$ that give the x- and y-coordinates of two ships at time t, how can you determine whether the ships will collide?

12. Suppose that the *Andrea Doria* had been equipped with technology that warned the captain that the ship was on a collision course with the *Stockholm*. Describe how the captain could have avoided the collision without changing direction, and tell how this method would affect the parametric equations $x(t) = at + b$ and $y(t) = ct + d$ for the *Andrea Doria*.

13. The function $f(x) = 113x$ gives the number of calories in x ounces of cheddar cheese. The function $g(x) = 0.35x$ gives the price in dollars of x ounces of cheddar cheese. Are the equations for $f(x)$ and $g(x)$ parametric equations? Explain.

LESSON 30-2 PRACTICE

In a science fiction movie, a crack in the ground is to expand across a field, while Rhena, an actress, races to cross the field before it is cut in half by the crack. Let $t = 0$ correspond to the time the crack begins to expand and suppose it expands according to the parametric equations $x(t) = 6t$ and $y(t) = 25 + 2t$, where t is measured in seconds and distance is measured in feet. Rhena's path is given by $x(t) = 240 - 4.5t$ and $y(t) = 15 + 3t$.

14. **Model with mathematics.** Write linear equations in terms of x and y that model Rhena's path and the path of the crack.

15. Find the point at which the paths of the crack and Rhena will cross.

16. What is the distance between Rhena and the tip of the crack at time $t = 10$ s? Explain how you determined your answer.

17. Find the amount of time it takes the crack to expand to the point of intersection and the time it takes Rhena to arrive at that point. Does Rhena get across the field before the crack splits it in half?

18. **a.** **Model with mathematics.** Develop a function $f(t)$ that gives the distance between Rhena and the tip of the crack at any time t since the crack begins to expand.

b. What is the minimum value of the function? How does the minimum value confirm your answer to Item 17?

My Notes

Learning Targets:

- Convert equations from rectangular to parametric, and vice versa.
- Use parametric equations to solve real-world problems.

SUGGESTED LEARNING STRATEGIES: Close Reading, Think-Pair-Share, Create Representations, Predict and Confirm

You may be able to convert a set of parametric equations $x(t)$ and $y(t)$ to a single rectangular relation in terms of x and y by eliminating the parameter t. To do this, you can start by solving one of the parametric equations for t and then substitute the expression for t into the other equation.

Example A

The parametric equations $x(t) = t^2 + 1$ and $y(t) = 1 - t^2$ model the position of a fishing boat on a rectangular grid in units of nautical miles for the domain $0 \le t \le 2$, where t is time in hours. Convert the parametric equations into a rectangular relation that represents the fishing boat's path. Then graph the rectangular relation.

Step 1: Solve one equation for t^2.

$$x = t^2 + 1$$
$$x - 1 = t^2$$

Step 2: Substitute the expression for t^2 into the second equation.

$$y = 1 - t^2$$
$$y = 1 - (x - 1)$$
$$y = 2 - x$$

The rectangular relation that models the path is $y = 2 - x$.

Step 3: Determine the domain of the rectangular relation and graph the fishing boat's initial position and final position.

The domain of the parametric equations is $0 \le t \le 2$.

Locate the ship at $t = 0$.

$x(0) = 0^2 + 1 = 1$

$y(0) = 1 - 0^2 = 1$

Locate the ship at $t = 2$.

$x(2) = 2^2 + 1 = 5$

$y(2) = 1 - 2^2 = -3$

The domain is $1 \le x \le 5$.

Graph the endpoints $(1, 1)$ and $(5, -3)$.

Step 4: Graph the fishing boat's path.

You can draw an arrowhead on the path to show the direction of the ship's movement.

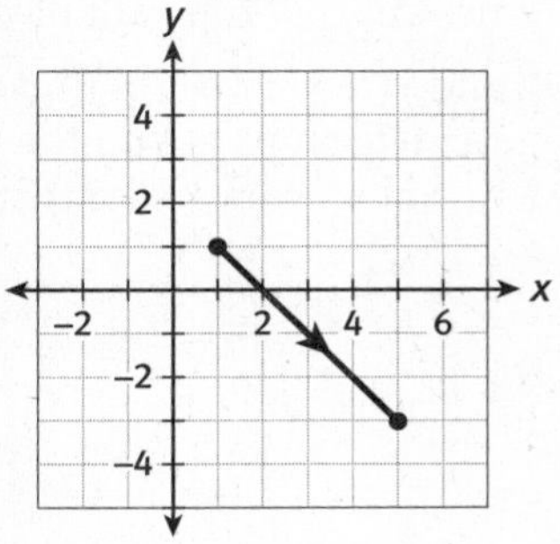

MATH TIP

Notice that both parametric equations in this example include t^2. Therefore, it is easier to solve one of the equations for t^2 rather than for t. Substitute the expression for t^2 into the other equation.

My Notes

Try These A

Convert each set of parametric equations into a rectangular relation. Then graph the rectangular relation.

a. $x(t) = t^2 + 3$ and $y(t) = 6t^2 + 16$ for the domain $0 \le t \le 3$

b. $x(t) = 2t + 1$ and $y(t) = 4(t - 1)^2 + 2$ for the domain $0 \le t \le 4$

Check Your Understanding

1. If the parametric equations that describe an object's position over time are quadratic, is the object's path necessarily a parabola? Explain.
2. Look back at Example A.
   a. What is the fishing boat's average speed between $t = 0$ and $t = 1$? What is the fishing boat's average speed between $t = 1$ and $t = 2$?
   b. Does a constant change in time result in a constant change in distance for the fishing boat? Explain.
3. **Use appropriate tools strategically.** Explain how you could use a graphing calculator to confirm the solution to Example A.

The movement of two more ships, HMS *Petticoat* and USS *Junction*, are shown on a tracking screen. The position of each ship is measured as x mm horizontally and y mm vertically from the lower left corner of the screen.

4. The linear path of the HMS *Petticoat* is given by $y = 2x + 50$. If $x = 3t$, express y as a function of t.

5. The parametric equations in Item 4 give the position of the HMS *Petticoat* at any time t in minutes. On the same screen an observer notices that the path of the USS *Junction* is described by $x(t) = \frac{5}{2}t + 10$ and $y(t) = 5t + 70$. The observer is concerned because she believes that the two ships are on the same path.
   a. Show work to confirm or contradict the observer's belief.

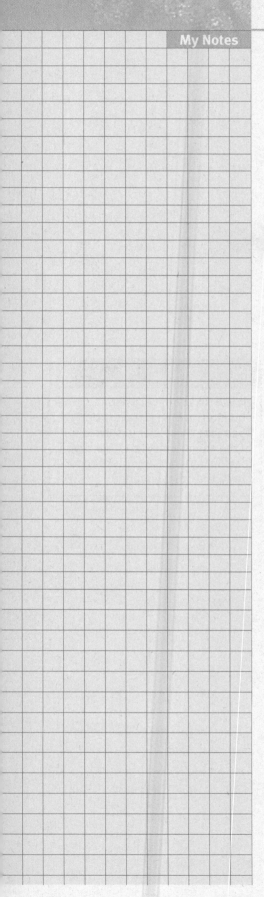

My Notes

b. The observer calculates that the ships will collide at $t = k$ minutes. Find k or refute the observer's claim.

6. The function $y = f(x)$ is defined parametrically by $x = t + 2$ and $y = t^2 + 3$. Write y as a function of x and sketch the graph of the function f.

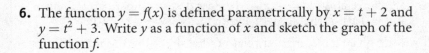

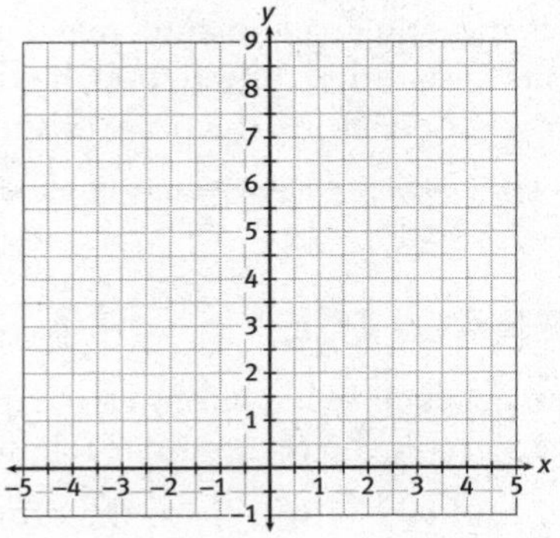

7. Make sense of problems. The equation $y = -2x + 120$ gives the path of a Coast Guard boat on a screen in units of millimeters. At time $t = 0$ minutes, the boat's position is at (50, 20) on the screen and it is moving 2 mm to the left each minute.

a. Write a parametric equation $x(t)$ that gives the boat's horizontal position at time t. Explain how you determined your answer.

b. Write a parametric equation $y(t)$ that gives the boat's vertical position at time t. Explain how you determined your answer.

c. A motorboat that ran out of fuel is at (20, 80) on the screen. How many minutes will it take the Coast Guard boat at (50, 20) to reach the motorboat, assuming that the motorboat does not drift? Explain your reasoning.

d. How can you check that your answer to Part c is reasonable?

My Notes

Check Your Understanding

8. Suppose the parametric equations $x(t)$ and $y(t)$ can be converted to the rectangular relation $y = -4x + 10$. How do the domain and range of $x(t)$ and $y(t)$ affect the domain and range of $y = -4x + 10$?

9. If you are given a rectangular relation that describes the path of an object, what other information do you need in order to convert the relation to a pair of parametric equations?

10. Suppose an object is moving at a constant speed. If you are given the parametric equations $x(t)$ and $y(t)$ that describe the object's position over time, how can you determine the object's speed?

LESSON 30-3 PRACTICE

For Items 11 and 12, convert each set of parametric equations into a rectangular relation. Then graph the rectangular relation.

11. $x(t) = (3t - 2)^2 + 2$ and $y(t) = 3t + 3$ for the domain $0 \le t \le 2$

12. $x(t) = -2t^2 + 16$ and $y(t) = t^2 + 12$ for the domain $0 \le t \le 4$

13. The parametric equations $x(t) = (t + 2)^2 + 9$ and $y(t) = -4(t + 2)^2 + 40$ model the position of a migrating hawk on a rectangular grid in units of kilometers for the domain $0 \le t \le 2$, where t is time in hours. Convert the parametric equations into a rectangular relation that represents the hawk's path. Then graph the rectangular relation.

Given a rectangular relation and one of the parametric equations that define it, write the other parametric equation.

14. $y = \frac{2}{3}(x - 6)$; $y(t) = 2t + 8$

15. $y = \sqrt{x + 8}$; $x(t) = 4t - 9$

16. **Make sense of problems.** The equation $y = \frac{1}{2}x$ gives the path of a hiker on a rectangular grid in units of miles. The hiker's starting position is (0, 0) and the x-coordinate of her position is changing at a constant rate of 2 mi/h.

a. Write parametric equations $x(t)$ and $y(t)$ that give the hiker's position at time t in hours.

b. To the nearest minute, how long will it take the hiker to hike 4 miles? Explain your reasoning.

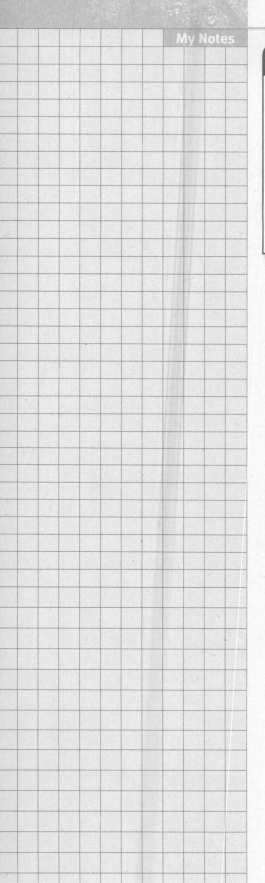

ACTIVITY 30 PRACTICE

Write your answers on notebook paper. Show your work.

Lesson 30-1

A football player carrying the ball has coordinates (39, 37) on a rectangular grid in units of yards. At the same time, a defensive player has coordinates (43, 41). After 1 second, the player with the ball has moved to (47, 31), and the defensive player has moved to (49, 33). Both players are running on linear paths at constant speeds. Use this information for Items 1–5.

1. Sketch the paths of the two players. Write linear equations to represent their paths.

2. At what point do the paths cross?

3. Find the speed in yards per second that both players are moving.

4. **a.** Make tables of values that show the horizontal position (x) and vertical position (y) of the players at time $t = 0$, 1, and 2 seconds.
b. Compare the positions of the players at $t = 2$ seconds. What can you conclude from the players' positions at this time?

5. Write rules for $x(t)$ and $y(t)$ to model the horizontal and vertical positions of the players as functions of time.

A jungle and wildlife preserve extends 80 miles north and 120 miles east of the ranger station. The ranger leaves from a point 100 miles east of the station along the southern boundary to survey the area. He travels to a point 0.6 mile north and 0.5 mile west every minute. A lion leaves the west edge of the preserve 51 miles north of the station at the same time the ranger leaves the southern border. Every minute the lion moves to a point 0.1 mile north and 0.3 mile east. The lion and the ranger are both traveling on linear paths. Use this information for Items 6–10.

6. Sketch the paths of the lion and the ranger. Write the linear equations to represent their paths.

7. Where do their paths cross?

8. Find the speed in miles per minute that both the lion and the ranger are moving.

9. Make tables of values that show the horizontal position (x) and vertical position (y) of the ranger and the lion at time $t = 0$, 1, 2, 3, 4, and 5 minutes.

10. Write rules for $x(t)$ and $y(t)$ to model the horizontal and vertical positions of the ranger and the lion as functions of time.

Lesson 30-2

Refer back to the scenario in Items 6–10.

11. How long does it take the lion and the ranger to get to the point where their paths cross?

12. Develop a function $f(t)$ that gives the distance between the lion and the ranger at any time t.

13. What is the closest the lion and ranger get to each other? Round to 3 decimal places.

An airplane appears on a radar tracking screen 55 mm to the right and 5 mm up from the lower left corner. At that same time, the operator notices a helicopter entering the screen 35 mm directly above the lower left corner of the screen. Each second the plane's position moves 2 mm left and 3 mm up and the helicopter's position moves 3 mm right and 1 mm up. Use this information for Items 14–19.

14. Write linear equations to represent their paths.

15. Write parametric equations for both the plane and the helicopter.

16. Show algebraically that the parametric equations for the plane are equivalent to the linear equation that you found in Item 14.

17. Determine the screen location of both the plane and the helicopter at time $t = 5$ min, and then find the distance between them to the nearest millimeter.

18. What is the closest the plane and the helicopter get to each other on the radar screen? Round to 3 decimal places.

19. At the time the plane and helicopter are closest, what are their coordinates on the radar screen rounded to the nearest integer?

20. Make sense of problems. Determine whether $(186, -268)$ is a point on the graph of the linear function $y(x)$ modeled by the parametric equations $x(t) = 6 + 2t$ and $y(t) = 5 - 3t$.

Lesson 30-3

21. Verify algebraically whether $y = 4x + 134$ represents the same path as the parametric equations $x(t) = 3.5t - 21$ and $y(t) = 14t + 50$.

Convert each set of parametric functions to a rectangular relation. Then sketch the graph of the relation.

22. $x(t) = 1 + 4t$ and $y(t) = t^2 - 3$

23. $x(t) = 2 - 3t$ and $y(t) = t^2 + 1$

The equation $x(t) = 160{,}000 - 200t$ models a plane's horizontal distance in feet from an airport at time t in seconds. The equation $y(t) = 12{,}000 - 15t$ models the plane's altitude in feet at time t. Use this information for Items 24–27.

24. How long will it take the plane to reach the airport?

25. Which rectangular relation models the plane's descent?

A. $y = -\frac{1}{200}x + 800$ **B.** $y = -\frac{1}{15}x + 800$

C. $y = \frac{3}{40}x$ **D.** $y = \frac{3}{40}x + 24{,}000$

26. What are the reasonable domain and range of the rectangular relation? Explain.

27. Graph the rectangular relation.

On Saturday morning Rashan is kayaking. The path of his trip on a coordinate grid measured in kilometers is $y = \frac{4}{3}x - 2$, with the positive y-axis pointing north. At time $t = 0$ hours, Rashan's boat is at $(6, 6)$ on the coordinate grid and is moving 4.8 km to the east each hour. Use this information for Items 28–30.

28. Which parametric equation gives the boat's east-west position at time t?

A. $x(t) = \frac{4}{3}t + 6$ **B.** $x(t) = \frac{4}{3}t + 4.8$

C. $x(t) = 4.8t$ **D.** $x(t) = 4.8t + 6$

29. Write a parametric equation $y(t)$ that gives the boat's north-south position at time t.

30. Alyssa's kayak can be described by the parametric equations $x(t) = 6t + 3$ and $y(t) = 8t + 2$.

a. Is Alyssa's kayak on the same path as Rashan's kayak? Explain.

b. How long will it take for Alyssa to catch up to Rashan?

Given a rectangular relation and one of the parametric equations that define it, write the other parametric equation.

31. $y = \frac{1}{2}(x - 1)^2 + 4$; $x(t) = 2t - 3$

32. $y = 4x + 5$; $y(t) = t^2 + 3$

MATHEMATICAL PRACTICES
Make Sense of Problems and Persevere in Solving Them

33. At time $t = 0$, the eight ball on a pool table is at $(1, 46)$ on a coordinate grid in units of inches, and the cue ball is at $(1, 6)$. The eight ball is moving along a linear path at constant speed so that 1 second later, the eight ball is at $(7, 43.5)$. The cue ball is moving at constant speed along a linear path given by $12y - 35x = 37$. If the cue ball hits the eight ball, what is the speed of each ball?

Parametric Equations Revisited

Keep Your Eye on the Ball

Lesson 31-1 Angular and Linear Velocity

My Notes

Learning Targets:

- Understand, calculate, and compare angular and linear velocities.
- Write equations to model circular motion.
- Sketch the graph of circular motion.

SUGGESTED LEARNING STRATEGIES: Marking the Text, Visualization, Vocabulary Organizer, Think-Pair-Share, Create Representations

Parametric equations are very powerful ways to describe motion. They model the path on which an object is moving and the location of the object at any particular moment.

A huge Ferris wheel, the London Eye, was built in London, England, to celebrate the new millennium. Very popular with tourists and locals, the London Eye is 135 m (just under 450 ft) high, makes one complete revolution every 30 minutes, and can carry 800 passengers per revolution. In this activity, let the radius of the wheel equal 67.5 m—exactly one-half the height of the London Eye.

1. Suppose the London Eye turns through one revolution.

a. Through how many degrees does it turn?

b. What distance, in meters, does a capsule on the rim of the wheel travel in that revolution?

2. The London Eye makes one revolution every 30 minutes.

a. Through how many degrees does it turn every minute?

b. What distance, in meters, does a capsule on the rim move every minute?

As an object rotates, its rate of rotation, called ***angular velocity***, is defined as $\frac{\Delta\theta}{\Delta t}$, where $\Delta\theta$ measures the change of the angle of rotation and Δt measures the change of time. Although the units may vary, the most frequent units are degrees per unit of time.

3. What is the angular velocity of a capsule on the London Eye in degrees per minute?

MATH TERMS

An object's **angular velocity** is the rate at which it rotates. Angular velocity is equal to $\frac{\Delta\theta}{\Delta t}$, where $\Delta\theta$ is the change in the angle of rotation and Δt is the change in time.

My Notes

MATH TERMS

An object's **linear velocity** is the ratio of the distance the object travels to the time needed to travel that distance. Linear velocity is equal to $\frac{\Delta s}{\Delta t}$, where Δs is distance traveled and Δt is the change in time.

MATH TIP

Any point that is moving has a linear velocity, even if its path is not linear.

When the linear distance that an object moves is divided by the time required to cover that distance, the resulting rate is called the ***linear velocity***. Linear velocity is defined as $\frac{\Delta s}{\Delta t}$, where Δs measures the distance traveled and Δt measures the change of time.

4. What is the linear velocity of a capsule on the London Eye in meters per minute?

5. Suppose that, to celebrate the opening of the ride, a brightly colored bow had been tied to a spoke of the London Eye at a point 13.5 m from the center.

a. What would be the angular velocity of the bow?

b. What would be the linear velocity of the bow?

c. **Reason quantitatively.** Explain why the angular velocities of the bow and the capsule are the same, but the linear velocities are different. Remember to use complete sentences and words such as *and, or, since, because* to make connections between your thoughts.

6. Locate the center of the London Eye at the origin in the coordinate plane, and let a capsule on the ride be represented by a point (x, y) on the grid on the next page.

a. Write an equation for the capsule's circular path as the Ferris wheel turns in terms of x and y. Recall that the radius is 67.5 m.

b. Solve your equation for y in terms of x and explain why your results confirm the fact that y is not a function of x.

My Notes

c. Write individual equations for the upper branch and lower branch of the circle and then graph these functions on your calculator. Sketch the graph on the grid.

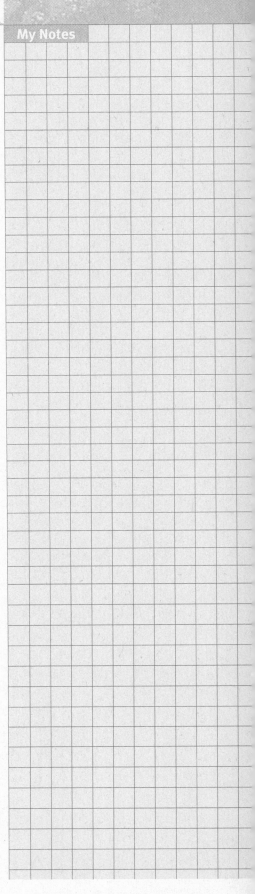

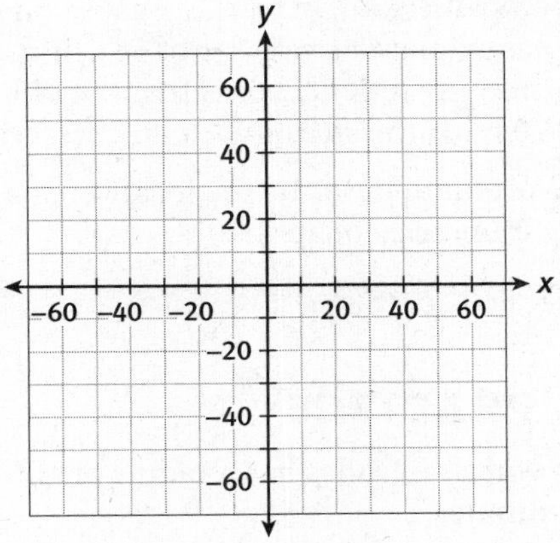

7. Some of the questions listed below can be answered using the model you created in Item 6 and some cannot. Answer the ones that can be answered using your model and explain why you cannot answer the others.

a. When the *x*-coordinate for the location of the capsule is 30, what are the possible *y*-coordinates?

b. How far, in meters, does the capsule travel in one revolution of the wheel?

c. Does the London Eye rotate clockwise or counterclockwise?

d. Where on the grid is the capsule located 10 minutes after the ride has started?

My Notes

Check Your Understanding

8. **Attend to precision.** Compare and contrast angular velocity with linear velocity.
9. **Critique the reasoning of others.** A cabin on the Suzhou Ferris wheel in China has an angular velocity of 18°/min and a linear velocity of about 18.8 m/min. A student claims that the radius of the Ferris wheel is about 120 m. Is the student's claim correct? Explain.
10. Why might it be useful to describe the location of a capsule on a Ferris wheel by using parametric equations?

LESSON 31-1 PRACTICE

The Texas Star Ferris wheel in Dallas has a radius of 106 ft and makes one revolution every 1.5 minutes.

11. Compute the angular and linear velocities of a rider on the rim of the Ferris wheel.
12. Locate the center of the Ferris wheel at the origin of a coordinate plane in units of feet, and let the position of a rider on the Ferris wheel be represented by a point (x, y). Write an equation for the rider's circular path as the Ferris wheel turns in terms of x and y.
13. When the x-coordinate for the location of the rider is -80, what are the possible y-coordinates?
14. Suppose a blue light bulb on the Texas Star is 95 feet from the center of the Ferris wheel.
    a. What are the angular and linear velocities of the light bulb as the Ferris wheel rotates?
    b. How do the angular and linear velocities of the light bulb compare to the angular and linear velocities of a rider on the Ferris wheel?
15. **Reason quantitatively.** Suppose a red light bulb on the Texas Star has a linear velocity of about 300 ft/min as the bulb rotates about the center of the wheel. Is the red light bulb closer to the center of the wheel than the blue light bulb described in Item 14? How do you know?

My Notes

Learning Targets:

- Sketch the graph of a moving object.
- Write parametric equations using trigonometry.
- Use technology to model motion.

SUGGESTED LEARNING STRATEGIES: Marking the Text, Visualization, Guess and Check, Look for a Pattern, Create Representations

A more useful model of the London Eye would describe the location of a capsule in terms of its x- and y-coordinates as a function of time.

1. Suppose Nigel built a model of the London Eye whose radius is 1 foot. Let the point (0, 0) represent the center of the wheel and (x, y) represent the coordinates of a capsule on the wheel. The model Ferris wheel completes 1 revolution in exactly 2π seconds. Assume the capsule starts at the point $(0, -1)$ and the wheel rotates clockwise.

a. Sketch a graph of the y-coordinate of the capsule as a function of time for the first 4π seconds after the ride has started.

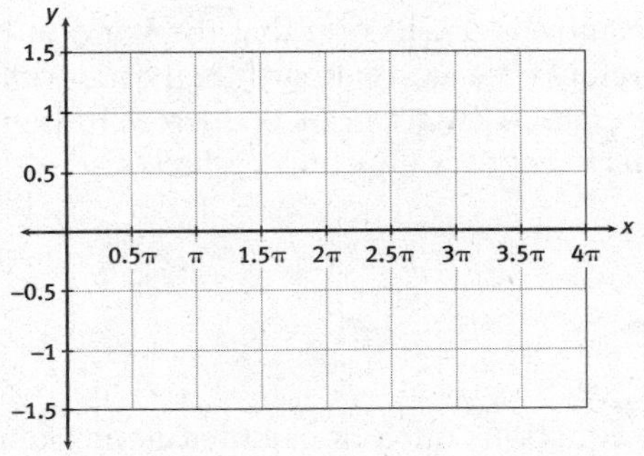

b. Sketch a graph of the x-coordinate of the capsule as a function of the time for the first 4π seconds after the ride has begun.

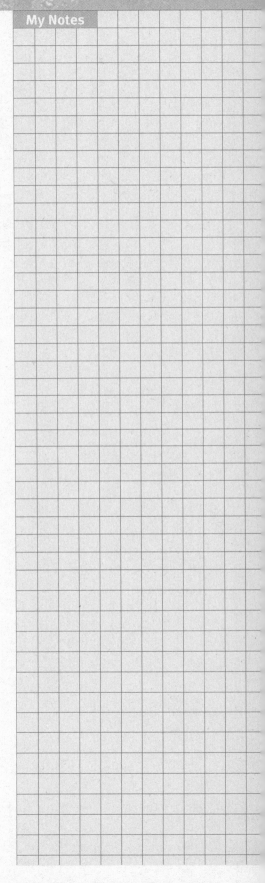

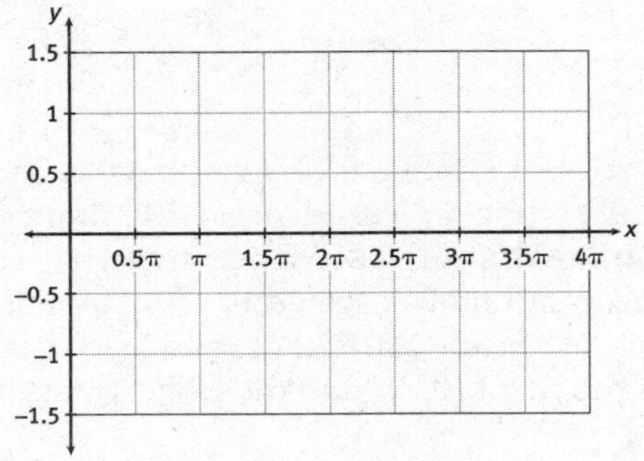

My Notes

c. Use your sketches to write parametric equations that represent the location of the capsule at time $t \geq 0$.

d. Use appropriate tools strategically. Set your calculator to PARAMETRIC mode and RADIAN mode and graph the equations. Choose appropriate values for the window to display 2 revolutions of the model Ferris wheel and then sketch the results. Indicate the direction of motion using arrows and the starting position of the capsule.

2. Nigel's friend Nancy later tells him that the London Eye Ferris wheel rotates counterclockwise as you board the Ferris wheel.

a. Adjust the parametric equations you wrote in Item 1 to represent the model Ferris wheel rotating counterclockwise.

b. Graph your equations on your calculator and sketch the results, indicating the direction of motion using arrows as well as the starting position of the capsule.

3. Recall that the radius of the London Eye Ferris wheel is 67.5 meters and the wheel completes one revolution every 30 minutes.

a. Model with mathematics. Write parametric equations to represent the location of a capsule as a function of time t minutes. Assume that the capsule starts at ground level, the center of the wheel is located at the point (0, 0), and the wheel rotates counterclockwise.

My Notes

b. Graph the equations on your calculator on the interval $0 \leq t \leq 30$ and sketch the results below. Indicate the direction of motion using arrows and the starting position of the capsule.

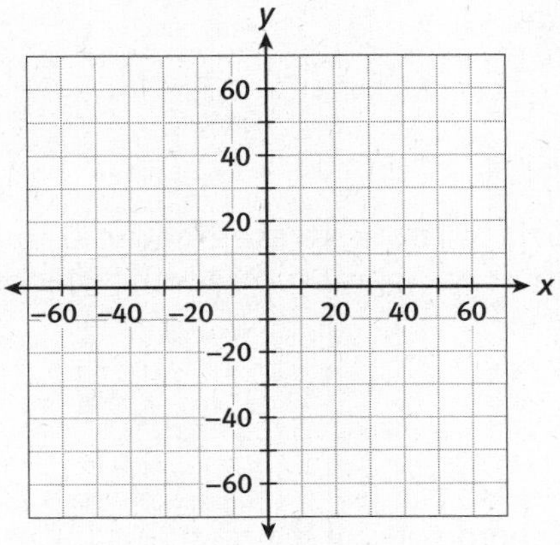

4. Let the point (0, 0) correspond to the location of a capsule when it is at ground level and let $t = 0$ represent the time when a particular capsule is at ground level.

a. Model with mathematics. Write parametric equations that represent the motion of this capsule on the London Eye over the course of a 30-minute ride.

b. Use appropriate tools strategically. Graph the equations on your calculator in an appropriate viewing window and sketch the results.

c. What are the coordinates of the capsule at the beginning and end of the ride?

d. Write a few sentences comparing and contrasting the equations and graphs from Item 3b and Item 4b.

My Notes

5. Let the point (0, 0) correspond to the location of a capsule when it is at ground level, and let $t = 0$ represent the time when a particular capsule is at the top of the Ferris wheel.

a. Model with mathematics. Write parametric equations to represent the position of this capsule over the course of a 30-minute ride.

b. Use appropriate tools strategically. Graph the equations on your calculator in an appropriate viewing window and sketch the results.

c. What are the coordinates of the capsule at the beginning and end of the ride?

d. Suppose a capsule starts at the top and completes one revolution, and then the ride stops when this capsule is at ground level. How long has the capsule been moving?

e. How high off the ground is the capsule after 10 minutes? After 25 minutes?

MATH TIP

The amplitude of a periodic function is half the difference of the maximum and minimum values. The period of a periodic function is the length of one cycle of the function measured in units of the independent variable.

Check Your Understanding

6. Reason quantitatively. What are the amplitude and period of the parametric equations in Item 3a, and how are the amplitude and period related to the London Eye Ferris wheel?

7. Are the parametric equations that represent the position of a capsule on a Ferris wheel functions? Explain.

8. The parametric equations $x(t) = 3\cos\left(\frac{2\pi}{10}t\right)$ and $y(t) = 3\sin\left(\frac{2\pi}{10}t\right)$ represent the position of a point on the rim of a rotating gear, where t is the time in seconds and x and y are in units of inches.

a. What is the radius of the gear?

b. How long does it take the gear to complete one revolution?

c. What is the rectangular relation that describes the path of the point on the rim of the gear? How do you know?

My Notes

LESSON 31-2 PRACTICE

Recall that the Texas Star Ferris wheel in Dallas has a radius of 106 ft and makes one revolution every 1.5 minutes. Assume that the wheel rotates counterclockwise.

9. **Model with mathematics.** Write parametric equations that would model the motion of a rider that starts at the bottom of the wheel at time $t = 0$ at the point (0, 0).
10. **Use appropriate tools strategically.** Graph the parametric equations on a graphing calculator. Then sketch a graph of the results. Indicate the direction of motion and the starting position of the rider.
11. In the first revolution, when will the rider be 159 feet off the ground?
12. What are the coordinates of the rider's position after 5 minutes?
13. How would the parametric equations change if the wheel rotated clockwise instead of counterclockwise?

My Notes

Learning Targets:

- Understand and apply the equations for projectile motion.
- Write and graph parametric equations.
- Solve real-world problems involving projectile motion.

SUGGESTED LEARNING STRATEGIES: Visualization, Identify a Subtask, Create Representations, Guess and Check, Group Presentation

The path of a projectile can also be modeled using parametric equations. You are familiar with projectile motion if you have ever shot a basket in basketball, thrown a baseball, or thrown a water balloon. The path of the projectile depends on the angle at which the object is thrown, its initial velocity and height, and the force of gravity.

MATH TIP

The acceleration due to gravity is a constant. On Earth, the acceleration due to gravity is -9.8 m/s^2, or -32 ft/s^2.

Parametric Equations for Projectile Motion

If an object starts at (x_0, y_0) at $t = 0$ with initial velocity v_0 in the direction θ, then its position at time t is given by

$$x(t) = x_0 + (v_0 \cos \theta)t$$

$$y(t) = y_0 + (v_0 \sin \theta)t + 0.5gt^2$$

where g is the acceleration due to gravity on Earth.

The regulation height of a basketball hoop is 10 feet. Let the location of the basket be represented in the coordinate plane by the point (0, 10). Let the ball be thrown at a 45° angle with the ground.

1. Suppose Nancy is standing a horizontal distance of 10 feet from the basket at the point (−10, 0), and she shoots a basket from 6 feet in the air with an initial velocity of 22 ft/s.

a. Write parametric equations that represent the ball's motion through the air.

b. Graph the parametric equations on your calculator in an appropriate window and sketch the results below.

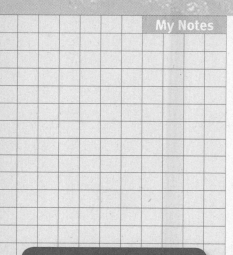

c. Will Nancy make the basket? Defend your reasoning.

d. Use appropriate tools strategically. Experiment on your calculator with different direction angles until the player makes a basket. What angle did you use?

To solve Item 1d algebraically, you would need to solve the system of equations $\begin{cases} x(t) = 0 \\ y(t) = 10 \end{cases}$.

2. Why do you set the x-coordinate equal to 0 and the y-coordinate equal to 10?

3. Reason abstractly. Substitute the parametric equations from Item 1 into the system of equations shown above Item 2 and solve the system for θ.

a. At what angle should the ball be thrown to make it through the hoop?

b. How long will it take to make the basket from the time Nancy releases the ball?

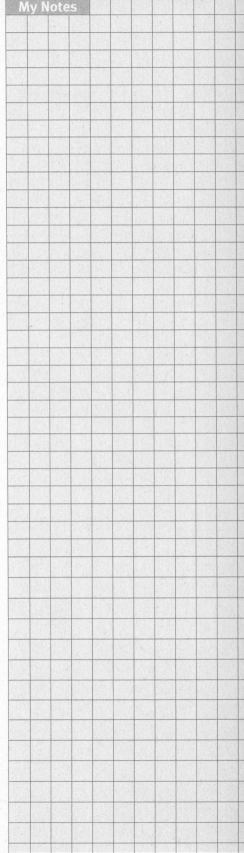

My Notes

4. Suppose Nancy is shooting from the free throw line located a horizontal distance of 15 feet from the basket and always releases the ball at a 45° angle from a height of 6 feet. Let the ball be thrown with an initial velocity of 22 feet per second.

a. Write parametric equations to represent the ball's motion through the air.

b. Graph the parametric equations on your calculator in an appropriate window and sketch the results.

c. Will she make the basket? Defend your reasoning.

d. Use appropriate tools strategically. Experiment on your calculator with different initial velocities until Nancy makes a basket. What velocity did you use?

5. Reason abstractly. Write and solve a system of equations to exactly determine an initial velocity that will guarantee the player makes the free throw.

Nigel and Nancy go to an amusement park. They find a carnival game that combines Nancy's love of basketball and Nigel's interest in Ferris wheels. Baskets are mounted on a rotating wheel. The players have to toss a basketball into the moving basket. If they get the ball in the blue basket, they win a big prize. The edge of the wheel faces the player and rotates toward the player (counterclockwise). The diagram shows a side view of the game.

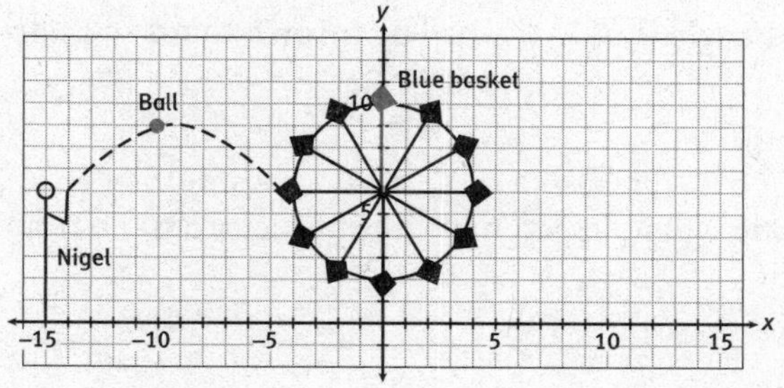

6. Let $t = 0$ be the time when the blue basket is at the top of the Ferris wheel. The center of the wheel is (0, 6). The wheel completes one revolution every 15 seconds.

a. Write parametric equations to represent the position of the blue basket as a function of time since it was at the top of the wheel.

My Notes

b. What are the coordinates of the basket when it has completed one-fourth of a revolution?

c. How long does it take the basket to get to that point?

7. Make sense of problems. The player stands a horizontal distance of 15 feet from the center of the wheel at $(-15, 0)$. Nigel decides to aim for the basket when it is at the point $(-4, 6)$. He releases the ball from a height of 6 feet at a 45° angle.

a. Write parametric equations to represent the location of the basketball as a function of time since the ball was thrown.

b. If Nigel throws with an initial velocity of 22 ft/sec, will the path of the basketball pass through the point $(-4, 6)$? Explain.

c. Solve a system of equations to determine an initial velocity that will guarantee the path of the basketball will pass through the point $(-4, 6)$.

d. How long does it take the basketball to get to the point $(-4, 6)$?

e. Nigel wants to get the ball in the blue basket. How long should Nigel wait after he sees the blue basket at the top of the wheel before shooting the ball?

My Notes

8. Use appropriate tools strategically. Use your answer in Item 7e to adjust your basketball parametric equations so that the ball and the blue basket meet at the point $(-4, 6)$ at the same time. Check your results on your graphing calculator, graphing both the basketball and wheel parametric equations. Write the equations you used.

Check Your Understanding

9. Explain how you adjusted the parametric equations for the basketball in Item 8 so that the ball would meet the basket.

10. What are the parametric equations for the motion of a projectile that is thrown straight up? Explain your reasoning.

11. What are some advantages of modeling problems by using parametric equations?

LESSON 31-3 PRACTICE

Cheerleaders are launching mini-basketballs into the crowd at a pep rally. Use this information for Items 12 and 13.

12. Let $x_0 = 0$. Write parametric equations to represent the path of the balls thrown by Sami and T'Aisha given the following conditions.

Sami: $v_0 = 15$ ft/s, $\theta = 35°$, $y_0 = 5.4$ ft

T'Aisha: $v_0 = 19$ ft/s, $\theta = 50°$, $y_0 = 5.8$ ft

13. Make sense of problems. The senior class section is located a horizontal distance of 40 feet from the cheerleaders and 15 feet in the air. Will either girl get her ball into the senior section? Explain your answer.

14. Let $x(t) = 3t - 6$ and $y(t) = t^2 - 2t$ model the path of one particle, and $x(t) = \sqrt{t + 6}$ and $y(t) = -3 + 2t$ model the path of a second particle for $t \geq 0$. Model the paths of two particles in the coordinate plane. Do these two particles ever collide? Explain.

Use appropriate tools strategically. For Items 15 and 16, graph the parametric equations on the interval $-4 \leq t \leq 4$. Use a "square window." Identify each as a conic section.

15. $x(t) = 3t^2 - 1, y(t) = 2t$

16. $x(t) = 3 \cos t + 1, y(t) = -2 \sin t$

ACTIVITY 31 PRACTICE

Write your answers on notebook paper. Show your work.

Lesson 31-1

A carousel makes 4 revolutions per minute. A wooden horse is 22 ft from the center of the carousel, and a wooden lion is 18 ft from the center of the carousel.

1. What is the angular velocity of a rider on the horse?
A. 12° per second
B. 15° per second
C. 24° per second
D. 90° per second

2. To the nearest foot per second, what is the linear velocity of a rider on the horse?
A. 2 ft/s
B. 3 ft/s
C. 6 ft/s
D. 9 ft/s

3. Compare the angular and linear velocities of a rider on the horse with a rider on the lion.

4. Locate the center of the carousel at the origin of a coordinate plane in units of feet, and let the position of a rider on the lion be represented by a point (x, y).
a. Write an equation for the rider's circular path in terms of x and y.
b. Sketch a graph of the circular path.

5. When the x-coordinate for the location of the rider on the lion is 9, what are the possible y-coordinates?

6. If a ride on the carousel lasts 3 minutes, how much farther will a rider on the horse travel than a rider on the lion? Explain how you determined your answer.

The minute hand of a clock face on the tower known as Big Ben in London is 4.2 m long. Use this information for Items 7–9.

7. What is the angular velocity of the minute hand? How do you know?

8. What is the linear velocity of the tip of the minute hand in meters per hour?

9. To the nearest kilometer, how far does the tip of the minute hand travel in one nonleap year?

Lesson 31-2

When you play "Spin the Wheel," you win when the Big Money spot stops at the top of the wheel. The parametric equations below represent the position of the Big Money spot on the wheel at time t seconds since the wheel started spinning. The wheel is computer-controlled so it always rotates at the same speed.

$$x(t) = -3\sin\left(\frac{\pi}{4}t\right) \qquad y(t) = 3\cos\left(\frac{\pi}{4}t\right)$$

10. How many seconds does it take the wheel to complete one revolution?

11. Where does the Big Money spot on the wheel start at time $t = 0$?

12. What is the radius of the wheel?

13. If the wheel spins for 150 seconds, where will the Big Money spot end up on the wheel?

14. If the Big Money spot is at the point $(-2.121, -2.121)$, how long will it take to return to the top of the wheel?

A scale model of Earth in a museum has a radius of 20 ft and makes one revolution about its axis every minute. Let the origin (0, 0) represent the center of the circle that corresponds to the equator of the model. The city of Pontianak, Indonesia, is on the equator. Let the position of Pontianak on the model at time $t = 0$ be the point (20, 0). Assume that Pontianak rotates counterclockwise about the center of the circle. Use this information for Items 15–19.

15. Sketch a graph of the y-coordinate of Pontianak as a function of time for the first 2 minutes the model rotates.

16. Sketch a graph of the x-coordinate of Pontianak as a function of the time for the first 2 minutes the model rotates.

17. Write the parametric equations that would model the motion of Pontianak.

18. Graph the parametric equations on a graphing calculator. Then sketch a graph of the results. Indicate the direction of motion and the starting position of Pontianak.

19. What are the coordinates of Pontianak after 40 seconds?

Lesson 31-3

Danny "The Arm" Robinson throws a mean pass. He releases the football from a height of 6 feet at an angle of 40°, and the initial velocity of the ball is 90 ft/sec. Use this information for Items 20–22.

20. Write parametric equations that represent the ball's motion through the air.

21. How far will the ball travel horizontally before it hits the ground?

22. What is the maximum height of the ball?

Danny's teammate Vernon kicks the football from ground level at an angle of 60° with an initial velocity of 60 ft/sec. Use this information for Items 23–26.

23. Write parametric equations that represent the ball's motion through the air.

24. Vernon is a horizontal distance of 30 yards from the goalpost when he kicks the football. The crossbar of the goalpost is 10 feet above the ground. Will the football go over the crossbar? Justify your answer.

25. If the angle of the kick is 60°, what initial velocity must the football have to pass 10 feet over the crossbar of the goalpost? Explain how you determined your answer.

26. If the initial velocity of the ball is 60 ft/sec, at what angle must the football be kicked to pass 10 feet over the crossbar of the goalpost? Explain how you determined your answer.

Point P is moving around a circle A of radius 4 with center at (5, 5). Point Q is moving around a circle O of radius 6 that is tangent to circle A at the point (1, 5). Use this information for Items 27–29.

27. Write parametric equations that could model the position of point P.

28. Write parametric equations that could model the position of point Q.

29. When $t = 0$, let P be located at (5, 9) and Q be located at (−5, 11). Adjust your equations so that P and Q meet at the point of tangency during their first revolution around the circle. Explain your answer.

For Items 30 and 31, graph the parametric equations on the interval $-4 \le t \le 4$. Use a "square window." Identify each as a conic section.

30. $x(t) = 3 \tan t + 1, y(t) = 2 \sec t$

31. $x(t) = \sin t - 3, y(t) = \cos t + 2$

MATHEMATICAL PRACTICES
Look For and Make Use of Structure

32. The parametric equations below represent the position of a point on a circular path centered at the origin, where t is the time in seconds and x and y are in units of centimeters.

$$x(t) = 12 \sin\left(\frac{2\pi}{3}t\right) \text{ and } y(t) = 12 \cos\left(\frac{2\pi}{3}t\right)$$

a. What part of the parametric equations indicates the radius of the circle? Give the radius.

b. What part of the parametric equations indicates the angular velocity of the point?

c. Is the point moving clockwise or counterclockwise around the circle? How do you know?

Parametric Equations for Projectile Motion

$x(t) = x_0 + (v_0 \cos \theta)t$

$y(t) = y_0 + (v_0 \sin \theta)t + 0.5gt^2$

$g = -9.8 \text{ m/s}^2$ or -32 ft/s^2

1. The pirate ship *Lucky Lucy* pulls alongside a freighter. When the ships are 100 meters apart, the pirate ship launches a cannonball with velocity 35 m/s and angle 25° from 12 meters above the water.

a. Write parametric equations for the path of the cannonball after it is shot from the *Lucky Lucy* at time $t = 0$. Let the cannonball start from the point (0, 12).

b. If the freighter rides 10 meters above the water and is 9 meters wide, will the cannonball hit the freighter? Explain your reasoning.

The pirate ship *Scurvy Shark* is chasing down a frigate loaded with treasure. Let the frigate be located at (0, 0) at time $t = 0$ and the pirate ship at (−20, −10) on a rectangular grid in units of kilometers. Half an hour later, the frigate is at (2, 7) and the pirate ship is at (−15, −5). Use this information for Items 2 and 3.

2. Both ships are following linear paths at constant speeds. Sketch the paths of the ships, and write the linear equations that model the paths.

3. a. Write parametric equations to represent the position of the frigate as a function of time in hours since $t = 0$.

b. Write parametric equations to represent the position of the pirate ship as a function of time in hours since $t = 0$.

c. Will the *Scurvy Shark* catch the frigate if neither ship changes course or speed? Explain.

4. The parametric equations $x(t) = 3t + 1$ and $y(t) = 4 + 4\sqrt{3t + 1}$ model the position of the pirate ship *Sea Serpent* on a rectangular grid in units of nautical miles for the domain $0 \le t \le 4$, where t is time in hours. Convert the parametric equations into a rectangular relation that represents the *Sea Serpent*'s path. Then graph the rectangular relation and indicate the direction of the ship's movement.

5. The equation $y = -0.2x + 6$ gives the path of the pirate ship *Doubloon* on a rectangular grid in units of nautical miles. The positive y-axis of the grid points north. At time $t = 0$ hours, the ship is located at (−10, 8), and it is moving 6 units to the east each hour.

a. Write parametric equations $x(t)$ and $y(t)$ that give the boat's position at time t.

b. The *Doubloon* is heading to an island at (30, 0). To the nearest hour, how long will it take the ship to reach the island? Explain your reasoning.

6. The position of an object on a coordinate plane over time is given by $x(t) = 1 - 8\cos\left(\frac{2\pi}{6}t\right)$ and $y(t) = -4 + 8\sin\left(\frac{2\pi}{6}t\right)$, where t is time in seconds.

a. Graph the equations on a graphing calculator and sketch the results. Indicate the direction of motion and the starting position of the object.

b. What are the angular velocity and linear velocity of the object?

c. What are the coordinates of the object at $t = 2$ s?

Scoring Guide	Exemplary	Proficient	Emerging	Incomplete
	The solution demonstrates these characteristics:			
Mathematics Knowledge and Thinking (Items 1a, 4, 5, 6)	• Clear and accurate understanding of parametric equations and their conversion into a rectangular function/ relation, and converting from rectangular into polar form; knows linear and angular velocity	• A functional understanding of parametric equations and their conversion into a rectangular function/ relation; may not understand linear and angular velocity	• Partial understanding of parametric equations and/or linear and angular velocity	• Little or no understanding of parametric equations and/or linear and angular velocity
Problem Solving (Items 1b, 2, 5)	• An appropriate and efficient strategy that results in a correct answer	• A strategy that may include unnecessary steps but results in a correct answer	• A strategy that results in some incorrect answers	• No clear strategy when solving problems
Mathematical Modeling / Representations (Items 2a, 2b, 4, 6)	• Clear and accurate understanding of parametric equations, including where time is the parameter, and using them to analyze scenarios	• A functional understanding of parametric equations and using them to analyze scenarios	• Partial understanding of parametric equations and using them to analyze scenarios	• Little or no understanding of parametric equations and using them to analyze scenarios
Reasoning and Communication (Items 1b, 2c)	• Precise use of appropriate math terms and language to convey meaning of how parametric equations connect to one another through their parameter, t	• Mostly correct interpretation of the answer, but may not have the exact answer	• Misleading or confusing characterization of how parametrics connect to the scenario	• Incomplete or inaccurate characterization of parametrics

Vectors and Complex Numbers

The Robotic Arm

Lesson 32-1 Introduction to Vectors

My Notes

Learning Targets:

- Understand and model rectilinear motion.
- Define and use vectors.
- Use the notation for position vectors.

SUGGESTED LEARNING STRATEGIES: Close Reading, Interactive Word Wall, Visualization, Create Representations, Quickwrite

Robots are widely used in manufacturing. One application is a robotic arm that can be used to quickly pick up and very accurately place objects. The position and motion of a robotic arm can be represented using vectors.

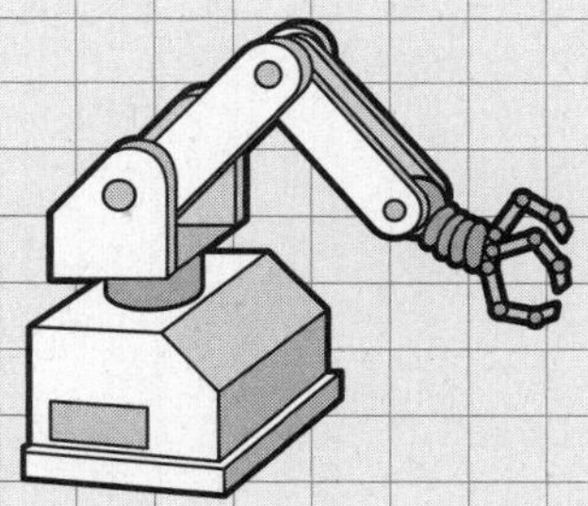

Vector Basics

A ***vector*** is a mathematical quantity that has both a magnitude and a direction. A vector is represented by a directed line segment.

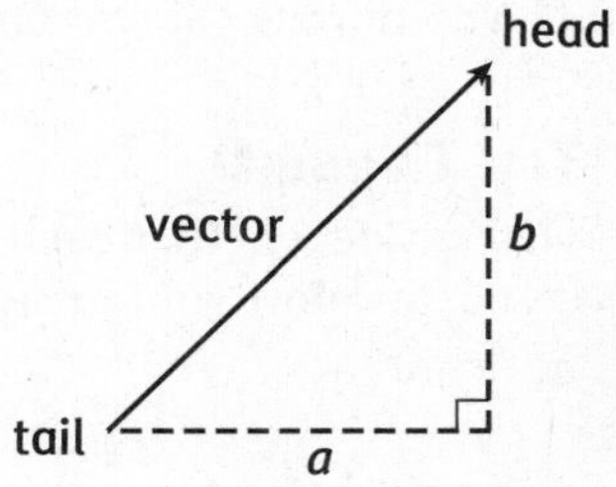

A two-dimensional vector $\vec{v} = \langle a, b \rangle$ has a horizontal component a and a vertical component b. A vector is said to be in standard position when its tail is at (0, 0).

The ***magnitude of a vector*** is the length of the directed line segment. Magnitude: $|\vec{v}| = \sqrt{a^2 + b^2}$.

Equal vectors have equal magnitude and point in the same direction.

MATH TERMS

A **vector** is a mathematical quantity that is described by its magnitude as well as its direction.

The **magnitude** of a vector is the length of the vector without regard to direction.

Example A

Draw each vector.

a. $\vec{v}$ with tail at (1, 2) and head at (3, −2)
b. $\vec{u} = \langle -4, 3 \rangle$ in standard position

In standard position the tail is at the origin.

To locate the head, start from the origin. Then move 4 units left and 3 units up.

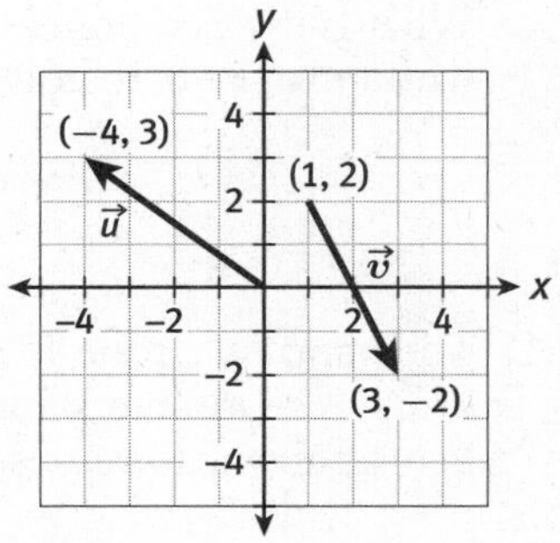

Try These A

Draw each vector on a coordinate plane.

a. $\vec{v} = \langle 2, -5 \rangle$ in standard position
b. $\vec{u}$ with tail at (−4, −2) and head at (−2, −2)
c. $\vec{t} = \langle 3, 3 \rangle$ with tail at (−1, 2)

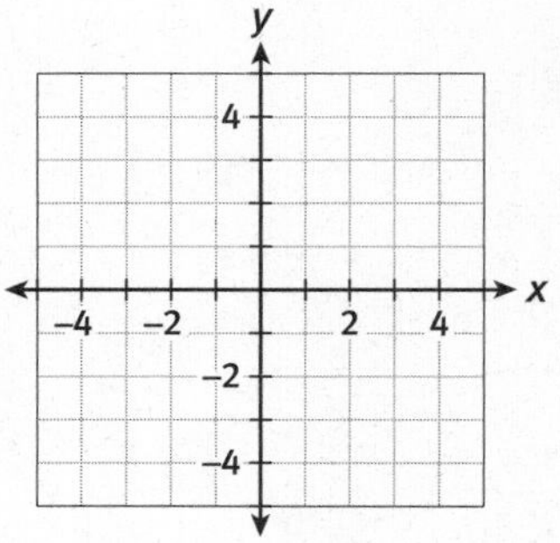

WRITING MATH

The component form of a vector with horizontal component a and vertical component b is written as $\langle a, b \rangle$. Notice the use of angle brackets.

My Notes

MATH TIP

Vectors are equal if they have the same component form.

Example B

Determine whether the vectors shown are equal.

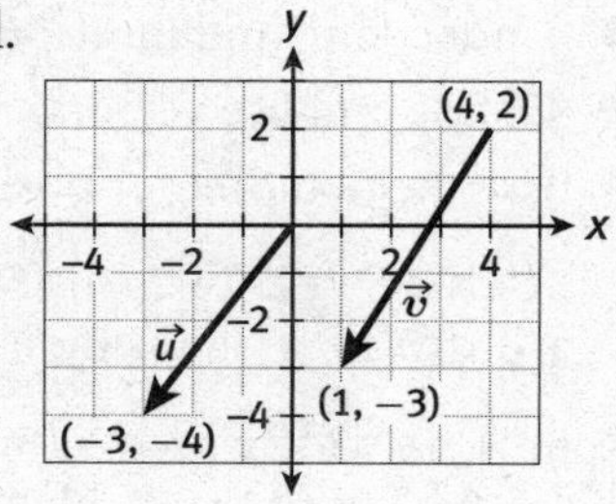

$\vec{u}$ is in standard position with its head at $(-3, -4)$, so $\vec{u} = \langle -3, -4 \rangle$.

To find the components of $\vec{v}$, subtract the coordinates of the tail from the coordinates of the head.

horizontal: $1 - 4 = -3$

vertical: $-3 - 2 = -5$

$\vec{v} = \langle -3, -5 \rangle$.

The component forms are not the same, so the vectors are not equal.

Try These B

Determine whether each pair of vectors are equal. Support your answers.

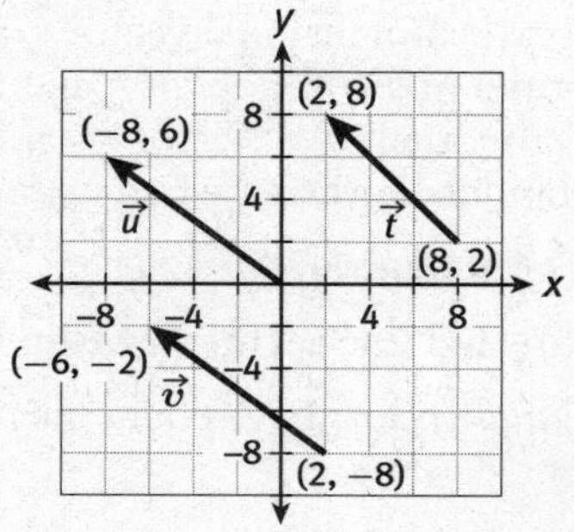

a. $\vec{v}$ and $\vec{u}$

b. $\vec{u}$ and $\vec{t}$

c. What is the component form of a vector with tail at $(-8, 6)$ and head at $(12, -15)$?

1. The hand on a robotic arm starts at (50, 120) on a coordinate grid in units of centimeters and moves to (98, 65). Explain why a vector would be useful way to represent the change in position of the hand.

My Notes

2. **Reason quantitatively.** Let $\vec{v}$ be the vector that describes the change in position of the robotic hand.
   a. What is the component form of $\vec{v}$? What does the component form indicate in this situation?

   b. What is the magnitude of $\vec{v}$? What does the magnitude indicate in this situation?

Check Your Understanding

3. **Construct viable arguments.** If two vectors have the same tail coordinates but different head coordinates, are the vectors equal? Explain your answer.
4. Give the meaning of each statement.
   a. $\vec{s} = \langle 12, -8 \rangle$ b. $|\vec{k}| = 27$
5. **Critique the reasoning of others.** A student claims that $\vec{m} = \langle -5, 4 \rangle$ and $\vec{n} = \langle 5, -4 \rangle$ are equal vectors. Is the student correct? Explain.

LESSON 32-1 PRACTICE

Use the graph for Items 6 and 7.

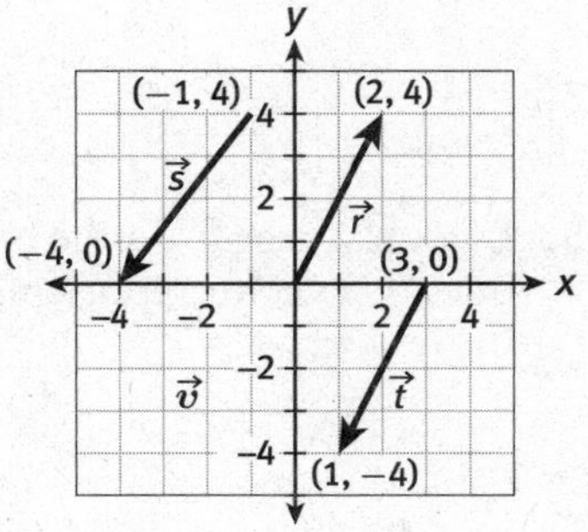

6. Are $\vec{s}$ and $\vec{t}$ equal? Explain.
7. Give the coordinates of the tail and head of a vector that is equal to $\vec{r}$. Explain how you determined your answer.

Write the component form of each vector, and determine its magnitude. Then draw each vector on a coordinate plane.

8. $\vec{v}$ with tail at (4, 8) and head at (−3, 1)
9. $\vec{u}$ in standard position with head at (9, −6)
10. **Reason quantitatively.** Biologists are using GPS technology to track a snow leopard. At 2:00 p.m., the leopard's coordinates are (12, 8) on a coordinate grid with units in kilometers. The positive y-axis points north. Twelve hours later, the leopard's coordinates are (20, 17). Let $\vec{p}$ represent the change in position of the leopard.
    a. What is the component form of $\vec{p}$? What does the component form indicate in this situation?
    b. What is the magnitude of $\vec{p}$? What does the magnitude indicate in this situation?

My Notes

Learning Targets:

- Find the magnitude and direction of a vector.
- Multiply a vector by a scalar.
- Add and subtract vectors.

SUGGESTED LEARNING STRATEGIES: Note Taking, Summarizing, Visualization, Create Representations, Group Presentation

Suppose the base of a robotic arm is secured at (0, 0) and its movement is limited to the *x*-*y* plane. A drawing of the arm is shown below.

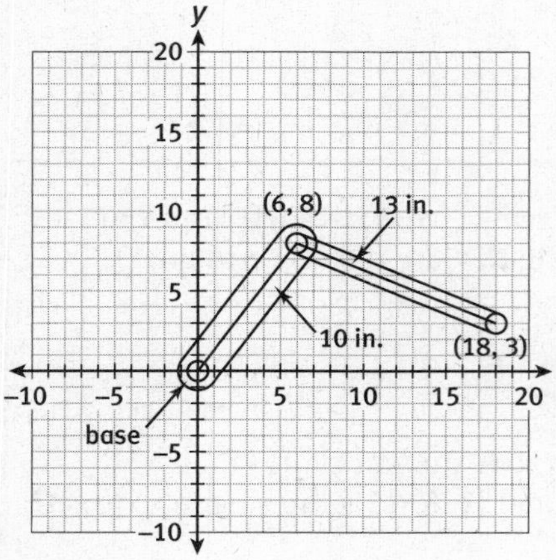

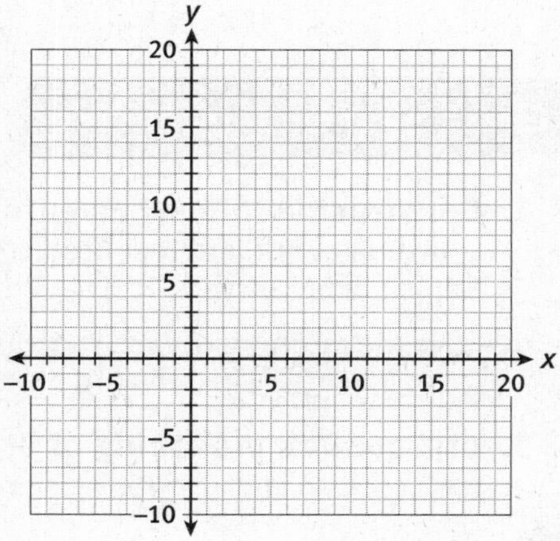

1. In the coordinate plane next to the diagram, draw two vectors to represent the 10-inch and 13-inch parts of the robotic arm and label them $\vec{u}$ and $\vec{v}$, respectively.
2. Write the vectors $\vec{u}$ and $\vec{v}$ in component form.
3. Draw a vector from the base of the arm to the end of the arm. What does this vector represent? What is its component form?
4. The third vector you drew represents the sum of $\vec{u}$ and $\vec{v}$, or $\vec{u} + \vec{v}$. Describe the relationship among the component forms of these three vectors.

MATH TIP

The sum of two vectors is also known as the *resultant vector*.

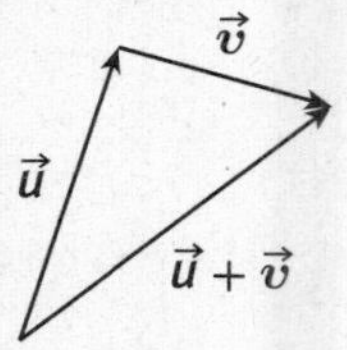

You saw above that you can add two vectors $\vec{u}$ and $\vec{v}$ geometrically by drawing $\vec{v}$ with its tail at the head of $\vec{u}$. The sum $\vec{u} + \vec{v}$ is then the vector from the tail of $\vec{u}$ to the head of $\vec{v}$.

You can also add two vectors geometrically by using properties of parallelograms, as shown in the next example.

My Notes

Example A

Add the vectors $\vec{u} = \langle 2, 4 \rangle$ and $\vec{v} = \langle 5, -2 \rangle$ both geometrically and symbolically.

Geometrically:

Step 1: Draw both vectors in standard position.

Step 2: Draw a parallelogram with $\vec{u}$ and $\vec{v}$ forming two of its sides.

Step 3: Draw a vector from (0, 0) to the opposite vertex of the parallelogram. This vector is $\vec{u} + \vec{v}$.

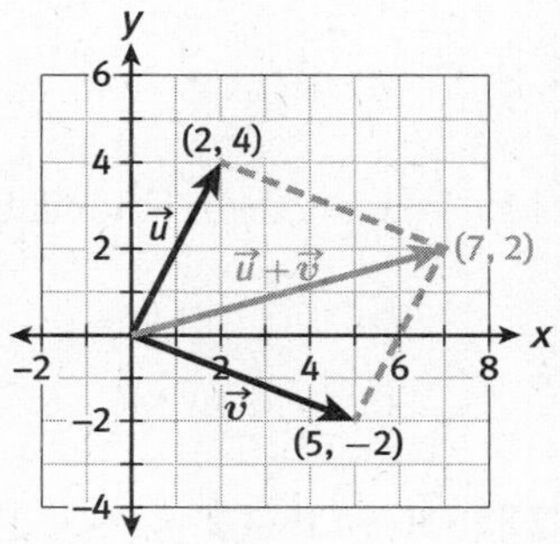

Symbolically:

Add the horizontal components and the vertical components of the vectors.

$\vec{u} + \vec{v} = \langle 2 + 5, 4 + (-2) \rangle = \langle 7, 2 \rangle$

Try These A

Add each pair of vectors both geometrically and symbolically.

a. $\vec{s} = \langle 4, 1 \rangle$ and $\vec{t} = \langle -3, 4 \rangle$

b. $\vec{q} = \langle -6, -5 \rangle$ and $\vec{r} = \langle 8, -5 \rangle$

Check Your Understanding

5. **Construct viable arguments.** Look back at Example A. Can you find the magnitude of $\vec{u} + \vec{v}$ by adding the magnitudes of $\vec{u}$ and $\vec{v}$? Explain.
6. Describe a method you could use to add three vectors geometrically.
7. **Express regularity in repeated reasoning.** Is vector addition commutative? In other words, is $\vec{u} + \vec{v}$ the same as $\vec{v} + \vec{u}$? Explain.

The additive inverse of a vector $\vec{w}$, denoted $-\vec{w}$, has the same magnitude as $\vec{w}$ but points in the opposite direction. You can subtract one vector from another by adding its additive inverse. In other words, $\vec{v} - \vec{w}$ is equivalent to $\vec{v} + (-\vec{w})$.

Use vectors $\vec{v} = \langle 3, 4 \rangle$ and $\vec{w} = \langle -2, 5 \rangle$ for Items 8–11.

8. What is the additive inverse of $\vec{w}$?

MATH TIP

Two vectors are additive inverses if their horizontal components are opposites and their vertical components are opposites.

My Notes

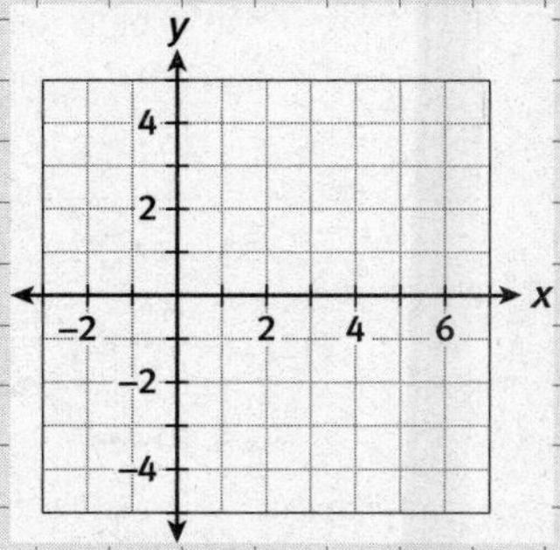

9. Use the coordinate grid to show how to find $\vec{v} + (-\vec{w})$ geometrically.

10. What is the component form of $\vec{v} - \vec{w}$? Explain your answer.

11. What is the relationship among the component forms of $\vec{v}$, $\vec{w}$, and $\vec{v} - \vec{w}$?

12. Given that $\vec{s} = \langle -2, 2 \rangle$ and $\vec{t} = \langle 1, -4 \rangle$, subtract each pair of vectors both geometrically and symbolically.

a. $\vec{s} - \vec{t}$

b. $\vec{t} - \vec{s}$

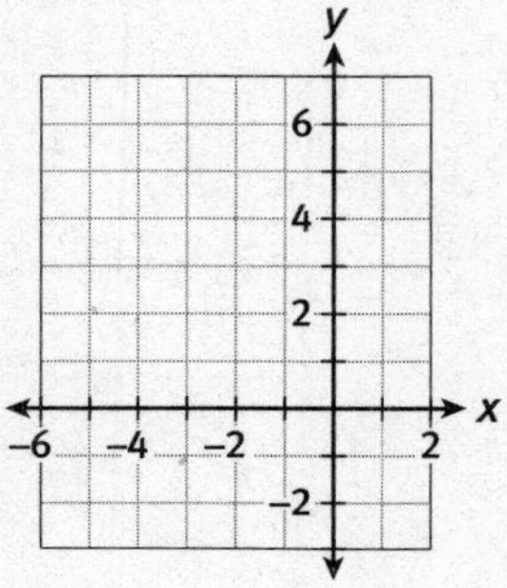

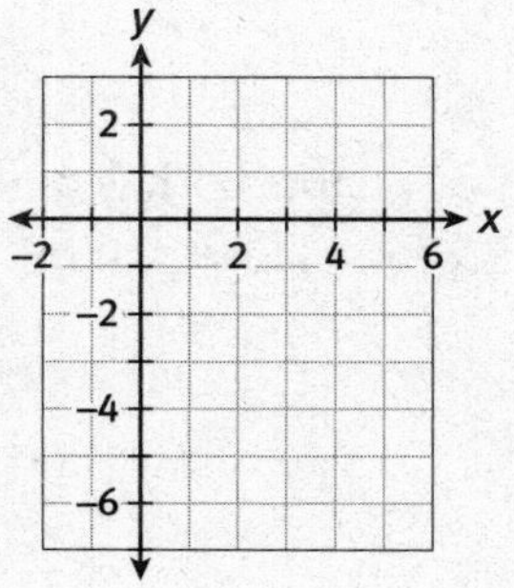

A scalar is a quantity that can be represented by a single real number. You can multiply a vector $\vec{u} = \langle a, b \rangle$ by a scalar h, as shown in the next example.

Example B

Multiply $\vec{u} = \langle 2, 1 \rangle$ by the scalar 3 both geometrically and symbolically.

Geometrically:

Step 1: Think of multiplication as repeated addition:
$3\vec{u} = \vec{u} + \vec{u} + \vec{u}$.

Step 2: Use the end-to-end method to find $\vec{u} + \vec{u} + \vec{u}$.

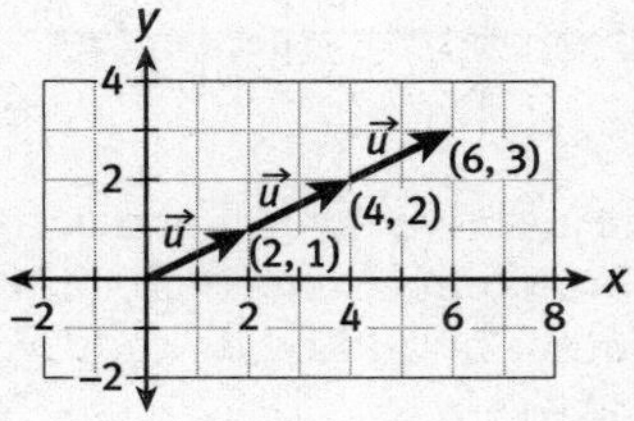

Step 3: Draw $3\vec{u}$ with the same magnitude and direction as $\vec{u} + \vec{u} + \vec{u}$.

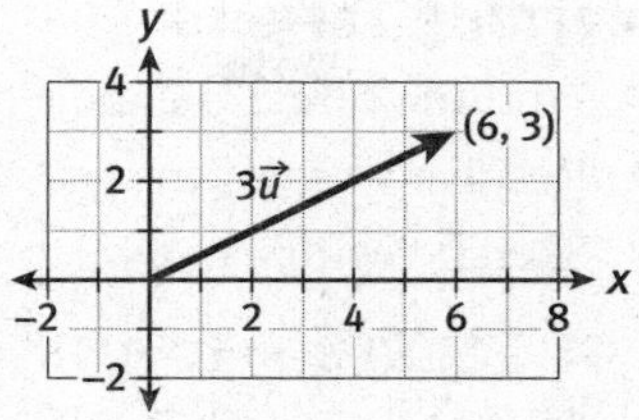

Symbolically:

Multiply each component by the scalar.

$3\vec{u} = \langle 3(2), 3(1) \rangle = \langle 6, 3 \rangle$

Try These B

Let $\vec{v} = \langle -2, 4 \rangle$ and $\vec{w} = \langle -3, -1 \rangle$. Find each vector both geometrically and symbolically.

a. $2\vec{v}$ **b.** $3\vec{w}$ **c.** $-2\vec{w}$

Check Your Understanding

13. Look back at Example B. Compare the direction of $3\vec{u}$ with the direction of $\vec{u}$, and compare the magnitude of $3\vec{u}$ with the magnitude of $\vec{u}$.

14. Express regularity in repeated reasoning. Explain the effect of the sign of the scalar h on the direction of $h\vec{v}$ compared to the direction of $\vec{v}$.

LESSON 32-2 PRACTICE

Let $\vec{u} = \langle 2, -3 \rangle$ and $\vec{v} = \langle -6, 4 \rangle$. Find each vector both graphically and symbolically.

15. $\vec{u} + \vec{v}$ **16.** $3\vec{u}$ **17.** $\vec{v} - \vec{u}$ **18.** $2\vec{u} + \vec{v}$

19. Critique the reasoning of others. Given that $\vec{s} = \langle 0. 5 \rangle$ and $\vec{t} = \langle 3, 4 \rangle$, a student states that $|\vec{s} + \vec{t}|$ is 10. What mistake did the student make? Give the correct magnitude of $\vec{s} + \vec{t}$.

20. Reason quantitatively. A coordinate grid is in units of miles. Henry's change in position on the grid during the first hour of a hike can be represented by $\vec{f} = \langle 3, -1 \rangle$. His change in position during the second hour of the hike can be represented by $\vec{g} = \langle -2, -2 \rangle$.

a. What vector represents Henry's overall change in position during the 2-hour hike? Explain.

b. Henry plans to walk directly back to his starting position. To the nearest tenth of a mile, how far will he walk on the return trip?

My Notes

My Notes

Learning Targets:

- Find the direction angle of a vector.
- Resolve a vector into its components.
- Sketch vectors and vector sums in the coordinate plane.

SUGGESTED LEARNING STRATEGIES: Note Taking, Think-Pair-Share, Visualization, Identify a Subtask, Group Presentation

Vectors can be described by their magnitude and a direction angle. The *direction angle* is the angle the vector would make with the positive x-axis when the tail (initial point) is located at the origin.

Recall from the previous lesson that $\vec{u} + \vec{v}$ represents the position of the end of a robotic arm compared to the base of the arm.

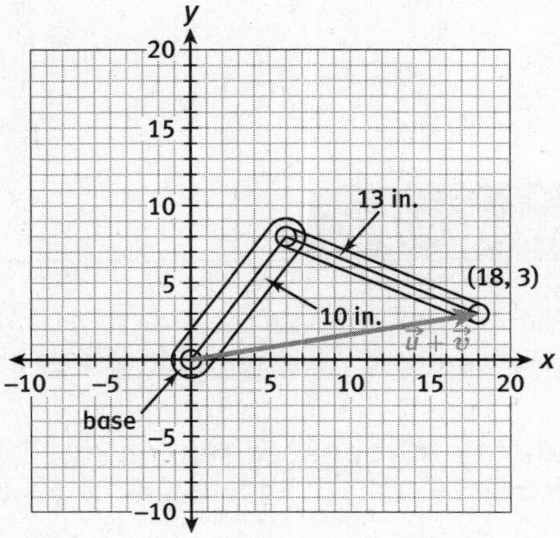

1. What is the magnitude of $\vec{u} + \vec{v}$?

2. Use trigonometry to compute the direction angle for $\vec{u} + \vec{v}$.

3. Compute the magnitude and direction angles for the following vectors.

a.

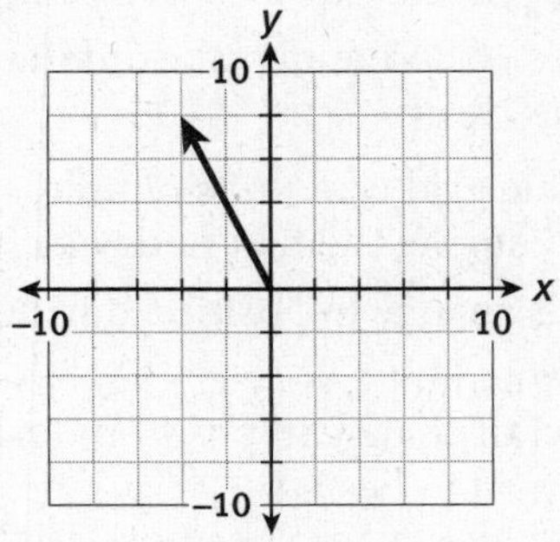

b.

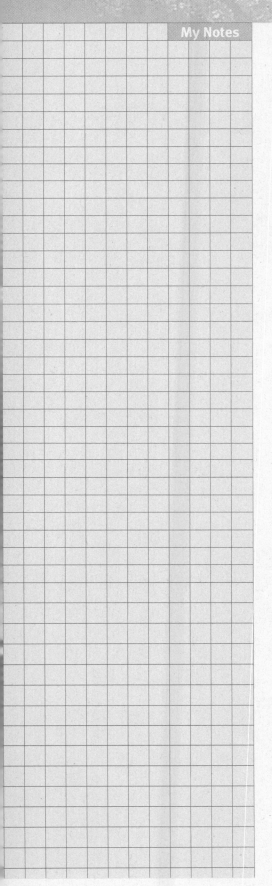

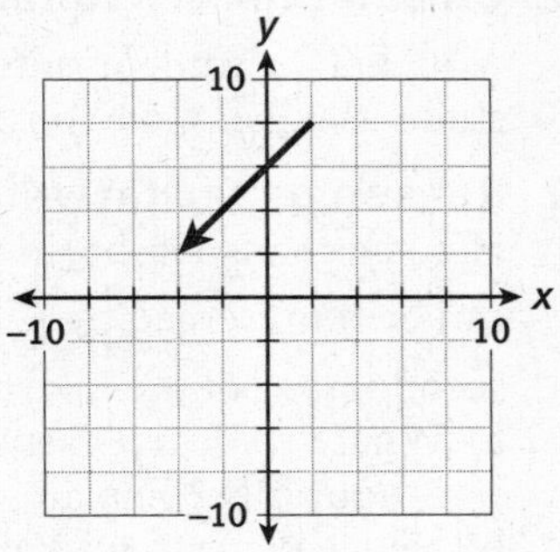

My Notes

c. $\langle 12, -4 \rangle$

d. the vector with tail at (1, 1) and head at (7, −10)

A vector can be resolved into its component parts if you know the magnitude and direction angle.

Resolving a Vector into Components

Given $\vec{v}$ in the direction θ with magnitude $|\vec{v}|$

$$\vec{v} = \left\langle |\vec{v}|\cos\theta,\ |\vec{v}|\sin\theta \right\rangle$$

Example A

A vector has a magnitude of 6 and a direction angle of 120°. Resolve the vector into its components.

Step 1: Find the horizontal component.

$$|\vec{v}|\cos\theta = 6\cos 120^\circ = 6\left(-\frac{1}{2}\right) = -3$$

Step 2: Find the vertical component.

$$|\vec{v}|\sin\theta = 6\sin 120^\circ = 6\left(\frac{\sqrt{3}}{2}\right) = 3\sqrt{3}$$

Solution: The component form of the vector is $\left\langle -3, 3\sqrt{3} \right\rangle$.

Try These A

Resolve each vector into its components.

a. magnitude = 8, direction = 225°

b. magnitude = 50, direction = −95°

c.

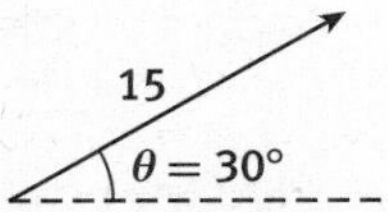

d.

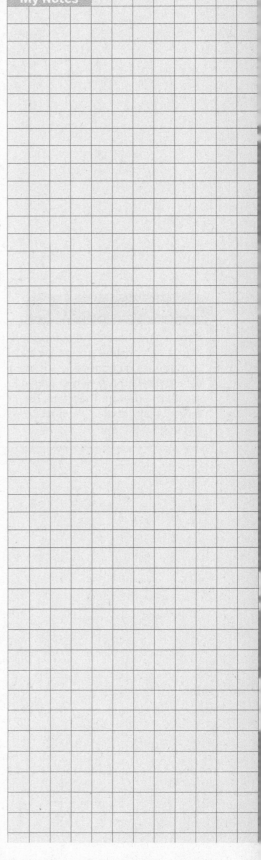

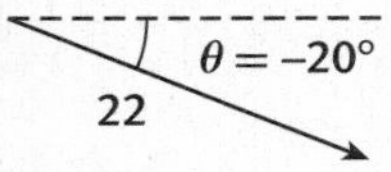

My Notes

4. Suppose that the 10-inch part of the robotic arm is pointing in the direction 110°. What are the coordinates of the point representing the joint connecting the two parts of the robotic arm?

Example B

The magnitude of $\vec{u}$ is 4, and its direction angle is 58°. The magnitude of $\vec{v}$ is 8, and its direction angle is −95°. What are the magnitude and direction of $\vec{u}+\vec{v}$?

Step 1: Find the component form of $\vec{u}$. $\vec{u} = \langle 4\cos(58°), 4\sin(58°)\rangle$

Step 2: Find the component form of $\vec{v}$. $\vec{v} = \langle 8\cos(-95°), 8\sin(-95°)\rangle$

Step 3: Find $\vec{u}+\vec{v}$.

$$\vec{u}+\vec{v} = \langle 4\cos(58°) + 8\cos(-95°),\ 4\sin(58°) + 8\sin(-95°)\rangle$$

$$\vec{u}+\vec{v} \approx \langle 1.422, -4.577\rangle$$

Step 4: Find $|\vec{u}+\vec{v}|$ and θ

$$|\vec{u}+\vec{v}| \approx \sqrt{1.422^2 + (-4.577)^2}$$

$$\approx 4.793$$

$$\tan\theta \approx \frac{-4.577}{1.422}, \text{ for } -90° < \theta < 0°$$

$$\theta \approx -72.741°$$

Solution: The magnitude of $\vec{u}+\vec{v}$ is approximately 4.793, and its direction angle is approximately −72.741°.

MATH TIP

Because the horizontal component of $|\vec{u}+\vec{v}|$ is positive and the vertical component is negative, $\vec{u}+\vec{v}$ must lie in Quadrant IV when drawn in standard position. Therefore, the direction angle of $\vec{u}+\vec{v}$ must be between −90° and 0°.

Try These B

The magnitude of $\vec{s}$ is 10, and its direction angle is 125°. The magnitude of $\vec{t}$ is 15, and its direction angle is −15°. Determine the magnitude and direction angle of each vector.

a. $\vec{s}-\vec{t}$ **b.** $\vec{t}-\vec{s}$ **c.** $2\vec{t}-\vec{s}$

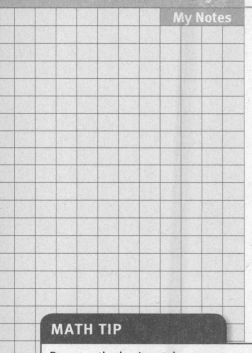

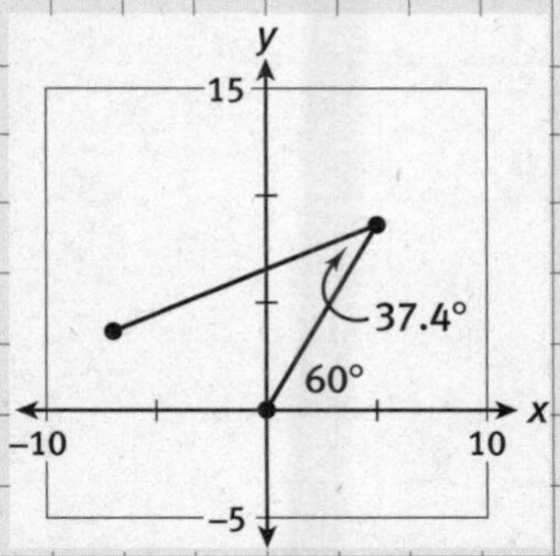

5. Make sense of problems. The robotic arm moves into the position as shown. Find the resultant vector that represents the location of the end of the robotic arm. Express this vector using its magnitude and direction angle, and then resolve it into component form.

My Notes

Check Your Understanding

6. Explain how to use trigonometry to determine the direction angle of a vector when you are given its component form.
7. **Make sense of problems.** Look back at Example B. Explain how you can determine whether the solution is reasonable.
8. **Construct viable arguments.** A vector has a magnitude of 16 and a direction angle of $-140°$. Without performing any calculations, how can you determine the signs of the horizontal component and the vertical component of the vector?
9. **Model with mathematics.** How do you think you could represent a complex number as a vector in the complex plane?

LESSON 32-3 PRACTICE

Compute the magnitude and direction angle of each vector.
Let $\vec{u} = \langle -2, 4 \rangle$ and $\vec{v} = \langle 3, 4 \rangle$.

10. $\vec{v}$ **11.** $\vec{u}$ **12.** $\vec{u} - \vec{v}$ **13.** $\vec{u} + \vec{v}$

Resolve each vector into its components.

14. magnitude 10 in the direction 225°

15. magnitude 15 in the direction 150°

16. Given that $\vec{v} = \langle 4, -6 \rangle$, what are the magnitude and direction angle of $4\vec{v}$? Explain your answer.

17. Attend to precision. Deana leaves a cabin and drives a snowmobile 60° north of east for 4.5 km. Then she turns and drives 30° south of east for 6.5 km.

a. If Deana turns and drives straight back to the cabin, what direction should she head? Round to the nearest tenth of a degree and justify your answer.

b. If Deana averages 20 km/h on her return trip, how long will the return trip take? Round to the nearest minute.

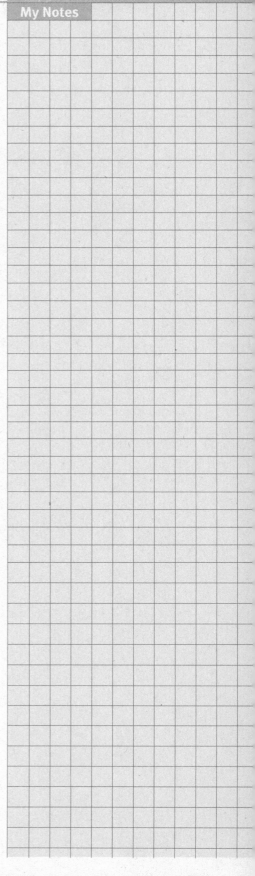

My Notes

Learning Targets:

- Represent complex numbers as vectors.
- Find the conjugate of a complex number.
- Add, subtract, multiply, and divide complex numbers.

SUGGESTED LEARNING STRATEGIES: Think-Pair-Share, Create Representations, Look for a Pattern, Quickwrite, Group Presentation

Complex numbers can be interpreted geometrically by representing them as vectors on the complex plane. If $z = a + bi$ is a complex number, where a and b are real numbers, then you can represent z on the complex plane by a vector in standard position with a horizontal component of a and a vertical component of b.

1. Let $z = a + bi$, where a and b are real numbers. Represent the following complex numbers as vectors on the complex plane.

a. $z = 1$ **b.** $z = 2i$
c. $z = 2 - i$ **d.** $z = -3 - 2i$

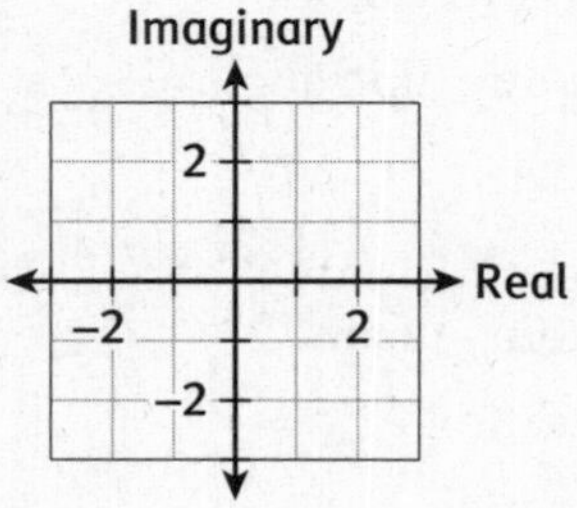

You can add and subtract complex numbers geometrically in the complex plane by using vector addition and subtraction.

2. Given that $z_1 = -2 + 4i$ and $z_2 = 3 - i$, find each sum or difference geometrically.

a. $z_1 + z_2$ **b.** $z_1 - z_2$

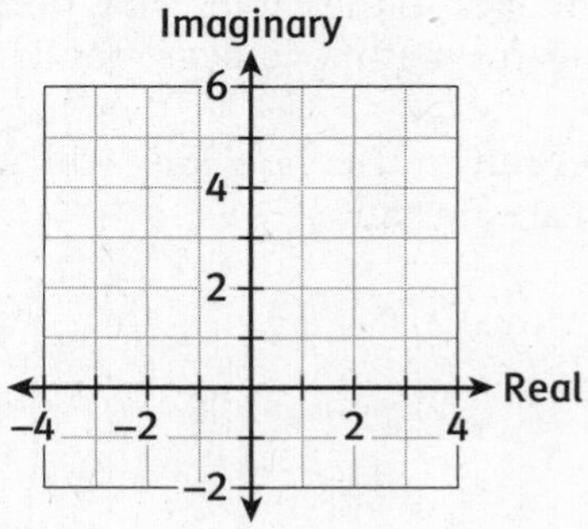

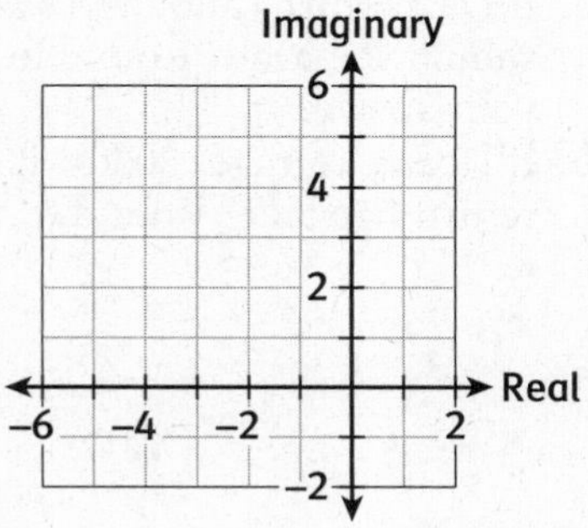

My Notes

3. **Express regularity in repeated reasoning.** Use your knowledge of vector addition and subtraction and your answers to Item 2 to answer the following.
   a. How can you add two complex numbers without representing them geometrically?

   b. How can you subtract two complex numbers without representing them geometrically?

4. Find each sum or difference.
   a. $(5 + 8i) + (-8 + 7i)$
   b. $(-4 + 3i) + (4 - 2i)$
   c. $(-12 + 8i) - (9 - 5i)$
   d. $(-6 + 7i) - (-2 + 7i)$

There are two definitions that are important to the geometric interpretation of two complex numbers. The ***absolute value***, or *modulus*, ***of a complex number*** $z = a + bi$, written as $|a + bi|$ or $|z|$, gives the distance from zero to $a + bi$ on the complex plane.

5. a. Write an expression in terms of a and b to determine the value of $|z|$.

   b. Consider the complex numbers $z_1 = -4 - i$ and $z_2 = 2 + 7i$ and the points $P(-4, -1)$ and $Q(2, 7)$. Find $|z_1 - z_2|$ and the distance between points P and Q. Compare your answers and make a conjecture about the distance between complex numbers.

   c. Explain how to find the midpoint of the segment whose endpoints are represented by z_1 and z_2 and make a conjecture about the midpoint of a segment whose endpoints are represented by two complex numbers.

MATH TERMS

The **absolute value**, or modulus, of a complex number z is the distance from the origin to z on the complex plane. It is written as $|z|$ or $|a + bi|$.

MATH TIP

The distance between two complex numbers on the complex plane is equal to the absolute value, or modulus, of their difference.

MATH TERMS

Recall that the distance between the points P and Q is given by

$$d = \sqrt{(x_2 - x_1)^2 + (y_2 - y_1)^2}$$

and the midpoint of the segment PQ is $\left(\frac{x_1 + x_2}{2}, \frac{y_1 + y_2}{2}\right)$.

My Notes

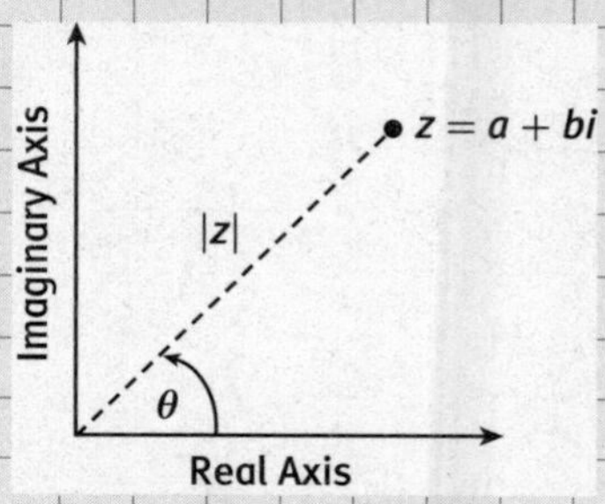

MATH TERMS

The **argument** of a complex number z is the angle formed by the positive real axis and the vector from the origin to z on the complex plane.

An ***argument of a complex number***, written $\theta = \arg(z)$, is an angle formed by the positive real axis and the vector representing z. Arguments of a complex number are not unique. To simplify calculations in this activity, let the argument of a complex number be the smallest positive angle whose terminal side is the vector representing z. The figure to the left illustrates both the absolute value of z, $|z|$, and the argument of z, $\arg(z)$.

6. Write an expression, in terms of a and b, to determine the value of the argument of z, or θ.

7. Determine the absolute value and the argument of each complex number below.

a. $z = 1$

b. $z = 2i$

c. $z = 2 - i$

d. $z = -3 - 2i$

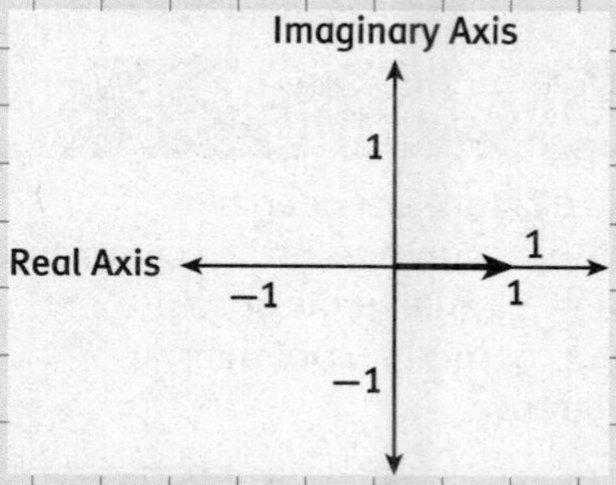

8. Explore the impact of repeatedly multiplying the complex number 1 by the complex number i. Find the following products and then show the results on the left. Draw a vector to represent each product. The vector representing 1 has been drawn.

a. $1 \cdot i =$

b. $1 \cdot i \cdot i =$

c. $1 \cdot i \cdot i \cdot i =$

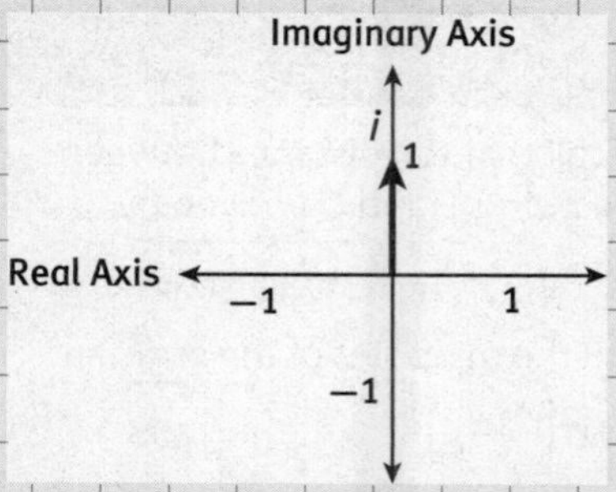

9. Explore the impact of repeatedly multiplying the complex number i by the complex number i. Find the following products and then show the results on the left. Draw a vector to represent each product. The vector representing i has been drawn.

a. $i \cdot i =$

b. $i \cdot i \cdot i =$

c. $i \cdot i \cdot i \cdot i =$

My Notes

10. Express regularity in repeated reasoning. Use your results in Items 8 and 9 to answer the following.

a. Describe the geometric pattern of repeatedly multiplying the numbers 1 and i by the complex number i.

b. State a hypothesis about multiplying a complex number by i. Then choose a complex number other than 1 or i and test your hypothesis.

c. Is there a geometric property about the vector that represents i in the complex plane that indicates why the overall effect of multiplication by i should be as you describe in Part a? Explain.

11. Investigate multiplication by a complex number with an argument other than 90°. Let w denote the complex number $\frac{\sqrt{2}}{2} + \frac{\sqrt{2}}{2}i$.

a. Find $|w|$ and $\arg(w)$ and draw the vector representing w on the complex plane.

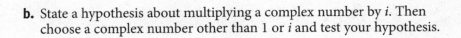

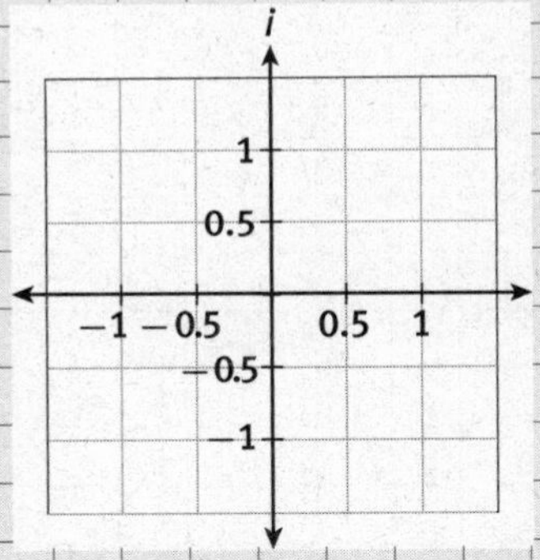

b. Compute the following products. Then draw vectors to represent each product. Label each vector.

$w^2 = w \cdot w =$

$w^3 = w \cdot w \cdot w =$

$w^4 = w \cdot w \cdot w \cdot w =$

c. Describe the effect that repeated multiplication by $w = \frac{\sqrt{2}}{2} + \frac{\sqrt{2}}{2}i$ has on the number w.

d. Use your answer in Part c to predict the solutions to the following.

$w^5 =$ $w^6 =$

$w^7 =$ $w^8 =$

My Notes

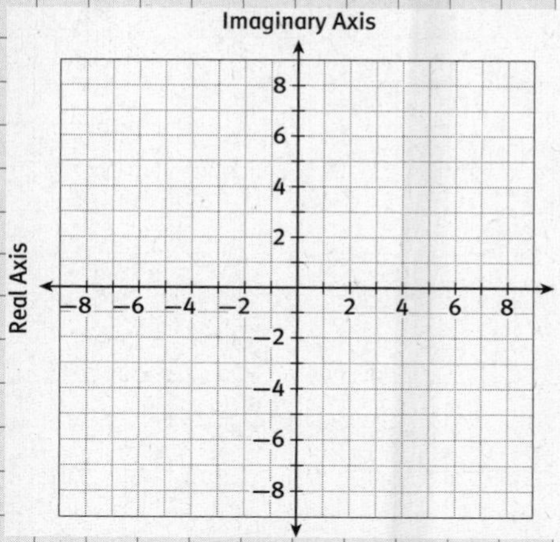

12. Now investigate the effects of multiplying complex numbers whose absolute value is a number other than 1. Let $z = \sqrt{2} + (\sqrt{2})i$.

a. Find $|z|$ and $\arg(z)$. Then draw the vector representing z.

b. Calculate z^2 and z^3.

c. Determine the absolute value and argument of z^2 and z^3. Then draw vectors to represent each product.

13. Consider the two complex numbers $w = \frac{\sqrt{2}}{2} + \frac{\sqrt{2}}{2}i$ and $z = \sqrt{2} + (\sqrt{2})i$.

a. Compare and contrast the two complex numbers.

b. Compare and contrast the products z^2 and z^3 with the products w^2 and w^3.

14. Find the following arguments, where $w = \frac{\sqrt{2}}{2} + \frac{\sqrt{2}}{2}i$.

a. $\arg(w) =$ **b.** $\arg(w^2) =$

c. $\arg(w^3) =$ **d.** $\arg(w^4) =$

15. Find the following arguments, where $z = \sqrt{2} + \sqrt{2}i$.

a. $\arg(z) =$ **b.** $\arg(z^2) =$

c. $\arg(z^3) =$ **d.** $\arg(z^4) =$

16. **Express regularity in repeated reasoning.** Based on your responses in Items 14 and 15, how is $\arg(z)$ related to $\arg(z^n)$? Explain.

My Notes

17. Let $z = 2\sqrt{3} + 2i$ and $w = 1 + (\sqrt{3})i$.

a. Find the absolute value of z and the absolute value of w.

b. Find $z \cdot w$.

c. Find $|z \cdot w|$.

d. Express regularity in repeated reasoning. What is the relationship between the absolute value of $z \cdot w$ and the absolute values of z and w?

18. Use z and w from Item 17. Find the following arguments.

a. $\arg(z) =$

b. $\arg(w) =$

c. $\arg(z \cdot w) =$

19. Express regularity in repeated reasoning. Based on your response to Item 18, how are the arguments of two complex numbers, z and w, related to the argument of their product, $\arg(z \cdot w)$?

20. For each product below, draw a vector for each factor on the complex plane. Next, predict the location of the corresponding product of these factors on the complex plane using your conclusions from Items 12–19. Finally, test your prediction by finding the product algebraically and determining its absolute value and argument.

a. $(i)(2 + 2i)$

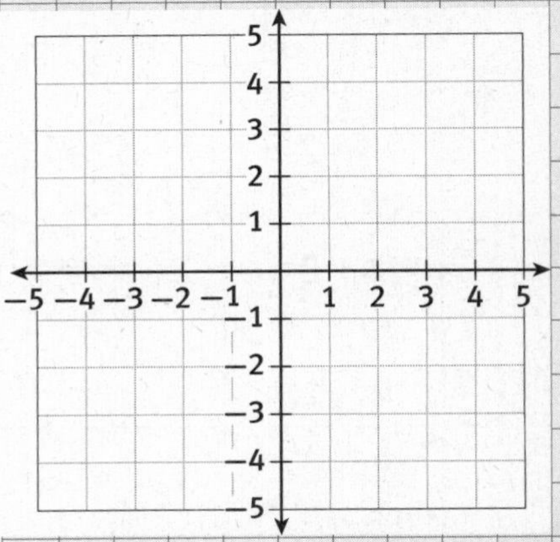

My Notes

b. $(-i)(2 + 2i)$

c. $(1 + i)(2 + 2i)$

d. $(i)(2\sqrt{3} + 2i)$

b.

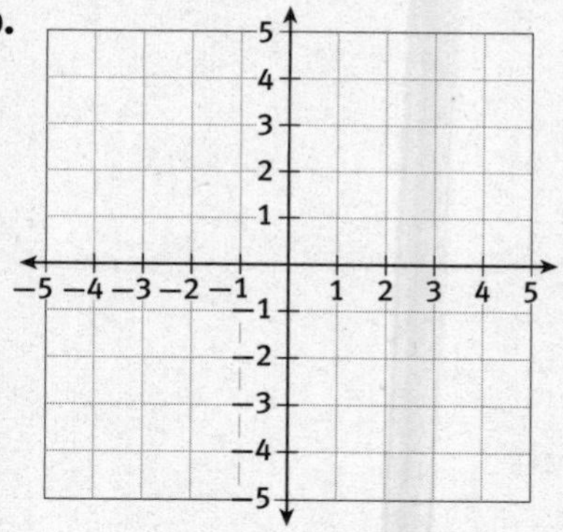

c.

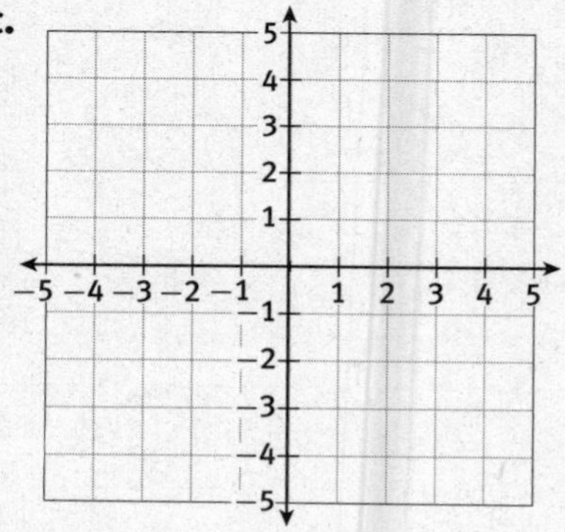

d.

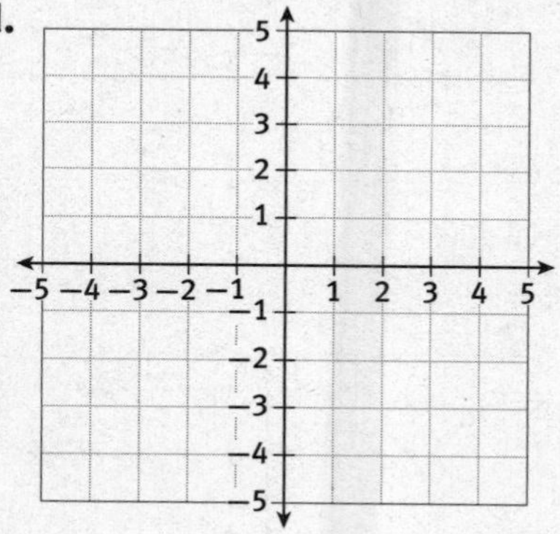

21. Use appropriate tools strategically. You can perform computations with complex numbers on a graphing calculator. To enter the imaginary unit i, press [2nd] [i]. Check that you calculated the products correctly in Item 20 by using a graphing calculator. Adjust your answers if needed.

Recall that the conjugate of a complex number $a + bi$ is $a - bi$. The real parts of a complex number and its conjugate are the same, and the imaginary parts are opposites. The conjugate of a complex number z can be denoted $\overline{z}$.

22. Determine the conjugate of each complex number. Then draw the vectors for each complex number and its conjugate on the complex plane.

a. $4 - 3i$
b. $-2 + 4i$
c. $2i$

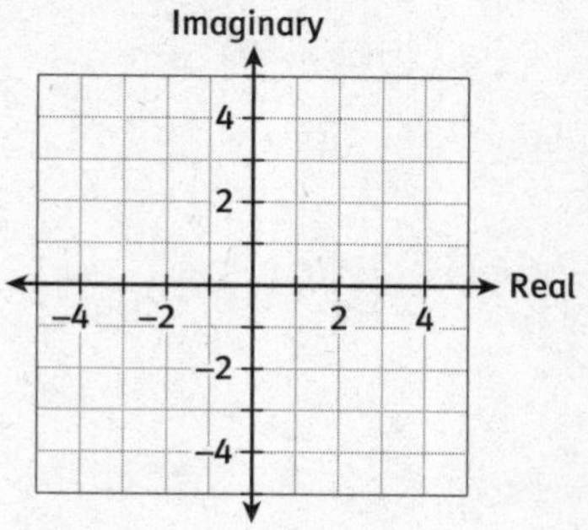

My Notes

23. Express regularity in repeated reasoning. Based on your answers to Item 22, what is the relationship between the vector that represents a complex number and the vector that represents its conjugate?

24. The formula $|z| = \sqrt{z\bar{z}}$ can be used to find the absolute value of a complex number $z = a + bi$ by using its complex conjugate. Show that this formula is equivalent to $|z| = \sqrt{a^2 + b^2}$.

25. Determine the absolute value of each complex number by using its conjugate. Show your work.

a. $12 + 5i$

b. $6 - 7i$

c. $-3 + 9i$

You also make use of conjugates when you divide complex numbers, as shown in the example below.

Example A

Write the quotient $\frac{1+4i}{2-3i}$ in the form $a + bi$.

Step 1: Multiply the dividend and divisor by the conjugate of the divisor. $\frac{1+4i}{2-3i}\left(\frac{2+3i}{2+3i}\right)$

Step 2: Apply the Distributive Property. $\frac{2+3i+8i-12}{4+6i-6i+9}$

Step 3: Simplify. $\frac{-10+11i}{13}$

Step 4: Write in the form $a + bi$. $-\frac{10}{13}+\frac{11}{13}i$

Try These A

Write each quotient in the form $a + bi$.

a. $\frac{-2+5i}{3i}$

b. $\frac{6}{6-8i}$

c. $\frac{3-4i}{-1+2i}$

My Notes

Check Your Understanding

26. What is the relationship between the magnitude and direction angle of a vector and the absolute value and argument of a complex number?

27. Show geometrically that the sum of a complex number $z = a + bi$ and its conjugate is equal to $2a$.

28. Use appropriate tools strategically. A student wants to evaluate i^{41}. He enters i^41 on his calculator, and it displays $-1\text{E}-13+i$.
   a. What is the actual value of i^{41}? Explain your answer.
   b. Why do you think the calculator displayed the result it did?

29. a. What is the product of $z = a + bi$ and its conjugate? What type of number is the product?
   b. Based on your answer to Part a, why does multiplying the dividend and divisor of a quotient of complex numbers by the conjugate of the divisor help you simplify the quotient?

LESSON 32-4 PRACTICE

30. Let $z = 4 - 3i$.
   a. Determine $\arg(z)$.
   b. Calculate $|z|$.
   c. Draw a vector that represents z on the complex plane.

For Items 31–36, given that $z = -6 + 4i$ and $w = 4 - 3i$, find each of the following. Write in the form $a + bi$ where appropriate.

31. $z + w$
32. $z - w$
33. zw
34. $\overline{z}$
35. $\frac{z}{w}$
36. distance between z and w

37. Let $w = \frac{\sqrt{3}}{2} + \frac{1}{2}i$.
   a. Calculate $|w|$ and $\arg(w)$.
   b. Determine w^2 and w^3.
   c. Describe the geometric pattern that results from repeated multiplication of $w = \frac{\sqrt{3}}{2} + \frac{1}{2}i$.

38. Make use of structure. What is the argument of $\left(6\sqrt{2} + 6\sqrt{2}i\right)\left(-2 + 2\sqrt{3}i\right)$? Explain your answer.

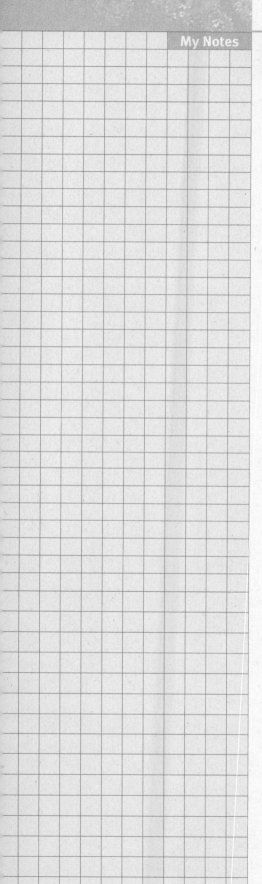

My Notes

Learning Targets:

- Find the polar form of a complex number.
- Represent complex numbers in polar form in the complex plane.

SUGGESTED LEARNING STRATEGIES: Marking the Text, KWL Chart, Think-Pair-Share, Look for a Pattern, Group Presentation

The ***polar form of a complex number*** z uses trigonometry to express a complex number in terms of its absolute value $|z|$ and argument $\theta = \arg(z)$. In the diagram shown below, $r = |z|$, and θ is the smallest positive angle formed by the positive real axis and the vector representing z.

MATH TERMS

The **polar form of a complex number** z is given by $r\cos\theta + (r\sin\theta)i$, where r is the absolute value of z and θ is the argument of z.

1. Use the diagram below to answer the following.

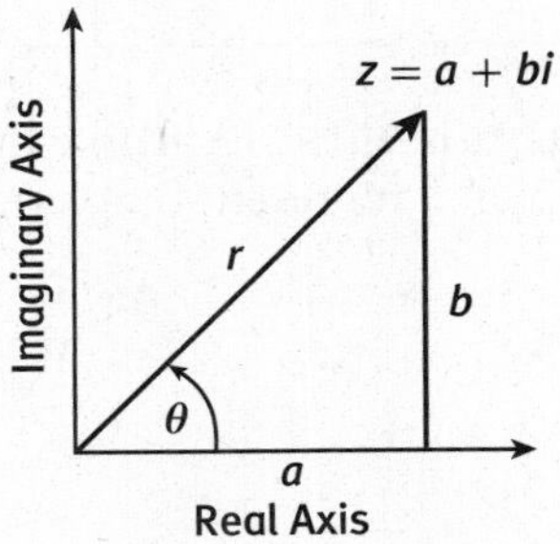

a. Express r in terms of a and b.

b. Use trigonometry to express a, the real part of z, in terms of r and θ.

c. Use trigonometry to express b, the imaginary part of z, in terms of r and θ.

d. Write the polar form of $z = a + bi$ by writing it in terms of r and θ.

My Notes

2. Complete the table below for each complex number.

Rectangular Form of z	$r = \|z\|$	θ	Polar Form of z
i	1	90°	$1(\cos 90° + i \sin 90°)$
$3i$			
$\frac{\sqrt{2}}{2} + \frac{\sqrt{2}}{2}i$			
$-\frac{\sqrt{2}}{2} + \frac{\sqrt{2}}{2}i$			
$-2 + 2i$			

3. **Construct viable arguments.** Explain why the rectangular and polar forms of $z = -2 + 2i$ represent the same number.

4. In the table below, z is the product of two complex numbers listed in the table for Item 2. Complete the table for each product by determining r and θ and expressing each product in polar form.

Rectangular Form of z	$r = \|z\|$	θ	Polar Form of z
$i \cdot \left(\frac{\sqrt{2}}{2} + \frac{\sqrt{2}}{2}i\right)$			
$3i \cdot \left(-\frac{\sqrt{2}}{2} + \frac{\sqrt{2}}{2}i\right)$			
$i \cdot (-2 + 2i)$			
$3i \cdot (-2 + 2i)$			

5. **Express regularity in repeated reasoning.** Compare the values in the tables for Items 2 and 4, and describe any patterns that you notice about the angle and the r-value of the products and factors.

My Notes

6. Make use of structure. Multiplying the polar forms of two complex numbers provides insight into the geometric properties of complex multiplication.

a. Multiply the following general forms of two complex numbers using binomial multiplication.

$$[r_1(\cos\theta_1 + i\sin\theta_1)] \cdot [r_2(\cos\theta_2 + i\sin\theta_2)] =$$

b. Write the real part of the result in Part a. What is a trigonometric identity that can be used to simplify this real part?

c. Write the imaginary part of the result in Part a. What is a trigonometric identity that can be used to simplify this imaginary part?

d. Explain how the work in Parts b and c confirms the two properties about the absolute value and argument of the product of complex numbers.

7. Draw a vector to represent each complex number on the complex plane.

a. $4(\cos(60°) + i\sin(60°))$
b. $3(\cos(180°) + i\sin(180°))$
c. $2(\cos(225°) + i\sin(225°))$
d. $5(\cos(270°) + i\sin(270°))$

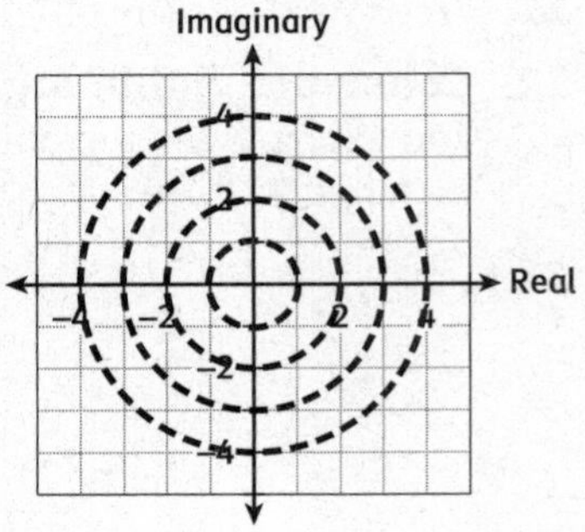

My Notes

TECHNOLOGY TIP

You can use a graphing calculator to convert the polar form of a complex number to the rectangular form. First, make sure your calculator is set to degree mode. Then enter the polar form of the complex number (without the degree symbols) and press ENTER.

8. **Use appropriate tools strategically.** Use a graphing calculator to write the rectangular form of each complex number. Use the rectangular form to check that the vectors you drew in Item 7 are correct.
   a. $4(\cos(60^\circ) + i \sin(60^\circ))$
   b. $3(\cos(180^\circ) + i \sin(180^\circ))$
   c. $2(\cos(225^\circ) + i \sin(225^\circ))$
   d. $5(\cos(270^\circ) + i \sin(270^\circ))$

Check Your Understanding

9. **Make use of structure.** The polar form of a complex number is $8(\cos 160^\circ + i \sin 160^\circ)$. Without performing any calculations, what can you conclude about the signs of a and b in the rectangular form of the complex number, $a + bi$? Explain your reasoning.
10. Explain how writing complex numbers in polar form can help you find the product of the complex numbers.
11. **Critique the reasoning of others.** A student claims that you can add two complex number in polar form $r(\cos\theta + i \sin\theta)$ by adding the values of r and adding the values of θ. Is the student correct? Provide an example to support your answer.
12. What is the polar form of the conjugate of $8(\cos 48^\circ + i \sin 48^\circ)$? Explain how you determined your answer.

LESSON 32-5 PRACTICE

Write each complex number in polar form.

13. $8 - 15i$

14. $-7 - 24i$

Calculate the value of each of the following. Write the product in polar form.

15. $3(\cos 40^\circ + i \sin 40^\circ) \cdot 5(\cos 60^\circ + i \sin 60^\circ)$
16. $8(\cos 120^\circ + i \sin 120^\circ) \cdot 8(\cos 80^\circ + i \sin 80^\circ)$

Write each complex number in rectangular form.

17. $7(\cos 240^\circ + i \sin 240^\circ)$

18. $12(\cos 315^\circ + i \sin 315^\circ)$

19. **Construct viable arguments.** Write the polar form of $-5 - 5\sqrt{3}i$, and explain why the polar form represents the same number as the rectangular form.

ACTIVITY 32 PRACTICE

Write your answers on notebook paper. Show your work.

Lesson 32-1

Draw each vector and find its magnitude.

1. $\vec{u} = \langle 10, 5 \rangle$ in standard position

2. $\vec{v} = \langle -6, -3 \rangle$ in standard position

3. $\vec{s}$ with tail at $(-5, 4)$ and head at $(-2, 1)$

4. $\vec{t} = \langle -3, 4 \rangle$ with head at $(2, -1)$

Use the graph for Items 5 and 6.

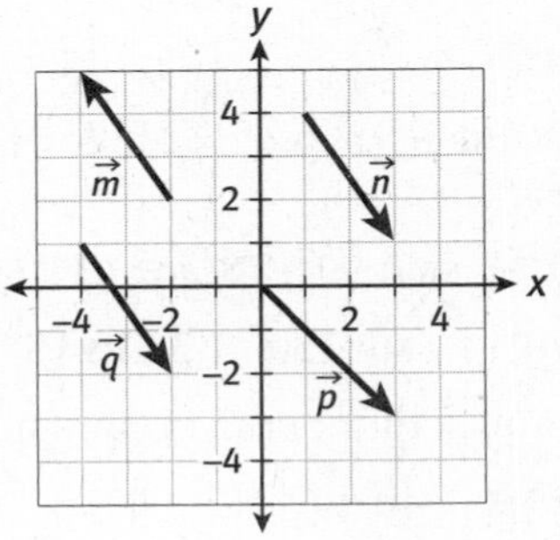

5. Which pair of vectors shown in the graph are equal? Explain.

6. Give the coordinates of the tail and head of a vector that is equal to $\vec{m}$. Explain how you determined your answer.

7. A ship's coordinates are (6, 8) on a coordinate grid in units of nautical miles in which the positive y-axis points north. Three hours later, the ship's coordinates are (12, 23). Let $\vec{p}$ represent the change in position of the ship.

a. What is the component form of $\vec{p}$? What does the component form indicate in this situation?

b. What is the magnitude of $\vec{p}$? What does the magnitude indicate in this situation?

Lesson 32-2

Let $\vec{r} = \langle -2, -1 \rangle$, $\vec{s} = \langle -4, 3 \rangle$, and $\vec{t} = \langle 1, -4 \rangle$. Find each sum, difference, or product both geometrically and symbolically.

8. $\vec{r} + \vec{s}$

9. $\vec{s} + \vec{t}$

10. $\vec{r} - \vec{s}$

11. $\vec{t} - \vec{r}$

12. $2\vec{s}$

13. $-3\vec{r}$

Let $\vec{u} = \langle 10, 5 \rangle$ and $\vec{v} = \langle -6, -3 \rangle$. Write the component form of each vector, and find its magnitude.

14. $\vec{u} + \vec{v}$

15. $2\vec{u}$

16. $2\vec{u} - \vec{v}$

17. $2\vec{v} - \vec{u}$

18. What is the additive inverse of $\vec{w} = \langle 4, -6 \rangle$?

19. How do the magnitude and direction of $-6\vec{c}$ compare with the magnitude and direction of $\vec{c}$?

20. The change in position of a queen on a chessboard on its first move can be represented by $\vec{u} = \langle -2, 2 \rangle$. Its change in position on its second move can be represented by $\vec{v} = \langle 0, 3 \rangle$. What vector represents the overall change in position of the queen for the two moves? Explain.

Lesson 32-3

Compute the magnitude and direction angle of each vector. Let $\vec{u} = \langle 4, 1 \rangle$ and $\vec{v} = \langle 5, 12 \rangle$.

21. $\vec{v}$

22. $\vec{u}$

23. $\vec{u} - \vec{v}$

24. $\vec{u} + \vec{v}$

Resolve each vector into its components.

25. magnitude 8 in the direction 45°

26. magnitude 9 in the direction 300°

27. magnitude 6 in the direction 125°

A whale-watching boat travels 80° north of east for 12 km. Then it turns and travels 20° south of east for 8 km.

28. To the nearest kilometer, how far is the boat from its starting point?
A. 10 km **B.** 13 km
C. 18 km **D.** 20 km

29. To the nearest degree, in what direction should the boat head to return directly to its starting point?
A. 34° south of west **B.** 43° south of west
C. 56° south of west **D.** 60° south of west

Lesson 32-4

30. Let $z = -5 - 12i$.
a. Draw the vector that represents z on the complex plane.
b. Determine $\arg(z)$.
c. Calculate $|z|$.

Let $z = 4 - 3i$ and $w = -2 - 4i$. Find each of the following both geometrically and symbolically.

31. $z + w$ **32.** $z - w$ **33.** $\overline{z}$

34. Let $w = -\frac{\sqrt{3}}{2} + \frac{1}{2}i$.
a. Calculate $|w|$ and $\arg(w)$.
b. Determine w^2 and w^3.
c. Describe the geometric pattern that results from repeated multiplication of $w = -\frac{\sqrt{3}}{2} + \frac{1}{2}i$.

35. Let z be a complex number with $|z| = 3$ and $\arg(z) = 35°$ and w be a complex number with $|w| = 7$ and $\arg(w) = 72°$.
a. Determine $|z^4|$ and $\arg(z^4)$.
b. Determine $|z \cdot w|$.
c. Calculate $\arg(z \cdot w)$.

Let $z = 2 + 5i$ and $w = -8 + i$. Find each of the following.

36. The distance between z and w

37. The midpoint of the segment connecting z and w on the complex plane

38. $\frac{z}{w}$ **39.** $\frac{w}{z}$

40. What is $(3 - 6i)(4 + 5i)$?
A. $-18 - 9i$ **B.** $12 - 39i$
C. $12 - 30i$ **D.** $42 - 9i$

Lesson 32-5

Write each number in polar form.

41. $-9 - 12i$ **42.** $40 - 9i$

Calculate the value of each of the following. Write the product in polar form.

43. $(7(\cos 90° + i \sin 90°))(8(\cos 135° + i \sin 135°))$

44. $(5(\cos 130° + i \sin 130°))(3(\cos 15° + i \sin 15°))$

Write each complex number in rectangular form.

45. $4(\cos 300° + i \sin 300°)$

46. $11(\cos 45° + i \sin 45°)$

Draw a vector to represent each complex number on the complex plane.

47. $z = 3(\cos(90°) + i\sin(90°))$

48. $w = 5(\cos(150°) + i\sin(150°))$

MATHEMATICAL PRACTICES
Construct Viable Arguments and Critique the Reasoning of Others

49. A student claims that $(-1 + \sqrt{3}i)^3 = 8$ because $(-1 + \sqrt{3}i)$ has an absolute value of 2 and an argument of 120°. Is the student correct? Explain.

Applications of Vectors

Moving Walkways

Lesson 33-1 Rectilinear Motion

My Notes

Learning Targets:

- Write equations to describe rectilinear motion.
- Use vectors to describe velocity of an object.
- Interpret speed as the magnitude of a velocity vector.

SUGGESTED LEARNING STRATEGIES: Levels of Questions, Paraphrasing, Visualization, Look for a Pattern, Quickwrite

Large public buildings, such as airport terminals and malls, use moving walkways to transport people efficiently over long distances. A top view of a moving walkway that moves at 2.5 feet per second (ft/s) is shown. The walkway moves people from west to east as indicated by the arrows.

Two adults walking at 6 ft/s approach the moving walkway. Anna, *A*, decides *not* to use the walkway and continues to maintain her same walking speed of 6 ft/s. Byron, *B*, on the other hand, chooses to use the moving walkway and continues to maintain the walking speed of 6 ft/s after entering the walkway.

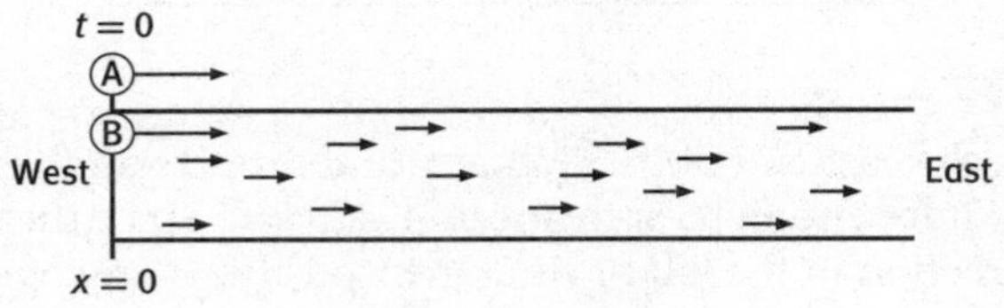

Let $x = 0$ mark the west end of the walkway and let $t = 0$ seconds represent the time that both Anna and Byron are located at the position $x = 0$.

1. Locate each adult's position from the west end of the walkway for the times $t = 1$, 2, and 4 seconds on the number line shown below.

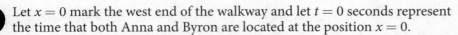

2. Explain how you determined your answer to Item 1.

3. Reason abstractly and quantitatively. Let x_A represent Anna's position and x_B represent Byron's position from the west end of the walkway at time *t*.

a. Write an expression that gives x_A in terms of time *t*.

b. Write an expression that gives x_B in terms of time *t*.

My Notes

c. Explain the meaning of the coefficients of t in each expression. Be sure to include units in your explanation.

Two children approach the same moving walkway, but this time, from its east end. The children also move at 6 ft/s, but in the opposite direction as the adults. Andre, A, runs *alongside* the moving walkway and maintains the running speed of 6 ft/s. Bella, B, enters the moving walkway and continues to maintain the running speed of 6 ft/s after entering the walkway.

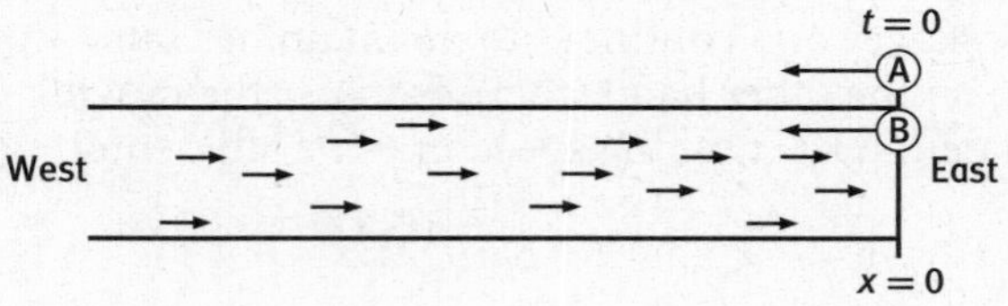

Let $x = 0$ mark the east end of the walkway and t represent the number of seconds since Andre and Bella were located at $x = 0$. Since the children are moving in a direction to the left of zero, their positions are represented by negative numbers.

4. Locate each child's position from the east end of the walkway for the times $t = 1$, 2, and 4 seconds on the number line shown below.

5. Explain how you determined your answer to Item 4.

6. Reason abstractly and quantitatively. Let x_A represent Andre's position and x_B represent Bella's position from the east end of the walkway at time t.

a. Write an expression that gives x_A in terms of time t.

b. Write an expression that gives x_B in terms of time t.

My Notes

c. Explain the meaning of the coefficients of t in each expression. Be sure to include units in your explanation.

7. Compare the algebraic expression for Anna from Item 3 with the algebraic expression for Andre from Item 6. How are they similar? How are they different?

Velocity can be described as directed motion. An object's velocity is a vector quantity. Therefore, velocity has both a direction and a magnitude. The magnitude of the velocity vector is the object's speed.

8. Complete the following table.

Person	Direction	Speed (including units)
Anna		
Andre		

The scenarios described in Items 1–8 illustrate motion along a line, called ***rectilinear motion***. These items show that a moving object's direction as well as its speed are both very important when describing its motion.

MATH TERMS

Rectilinear motion is motion along a line.

9. Describe the rectilinear motion along a number line using your work in Items 1–8.

a. What vector describes Anna's velocity?

b. What vector describes Andre's velocity?

c. What vector describes Byron's velocity?

d. What is Bella's velocity?

e. Explain how the direction of their velocities is indicated.

f. Explain how their speeds are indicated.

MATH TIP

When describing rectilinear motion, vectors are indicated using signed numbers.

For example, a velocity of 4 ft/s in the positive direction along a line can be represented by $\vec{v} = 4$ ft/s. A velocity of 4 ft/s in the negative direction along a line can be represented by $\vec{v} = -4$ ft/s.

10. Let $\vec{v}$ equal the velocity of an object moving along a horizontal number line.

a. What is the direction of motion when $\vec{v}$ is positive?

b. What is the direction of motion when $\vec{v}$ is negative?

c. Explain how you could represent the magnitude of $\vec{v}$.

d. Describe the similarities and differences between velocity and speed.

Typical moving walkways are about 5–6 feet wide. Suppose there is a moving walkway that is 120 feet wide. An illustration of an extra-wide walkway is shown below.

The direction of motion is indicated by arrows. We will locate the walkway on a coordinate grid with the origin at the southwest end of the walkway.

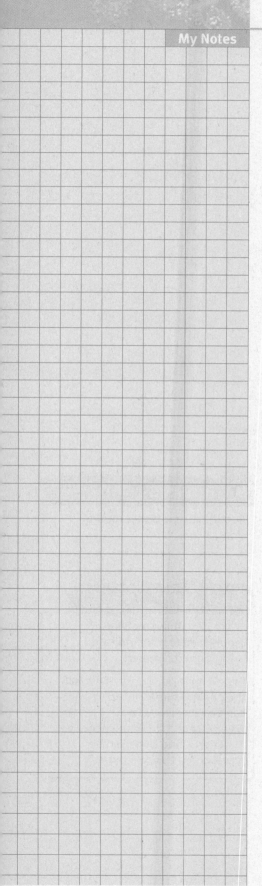

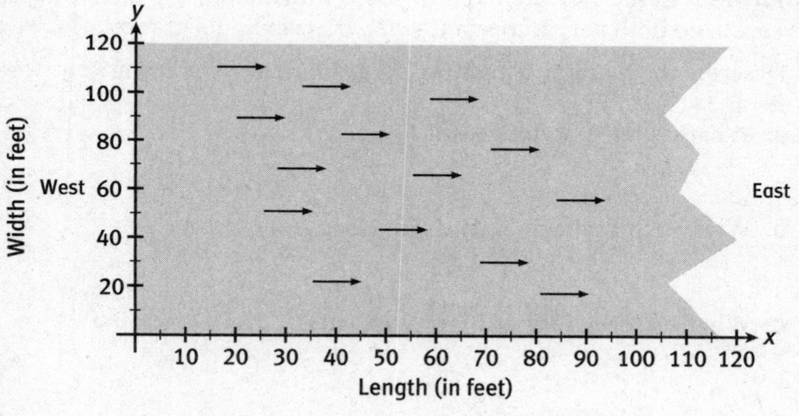

11. If the walkway were not moving, how long would it take for a person walking 6 ft/s to cross from the south side to the north side of the walkway? Show work to support your answer.

My Notes

12. Model with mathematics. The walkway begins to move at 2.5 ft/s. Sally starts at (0, 0) and walks south to north at 6 ft/s, moving at a right angle to the direction of the walkway's motion. Let t equal the seconds since Sally started walking.

a. Complete the table to represent Sally's position.

Time t (in seconds)	x (in feet)	y (in feet)
0		
2		
4		
6		
8		
10		
12		

CONNECT TO AP

Vectors and parametric equations are used to algebraically model the motion of objects as a function of time in physics and AP Calculus.

b. Use the patterns in the table to write parametric equations that represent Sally's motion on the walkway.

WRITING MATH

Parametric equations for x and y can also be written in ordered pair notation as shown.

$$(x, y) = (f(t), g(t))$$

c. Write the parametric equations in Part b as an ordered pair.

d. What is Sally's position at $t = 5\frac{1}{4}$ seconds?

e. What is Sally's position at $t = 10.75$ seconds?

f. Where will Sally be located when she is 27 feet from the north end of the moving walkway?

g. Graph the parametric equations that show Sally's path as she walks from south to north along the moving walkway. Indicate the direction of her movement.

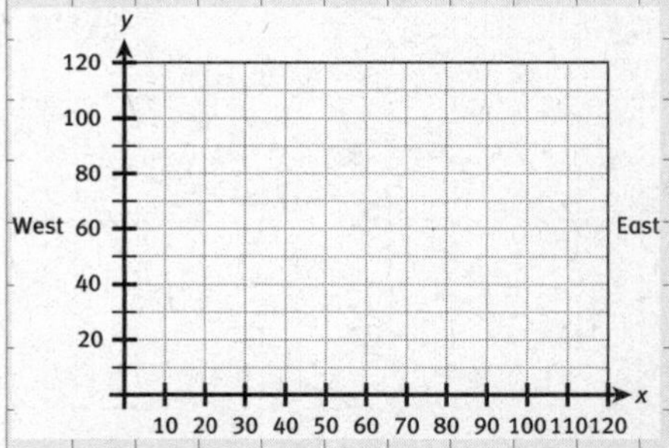

My Notes

h. Is the graph a reasonable description of Sally's position as she walks at a right angle to the motion of the moving walkway? Explain.

13. After reaching the north end, Sally walks from *north to south across* the moving walkway at 6 ft/s. Let t equal the seconds since Sally started walking from the position (50, 120).

a. Reason quantitatively. Explain the significance of the point (50, 120).

b. Model with mathematics. Write and graph the parametric equations that describe Sally's position as she walks from north to south along the moving walkway. Use the coordinate grid in Item 12 for your graph.

Check Your Understanding

14. Explain how two cars can have the same speed but different velocities.

15. How would you determine the sign of the velocity vector for an object moving along a vertical line?

16. Model with mathematics. In still air, an airplane's cruising speed is 850 km/h.

a. Write a vector for the airplane's velocity when it flies from south to north in still air.

b. Write a vector for the wind velocity when it blows from north to south at 40 km/h.

c. Write a vector for the plane's overall velocity when it flies from south to north in the wind described in Part b. What vector operation did you perform to find the overall velocity?

17. Refer back to Item 12. How could you use a vector to represent Sally's position with respect to the southwest corner of the walkway 3 seconds after she starts walking north? What is the component form of this vector?

My Notes

LESSON 33-1 PRACTICE

18. Penelope moves across a 50 ft tightrope strung horizontally with the ground. The audience watches her walk from left to right at a steady pace of 0.25 ft/s. Let t represent the number of seconds since she stepped onto the tightrope.

a. How long does it take her to get to the middle of the tightrope?

b. Write a vector for her velocity in ft/s.

19. When Penelope reaches the middle of the rope she stops moving, and her partner Paulo starts from the right side and walks toward her. Paulo reaches Penelope in 1 minute.

a. What is his speed in ft/s?

b. Write a vector for his velocity in ft/s.

Steven rows his kayak across a 200-ft-wide river. The current flows at 1.5 ft/s from west to east. He rows from the south shore heading due north at a speed of 4 ft/s. Let t equal the number of seconds since Steven left the south shore. Assume he starts at (0, 0).

20. Model with mathematics. Write parametric equations that represent Steven's motion.

21. Graph the parametric equations that show Steven's path as he crosses the river. Indicate the direction of his movement.

22. Write the component form of a vector that represents Steven's position compared to (0, 0) after he has been paddling for 30 seconds.

23. Critique the reasoning of others. A student claims that if the current of the river were twice as fast, it would take Steven twice as long to cross the river. Is the student correct? Explain your reasoning.

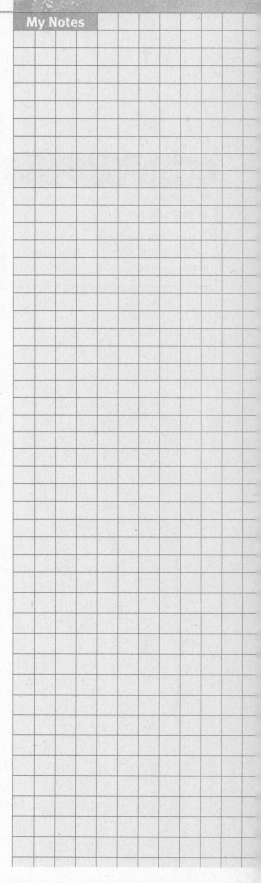

My Notes

Learning Targets:

- Use vectors to describe planar motion.
- Graph position vectors in the coordinate plane.
- Write a vector equation to model a real-world context.

SUGGESTED LEARNING STRATEGIES: Paraphrasing, Look for a Pattern, Create Representations, Discussion Groups, Quickwrite

MATH TERMS

Planar motion is motion in a coordinate plane.

A **position vector** indicates the distance and direction from the origin or another fixed point.

Motion in a coordinate plane (walking across a moving walkway) is two-dimensional and called ***planar motion***. The parametric equations $(2.5t, 6t)$ represent Sally's position as a point in the plane at time t as she walks from south to north.

Since position includes both a distance and a direction from a fixed reference point, it can also be represented as a vector. A ***position vector*** $\vec{s} = \langle 2.5t, 6t \rangle$ represents Sally's position in the plane at time t with reference to the point $(0, 0)$ as she walks from south to north.

1. **Model with mathematics.** Now consider Sally's position as she moves from *north to south* across the moving walkway.
   a. Express her position from the point $(0, 0)$ as a vector for $0 \le t \le 20$ ($t = 0$ represents the time at which she begins to walk from north to south).

   b. Evaluate Sally's position vector for $t = 0$ and $t = 10$.

      Sally's position vector when $t = 0$ is ________________.

      Sally's position vector when $t = 10$ is ________________.

   c. Graph Sally's two position vectors for $t = 0$ and $t = 10$ on the coordinate grid.

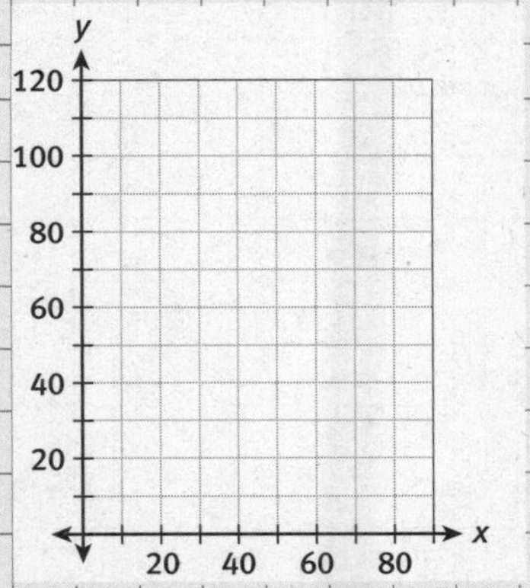

   d. After 10 seconds have elapsed, how many feet has Sally moved horizontally and vertically? Express this displacement as a vector.

   e. Draw a vector from Sally's position at $t = 0$ to her position at $t = 10$. Compare this vector to the displacement vector in Part d.

   f. How could you use Sally's position vector at $t = 0$ and the displacement vector from part d to find her position vector at $t = 10$?

2. Sally's position vector representing her *south-to-north* movement across the walkway is $\langle 2.5t, 6t \rangle$.

a. Reason quantitatively. Each component of her position vector gives information about her velocity. Describe what each component in the position vector indicates about her velocity.

b. Write a vector that represents Sally's velocity.

3. Consider Sally's position from Item 2 as she moves from *south to north*.

a. Use scalar multiplication to write her position as a vector multiplied by a scalar t.

b. What is Sally's speed? Show work to support your answer.

c. How far is Sally from the origin after 5 seconds? Use this information to determine Sally's speed.

4. Consider Sally's position from Item 1a as she moves from *north to south*.

a. What is Sally's velocity vector?

b. Reason abstractly. Use vectors and scalar multiplication to write her position at time t and explain the meaning of each vector quantity.

c. What is Sally's speed? Show work to support your answer.

5. Are Sally's velocity vectors from Items 2b and 4a equal? Explain.

My Notes

MATH TIP

The vector position equation is

$$\vec{y} = \vec{v}t + \vec{s}_0$$

where
$\vec{v}$ is the velocity vector, t is time, and $\vec{s}_0$ is the position vector at time $t = 0$.

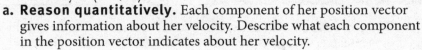

My Notes

CONNECT TO PHYSICS

Newton's First Law of Motion states that an object in motion will continue to move at a constant velocity unless it is acted upon by a net force with a positive magnitude.

Check Your Understanding

6. To the nearest tenth of a degree, what is the direction angle of Sally's movement as she walks from *south to north* across the walkway? Explain your answer.

7. Attend to precision. How does a position vector differ from a displacement vector?

8. A force that acts on an object has both magnitude and direction, so a force can be represented by a vector. If there are two different forces acting on an object, how could you determine magnitude and direction of the overall, or net, force on the object?

9. What are the advantages of representing physical quantities such as position and velocity with vectors?

LESSON 33-2 PRACTICE

Steven rows his kayak across a 200-ft-wide river. He rows from the south shore heading due north. Steven starts from (0, 0) at time $t = 0$. On this trip his velocity is $\langle 3.6, 4.8 \rangle$ ft/s.

10. What is Steven's speed?

11. Model with mathematics. Write Steven's position as a vector equation in terms of t.

12. To the nearest second, how long will it take Steven to reach the north shore of the river? Explain your answer.

Make sense of problems. The vector $\vec{y} = \langle -5, -9 \rangle t + \langle 200, 360 \rangle$ represents the position of an oil tanker at time t in hours on a coordinate grid in units of miles, where the positive y-axis points north.

13. What is the ship's velocity vector? What is its speed to the nearest mile per hour?

14. What are the coordinates of the ship's position at $t = 3$ hours? Explain how you determined your answer.

15. Write the component form of the displacement vector that describes the oil tanker's change in position from $t = 0$ hours to $t = 3$ hours.

16. How long will it take the oil tanker to reach a port at (0, 0)?

ACTIVITY 33 PRACTICE

Write your answers on notebook paper. Show your work.

Lesson 33-1

Rudy leaves home and walks to school at a steady pace of 2 ft/s. His sister Rosa leaves at the same time but rides a bike at a speed of 8 ft/s. On a number line, let $x = 0$ represent their home and $t = 0$ the time since they left the house.

1. Sketch the distance each one has traveled from home on a number line. Mark their locations at 30-second intervals for the first 3 minutes.
2. Suppose the school is 5000 feet to the east of Rudy and Rosa's home. On the way home, Rudy rides the bike at 8 ft/s and Rosa walks at 2 ft/s. Let x_A represent Rudy's position and x_B represent Rosa's position compared to their home at time t in seconds. Write expressions for x_A and x_B.
3. What are the values of x_A and x_B when $t = 600$? What do these values represent?
4. How do Rudy and Rosa's *biking speeds* compare to each other?
5. How do Rudy and Rosa's *walking velocities* compare to each other?

A crane pulls upward on a shipping container with a force of 180,000 newtons. At the same time, gravity pulls downward on the container with a force of 176,000 newtons.

6. Write a vector that represents the force of the crane on the shipping container.
7. Write a vector that represents the force of gravity on the shipping container.
8. Write a vector for the net, or overall, force on the container. What are the magnitude and direction of this force?
9. A speed skater skates around a track. Explain why the skater's motion is *not* an example of rectilinear motion.

An escalator moves passengers to the right at a speed of 0.44 m/s and upward at a speed of 0.25 m/s. Let t equal the number of seconds since Krista steps on the escalator. Assume she starts at (0, 0).

10. Complete the table to represent Krista's position.

Time t (in s)	x (in s)	y (in m)
0		
1		
2		
3		
4		

11. Write parametric equations that represent Krista's motion.
12. The escalator lifts passengers to a height of 9 m. How long will it take Krista to reach the top of the escalator?
13. Graph the parametric equations that show Krista's path as she rides the escalator. Indicate the direction of her movement.
14. Write the component form of a vector that represents Krista's position compared to (0, 0) after she has been riding the escalator for 30 seconds.
15. What does the magnitude of the vector you wrote in Item 14 represent?
    A. Krista's speed after 30 s
    B. Krista's velocity after 30 s
    C. Krista's height above ground after 30 s
    D. Krista's distance from the base of the escalator after 30 s

Lesson 33-2

Jin and Kin are standing on the side of a soccer field 100 feet apart. Both run directly toward a soccer ball that is not moving. Jin starts at (0, 0) and Kin at (100, 0). Jin's velocity is $\langle 10, 12 \rangle$ ft/s and Kin's velocity is $\langle -9, 13 \rangle$ ft/s.

16. Write each boy's position vector at time t in seconds.

17. What is each boy's speed?

18. What are the coordinates of the ball rounded to the nearest integer? Explain your answer.

19. Who gets to the ball first and how much faster?

Three forces act on a crate sitting on a ramp. The force of gravity is given by $\langle 0, -490 \rangle$, and the force of friction is given by $\langle 191, 110 \rangle$. The normal force exerted by the ramp on the block is given by $\langle -212, 368 \rangle$. Each force is in units of newtons.

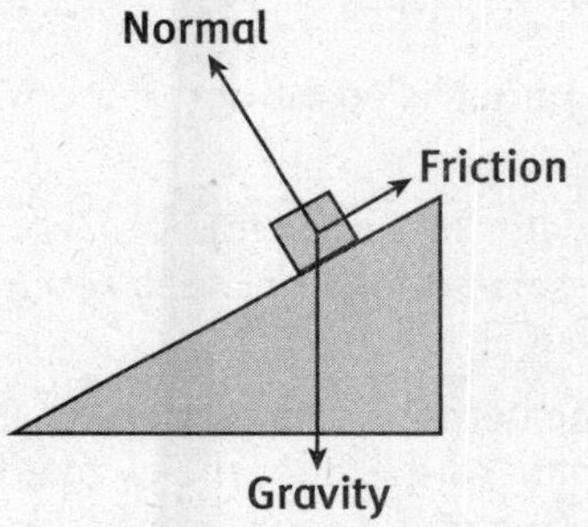

20. What is the component form of the net, or overall, force on the crate?

21. What are the magnitude and direction angle of the net force? Round to the nearest tenth.

22. The vector equation $\vec{F} = m\vec{a}$ relates the net force $\vec{F}$ on an object in newtons, its mass m in kilograms, and its acceleration $\vec{a}$ in m/s^2. Given that the crate has a mass of 50 kg, write the component form of its acceleration.

23. What are the magnitude and direction of the crate's acceleration?

24. What is the relationship between the direction angles of the net force and the acceleration?

Macy is floating in an inner tube down a river. Each minute, the current pushes her 105 ft north and 88 ft east.

25. Write Macy's position vector at time t in minutes, assuming that she starts from (0, 0).

26. Evaluate Macy's position vector for $t = 15$ minutes.

27. What is the approximate direction of Macy's motion?

A. 33° north of east
B. 40° north of east
C. 50° north of east
D. 57° north of east

28. About how far will Macy travel in one hour?

A. 1.2 miles
B. 1.6 miles
C. 2.2 miles
D. 2.6 miles

MATHEMATICAL PRACTICES
Reason Abstractly and Quantitatively

29. The vector $\vec{y} = \langle 5, -3 \rangle t + \langle 0, 200 \rangle$ represents the position of a tractor at time t in seconds on a coordinate grid in units of feet, where the positive y-axis points north.

a. To the nearest foot per second, what is the tractor's speed?

b. To the nearest degree, what is the tractor's direction?

c. Write the component form of the displacement vector that describes the change in the tractor's position from $t = 0$ seconds to $t = 30$ seconds.

d. The tractor will make a turn when it is 1000 ft to the east of its starting position. After how many minutes will the tractor begin the turn?

In an electric circuit with an alternating current, voltage has both a magnitude and a direction. As a result, electrical engineers use complex numbers in the form of vectors to represent voltage in these types of circuits.

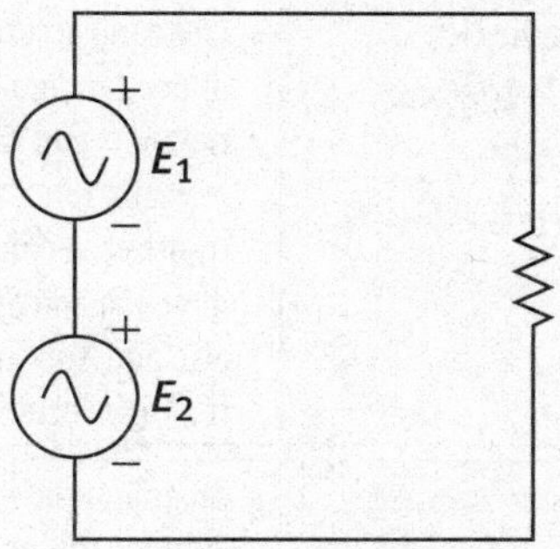

1. The diagram shows two voltage sources, E_1 and E_2, connected in series in a circuit with an alternating current. In this circuit, the voltage of E_1 is given by $20(\cos 25° + i \sin 25°)$ and the voltage of E_2 is given by $15(\cos 130° + i \sin 130°)$, where the unit of measure is volts.
   a. Write the rectangular form of the complex numbers representing E_1 and E_2.
   b. The total voltage of the circuit is equal to the sum of E_1 and E_2. Find the sum both geometrically and symbolically.
   c. Write the total voltage of the circuit in polar form.
2. An engineer adds a third voltage source, E_3, to the circuit. Afterward, the total voltage of the circuit is equal to $20(\cos 323° + i \sin 323°)$. Find the voltage of E_3, and explain how you determined your answer.

A wind turbine generates electricity from the wind's energy. A wind farm is a group of wind turbines. Wind turbines produce the most electricity when their blades face directly into the wind. Computer controls can rotate the turbines to change the direction that the blades face.

3. A cold front results in a shift in the wind. The new wind velocity in miles per hour is given by the vector $\langle -26, -15 \rangle$, on a coordinate grid in which the positive y-axis points north.
   a. What are the magnitude and direction of the wind's velocity?
   b. If the blades of a turbine point due north, how many degrees and in what direction should the turbine rotate so that its blades will face directly into the wind?
4. The speed of the wind increases to 40 mi/h, but its direction stays the same. Write a vector in component form to represent the new velocity of the wind.
5. A map of a wind farm is based on a coordinate grid in units of feet in which the positive y-axis points north. A technician just finished working on a turbine with a position vector of $\langle 2340, 2080 \rangle$. The next turbine he must work on has a position vector of $\langle 2730, 4160 \rangle$.
   a. How far and in what direction does the technician need to travel to reach the next turbine? Explain how you determined your answer.
   b. Write the technician's position vector equation in terms of time t in minutes given that he travels at a speed of 1760 ft/min.
6. Find each of the following.
   a. the quotient of $4 + 3i$ and $2 - 5i$
   b. the product of $3(\cos 25° + i \sin 25°)$ and $6(\cos 35° + i \sin 35°)$
   c. the distance between $-2 - 6i$ and $5 + 8i$ on the complex plane
   d. $2\vec{v} + \vec{u}$ given that $\vec{v} = \langle -10, 8 \rangle$ and $\vec{u} = \langle 12, -15 \rangle$

Scoring Guide	Exemplary	Proficient	Emerging	Incomplete
	The solution demonstrates these characteristics:			
Mathematics Knowledge and Thinking (Items 1, 3, 5, 6)	• Clear and accurate understanding of complex numbers and writing them in vector form; able to translate vectors into direction and distance; can also add, subtract, and multiply vectors	• A functional understanding of vectors; can functionally understand complex numbers, but may not be able to marry the two concepts completely	• Partial understanding of vectors and complex numbers	• Little or no understanding of vectors and complex numbers
Problem Solving (Items 1c, 3b, 5a)	• An appropriate and efficient strategy that results in a correct answer when interpreting vectors as a sum	• A strategy that may include unnecessary steps but results in a correct answer	• A strategy that results in some incorrect answers	• No clear strategy when solving problems
Mathematical Modeling / Representations (Items 3, 4, 5)	• Clear and accurate understanding of the application of vectors to the compass rose in the context of the problem to find distance and directions	• A functional understanding of the application of vectors to the compass rose in the context of the problem	• Partial understanding of vectors, especially in a contextual situation	• Little or no understanding of vectors, especially in a contextual situation
Reasoning and Communication (Items 2, 5a)	• Precise use of appropriate math terms and language to describe the results of vectors within the context of the problem	• Mostly correct interpretation to describe the results of vectors within the context of the problem	• Misleading or confusing characterization to describe the results of vectors within the context of the problem	• Incomplete or inaccurate attempt at a solution to the scenario

Matrices, Systems of Equations, and Volume

6

Unit Overview

In this unit, you will study matrices and how they are used to store and manipulate data. You will also write and solve matrix equations to find solutions to systems of equations. In addition, you will use Cavalieri's principle and the concept of a limit to derive the formula for the volume of a sphere.

Key Terms

As you study this unit, add these and other terms to your math notebook. Include in your notes your prior knowledge of each word, as well as your experiences in using the word in different mathematical examples. If needed, ask for help in pronouncing new words and add information on pronunciation to your math notebook. It is important that you learn new terms and use them correctly in your class discussions and in your problem solutions.

Academic Vocabulary

- image
- unique

Math Terms

- matrix
- elements
- entries
- dimension
- order
- scalar
- determinant
- multiplicative inverse
- column matrix
- row matrix
- perpendicular
- dilation
- matrix equation
- coefficient matrix
- variable matrix
- constant matrix
- Cavalieri's Principle
- converse
- sphere
- annulus
- limit

ESSENTIAL QUESTIONS

How are matrices used to represent real-world problems in business?

How can systems of equations be solved using matrix equations and technology?

EMBEDDED ASSESSMENTS

This unit has two embedded assessments, following Activities 35 and 37. In completing the embedded assessments you will demonstrate your ability to use matrices to solve problems, including transformations in the coordinate plane. You will also have an opportunity to demonstrate your understanding of solving a system with matrix equations and find volumes of solid figures.

Getting Ready

Write your answers on notebook paper.
Show your work.

1. Solve the system.

   $x - 6y = -5$

   $4x + 6y = 10$

2. Jen has a bunch of nickels and dimes, worth \$1.85. She has 24 coins altogether. How many dimes does Jen have?

   A. 9 **B.** 11

   C. 13 **D.** 17

3. A company manufactures an exercise ball, which is shown below with its radius of 12 inches.

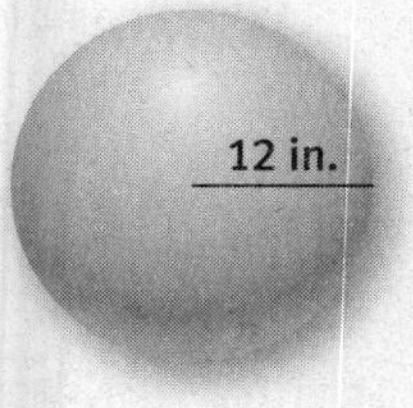

   a. Find the exact volume of the exercise ball, and the volume to the nearest cubic inch.

   b. If the company wants to increase the volume by 15%, by how much should the company increase the radius?

4. The point $(-5, 3)$ is reflected over the y-axis. What is the y-coordinate of the image point?

   A. -5 **B.** -3

   C. 3 **D.** 5

5. Find the value of b so that the system below has no solution.

   $x - by = 2$

   $2x + 3y = 3$

6. Mandy plays on the basketball team. Free throws are worth 1 point, field goals are worth 2 points, and 3-pointers are worth 3 points. Last season, she scored 164 points. She made 14 fewer 3-pointers than free throws, and 3 times as many field goals as 3-pointers.

   a. Define variables and write a system of equations to represent this situation.

   b. Determine how many of each type of basket that Mandy made last season.

7. The figure below is translated 4 units left, and then rotated 180° about the origin. What are the coordinates of A', the image of point A?

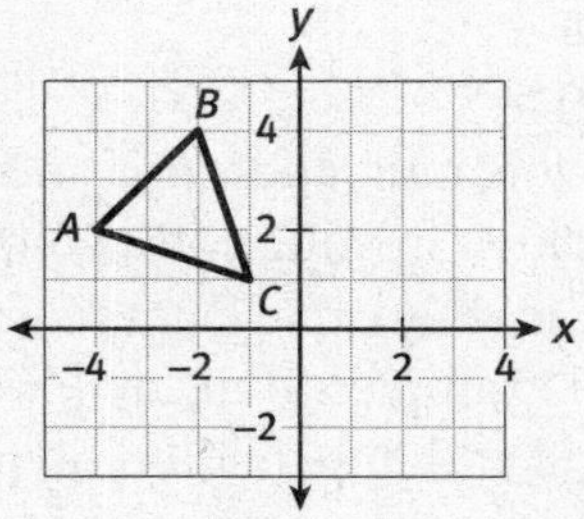

8. A racquetball has a diameter of 57 mm. A company sells two racquetballs in plastic cylindrical containers. If the two balls fit snugly inside the container, what is the volume of the container?

9. Solve the system:

   $2x - y + z = -1$

   $x + y + z = -1$

   $x - 3y - 2z = 7$

Matrix Operations

How Much Wood Would You Need?

Lesson 34-1 Representing Data with Matrices

Learning Targets:

- Use matrices to represent numeric data.
- Add and subtract matrices.
- Define and use scalar multiplication.

SUGGESTED LEARNING STRATEGIES: Marking the Text, Graphic Organizer, Vocabulary Organizer, Create Representations

Monique and Shondra have created their own after-school business making designer cutting boards, as shown at the right. They purchase different varieties of hardwood strips from a craft supply store and use them to construct the cutting boards.

Style I uses four strips of walnut, three strips of maple, and two strips of cherry. Style II uses five strips of maple and four strips of cherry. Style III uses eight strips of walnut and five strips of maple.

1. Complete the table below, using the information about the number of strips of wood needed to construct each style of cutting board.

Number of Hardwood Strips

	Walnut	Maple	Cherry
Style I			
Style II			
Style III			

A ***matrix*** (plural: matrices) is a rectangular arrangement of numbers written inside brackets. The numbers in a matrix are organized in rows and columns. They are called the ***elements***, or ***entries***, of the matrix.

2. Make use of structure. Complete matrix S below, using the information in the table.

$$S = \begin{array}{r} \text{Style I} \\ \text{Style II} \\ \text{Style III} \end{array} \begin{array}{c} \begin{array}{ccc} \text{Walnut} & \text{Maple} & \text{Cherry} \end{array} \\ \begin{bmatrix} \_\_\_\_ & \_\_\_\_ & \_\_\_\_ \\ \_\_\_\_ & \_\_\_\_ & \_\_\_\_ \\ \_\_\_\_ & \_\_\_\_ & \_\_\_\_ \end{bmatrix} \end{array}$$

The ***dimension*** of a matrix, also called the ***order*** of a matrix, gives the number of rows and columns. A matrix A with m rows and n columns is an $m \times n$ matrix with a dimension of $m \times n$ (read: m by n). You can represent matrix A as $A_{m \times n}$. Similarly, a_{mn} represents the element that is in row m, column n of A.

3. What is the dimension of matrix S in Item 2?

4. What is the value of element s_{31}?

My Notes

Style I

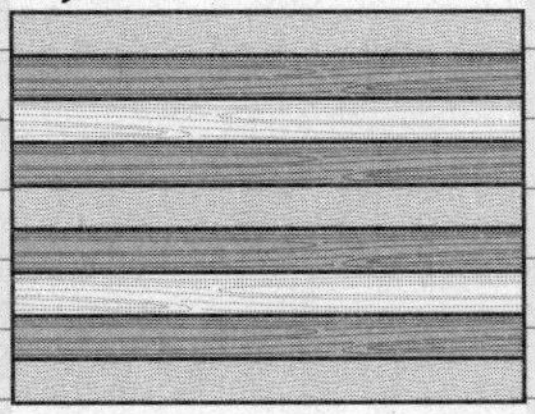

Style II

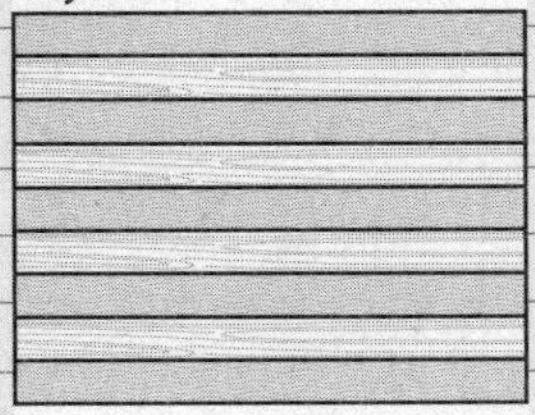

Style III

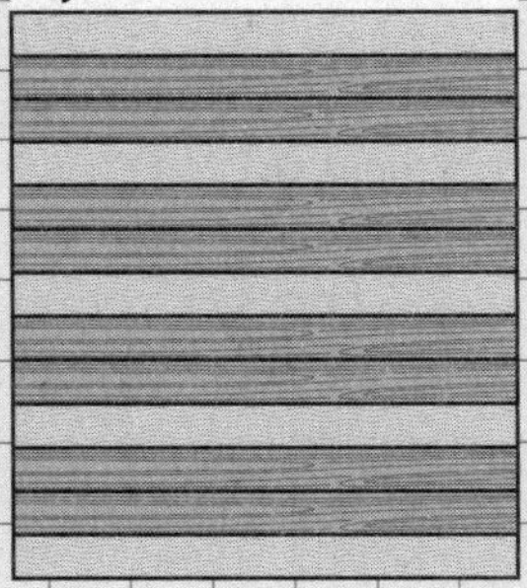

WRITING MATH

You can identify a matrix entry by its position in the matrix. The *notation* is a two-digit subscript that represents the entry's row and column number. For example, the notation e_{23} indicates the entry in the second row and third column.

My Notes

MATH TIP

Matrix row and column sums can be used to analyze data. For matrix *D*, the column sums give the total number of each style of cutting board for the December contracts. The row sums give the number of boards for each person for December.

Properties of matrices used in a contextual situation are described using row-by-column information. Matrix *S* refers to a style-by-wood matrix. The numbers of strips for each style of board are recorded in the rows, and the numbers of strips for each variety of wood are recorded in the columns.

5. In November, Monique had a contract for six cutting boards in Style I, five in Style II, and three in Style III. Shondra had a contract for four cutting boards in Style I, five in Style II, and four in Style III. Write matrix *N*, a person-by-style matrix, that gives the number of each style of cutting board in the contract for each person in November. Give the dimension of matrix *N*.

The matrix below gives the number of cutting boards in the December contract for each person.

$$D = \begin{array}{c} \\ \text{Monique} \\ \text{Shondra} \end{array} \begin{array}{c} \begin{array}{ccc} \text{Style I} & \text{Style II} & \text{Style III} \end{array} \\ \begin{bmatrix} 5 & 3 & 4 \\ 4 & 4 & 2 \end{bmatrix} \end{array}$$

6. Shondra wants to know the total number of cutting boards in the contracts for both November and December.

a. Write a matrix *T* that represents the number of cutting boards in each style for both months for each person.

b. How does your matrix *T* compare to the individual matrices for November and for December? Describe the relationship in terms of an operation on those matrices. Write your answer in the My Notes space.

My Notes

7. If possible, find the sum or difference of the following matrices. If not possible, explain why.

a. $\begin{bmatrix} 10 & 5 \\ 0 & 1 \end{bmatrix} + \begin{bmatrix} 6 & 7 \\ -8 & 3 \end{bmatrix}$

b. $\begin{bmatrix} 4 & 8 & -2 \\ 6 & 7 & 4 \end{bmatrix} + \begin{bmatrix} 6 & 12 \\ 4 & 8 \end{bmatrix}$

c. $\begin{bmatrix} 8 & -6 \\ 3 & 6 \\ 9 & 10 \end{bmatrix} - \begin{bmatrix} -4 & 7 \\ 5 & 6 \\ 4 & -3 \end{bmatrix}$

8. What must be true about the number of rows and columns of two matrices in order to be able to add or subtract the matrices?

9. Suppose that A is any $m \times n$ matrix.

a. The ***identity matrix for addition*** is a matrix O such that $A + O = A$ and $O + A = A$. What is the dimension and what are the elements of matrix O?

b. The ***additive inverse*** for matrix A is the matrix $-A$ such that $A + (-A) = O$. Describe $-A$.

DISCUSSION GROUP TIP

As needed, refer to the Glossary to review translations of key terms. Incorporate your understanding into group discussions to confirm your knowledge and use of key mathematical language.

A ***scalar product*** is the product of a real number and a matrix. The real number is called a ***scalar***. In ***scalar multiplication***, each element in the matrix is multiplied by the scalar.

10. Use the elements of matrix S from Item 2 to find the scalar product $4S$. Tell what the product represents in the contextual situation.

My Notes

11. Monique and Shondra want to know how much wood they need to purchase to meet their contracts.

a. How many strips of walnut wood does Monique need to buy to fill her contract for cutting boards for December?

b. How many strips of cherry wood does Shondra need to buy to fill her contract for cutting boards for December?

c. What operations did you use to find your answers to Parts a and b?

Check Your Understanding

12. Matrix W has dimension 4×2. Write the matrix that represents the sum of W and its additive inverse.

13. Look for and make use of structure. For matrix S from Item 2, could the rows have represented the styles and the columns the hardwoods? Explain your reasoning.

LESSON 34-1 PRACTICE

14. Find each sum or difference. State if the operation is not possible.

a. $\begin{bmatrix} 4 & -8 \\ -2 & 7 \end{bmatrix} - \begin{bmatrix} 3 & -7 \\ 5 & 7 \end{bmatrix}$

b. $\begin{bmatrix} 8 & -1 & 0 \\ 9 & 12 & 3 \end{bmatrix} + \begin{bmatrix} -5 & 8 & 3 \\ 6 & 1 & 4 \end{bmatrix}$

c. $\begin{bmatrix} -4 & 9 \\ 2 & 7 \end{bmatrix} - \begin{bmatrix} 1 & -3 & 4 \\ 6 & 2 & 8 \end{bmatrix}$

d. $\begin{bmatrix} 2 \\ -1 \\ 3 \end{bmatrix} + \begin{bmatrix} 0 \\ 19 \\ -4 \end{bmatrix}$

15. How can you use a scalar to represent the additive inverse of a matrix?

16. Model with mathematics. The matrix C represents the cost in dollars of items at a theater.

	S	M	L
Popcorn	1	2.5	4
Ice Cream	1.5	3	4.5
Drink	2	3	3.5

a. Write a sentence to describe what the element c_{32} represents.

b. Use matrix addition to represent a price increase of $0.50 per item. Show your matrices.

c. Use scalar multiplication to represent a price increase of 10 percent per item.

My Notes

Learning Targets:

- Determine if two matrices can be multiplied.
- Find the matrix product of two matrices.
- Explore properties of matrix operations.

SUGGESTED LEARNING STRATEGIES: Vocabulary Organizer, Marking the Text, Look for a Pattern, Close Reading, Think-Pair-Share, Quickwrite

Matrix multiplication uses the arithmetic operations of both multiplication and addition.

1. The product of matrices *D* and *S* gives the number of strips of each variety of hardwood that each person needs to purchase for the month of December. The product of matrix *D*, a person-by-style matrix, and matrix *S*, a style-by-wood matrix, gives $D \cdot S$, a person-by-wood matrix. The computation for the first element in the product is shown below. Use this as an example to complete the remaining elements in the matrices.

$$D \cdot S = \begin{array}{c} \\ \text{Monique} \\ \text{Shondra} \end{array} \begin{array}{c} \begin{array}{ccc} \text{Style I} & \text{Style II} & \text{Style III} \end{array} \\ \begin{bmatrix} 5 & 3 & 4 \\ 4 & 4 & 2 \end{bmatrix} \end{array} \cdot \begin{array}{c} \\ \text{Style I} \\ \text{Style II} \\ \text{Style III} \end{array} \begin{array}{c} \begin{array}{ccc} \text{Walnut} & \text{Maple} & \text{Cherry} \end{array} \\ \begin{bmatrix} 4 & 3 & 2 \\ 0 & 5 & 4 \\ 8 & 5 & 0 \end{bmatrix} \end{array}$$

$$= \begin{array}{c} \\ \text{Monique} \\ \text{Shondra} \end{array} \begin{array}{c} \begin{array}{ccc} \text{Walnut} & \text{Maple} & \text{Cherry} \end{array} \\ \begin{bmatrix} 5(4)+3(0)+4(8) & \underline{\qquad\qquad} & \underline{\qquad\qquad} \\ \underline{\qquad\qquad} & \underline{\qquad\qquad} & 4(2)+4(4)+2(0) \end{bmatrix} \end{array}$$

$$= \begin{array}{c} \\ \text{Monique} \\ \text{Shondra} \end{array} \begin{array}{c} \begin{array}{ccc} \text{Walnut} & \text{Maple} & \text{Cherry} \end{array} \\ \begin{bmatrix} 52 & \underline{\qquad} & \underline{\qquad} \\ \underline{\qquad} & \underline{\qquad} & 24 \end{bmatrix} \end{array}$$

Each entry of matrix $D \cdot S$ is calculated by using entries in matrices *D* and *S*. To find the entry in row *i* and column *j*, multiply the corresponding entries from row *i* in matrix *D* and column *j* in matrix *S*. Then add the three products. The following visual may be helpful in understanding the process.

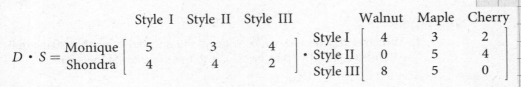

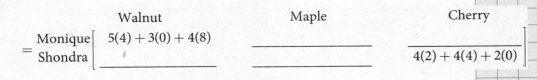

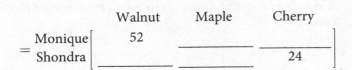

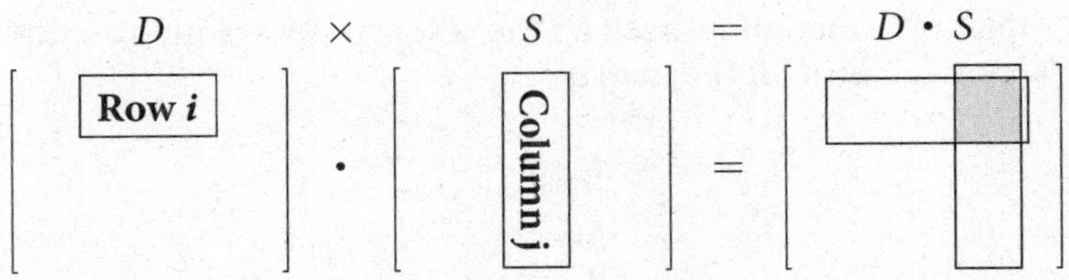

My Notes

2. Information from matrices D and S was used to create matrix $D \cdot S$.

a. Which row in matrix D was used to calculate the number of maple strips that Monique needed to purchase?

b. Which column in matrix S was used to calculate the number of maple strips that Monique needed to purchase?

c. Which entry in matrix $D \cdot S$ shows the number of maple strips that Monique needed to purchase? Write the *notation* of the entry.

d. Which row in matrix D was used to calculate the number of walnut strips that Shondra needed to purchase?

e. Which column in matrix S was used to calculate the number of walnut strips that Shondra needed to purchase?

f. Which entry in matrix $D \cdot S$ shows the number of walnut strips that Shondra needed to purchase? Write the *notation* of the entry.

3. Answer using the contextual situation represented by the matrices.

a. Describe matrix $D \cdot S$, using a row-by-column name.

b. Construct viable arguments. What category of information that was common to matrices D and S is missing from matrix $D \cdot S$? Why is it missing?

c. What information is given by the entry in the first row and the third column of matrix $D \cdot S$?

d. What information is given by the entry in the second row and the second column of the matrix?

My Notes

In the previous examples, D was a 2×3 matrix and S was a 3×3 matrix. Their product $D \cdot S$ was a 2×3 matrix.

4. **Express regularity in repeated reasoning.** Consider the process used to multiply the matrices. Make a conjecture concerning what must be true about the dimensions of two matrices for their product to be defined. In other words, what must be true about the number of rows and columns in the two matrices in order to be able to multiply the matrices?

5. Suppose R is a 3×2 matrix, S is a 2×4 matrix, and T is a 4×3 matrix. Use the notation $R_{3\times2}$, $S_{2\times4}$, and $T_{4\times3}$ to list all possible products that are defined for matrices R, S, and T, where the dimensions of the matrices are the only restriction on the multiplication. Give the dimension of the resulting matrix.

6. **Reason abstractly.** If L is an $m \times n$ matrix and matrix T is an $n \times p$ matrix, what are the dimensions of the matrix $L \cdot T$?

Check Your Understanding

7. Find each product. State if it is not possible.

   a. $\begin{bmatrix} 4 & -1 \\ -2 & 6 \end{bmatrix} \cdot \begin{bmatrix} 3 & -2 \\ 5 & 1 \end{bmatrix}$

   b. $\begin{bmatrix} 4 & -1 & 0 \\ 9 & 2 & 3 \end{bmatrix} \cdot \begin{bmatrix} -3 & 8 & 3 \\ 1 & 4 & 2 \end{bmatrix}$

   c. $\begin{bmatrix} -4 & 1 \\ 2 & 7 \end{bmatrix} \cdot \begin{bmatrix} 1 & -3 & 4 \\ 6 & 2 & 0 \end{bmatrix}$

8. If H is an $m \times n$ matrix and G is a $p \times q$ matrix, what restrictions must be placed on the numbers m, n, p, and q for the matrix $H \cdot G$ to be defined?

My Notes

There are many properties that hold true for real numbers. Some of these same properties also hold true for matrices.

9. Use these matrices.

$$A = \begin{bmatrix} 4 & 2 \\ 5 & -2 \end{bmatrix} \qquad B = \begin{bmatrix} 5 & 6 \\ 2 & 4 \end{bmatrix}$$

a. Find $A + B$ and $B + A$.

b. Find AB and BA.

10. For any two real numbers a and b, it is true that $a + b = b + a$ and $ab = ba$.

a. What property do these statements demonstrate?

b. Does this property hold true for matrix addition and matrix multiplication? Explain.

11. Use these matrices.

$$B = \begin{bmatrix} 5 & 6 \\ 2 & 4 \end{bmatrix} \qquad C = \begin{bmatrix} 1 & 0 \\ 0 & 1 \end{bmatrix} \qquad D = \begin{bmatrix} 5 & 0 & -2 \\ 4 & 1 & 3 \\ 2 & 2 & 1 \end{bmatrix} \qquad E = \begin{bmatrix} 1 & 0 & 0 \\ 0 & 1 & 0 \\ 0 & 0 & 1 \end{bmatrix}$$

a. Find BC and CB.

b. Find DE and ED.

c. For a square matrix, describe what the **multiplicative identity matrix** I appears to be.

MATH TIP

Recall the following properties for real numbers a, b, and c.

Addition Properties

Commutative
$a + b = b + a$

Associative
$(a + b) + c = a + (b + c)$

Identity
$a + 0 = a, 0 + a = a$

Inverse
$a + (-a) = 0$

Multiplication Properties

Commutative
$ab = ba$

Associative
$(ab)c = a(bc)$

Identity
$a \cdot 1 = a, 1 \cdot a = a$

Inverse
$a \cdot \frac{1}{a} = 1, a \neq 0$

Distributive Properties

$a(b + c) = ab + ac$
$(a + b)c = ac + bc$

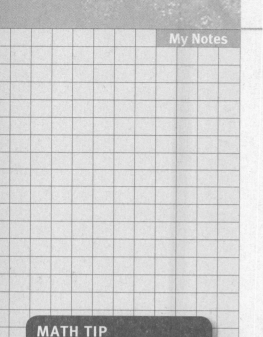

My Notes

Check Your Understanding

12. Let A and B be two matrices with $A + B = \begin{bmatrix} 2 & 9 \\ 3 & 5 \end{bmatrix}$. If possible, determine the value of $B + A$. If not possible, explain why.

13. Let A and B be two matrices with $A \cdot B = \begin{bmatrix} -3 & 9 \\ 9 & 15 \end{bmatrix}$. If possible, determine the value of $B \cdot A$. If not possible, explain why.

14. Reason quantitatively. Use three 2×2 matrices A, B, and C, to show that $A(B + C) = AB + BC$. Name the property used.

LESSON 34-2 PRACTICE

For Items 15–22, use matrices A, B, C, and D below. Evaluate each expression or explain why it is not possible.

$$A = \begin{bmatrix} 2 & -3 \\ 4 & 1 \end{bmatrix} \qquad B = \begin{bmatrix} 5 & 3 \\ -2 & 6 \end{bmatrix}$$

$$C = \begin{bmatrix} 1 & 0 & 3 \\ 2 & 4 & -2 \end{bmatrix} \qquad D = \begin{bmatrix} -4 & 1 \\ 0 & 2 \\ 2 & 3 \end{bmatrix}$$

15. $A + B$

16. $B - A$

17. $A + C$

18. $3C$

19. $A \cdot B$

20. $A \cdot C$

21. $C \cdot D$

22. $C \cdot B$

23. Model with mathematics. Matrix A gives the number of cutting boards that Monique and Shondra contracted to make in August. Matrix B gives the number of wood strips needed to make each style.

$A =$

	Style I	Style II	Style III
Monique	10	6	8
Shondra	8	8	4

$B =$

	Walnut	Maple	Cherry
Style I	4	3	2
Style II	0	5	4
Style III	8	5	0

Walnut costs \$1.50 per strip, maple costs \$0.85 per strip, and cherry costs \$1.10 per strip. Write matrix C to represent these costs. Use matrices A, B, and C and matrix multiplication to find the total cost of Monique's wood and of Shondra's wood. Show the matrix product you used. Then describe your solution method.

24. Decide whether matrix addition and multiplication are associative. Justify your answers.

My Notes

Learning Targets:

- Determine if a matrix has an inverse.
- Find the determinant and inverse of a matrix.
- Justify properties of matrix operations.

SUGGESTED LEARNING STRATEGIES: Quickwrite, Marking the Text, Create Representations, Vocabulary Organizer, Summarizing, Paraphrasing

Each square matrix is associated with a real number called the ***determinant***.

For a 2×2 matrix $\begin{bmatrix} a & b \\ c & d \end{bmatrix}$, the determinant is written $\begin{vmatrix} a & b \\ c & d \end{vmatrix}$ or det $|A|$. Its value is $ad - bc$.

WRITING MATH

You can write two different symbols for the determinant:

$\begin{vmatrix} a & b \\ c & d \end{vmatrix} = \det A$

Do not confuse the straight line segments used for the determinant with absolute value signs. For the absolute value of a determinant, you can write $|\det A|$.

1. Use the definition to find the determinant of $\begin{bmatrix} 4 & -2 \\ 5 & -2 \end{bmatrix}$.

Every square matrix A has a ***multiplicative inverse*** A^{-1}, except when $\det A = 0$.

For the matrix $A = \begin{bmatrix} a & b \\ c & d \end{bmatrix}$, if $\det A \neq 0$,

$$\text{then } A^{-1} = \frac{1}{\det A}\begin{bmatrix} d & -b \\ -c & a \end{bmatrix} = \frac{1}{ad - bc}\begin{bmatrix} d & -b \\ -c & a \end{bmatrix}.$$

2. For $A = \begin{bmatrix} 4 & -2 \\ 5 & -2 \end{bmatrix}$, use the definition above to find A^{-1}.

MATH TIP

In the set of real numbers, every real number has an additive inverse $-a$ and every real number except 0 has a multiplicative inverse $\frac{1}{a}$.

3. Find $A \cdot A^{-1}$ and $A^{-1} \cdot A$. Explain why these products verify that the matrices are inverses.

4. Use the definition of A^{-1} to show that the inverse matrix does not exist when $\det A = 0$.

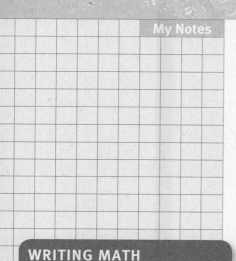

My Notes

5. Explain in words how to find the inverse of a 2 × 2 matrix.

Techniques to calculate determinants and inverses of larger square matrices by hand can be tedious. You can use a graphing calculator to find these determinants and matrices.

Let $B = \begin{bmatrix} 1 & -3 & -2 \\ 0 & 3 & 1 \\ 1 & 5 & 1 \end{bmatrix}$.

6. Show that $B^{-1} = \begin{bmatrix} -2 & -7 & 3 \\ 1 & 3 & -1 \\ -3 & -8 & 3 \end{bmatrix}$ by using matrix multiplication.

7. Use appropriate tools strategically. Enter the values for matrix B into your graphing calculator. You may first need to enter the dimension of the matrix.

a. Verify that the inverse of B is as shown in Item 6.

b. Determine det B.

8. Construct viable arguments. Suppose a 2 × 2 matrix has integer elements and its inverse exists. Use the definition of the inverse of a 2 × 2 matrix to determine when the inverse will also have integer values. Explain your reasoning.

My Notes

9. Do you think your conclusion in Item 8 applies to any square matrix with integer elements and an inverse? Use results from previous items to justify your answer.

Check Your Understanding

10. Find the determinant and inverse of each matrix, if possible. If not possible, explain why. Show your work.

a. $A = \begin{bmatrix} -2 & 3 \\ -5 & 8 \end{bmatrix}$ **b.** $B = \begin{bmatrix} 8 & 6 \\ 4 & 2 \end{bmatrix}$

11. Critique the reasoning of others. Amanda says that $\begin{vmatrix} 4 & 1 \\ -5 & 10 \end{vmatrix}$ represents a matrix with dimension 2×2. What mistake is Amanda making?

12. Square matrices with nonzero determinants have an inverse. What is a square matrix?

LESSON 34-3 PRACTICE

13. Find the determinant and inverse of each matrix. Use a graphing calculator for the 3×3 matrices.

a. $A = \begin{bmatrix} \frac{1}{2} & 5 \\ 3 & -12 \end{bmatrix}$ **b.** $B = \begin{bmatrix} 5.5 & -0.5 \\ 2 & 3 \end{bmatrix}$

c. $C = \begin{bmatrix} 8 & 4 & -3 \\ 2 & 0 & 0 \\ 3 & -2 & 1 \end{bmatrix}$ **d.** $D = \begin{bmatrix} 5 & 2 & -3 \\ 16 & 1 & -8 \\ 2 & 0 & -1 \end{bmatrix}$

14. Make sense of problems. Determine the value(s) of x so that the matrix $\begin{bmatrix} 3x & 2x-3 \\ -2 & x+1 \end{bmatrix}$ has an inverse.

15. The 2×2 matrix T has a determinant of 22. Matrix V is equal to matrix T times the scalar m. Write an expression for det V. Explain your reasoning or show your work.

16. Mario says that if the 2×2 matrix A has an inverse B, then $A + B = 0$.

a. Describe Mario's error. Write an equation that relates A and B.

b. Rewrite the equation that Mario wrote, replacing B with the matrix that makes the equation true.

ACTIVITY 34 PRACTICE

Write your answers on notebook paper. Show your work.

Lesson 34-1

1. The dimension of matrix A is 3×2. If the matrix sum $A + B$ exists, what could be the dimension of matrix B?

   I. 2×3 **II.** 3×2 **III.** 2×5

   A. I only
   B. I and II
   C. I, II, and II
   D. II only

2. Solve for x and y.

$$\begin{bmatrix} 9 & 3-x \\ -2y & -1 \end{bmatrix} + \begin{bmatrix} 2 & 2 \\ -3 & 1 \end{bmatrix} = \begin{bmatrix} 0 & 24 \\ 11 & 7 \end{bmatrix}$$

3. Matrix A is shown below.

$$A = \begin{bmatrix} 2 & -1 & 5 \\ 9 & 0 & 8 \\ 3 & -2 & 7 \\ 4 & -3 & 9 \end{bmatrix}$$

   a. What is the value of a_{42}?
   b. Which two elements of the matrix have the same value?
   c. Calculate $a_{13} + a_{23}$.
   d. Write the matrix $-2A$ without the scalar.

4. Add: $\begin{bmatrix} 7 & 0 \\ -3 & 2 \end{bmatrix} + \begin{bmatrix} -3 & 4 \\ 11 & -3 \end{bmatrix}$

5. Subtract: $\begin{bmatrix} 54 & 98 \\ 70 & 80 \\ 56 & 77 \end{bmatrix} - \begin{bmatrix} 44 & 69 \\ 77 & 91 \\ 55 & 70 \end{bmatrix}$

6. Determine when two matrices can be added. Give your answer in terms of the dimension and explain whether the order in which the matrices are added matter.

7. Amy, Elaine, and Hector all work part time at Samantha's Beauty. The shop is open Wednesday through Saturday. The table shows their hours for the week.

	Amy	Elaine	Hector
Wed	4	0	6
Thu	5	6	0
Fri	3	4	3
Sat	6	5	4

   a. Organize the information into a 4×3 matrix. What do the elements of the third column represent?
   b. Next week, Samantha asks everyone to work the same hours. Write a matrix sum to represent how many hours each person works over the two-week period.
   c. Suppose everyone works the same hours for the summer, or 13 weeks. Use a scalar to write a matrix that represents how many hours each person works over the summer.

Lesson 34-2

8. Use the matrix for Item 7. Suppose Amy earns \$11 per hour, and Elaine and Hector each earn \$9 per hour. Write a matrix product that shows how much Samantha must pay out to her employees each day of the week.

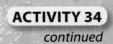

9. Multiply each pair of matrices. If the product does not exist, explain why.

a. $\begin{bmatrix} 2 & 3 \\ 1 & -7 \end{bmatrix}$ and $\begin{bmatrix} 2 & 3 \\ 2 & -4 \end{bmatrix}$

b. $\begin{bmatrix} 8 & 0 & 4 \\ 1 & 0 & 8 \\ 3 & -3 & -6 \end{bmatrix}$ and $\begin{bmatrix} 3 & -2 \\ 4 & 0 \\ -1 & 5 \end{bmatrix}$

c. $\begin{bmatrix} 3.2 \\ 2.5 \\ 1.6 \end{bmatrix}$ and $\begin{bmatrix} 5 & 5 & 5 \end{bmatrix}$

10. Determine when two matrices can be multiplied, in terms of the dimension of each matrix. Does the order in which the matrices are multiplied matter? Explain.

11. Find the values of *x* and *y*.

$$\begin{bmatrix} x & -2 \\ y & 3 \end{bmatrix}\begin{bmatrix} 2 \\ 5 \end{bmatrix} = \begin{bmatrix} 10 \\ 1 \end{bmatrix}$$

12. The dimension of matrix *A* is 3×6. If the matrix product *AB* exists, what could be the dimension of matrix *B*?

I. 6×3 **II.** 3×6 **III.** 6×5

A. I only
B. I and III
C. I, II, and II
D. II only

Lesson 34-3

13. The 2×2 matrix *D* does not have an inverse. What is the value of det *D*?

14. Find the inverse of each matrix, if it exists.

a. $\begin{bmatrix} 2 & -3 \\ 1\frac{1}{2} & -1 \end{bmatrix}$

b. $\begin{bmatrix} 4 & 6 \\ -2 & 3 \end{bmatrix}$

c. $\begin{bmatrix} 9 & -4.5 \\ -2 & 1 \end{bmatrix}$

15. Use a graphing calculator to find the inverse of the matrix.

$$A = \begin{bmatrix} 0 & 1 & 0 \\ -1 & -4 & -2 \\ 1 & 4 & 1 \end{bmatrix}$$

16. The rows of the 2×2 matrix *B* are identical (they have the same elements in the same positions). Prove algebraically that *B* does not have an inverse.

17. Find the value(s) of *x* so that the matrix has a determinant of 8.

$$\begin{bmatrix} x+1 & -3 \\ 2 & x \end{bmatrix}$$

MATHEMATICAL PRACTICES
Model with Mathematics

18. Describe a way that you could use a matrix to store your own personal data. It may be from a hobby you have or a sport that you play. How might you use matrix operations to transform the data?

Matrices and Transformations

Sizing Up Real Estate

Lesson 35-1 Translations and Reflections

My Notes

Learning Targets:

- Use matrices as vectors to translate figures in the plane.
- Use matrices as vectors to reflect figures in the plane.

SUGGESTED LEARNING STRATEGIES: Critique Reasoning, Paraphrasing, Quickwrite, Predict and Confirm

A development company is selling a triangular plot of land. The size and location of the plot are represented in the graph.

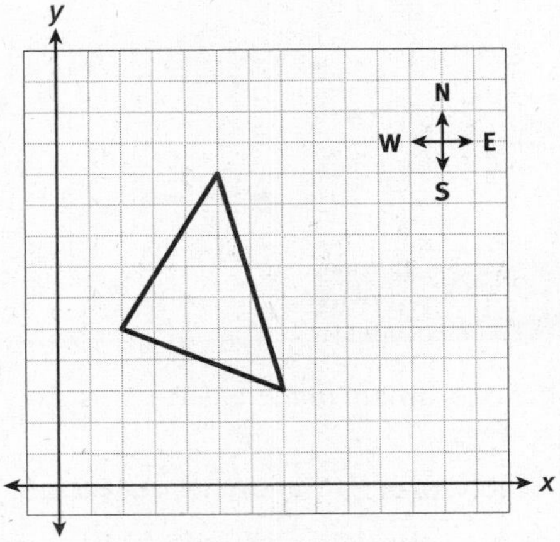

1. Use vectors in standard position to represent each vertex of the plot. Write each vector as a ***column matrix***.

MATH TERMS

A **column matrix** is matrix that has dimension $m \times 1$. Similarly, a **row matrix** has dimension $1 \times n$.

2. Write one matrix to represent the vectors from Item 1. What is the dimension of the matrix?

3. Each square unit of the grid represents 10,000 square feet. The developer's assistant notices that the plot should actually be plotted 200 feet east and 100 feet north of where it is.

a. Attend to precision. Determine the correct vertices for the plot and graph the plot on the grid above. Explain your reasoning.

b. Write a new matrix C to represent the correct vectors.

My Notes

c. **Make use of structure.** Write the matrix C as a sum of the matrix from Item 2 and another matrix.

4. Explain how a matrix can represent a figure in the coordinate plane, and how matrix addition can be used to translate the figure m units horizontally and n units vertically.

Check Your Understanding

5. A rectangle in the coordinate plane has vertices $A(1, 3)$, $B(1, 7)$, $C(6, 7)$, and $D(6, 3)$.

a. Write a matrix to represent the vertices of rectangle $ABCD$.

b. Write a matrix T to translate rectangle $ABCD$ down 3.5 units and left 2.5 units. Then write and simplify the matrix sum to represent the new position of the rectangle in the plane.

c. How would the matrix $-T$ translate the original rectangle? Explain your reasoning.

The city is interested in purchasing the plot to create a garden. However, the mayor would like a symmetrical arrangement of four gardens with the same shape, centered about the intersection of Main Street and Bay Road.

6. In the graph on the previous page, the x-axis represents Main Street and the y-axis represents Bay Road.

a. **Reason abstractly.** For the plot you graphed in Item 3a, determine vertices for a new plot such that each vertex is the same distance from Main Street.

b. What is the relationship between the coordinates of the new plot and those of the original plot?

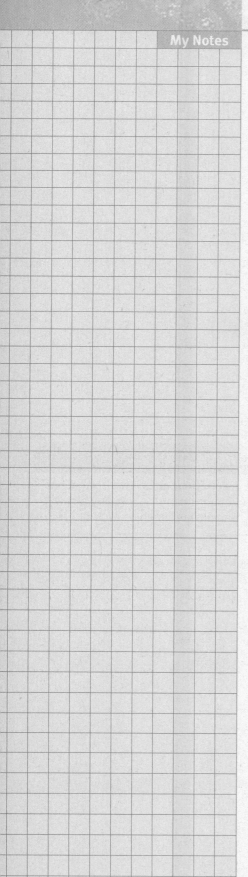

My Notes

7. The matrix $R_x = \begin{bmatrix} 1 & 0 \\ 0 & -1 \end{bmatrix}$ is called a reflection matrix.

a. Find the matrix product R_xC, where C is your matrix from Item 3b.

b. Use transformations in the coordinate plane to describe the effect that matrix R_x plays in terms of transformations in the coordinate plane. Justify your answer.

8. Critique the reasoning of others. Theo says that he does not need to multiply by the reflection matrix R_x. Instead, the elements in the second row of matrix C can be multiplied by the scalar -1. Explain the error in Theo's reasoning.

9. Write the reflection matrix R_y and explain its effect.

10. Use the matrices R_y and C to write a matrix that represents the vertices for a new plot such that each vertex is the same distance from Bay Road.

11. Find the matrix products R_xR_x and R_yR_y. Relate the results to applying these reflections twice to the same figure.

READING MATH

Repeated multiplication of the same matrix can be represented with an exponent.

$$R_xR_x = R_x^2$$

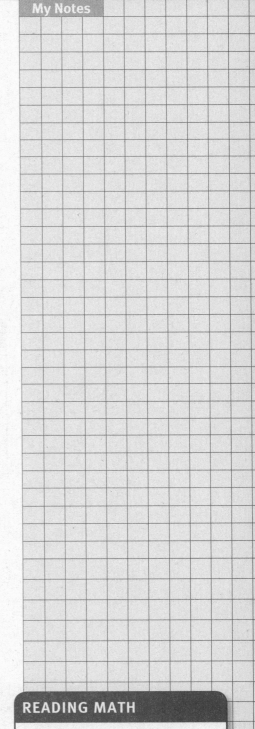

My Notes

12. The fourth and final garden should appear in Quadrant III of the graph.
   a. Find the matrix product $R_O = R_xR_y$. How could the result be used to write the matrix that represents the coordinates of the final garden? Explain.

   b. **Make use of structure.** Explain in terms of a reflection why, in the notation R_O, the O stands for "origin."

Check Your Understanding

13. When reflecting a figure over the x-axis and the y-axis, does the order matter? Use matrix multiplication to justify your response.
14. **Reason abstractly.** Suppose you wanted to reflect a regular hexagon, with vertices represented by matrix H, over the y-axis. What is the dimension of H? How does the dimension relate to the product R_yH?

LESSON 35-1 PRACTICE

15. A parallelogram in the coordinate plane has vertices $F(4, -3)$, $G(2, -3)$, $H(0, 1)$, and $J(2, 1)$.
   a. Write and simplify a matrix sum to represent a translation of the figure 1 unit down and 4 units right.
   b. Write and simplify a matrix product to represent a reflection over the x-axis of the translation in Part a.
16. The notation $R_x^{\ 3}$ represents the matrix product $R_x \cdot (R_x \cdot R_x)$. Calculate $R_x^{\ 3}$, and then make a conjecture about $R_x^{\ n}$, where n is a positive integer. Justify your conjecture in terms of reflections.
17. **Construct viable arguments.** Suppose a matrix uses the first column for the x-coordinates of each vertex of a figure and the second column for the y-coordinates. Must the rotation matrices be used differently than in Item 8a? Use an example to support your answer.

My Notes

Learning Targets:

- Use matrices as vectors to rotate figures in the plane.
- Use matrices as vectors to dilate figures in the plane.

SUGGESTED LEARNING STRATEGIES: Debriefing, Paraphrasing, Create a Plan, Construct an Argument, Visualization

The mayor organizes a team to help with the planning of the new city gardens. An arrangement of six triangular flower beds will be placed symmetrically around a fountain. Aimee draws the sketch below, which shows the location of one flower bed. With the fountain located at the origin, she will rotate this triangle to locate the other triangles.

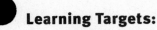

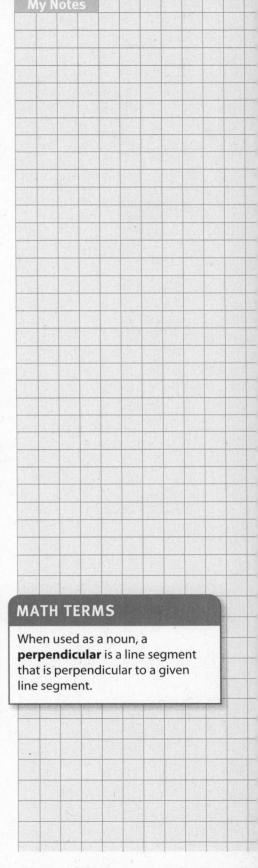

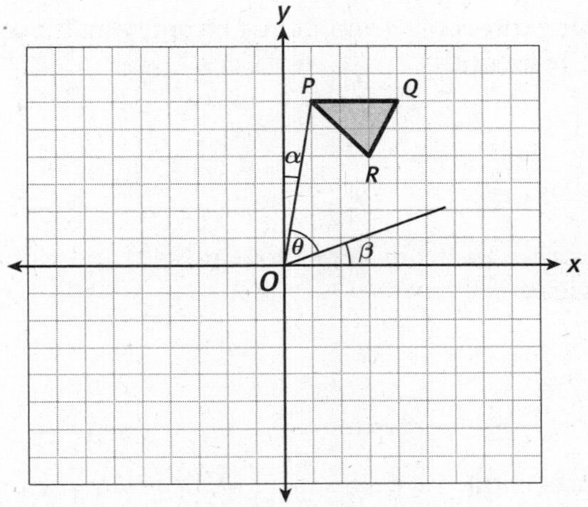

1. Aimee wants to find the coordinates of $P' = (x', y')$ after a clockwise rotation of θ degrees of $P = (x, y)$.

a. What will be the value of θ? Explain.

b. Label the distance OP as r. What is the distance OP'?

2. Draw perpendiculars from P and from P' to the x-axis, forming two right triangles.

a. What is the angle measure at point P? How do you know?

b. What is the measure of $\alpha + \beta + \theta$? Use this fact to write the angle measure at point P' in terms of $\alpha + \theta$. Explain your reasoning.

MATH TERMS

When used as a noun, a **perpendicular** is a line segment that is perpendicular to a given line segment.

My Notes

3. Use a triangle to write trigonometric expressions for x and y in terms of r and α.

4. Express regularity in repeated reasoning. Write trigonometric expressions for x' and y' in terms of r, α, and θ.

5. Rewrite your expressions from Item 4 by applying the appropriate sum trigonometric identity.

6. Use your expressions from Item 3 to express x' and y' in terms of x, y, and the angle θ.

7. Attend to precision. Let each square of the grid represent 9 square feet. Determine the value of r to the nearest hundredth. Show your work.

Check Your Understanding

8. The original triangle had a horizontal segment for a side containing P. Will this be true for the rotated triangle and point P'? Explain your response.

9. Show that triangle POP' is equilateral.

10. Suppose Aimee repeats this procedure for an obtuse angle that has twice the measure of θ. How can she use the location of P' to test whether or not the expressions from Item 6 will work for obtuse θ?

The rotation matrix R_θ can be used to rotate a point (x, y) in the coordinate plane clockwise θ degrees about the origin.

$$R_\theta = \begin{bmatrix} \cos\theta & \sin\theta \\ -\sin\theta & \cos\theta \end{bmatrix}$$

Example A

Find the coordinates of vertex P of triangle PQR after a clockwise rotation of 60° about the origin.

Step 1: Write P as a column matrix. $P = \begin{bmatrix} 1 \\ 6 \end{bmatrix}$

Step 2: Write the matrix product $R_\theta P$.

$$(x', y') = \begin{bmatrix} \cos 60^\circ & \sin 60^\circ \\ -\sin 60^\circ & \cos 60^\circ \end{bmatrix}\begin{bmatrix} 1 \\ 6 \end{bmatrix}$$

Step 3: Multiply.

$$(x', y') = \begin{bmatrix} \frac{1}{2} & \frac{\sqrt{3}}{2} \\ -\frac{\sqrt{3}}{2} & \frac{1}{2} \end{bmatrix}\begin{bmatrix} 1 \\ 6 \end{bmatrix} = \begin{bmatrix} \frac{1+6\sqrt{3}}{2} \\ \frac{6-\sqrt{3}}{2} \end{bmatrix}$$

Solution: To the nearest hundredth, $P' = (5.70, 2.13)$.

Try These A

a. Use the rotation matrix to find the points Q' and R'. Round to the nearest hundredth.

b. Sketch triangle $P'Q'R'$ on the coordinate plane above Item 1.

c. Write and simplify the rotation matrix R_θ for $\theta = 90^\circ$.

Check Your Understanding

11. Explain how the application of the rotation matrix is equivalent to the equations you wrote in Item 6.

12. Explain how Aimee needs to calculate only one rotation matrix to find the coordinates of all six triangular flower beds.

My Notes

Jackson drew the sketch below to represent part of a garden that will have lilac bushes. Each square represents 25 square feet.

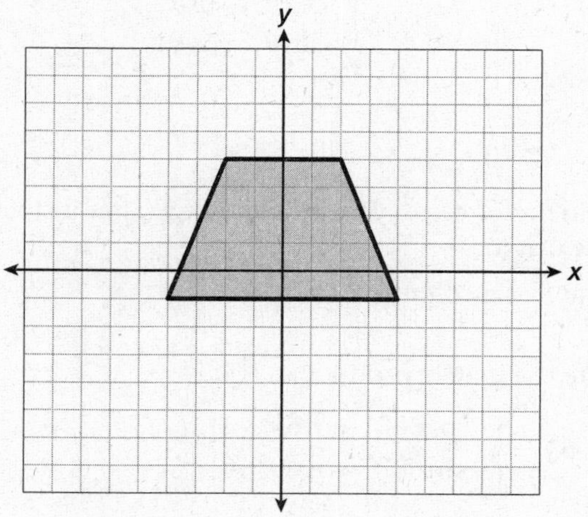

13. Write a matrix with dimension 2×4 to represent the vertices of the figure.

14. Multiply the matrix by the scalar 2. Plot the points represented by the new matrix on the coordinate plane above.

15. Multiply the matrix (from Item 13) by the scalar 0.5. Plot the points represented by the new matrix on the coordinate plane above.

16. Reason quantitatively. What is the relationship between the value of the scalar and the lengths of the sides of the figure?

My Notes

17. How would a negative scalar affect the figure? Test your hypothesis by multiplying by the scalar -2.

18. Suppose that instead of multiplying by the scalar 2 in Item 14, the matrix product $\begin{bmatrix} 2 & 0 \\ 0 & 2 \end{bmatrix}\begin{bmatrix} -2 & -4 & 4 & 2 \\ 4 & -1 & -1 & 4 \end{bmatrix}$ is used.

a. Is this equivalent to multiplying by the scalar 2?

b. Jackson is told to stretch the lilac area horizontally by doubling each base length of the trapezoid shape. Explain how he can do this.

19. A ***dilation*** of a figure in the coordinate plane results in an ***image*** that is similar to the original figure. Complete the following table.

Multiplier	Change in Figure	Is This a Dilation?
Scalar c, $0 < c < 1$		
Scalar c, $c > 1$		
Matrix $\begin{bmatrix} c & 0 \\ 0 & c \end{bmatrix}$ $c > 1$		
Matrix $\begin{bmatrix} 1 & 0 \\ 0 & c \end{bmatrix}$ $c > 1$		

ACADEMIC VOCABULARY

An ***image*** is the resultant figure after a transformation.

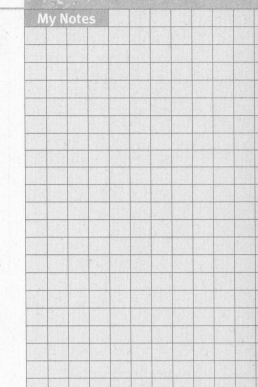

My Notes

Check Your Understanding

20. A scalar multiplies a matrix that represents the vertices of a figure in the plane. The new figure is congruent to the original figure. What is the value of the scalar?

21. The vertices of a square in the coordinate plane are represented by the matrix $\begin{bmatrix} 0 & 4 & 4 & 0 \\ 4 & 4 & 0 & 0 \end{bmatrix}$.

a. Write a matrix product that stretches the square horizontally by a factor of 2.

b. **Reason quantitatively.** Can you achieve the same result as Item 21a using a scalar?

c. Use a scalar to double the area of the square.

LESSON 35-2 PRACTICE

22. Refer to the figure above Item 1.

a. Use matrix rotations to graph the remaining five triangles for the city gardens.

b. Describe the "opposite" triangles in terms of a rotation. How can this help to determine the coordinates of a triangle's vertices?

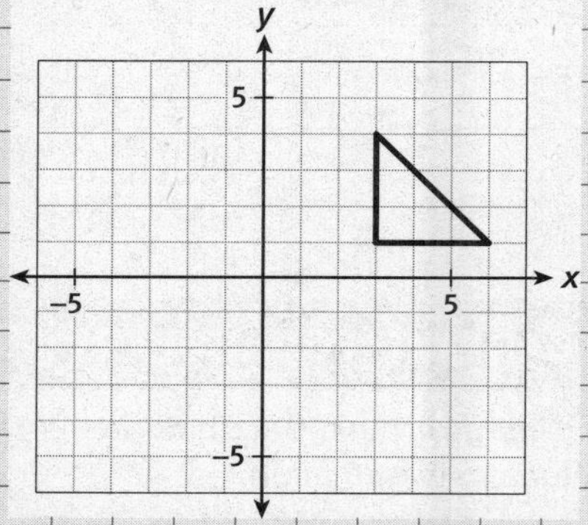

23. Consider the matrix to represent the vertices of the triangle shown.

a. Write a matrix product to represent a clockwise rotation of the figure by 270°.

b. Write a matrix product to represent a dilation of the figure by a factor of 2.5.

c. Graph the transformations in the coordinate plane.

24. **Construct viable arguments.** Reggie claims that a 180° rotation about the origin can be attained by multiplying by the scalar −1. Do you agree? Justify your response.

25. Suppose a rectangle in the coordinate plane is stretched horizontally using the matrix $\begin{bmatrix} 5 & 0 \\ 0 & 1 \end{bmatrix}$. What must be true of the orientation of the rectangle if two side lengths increase by a factor of 5?

My Notes

Learning Targets:

- Work with matrices to represent real-world situations.
- Interpret absolute value of determinants as areas.

SUGGESTED LEARNING STRATEGIES: Construct an Argument, Visualization, Sharing and Responding, Create Representations

The development company wants to divide a large piece of property into smaller lots so that homes can be constructed on them. It is necessary to know the area of each property in the development to determine selling prices and estimate taxes.

1. Triangle *OAB* is shown below.

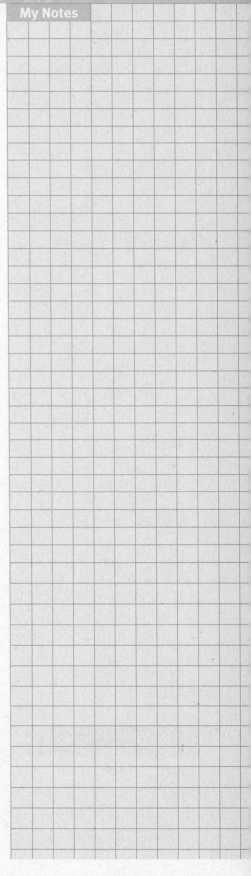

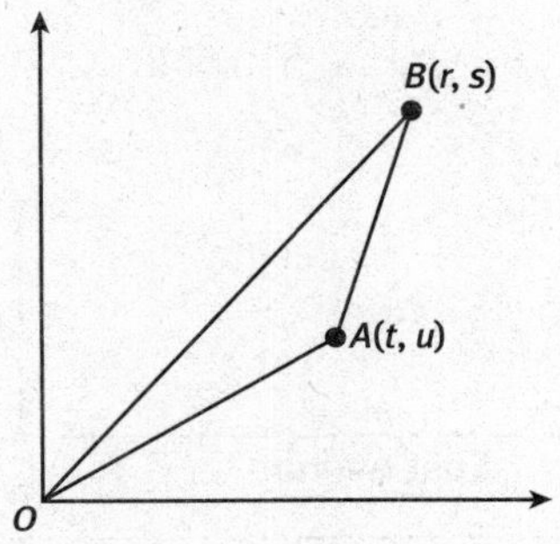

a. Derive a formula for the area of the triangle in terms of the coordinates shown.

b. Write your answer from Part a in the form of a determinant of a 2×2 matrix.

c. **Construct viable arguments.** Suppose points *O*, *A*, and *B* were collinear. Show or explain why the value of the determinant is 0.

My Notes

You own the two triangular pieces of property shown on the map as Lot 1 and Lot 2. The coordinate values represent distances in feet.

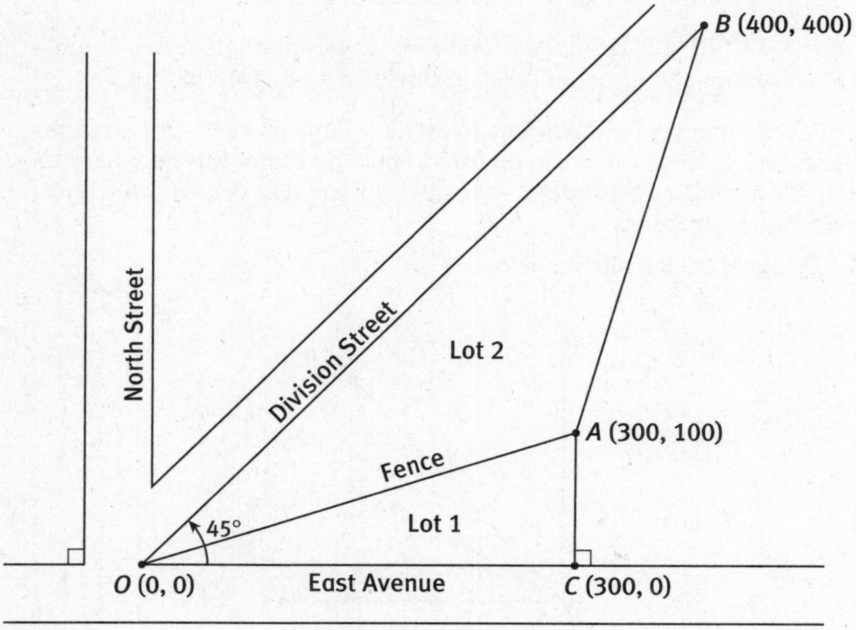

2. Calculate the square footage of Lot 1 and Lot 2.

3. Make sense of problems. Verify the determinant you wrote in Item 1b is correct by using it to check the values you calculated in Item 2.

Check Your Understanding

4. Using determinants, calculate the areas of the triangular lots whose vertices are given.

a. (100, 300), (200, −100), (0, 0)

b. (−200, 300), (40, 50), (0, 0)

c. (40, 20), (−30, −50), (0, 0)

5. Lots are sometimes given in acres instead of square feet. Convert your answers from Item 4 to acres. Round to four decimal places.

MATH TIP

43,560 ft^2 = 1 acre

My Notes

6. You want to sell a 25,000-square-foot portion of Lot 2. You want to keep 15,000 feet in the form of a triangular piece with two vertices at O and at A. The final vertex is located along Division Street.

a. Use determinants to find the coordinates of point D.

b. Point D is what fraction of the distance from O to B?

7. Not all triangular lots will have a vertex at the origin.

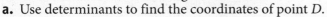

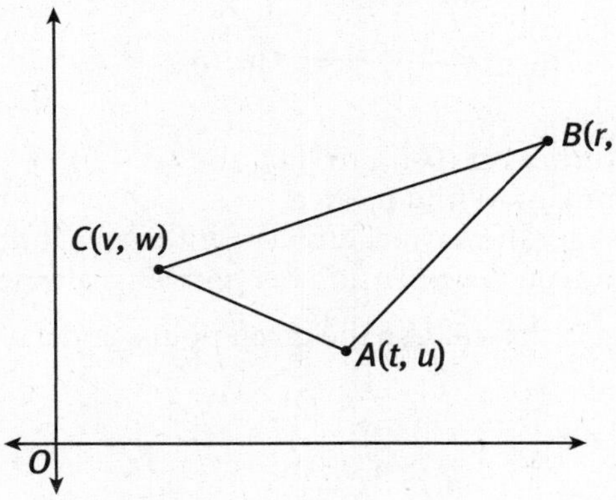

a. The triangle can be translated so that point A' (the translated point A) is at the origin. Write the coordinates of A', B', and C'.

b. Express regularity in repeated reasoning. Write the area of triangle ABC using a determinant.

My Notes

8. Describe a method for determining the area of any polygonal-shaped lot, given its vertices in the coordinate plane.

LESSON 35-3 PRACTICE

9. Use the method you described in Item 8 to find the area of the polygonal figure.

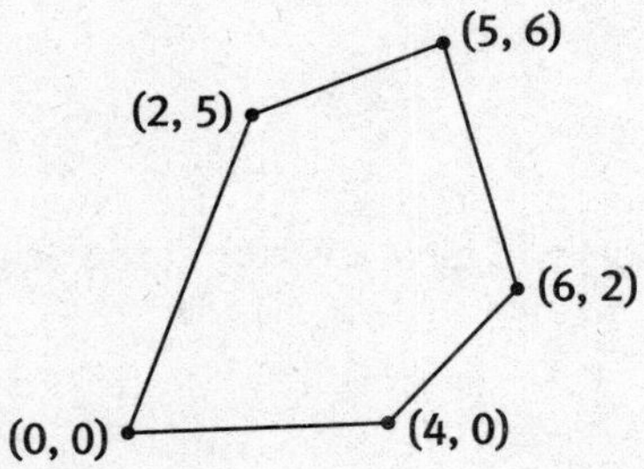

10. A triangle has vertices at (0, 0), (6, 11), and (2, −5).

a. Use a determinant to find its area.

b. Gwen almost got the correct answer for the area, but the value was negative. How can Gwen ensure her answer is always positive?

11. A parallelogram is shown. Use the given points and a determinant to find its area.

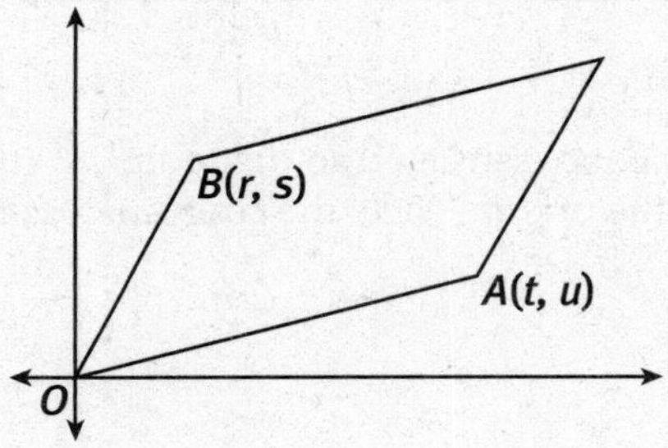

12. **Express regularity in repeated reasoning.** For the parallelogram in Item 11, find the coordinates of the vertex opposite the origin. Verify the area you found in Item 11 in another way.

ACTIVITY 35 PRACTICE

Write your answers on notebook paper. Show your work.

Lesson 35-1

1. A matrix M represents the vertices of a triangle in the coordinate plane. Which of the following will translate the figure 5 units right and 2 units down?

   A. Multiply $\begin{bmatrix} 5 & 1 \\ 1 & -2 \end{bmatrix}$ by matrix M.

   B. Add $\begin{bmatrix} 5 & 5 & 5 \\ -2 & -2 & -2 \end{bmatrix}$ to matrix M.

   C. Multiply $\begin{bmatrix} 5 & 1 \\ 1 & 5 \end{bmatrix}$ by matrix M.

   D. Add $\begin{bmatrix} 5 & -2 \\ 5 & -2 \end{bmatrix}$ to matrix M.

2. Triangle ABC has vertices $A(3, -2)$, $B(4, 5)$, and $C(7, 0)$. Write a matrix product that reflects the coordinates of the vertices over the x-axis. Perform the multiplication.

3. The endpoints of line segment TV are $T(3, 7)$ and $V(-3, -3)$.
   a. Write a matrix sum to translate the segment 8 units up. Add the matrices.
   b. Write a matrix product to reflect the translated segment over the y-axis. Multiply the matrices.
   c. If the figure was first reflected over the y-axis and then translated, would the end result be the same? Verify your answer using matrices.

4. A figure is to be reflected over the vertical line $x = a$. Explain how this can be done by first multiplying by a certain matrix, and then adding a certain matrix. Confirm your answer by graphing a figure and performing the operations.

Lesson 35-2

5. Which of the following matrices rotate a figure in the plane clockwise 180°?

   A. $\begin{bmatrix} -1 & 0 \\ 0 & 1 \end{bmatrix}$

   B. $\begin{bmatrix} 0 & 1 \\ -1 & 0 \end{bmatrix}$

   C. $\begin{bmatrix} -1 & 1 \\ -1 & 1 \end{bmatrix}$

   D. $\begin{bmatrix} -1 & 0 \\ 0 & -1 \end{bmatrix}$

6. The vertices of the figure below are represented by matrix F.

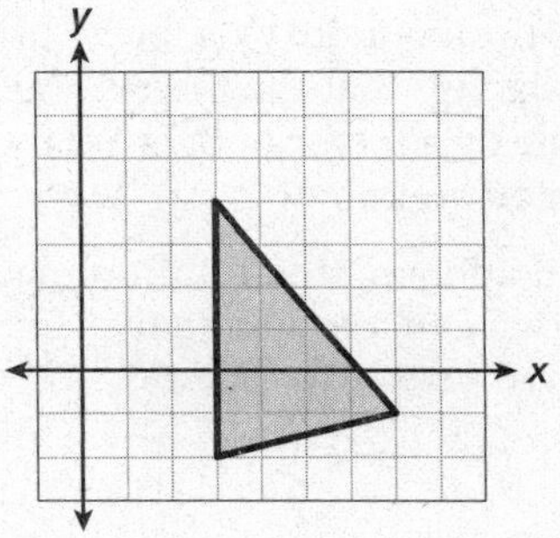

   a. Find the coordinates of the figure after a clockwise rotation of 90° about the origin. Use a matrix product. Round all values to the nearest thousandth.
   b. Find the coordinates of the figure after a dilation of 1.5. Use a matrix product.
   c. Consider the matrix product from Part b. What scalar could you multiply this matrix by so that the matrix represents the vertices of the original figure?

7. The rotation matrix $R_\theta = \begin{bmatrix} \cos\theta & \sin\theta \\ -\sin\theta & \cos\theta \end{bmatrix}$ rotates a figure clockwise θ degrees about the origin. Assume that $0° < \theta < 180°$. Suppose $-\theta$ is used in the matrix.
   a. Write an expression for the angle that represents a clockwise rotation equivalent to the counterclockwise rotation $-\theta$.
   b. Explain why using the angle $-\theta$ is equivalent to a counterclockwise rotation of θ degrees. Use your expression from Part a and trigonometric identities.

8. Yolanda writes a matrix T with dimension 3×2 to represent the vertices of a triangle.
   a. Write a matrix V such that VT will stretch the figure vertically by a factor of 3.
   b. Write a matrix H such that HT will stretch the figure horizontally by a factor of 3.
   c. Yolanda says that the matrix VH will dilate the triangle by a factor of 3. Is Yolanda correct? How do you know?

9. Show that applying the rotation matrix for $\theta = 45°$ twice in a row is equivalent to applying the rotation matrix for $\theta = 90°$.

Lesson 35-3

10. What is the area of a triangle with vertices at (2, 5), (4, 6), and (3, 1)?
   A. 4.5 square units
   B. 5.5 square units
   C. 7 square units
   D. 9 square units

11. Determine the area of the polygonal figure by using determinants.

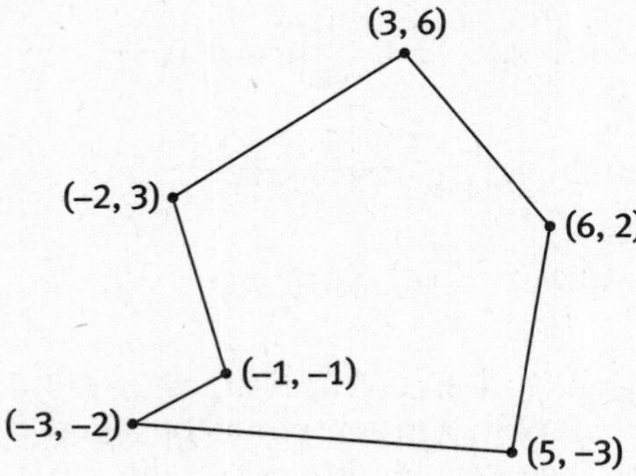

12. Find the area of a quadrilateral with vertices at (1, 10), (6, 2), (1, −5), and (−3, 5).

13. Use the points (0, 0), $(b_1, 0)$, (b_1, h), and $(b, 0)$, where $0 < b_1 < b$, to prove the formula for the area of a triangle with base length b and height h.

MATHEMATICAL PRACTICES
Model with Mathematics

14. Determine other real-life applications besides the acreage of real estate that might use matrices to represent and transform figures in the coordinate plane.

A produce company has two apple orchards. The orchards produce three varieties of apples: Rome, Jazz, and Fuji. The manager of the company wants to know if the orchards are meeting their goal of producing at least 500 bushels of apples per acre. The manager has provided the following data about the harvest, which takes place during four weeks in October. You have been hired to analyze the data and report back to the manager.

Yield per Tree (bushels)			
Week of Harvest	Variety		
	Rome	Jazz	Fuji
Week 1	2	0	0
Week 2	2	1	0
Week 3	1	1	2
Week 4	0	2	2

Number of Trees		
Variety	Orchard 1	Orchard 2
Rome	500	600
Jazz	400	750
Fuji	300	480

1. Use matrices to analyze the data in the tables.

a. Write a matrix Y that represents the data in the Yield per Tree table and a matrix N that represents the data in the Number of Trees table.

b. Write the matrix given by the scalar product $2N$. What does this matrix represent?

c. Let P be the product matrix $Y \cdot N$. Find P and explain what information is contained in the matrix.

d. What is the entry p_{32}? What does it represent?

2. The manager tells you that Orchard 1 can be represented by a triangle with vertices $O(0, 0)$, $A(6, 1)$, and $B(2, 4)$, where each square unit of the coordinate plane represents one acre.

a. Show how you can use the determinant of a 2×2 matrix to find the area of Orchard 1.

b. Does the inverse of the matrix from Part a exist? If so, find it. If not, explain why it does not exist.

c. Orchard 2 is a clockwise rotation of Orchard 1 by 90° about the origin. Show how to use matrices to find the coordinates of the vertices of Orchard 2.

d. What is the area of Orchard 2? Why?

3. Use your findings to write a short report to the manager of the produce company. Explain whether each of the orchards is meeting the goal of producing at least 500 bushels of apples per acre.

Scoring Guide	Exemplary	Proficient	Emerging	Incomplete
	The solution demonstrates these characteristics:			
Mathematics Knowledge and Thinking (Items 1 and 2)	• Clear and accurate understanding of matrices, including creating matrices to solve problems, multiplying scalars by a matrix, using the matrix formula for the area of a triangle, finding inverse matrices, and using the rotation matrix	• A functional understanding of matrices and using them to solve equations; may or may not successfully find the area of a triangle using matrices or know how to rotate a shape using matrices	• Partial understanding of using matrices to solve systems of equations	• Little or no understanding of matrices or how to create systems of equations with them
Problem Solving (Item 3)	• An appropriate and efficient strategy that results in a correct answer	• A strategy that may include unnecessary steps but results in a correct answer	• A strategy that results in some incorrect answers	• No clear strategy when solving problems
Mathematical Modeling / Representations (Items 1b, 1c, 1d)	• Clear and accurate understanding of representations of situations using matrices • Clear and accurate understanding of creating matrices to simplify more complicated systems	• A functional understanding of matrices when modeling a real scenario • Mostly accurate understanding of using matrices to model a system	• Partial understanding of matrices when modeling a real scenario • Partial understanding of using matrices to model a system	• Little or no understanding of representations of matrices • Inaccurate or incomplete understanding of systems modeled with matrices
Reasoning and Communication (Item 3)	• Precise use of appropriate math terms and language to describe an entry in a matrix, and use of the data acquired to determine information in the context of the problem	• Correct characterization of information from the matrices, but perhaps with some minor errors	• Misleading or confusing characterization of information from the matrices	• Incomplete or inaccurate characterization of information from the matrices

Matrices and Systems of Equations

ACTIVITY 36

Hit the Trail

Lesson 36-1 Representing Linear Systems with Matrices

My Notes

Learning Targets:

- Write a linear system of equations as a matrix equation.
- Represent a real-world situation with a matrix equation.
- Identify the coefficient matrix, variable matrix, and constant matrix.

SUGGESTED LEARNING STRATEGIES: Close Reading, KWL Chart, Interactive Word Wall, Create Representations, Think-Pair-Share

A snack company is planning a new type of trail mix that will contain almonds and sunflower seeds. The table shows information about the nutrition content of these foods.

Nutrition Data

Food	Carbohydrates (grams per ounce)	Protein (grams per ounce)
Almonds	5	6
Sunflower seeds	6	5

The company wants the trail mix to contain 16 grams of carbohydrates and 17 grams of protein per serving.

1. **Model with mathematics.** Let x represent the weight in ounces of almonds in one serving of trail mix and y represent the weight in ounces of sunflower seeds in one serving. Write a system of equations that can be used to solve for x and y.

MATH TIP

The standard form of a linear equation in two variables is $Ax + By = C$, where A, B, and C are real numbers.

You can use matrices to represent systems of linear equations, such as the one you wrote in Item 1. A ***matrix equation*** that represents a system of linear equations includes a ***coefficient matrix***, a ***variable matrix***, and a ***constant matrix***.

MATH TERMS

A **matrix equation** has the form $AX = B$, where A is the coefficient matrix, X is the variable matrix, and B is the constant matrix.

A **coefficient matrix** is the matrix consisting of the coefficients of the variable terms in a system of linear equations in standard form.

A **variable matrix** is the matrix consisting of the variables in a system of linear equations.

A **constant matrix** is the matrix consisting of the constant terms in a system of linear equations in standard form.

Example A

Write a matrix equation to represent the system $\begin{cases} 3x - 4y = -11 \\ y = 5x - 3 \end{cases}$.

Step 1: Write each equation in standard form.

$$\begin{cases} 3x + (-4)y = -11 \\ -5x + (1)y = -3 \end{cases}$$

Step 2: Write the coefficient matrix, A.

Use the coefficients of the first equation in the first row, and the coefficients of the second equation in the second row.

$$\begin{bmatrix} 3 & -4 \\ -5 & 1 \end{bmatrix}$$

My Notes

Step 3: Write the variable matrix, X.

Write a column matrix for the variables. $\begin{bmatrix} x \\ y \end{bmatrix}$

Step 4: Write the constant matrix, B.

Write a column matrix for the constants. $\begin{bmatrix} -11 \\ -3 \end{bmatrix}$

Step 5: Write the matrix equation, $AX = B$. $\begin{bmatrix} 3 & -4 \\ -5 & 1 \end{bmatrix}\begin{bmatrix} x \\ y \end{bmatrix} = \begin{bmatrix} -11 \\ -3 \end{bmatrix}$

Try These A

Write a matrix equation to represent each system. Then identify the coefficient matrix, the variable matrix, and the constant matrix.

a. $\begin{cases} 6x + 4y = 18 \\ 8x = 5y \end{cases}$

b. $\begin{cases} x + y + z = 24 \\ 3x + y - 2z = 18 \\ 4x = -8z \end{cases}$

2. Reason abstractly and quantitatively. Look back at the system of equations you wrote in Item 1.

a. Write the system of equations as a matrix equation.

b. What do the entries in the first column of the coefficient matrix represent in this situation?

c. What does the entry in the second row of the constant matrix represent in this situation?

d. Multiply the coefficient matrix by the variable matrix. What is the relationship between the matrix product and the system of equations?

My Notes

Check Your Understanding

3. A system of 4 linear equations involves 4 variables. What are the dimensions of the coefficient matrix, the variable matrix, and the constant matrix of the matrix equation that models this system?

4. Critique the reasoning of others. A student wrote the matrix equation $\begin{bmatrix} 3 & -6 \\ 8 & 2 \end{bmatrix}\begin{bmatrix} x & y \end{bmatrix} = \begin{bmatrix} 24 \\ 40 \end{bmatrix}$ to represent $\begin{cases} 3x - 6y = 24 \\ 8x + 2y = 40 \end{cases}$. Describe the mistake that the student made.

5. Construct viable arguments. Does the order of the variables in the variable matrix of a matrix equation matter? Give an example to support your answer.

LESSON 36-1 PRACTICE

Write a matrix equation to represent each system in Items 6 and 7.

6. $\begin{cases} 4p + 3q = 79 \\ 25p = q \end{cases}$

7. $\begin{cases} 3x + 4y = 2z \\ x - y = 8 \\ x + y + 5z = 20 \end{cases}$

8. Model with mathematics. Let t represent the cost of a tube of oil paint and p represent the cost of a paintbrush. An oil paint set that contains 14 tubes of paint and 2 brushes costs \$22. An oil paint set that contains 10 tubes of paint and 6 brushes costs \$26.

a. Write a system of equations that can be used to solve for t and p.
b. Write the system of equations as a matrix equation.
c. What do the entries in the constant matrix represent?

9. Model with mathematics. Some of the tables at a wedding reception will seat 6 people, and some will seat 8 people. There will be 7 tables in all, with seats for 46 people.

a. Write a system of equations in two variables that can be used to find the number of tables with 6 seats and the number of tables with 8 seats.
b. Write the system of equations as a matrix equation.
c. Identify the coefficient matrix of the matrix equation.

10. Make use of structure. What system of equations does the matrix equation $\begin{bmatrix} 1 & -4 \\ 3 & -2 \end{bmatrix}\begin{bmatrix} a \\ b \end{bmatrix} = \begin{bmatrix} -4 \\ 8 \end{bmatrix}$ represent?

My Notes

Learning Targets:

- Use an inverse matrix to solve a matrix equation.
- Connect the existence of an inverse matrix to solutions of systems.

SUGGESTED LEARNING STRATEGIES: Close Reading, Note Taking, Identify a Subtask, Discussion Groups, Quickwrite

Recall that a snack company is planning a new type of trail mix containing almonds and sunflower seeds. In the previous lesson, you used a matrix equation to represent a system of linear equations in which x is the weight in ounces of almonds in one serving of the trail mix and y is the weight in ounces of sunflower seeds in one serving.

In this lesson, you will learn how to solve matrix equations by using an inverse matrix. To solve the matrix equation $AX = B$, multiply both sides of the matrix equation by A^{-1}, the inverse of A. The solution of the matrix equation is $X = A^{-1}B$.

Example A

Use an inverse matrix to solve the matrix equation

$$\begin{bmatrix} 3 & -4 \\ -5 & 1 \end{bmatrix}\begin{bmatrix} x \\ y \end{bmatrix} = \begin{bmatrix} -22 \\ 14 \end{bmatrix}.$$

Step 1: Find the determinant of the coefficient matrix, A.

$$\det A = (3)(1) - (-4)(-5)$$
$$\det A = -17$$

Step 2: Find the inverse of the coefficient matrix, A.

$$A^{-1} = \frac{1}{-17}\begin{bmatrix} 1 & 4 \\ 5 & 3 \end{bmatrix}$$

$$A^{-1} = \begin{bmatrix} -\frac{1}{17} & -\frac{4}{17} \\ -\frac{5}{17} & -\frac{3}{17} \end{bmatrix}$$

Step 3: Solve the matrix equation.

$$X = A^{-1}B$$

$$X = \begin{bmatrix} -\frac{1}{17} & -\frac{4}{17} \\ -\frac{5}{17} & -\frac{3}{17} \end{bmatrix}\begin{bmatrix} -22 \\ 14 \end{bmatrix}$$

$$X = \begin{bmatrix} -2 \\ 4 \end{bmatrix}$$

Solution: The solution of the matrix equation is $X = \begin{bmatrix} x \\ y \end{bmatrix} = \begin{bmatrix} -2 \\ 4 \end{bmatrix}.$

MATH TIP

For a 2×2 matrix $A = \begin{bmatrix} a & b \\ c & d \end{bmatrix}$, the determinant of A is $ad - bc$, and the inverse of A is $\frac{1}{\det A}\begin{bmatrix} d & -b \\ -c & a \end{bmatrix}$.

My Notes

Try These A

Use an inverse matrix to solve each matrix equation.

a. $\begin{bmatrix} 3 & 8 \\ -2 & 5 \end{bmatrix}\begin{bmatrix} x \\ y \end{bmatrix} = \begin{bmatrix} 14 \\ 32 \end{bmatrix}$

b. $\begin{bmatrix} 4 & 3 \\ -2 & 2 \end{bmatrix}\begin{bmatrix} x \\ y \end{bmatrix} = \begin{bmatrix} 17 \\ 9 \end{bmatrix}$

1. Make sense of problems. The matrix equation $\begin{bmatrix} 5 & 6 \\ 6 & 5 \end{bmatrix}\begin{bmatrix} x \\ y \end{bmatrix} = \begin{bmatrix} 16 \\ 17 \end{bmatrix}$ can be used to determine the weight x in ounces of almonds in one serving of the new trail mix and the weight y in ounces of sunflower seeds in one serving.

a. Use an inverse matrix to solve the matrix equation.

b. Interpret the solution of the equation in the context of the problem.

c. Determine whether your solution is reasonable. Explain.

2. Consider the linear system $\begin{cases} 3x + 4y = 6 \\ 6x + 8y = 24 \end{cases}$.

a. Write a matrix equation to represent the system.

b. What is the determinant of the coefficient matrix of the matrix equation?

c. What can you conclude about the coefficient matrix based on the value of its determinant? Why?

My Notes

d. Graph the linear system on the coordinate plane.

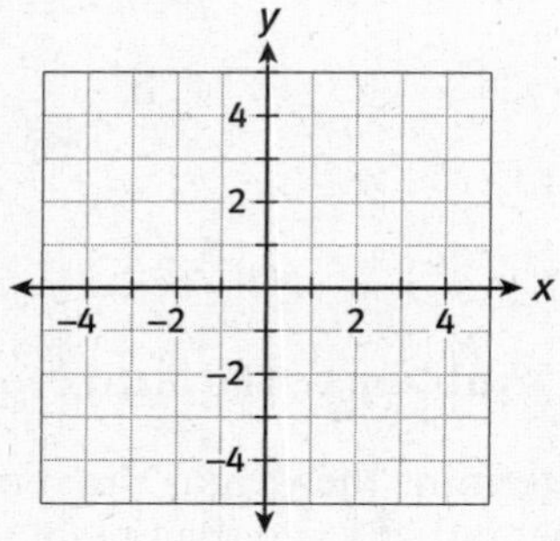

e. What does the graph indicate about the number of solutions of the system?

3. Consider the linear system $\begin{cases} x - 3y = 8 \\ 3x - 9y = 24 \end{cases}$.

a. Write a matrix equation to represent the system.

b. What is the determinant of the coefficient matrix of the matrix equation?

c. What can you conclude about the coefficient matrix based on the value of its determinant?

d. Graph the linear system on the coordinate plane.

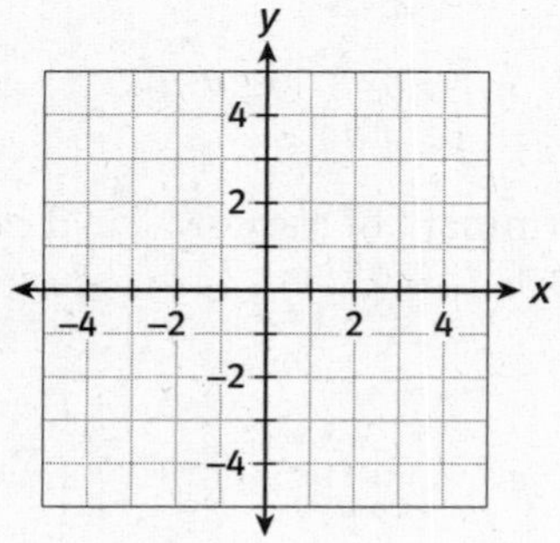

e. What does the graph indicate about the number of solutions of the system?

My Notes

4. Express regularity in repeated reasoning. Make a conjecture about a matrix equation whose coefficient matrix has a determinant of 0.

Check Your Understanding

5. Construct viable arguments. Explain why the matrix equation $AX = B$ is equivalent to $X = A^{-1}B$.

6. How is solving a matrix equation of the form $AX = B$ for X similar to solving a linear equation of the form $ax = b$ for x?

LESSON 36-2 PRACTICE

Use an inverse matrix to solve each matrix equation.

7. $\begin{bmatrix} 2 & -3 \\ -6 & 8 \end{bmatrix}\begin{bmatrix} x \\ y \end{bmatrix} = \begin{bmatrix} 1 \\ 2 \end{bmatrix}$

8. $\begin{bmatrix} 3 & -6 \\ 9 & 4 \end{bmatrix}\begin{bmatrix} x \\ y \end{bmatrix} = \begin{bmatrix} -22 \\ 22 \end{bmatrix}$

9. Model with mathematics. Jason has 24 ft of fencing to enclose a rectangular garden. The length of the garden will be twice the width.

a. Write a system of equations in two variables that can be used to determine the length and width of the garden.

b. Write the system of equations as a matrix equation.

c. Solve the matrix equation, and interpret the solution.

10. Model with mathematics. A marching band is selling T-shirts to raise money. Adult shirts sell for \$16.25, and children's shirts sell for \$10.75. On Friday, the band sold 31 shirts for a total of \$476.25.

a. Write a matrix equation that can be used to determine the number of adult shirts and the number of children's shirts the band sold.

b. Solve the matrix equation, and interpret the solution.

11. Explain how you can use a determinant to determine whether a system of two linear equations is independent.

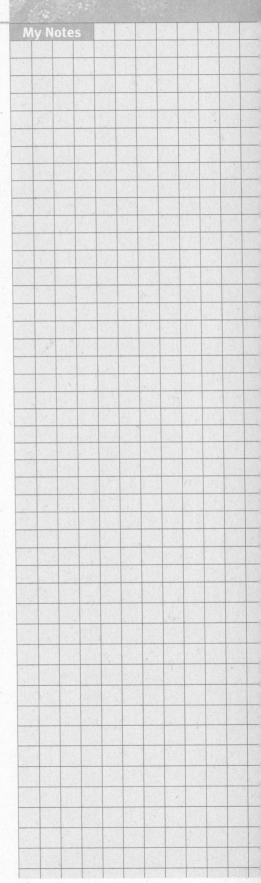

My Notes

Learning Targets:

- Use technology to solve large linear systems.
- Solve a 3×3 matrix equation using technology.

SUGGESTED LEARNING STRATEGIES: Close Reading, Note Taking, Create Representations, Sharing and Responding, Quickwrite

The snack company decides to add dried cranberries to its new trail mix along with almonds and sunflower seeds. The table shows information about the nutritional content of these foods.

Nutrition Data

Food	Carbohydrates (grams per ounce)	Protein (grams per ounce)	Fat (grams per ounce)
Almonds	5	5	15
Sunflower seeds	6	6	16
Cranberries	23	0	0

The new version of the trail mix will contain 33.5 grams of carbohydrates, 10.5 grams of protein, and 30.5 grams of fat per serving.

1. **Model with mathematics.** For one serving of trail mix, let x represent the weight in ounces of almonds, y represent the weight in ounces of sunflower seeds, and z represent the weight in ounces of cranberries. Write a system of equations that can be used to determine the values of x, y, and z.

2. **Reason quantitatively.** Explain what each equation in the system represents.

3. Write a matrix equation to represent the system in Item 1.

My Notes

To solve a matrix equation that represents a system of three or more linear equations, you can use a graphing calculator.

Example A

Use technology to solve the matrix equation

$$\begin{bmatrix} 4 & 5 & -3 \\ -2 & -6 & 8 \\ 9 & -4 & -1 \end{bmatrix}\begin{bmatrix} x \\ y \\ z \end{bmatrix} = \begin{bmatrix} 19.4 \\ -23 \\ 17.5 \end{bmatrix}.$$

Step 1: Enter the coefficient matrix A into a graphing calculator.

```
MATRIX[A] 3 × 3
[ 4    5    -3  ]
[-2   -6     8  ]
[ 9   -4    -1  ]
```

Step 2: Enter the constant matrix B into a graphing calculator.

```
MATRIX[B] 3 × 1
[ 19.4          ]
[-23            ]
[ 17.3          ]
```

Step 3: Use the calculator to find $A^{-1}B$.

```
[A]^-1 * [B]
            [ [2.3]
              [1.2]
              [-1.4]
]
```

Solution: The solution of the matrix equation is $X = \begin{bmatrix} x \\ y \\ z \end{bmatrix} = \begin{bmatrix} 2.3 \\ 1.2 \\ -1.4 \end{bmatrix}$.

TECHNOLOGY TIP

To key in A^{-1} on a graphing calculator, select [A] from the Names submenu of the Matrix menu. Then press $\boxed{x^{-1}}$. Your screen should now show $[A]^{-1}$.

Try These A

Use appropriate tools strategically. Use technology to solve each matrix equation.

a. $\begin{bmatrix} 2 & 2 & -1 \\ 1 & -5 & 6 \\ 9 & 4 & 8 \end{bmatrix}\begin{bmatrix} x \\ y \\ z \end{bmatrix} = \begin{bmatrix} -9 \\ 0.5 \\ -8 \end{bmatrix}$

b. $\begin{bmatrix} 1 & 2 & 1 & 3 \\ -2 & 4 & 6 & 0 \\ 3 & 1 & 5 & -4 \\ 0 & -8 & 1 & 7 \end{bmatrix}\begin{bmatrix} w \\ x \\ y \\ z \end{bmatrix} = \begin{bmatrix} -11 \\ 22 \\ 41 \\ -104 \end{bmatrix}$

My Notes

4. Refer back to the matrix equation you wrote in Item 3 to model the new version of the trail mix.

a. **Use appropriate tools strategically.** Use technology to solve the matrix equation.

b. **Reason quantitatively.** Interpret the solution of the matrix equation.

c. How could you check that the solution is correct?

A food researcher at the snack company determines the number of calories in three different mixtures of almonds, sunflower seeds, and dried cranberries. The results are shown in the table.

Mixture	Weight (oz)			Total Calories
	Almonds	Sunflower Seeds	Cranberries	
1	2	1	3	765
2	3	3	4	1364
3	4	2	6	1530

5. **Use appropriate tools strategically.** The researcher uses the data in the table to write the matrix equation $\begin{bmatrix} 2 & 1 & 3 \\ 3 & 3 & 4 \\ 4 & 2 & 6 \end{bmatrix}\begin{bmatrix} x \\ y \\ z \end{bmatrix} = \begin{bmatrix} 765 \\ 1364 \\ 1530 \end{bmatrix}$, where x is the number of calories per ounce of almonds, y is the number of calories per ounce of sunflower seeds, and z is the number of calories per ounce of cranberries.

a. What happens when you try to use a graphing calculator to solve the matrix equation?

b. What does the result in Part a indicate about the coefficient matrix of the matrix equation?

MATH TIP

A singular matrix is a matrix that does not have an inverse.

My Notes

c. What does the result in Part a indicate about the solution(s) of the matrix equation?

d. Notice that the weights and calories in mixture 3 are twice the weights and calories in mixture 1. What does this pattern indicate about these mixtures?

e. How could the researcher change the experiment in order to find the values of x, y, and z?

Example B

Use technology to identify whether the linear system below has a ***unique*** solution. If so, solve the system.

$$\begin{cases} 2x + y - 3z = 8 \\ 3x + 6y - 4z = 10 \\ 6x + 3y - 9z = 30 \end{cases}$$

Step 1: Write a matrix equation for the system.

$$\begin{bmatrix} 2 & 1 & -3 \\ 3 & 6 & -4 \\ 6 & 3 & -9 \end{bmatrix}\begin{bmatrix} x \\ y \\ z \end{bmatrix} = \begin{bmatrix} 8 \\ 10 \\ 30 \end{bmatrix}$$

Step 2: Enter the coefficient matrix A into a graphing calculator.

```
MATRIX[A] 3 × 3
[2    1    -3  ]
[3    6    -4  ]
[6    3    -9  ]
```

Step 3: Find the determinant of A.

```
det([A])
                0
```

Solution: The determinant of A is 0, so A does not have an inverse. This means that the linear system does not have a unique solution. Instead, it either has no solution or infinitely many solutions.

ACADEMIC VOCABULARY

A system with a ***unique*** solution has exactly one solution.

My Notes

Try These B

Use appropriate tools strategically. Use technology to identify whether each linear system has a unique solution. If so, solve the system.

a. $\begin{cases} 3x + 5y - 2z = -34.5 \\ x + 2y + 2z = -1.5 \\ -4x - 3y + z = 16.5 \end{cases}$

b. $\begin{cases} -4x + y + z = 12.4 \\ 3x + 6y - 4z = 6.6 \\ 8x - 2y - 2z = -24.8 \end{cases}$

Check Your Understanding

6. Use tools strategically. Explain why a graphing calculator is useful for solving systems of three or more linear equations.

7. Suppose you use a matrix equation to determine that a system of three linear equations does not have a unique solution. How could you determine whether the system has no solution?

LESSON 36-3 PRACTICE

Use technology to solve each matrix equation.

8. $\begin{bmatrix} 2 & 1 & 1 \\ 3 & 3 & -9 \\ 1 & 8 & 6 \end{bmatrix}\begin{bmatrix} x \\ y \\ z \end{bmatrix} = \begin{bmatrix} -9 \\ 12.6 \\ 0 \end{bmatrix}$

9. $\begin{bmatrix} 2 & 4 & -1 & 1 \\ 1 & 1 & 3 & 4 \\ 0 & -3 & 2 & -1 \\ 5 & 6 & 1 & -2 \end{bmatrix}\begin{bmatrix} a \\ b \\ c \\ d \end{bmatrix} = \begin{bmatrix} 24 \\ 13 \\ -26 \\ 11 \end{bmatrix}$

10. Model with mathematics. The number of points a player earns in a video game depends on the number of keys, treasures, and health packs the player finds. The table shows the results for three players on the first level of the game. Write and solve a matrix equation to determine the number of points a player earns for finding each type of item.

Player	Keys	Treasures	Health Packs	Total Points
Marci	2	8	4	1000
Cameron	1	12	8	1250
Amya	1	6	2	650

Use technology to identify whether each linear system has a unique solution. If so, solve the system.

11. $\begin{cases} 4x - 6y + 2z = 15 \\ -3x + 9y - 6z = 24 \\ -2x + 6y - 4z = 8 \end{cases}$

12. $\begin{cases} -3x + 5y - 3z = -50 \\ 4x - 2y + z = 42 \\ -6x + 8y + 6z = -68 \end{cases}$

ACTIVITY 36 PRACTICE

Write your answers on notebook paper. Show your work.

Lesson 36-1

In an election for mayor, 42,642 votes were cast for candidates Harrison and Cho. Harrison received 6% more votes than Cho did. Use this information for Items 1–3.

1. Let h represent the number of votes Harrison received and c represent the number of votes Cho received. Write a system of equations that can be used to solve for h and c.

2. Write a matrix equation to represent the system of equations.

3. Identify the coefficient matrix and the variable matrix of the matrix equation.

4. If you write a matrix equation to represent the system $\begin{cases} x+y=z \\ 2x+3y+z=-14 \\ 5x=-2y \end{cases}$, what will be the dimension of the constant matrix?

A. 1×1 **B.** 1×3
C. 3×1 **D.** 3×3

Write a matrix equation to represent each system.

5. $\begin{cases} 4m+2n=18 \\ 3m-n=1 \end{cases}$

6. $\begin{cases} 2x+3y=36 \\ 4x=3y \end{cases}$

7. $\begin{cases} a+b+c=4 \\ -7a+b=c \\ 5a-b=0 \end{cases}$

8. What system of equations does the matrix equation $\begin{bmatrix} 2 & 5 \\ 7 & -4 \end{bmatrix}\begin{bmatrix} x \\ y \end{bmatrix}=\begin{bmatrix} 42 \\ 18 \end{bmatrix}$ represent?

A chemist has two salt solutions. Solution A has a concentration of 5 g of salt per 100 mL of solution. Solution B has a concentration of 8 g of salt per 100 mL of solution. When the solutions are combined, the resulting solution has a volume of 500 mL and a concentration of 6.8 g of salt per 100 mL of solution. Use this information for Items 9–11.

9. Let x represent the volume in milliliters of the first solution and y represent the volume in milliliters of the second solution. Write a system of equations that can be used to solve for x and y.

10. Write a matrix equation to represent the system of equations.

11. Explain what each entry in the constant matrix of the matrix equation represents.

Lesson 36-2

Use an inverse matrix to solve each matrix equation.

12. $\begin{bmatrix} 2 & 3 \\ 4 & -5 \end{bmatrix}\begin{bmatrix} x \\ y \end{bmatrix}=\begin{bmatrix} 6 \\ -32 \end{bmatrix}$

13. $\begin{bmatrix} 1 & -4 \\ 3 & 2 \end{bmatrix}\begin{bmatrix} p \\ q \end{bmatrix}=\begin{bmatrix} 30 \\ 6 \end{bmatrix}$

14. $\begin{bmatrix} -3 & 2 \\ 6 & 1 \end{bmatrix}\begin{bmatrix} s \\ t \end{bmatrix}=\begin{bmatrix} 3 \\ 4 \end{bmatrix}$

A movie theater offers two gift packages. One package costs $21 and includes 2 movie tickets and 1 regular popcorn. The other package costs $50 and includes 4 movie tickets and 4 regular popcorns. Use this information for Items 15–18.

15. Write a system of equations in two variables that can be used to determine the cost of one movie ticket and the cost of one regular popcorn.

16. Write the system of equations as a matrix equation.

17. Use an inverse matrix to solve the matrix equation, and interpret the solution.

18. Show that your solution is reasonable.

Find the determinant of the coefficient matrix of each matrix equation. What does the determinant indicate about the number of solutions of the matrix equation?

19. $\begin{bmatrix} 4 & -12 \\ -6 & 18 \end{bmatrix}\begin{bmatrix} x \\ y \end{bmatrix} = \begin{bmatrix} 16 \\ -24 \end{bmatrix}$

20. $\begin{bmatrix} 2 & 4 \\ 6 & -2 \end{bmatrix}\begin{bmatrix} x \\ y \end{bmatrix} = \begin{bmatrix} 6 \\ 32 \end{bmatrix}$

21. What is the missing number in the following matrix equation given that its solution is $\begin{bmatrix} x \\ y \end{bmatrix} = \begin{bmatrix} 6 \\ -2 \end{bmatrix}$?

$$\begin{bmatrix} 4 & -1 \\ -3 & 2 \end{bmatrix}\begin{bmatrix} x \\ y \end{bmatrix} = \begin{bmatrix} ? \\ -22 \end{bmatrix}$$

A. 22 **B.** 24
C. 26 **D.** 30

Lesson 36-3

The table gives information about three acids, each consisting of carbon (C), hydrogen (H), and oxygen (O).

Use this information for Items 22–24.

Data for 1 Mole of Acid

Acid	Moles of C	Moles of H	Moles of O	Mass (g)
acetic	2	4	2	60.052
citric	6	8	7	192.123
formic	1	2	2	46.025

22. Write a system of equations that can be used to determine the masses of 1 mole of carbon, 1 mole of hydrogen, and 1 mole of oxygen.

23. Write a matrix equation to represent the system of equations.

24. Solve the matrix equation, and interpret the solution.

Use technology to solve each matrix equation.

25. $\begin{bmatrix} 2 & 1 & 3 \\ -1 & 4 & 2 \\ 5 & -6 & 1 \end{bmatrix}\begin{bmatrix} x \\ y \\ z \end{bmatrix} = \begin{bmatrix} 3.6 \\ 0.9 \\ 3.8 \end{bmatrix}$

26. $\begin{bmatrix} 1 & 2 & -5 \\ 0.5 & 3 & 1 \\ 3 & -1 & 2.6 \end{bmatrix}\begin{bmatrix} r \\ s \\ t \end{bmatrix} = \begin{bmatrix} -52 \\ 14 \\ 2.5 \end{bmatrix}$

27. $\begin{bmatrix} 1 & 1 & 1 & 0 \\ 2 & 3 & -1 & 1 \\ 5 & -2 & 0 & 4 \\ -2 & 1 & 2 & -3 \end{bmatrix}\begin{bmatrix} a \\ b \\ c \\ d \end{bmatrix} = \begin{bmatrix} 1 \\ -2 \\ -52 \\ 30 \end{bmatrix}$

Use technology to identify whether each linear system has a unique solution. If so, solve the system.

28. $\begin{cases} 2x + 3y - z = -12 \\ 5x - 4y + 2z = 14 \\ -x + 6y - 5z = -15 \end{cases}$

29. $\begin{cases} 3x - 2y + z = 8 \\ 2x + y - 4z = -6 \\ -6x + 4y - 2z = 12 \end{cases}$

MATHEMATICAL PRACTICES
Use Appropriate Tools Strategically

30. Explain how you could use a graphing calculator to solve a system of 5 linear equations in 5 variables.

Volume
Stack 'em High
Lesson 37-1 Cavalieri's Principle

My Notes

Learning Targets:

- Understand Cavalieri's Principle.
- Relate Cavalieri's Principle to volume formulas.

SUGGESTED LEARNING STRATEGIES: Create Representations, Construct an Argument, Use Manipulatives, Quickwrite

The dimensions of a CD case are shown.

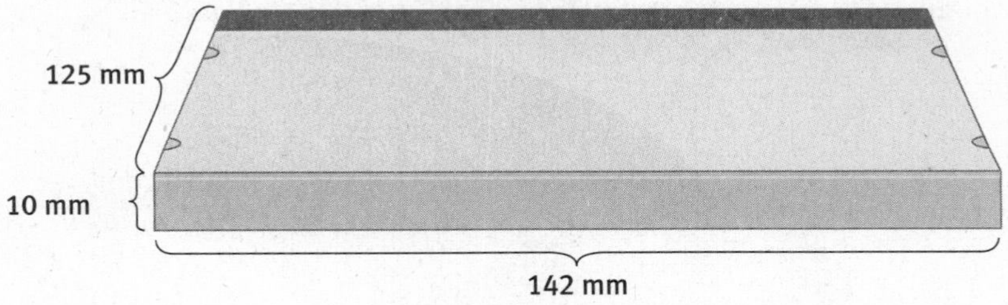

Recall that ***volume*** is the number of cubic units in a solid figure.

1. Write the formula for the volume of a rectangular prism. What is the volume of the CD case?

2. **Express regularity in repeated reasoning.** Explain how you could apply the same formula to a vertical stack of 10 CD cases. Is there an easier way to find the volume of the stack?

3. You stack 10 CD cases as shown at the right. Would you apply the same volume formula to find the volume of the stack? What is the volume?

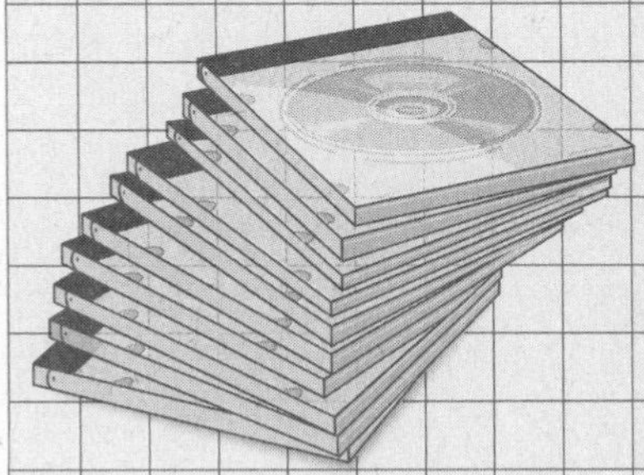

Suppose two solid figures lie between two parallel planes. ***Cavalieri's Principle*** states that if every plane parallel to these two planes intersects both figures with equal cross sections, then the two figures have equal volumes.

My Notes

CONNECT TO HISTORY

Bonaventura Cavalieri was an Italian mathematician who lived in the 1600s. His principle is part of his geometric approach to calculus.

4. How does Cavalieri's Principle apply to the stacks of CD cases from Items 1 and 2? Explain.

5. A CD has a diameter of 120 mm. Your friend would like to see how many CDs can be stacked before it tips over. He stacks 25 CDs.

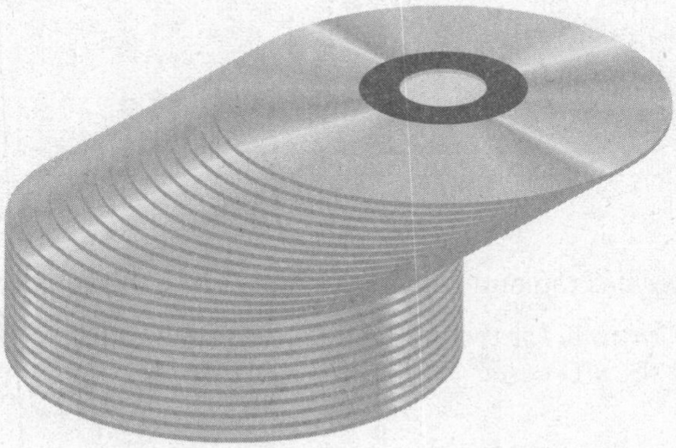

a. Name the solid figure that would allow you to use Cavalieri's Principle to determine the volume of the stack of CDs.

b. Explain how you could determine the volume of the stack using a centimeter ruler.

c. **Attend to precision.** The height of the stack is 30 mm. What is the volume of the stack of CDs? Round to the nearest cubic millimeter.

d. How thick is one of the CDs? Did you need to know the volume of the stack to answer this question?

The figures below are examples of *oblique solids.*

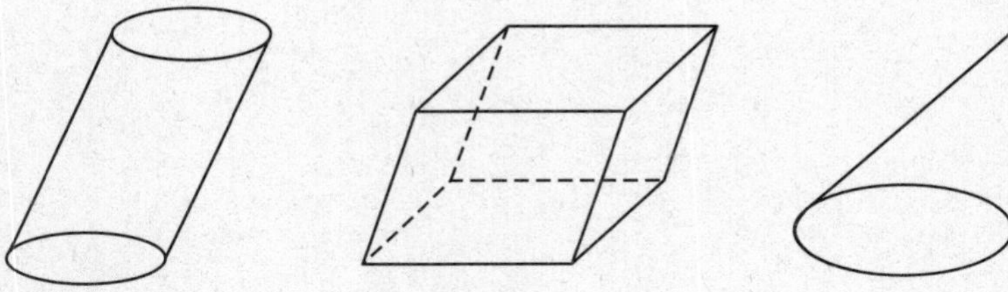

My Notes

MATH TERMS

An **oblique angle** is an angle whose measure is not 90°.

6. What common solids do you recognize from the drawings? Describe what differentiates an oblique solid from a right solid for each of these figures.

7. Do you think you can apply the volume formulas for the common solids listed in Item 6 to the oblique solids? Explain.

Check Your Understanding

8. **Construct viable arguments.** Explain how you would calculate the volume of the stack of papers shown by applying Cavalieri's Principle.

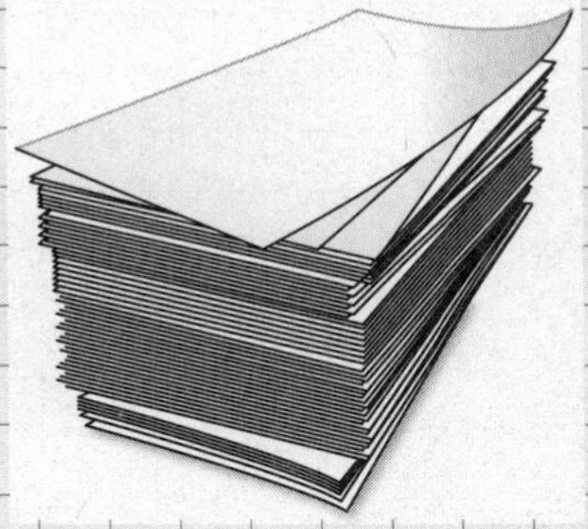

9. Cavalieri's Principle can also be applied to show that two regions have the same area. Complete Cavalieri's principle for the two-dimensional version:

   Suppose two plane figures lie between the same two parallel lines. Cavalieri's Principle states that if every _______ parallel to these two lines intersects both figures with equal _______, then the two figures have equal _______.

Suppose two solid figures lie between the same two parallel planes. The ***converse*** of Cavalieri's Principle is stated as follows:

If the two figures have equal volumes, then every plane parallel to these two planes intersects both figures with equal cross sections.

MATH TERMS

The **converse** of the statement "if *p* then *q*" is "if *q* then *p*."

My Notes

10. Critique the reasoning of others. Petra claims that the converse is false. She draws the following two solids to serve as a counterexample. Explain Petra's error.

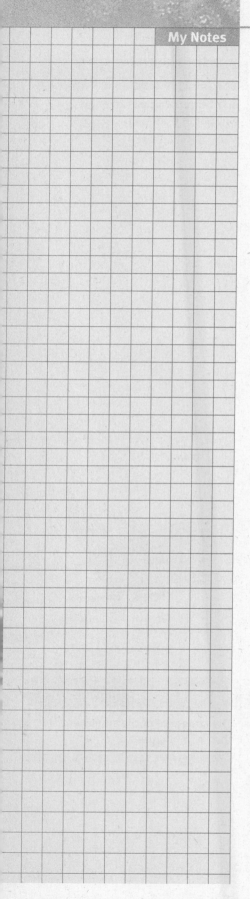

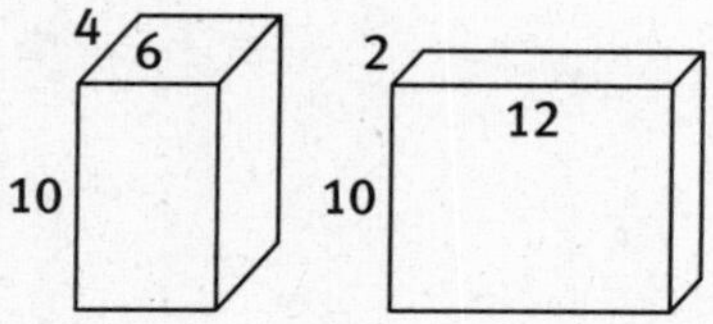

11. To prove the converse is false, you can use a square pyramid and a cylinder. Assume each figure has a height of 10 cm.

a. Write the formulas for the volume of the cylinder and the square pyramid. To prove the converse false, what must be true about the volumes of the figures?

b. Suppose the square pyramid has a base area of 42 cm^2. Find the radius of the cylinder so that what you wrote in part a is true.

c. Without doing any calculations, explain why the figures do not have equal cross-sectional areas.

LESSON 37-1 PRACTICE

12. Helena wants to find the volume of an oblique cone. She knows she can use the formula $V = \frac{1}{3}\pi r^2 h$, but she isn't sure how to find the slanted height h. Explain Helena's error.

13. Reason abstractly. Explain why Cavalieri's Principle states that the two solid figures must lie *between two parallel planes.*

14. An oblique pentagonal prism has a height of 12 inches and a base area of 54 square inches. Find its volume.

15. Compare the volume of the prism from Item 14 with that of a right hexagonal prism with the same height and same base area.

My Notes

Learning Targets:

- Informally derive the formula for the volume of a sphere.
- Use volume formulas to solve real-world problems.

SUGGESTED LEARNING STRATEGIES: Create Representations, Prewriting, Simplify the Problem, Quickwrite

A ***sphere*** is a set of points in space that are equidistant from a given point, called the center of the sphere.

The figure below shows a cylinder with a cone inside. The base of the cone is a base of the cylinder.

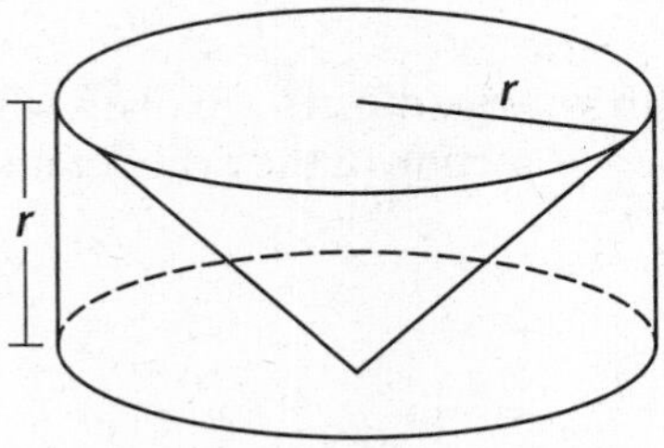

1. Write the formula for the volume of a cylinder. Then write an equation for the volume of the cylinder shown above.

2. Write the formula for the volume of a cone. Then write an equation for the volume of the cone above.

3. **Attend to precision.** How much of the total volume of the cylinder lies outside of the cone? Does your answer depend on the radius or height of the cylinder?

4. Write an expression for the volume of the region inside the cylinder and outside the cone.

My Notes

A hemisphere of radius r is placed next to the cylinder. The height of the hemisphere is also r, the same as the cylinder. Suppose a plane parallel to the base of the cylinder passes through both solids at a height x, as illustrated in the diagram.

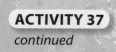

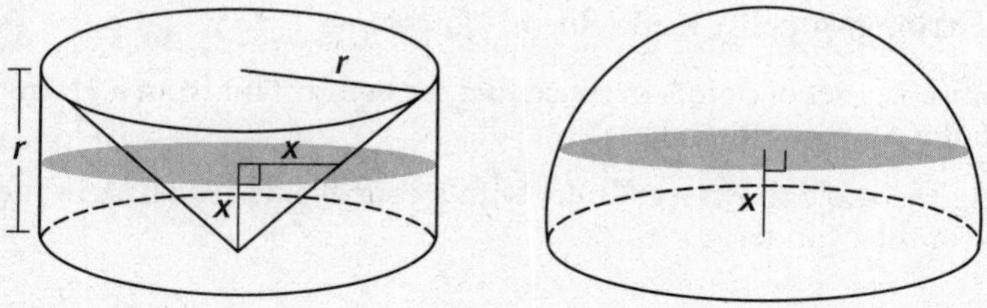

5. **Construct viable arguments.** Explain why the horizontal segment in the cross section of the cylinder and cone is also labeled x.

6. The cross section of the cylinder that lies outside the cone forms an ***annulus***, or ring shape.
   a. How can you use the formula for the area of a circle to find the area of an annulus?

   b. Write an expression for the area of the cross-sectional annulus.

7. The cross section of the hemisphere is a circle. Draw a triangle to help determine an expression for the radius of this circle. Explain what you did.

8. Show that the cross sections of the hemisphere and the region of the cylinder that lies outside the cone have the same area.

My Notes

9. Use the information from the previous items to derive the formula for the volume of a sphere. Write a paragraph to explain your reasoning.

10. Model with mathematics. A grain silo is in the shape of a cylinder with a hemispherical top. Its radius is 15 feet and its height (including the top) is 80 feet. Find the volume of the silo.

Check Your Understanding

11. Refer to the figure before Item 5. How do you know that the hemisphere of radius r was the same height as the cylinder of height r?

12. Reason abstractly. Explain why the cross-sectional areas are equal for the parallel bases that contain the bases of the cylinders.

LESSON 37-2 PRACTICE

13. A sphere of radius r fits snugly inside a cylinder.
a. What is the height of the cylinder?
b. Write an expression for the volume of the cylinder that lies outside of the sphere. Justify your work.

14. Consider the silo from Item 10.
a. Another silo will be built with the same shape and height, but a different radius. If the volume must increase by 10 percent, what should the new radius be? Round to the nearest tenth of a foot.
b. By how much would the height need to change to increase the volume of the silo by 10 percent? Assume the radius stays the same.

15. A wooden bead is in the shape of a sphere with radius R cm. A hole is drilled through the bead that has a radius r cm.
a. Use volume formulas to show that the volume of wood for the bead is approximately $2\pi R\left(\frac{2}{3}R^2 - r^2\right)$.
b. Reason quantitatively. Does the expression overestimate or underestimate the volume? Explain how you know.

My Notes

Learning Targets:

- Informally derive the formula for the volume of a sphere.
- Understand the concept of a limit.
- Represent a volume using sums and limits.

SUGGESTED LEARNING STRATEGIES: Create Representations, Think-Pair-Share, Sharing and Responding, Paraphrasing

Most all of the parallel cross sections of a sphere are circles. If these circles were cylinders with a very small height, summing the volumes of the cylinders approximates the volume of the sphere. In the figure below, the *bottom edge* of each cylinder lies on the surface of the hemisphere.

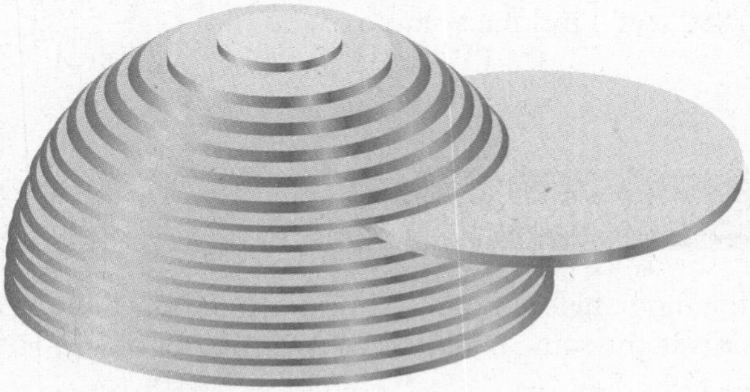

1. Suppose the hemisphere above has radius r, and is composed of n cylinders with the same height. Write an expression for the height of a cylinder in terms of r.

2. Use Parts a, b, and c below to find an expression for the radius of the ith cylinder, where the first cylinder has a radius r.

a. What is the distance from the center of the base of the hemisphere to the center of the bottom of the ith cylinder? Use your answer from Item 1.

b. Make sense of problems. What is the distance from the center of the base of the hemisphere to any point on the edge of the bottom of the ith cylinder? How do you know?

My Notes

c. Use your answers from Parts a and b to find an expression for the radius of the ith cylinder. Explain your reasoning or show your work.

3. Explain or show why the expression for the volume of the ith cylinder can be written as $\frac{\pi r^3}{n}\left(1-\left(\frac{(i-1)}{n}\right)^2\right)$.

4. Using sigma notation and the expression from Item 3, the total volume of the cylinders is given by $\sum_{i=1}^{n}\frac{\pi r^3}{n}\left(1-\left(\frac{(i-1)}{n}\right)^2\right)$.

a. Make use of structure. Why can this also be written as $\frac{\pi r^3}{n}\sum_{i=1}^{n}\left(1-\left(\frac{(i-1)}{n}\right)^2\right)$?

b. By breaking the summation into two separate sums, show that the expression can be written as $\pi r^3 - \frac{\pi r^3}{n^3}\sum_{i=1}^{n}(i-1)^2$.

MATH TIP

A property of summation is that $\sum_{i=1}^{n}(a_i + b_i) = \sum_{i=1}^{n}a_i + \sum_{i=1}^{n}b_i$.

My Notes

c. Explain why the expression $\pi r^3 - \frac{\pi r^3}{n^3}\sum_{i=1}^{n-1} i^2$ is equivalent to the expression from Part b by considering the terms of the sum.

5. Previously, you used mathematical induction to prove that $\sum_{i=1}^{n} i^2 = \frac{n(n+1)(2n+1)}{6}$.

a. If you replace n with $n - 1$ on each side of the equation, is the equation still true? Justify your answer.

b. Rewrite the equation with n replaced by $n - 1$.

6. Using information from Items 4 and 5, show that the total volume of the cylinders is given by $\pi r^3\left(\frac{4n^3 + 3n^2 - n}{6n^3}\right)$.

Check Your Understanding

7. In general, will the stack of n cylinders underestimate or overestimate the volume of the sphere? Refer to the description of the diagram to help explain your answer.

8. Evaluate the expression in Item 6 for $n = 1$. Explain the result in terms of the previous Item.

My Notes

Recall that the value to which a convergent sequence approaches is its ***limit***. In general, the limit of an expression or function is the value it approaches when the variable approaches some value.

The notation $\lim_{x \to a}$ is read "the limit as x approaches a" and can be used in a variety of situations.

9. The sequence $\{a_n\} = \frac{1}{2}, \frac{3}{4}, \frac{5}{6}, \frac{7}{8}, \ldots$ is convergent.

a. As n increases without bound, what happens to a_n?

b. Complete: $\lim_{n \to \infty} \{a_n\} =$ ____

10. The function $f(x) = \frac{3x-2}{5x+1}$ has both a vertical asymptote and a horizontal asymptote.

a. As x increases without bound, what happens to $f(x)$? Write this using limit notation.

b. Reason abstractly. Complete: $\lim_{n \to \_} f(x)$ does not exist. Describe what this means.

11. Use a calculator to complete the table.

n	$\frac{4n^3 + 3n^2 - n}{6n^3}$
1	1
10	0.715
100	
1000	
10,000	

My Notes

12. What do you think the exact value of $\lim_{n\to\infty} \frac{4n^3 + 3n^2 - 6n}{6n^3}$ is? Support your answer with evidence from the preceding items.

13. Write an equation using a limit that shows the volume of the stack of cylinders as the number of cylinders increases without bound. Use it to justify the formula for the volume of a sphere.

Check Your Understanding

14. Determine $\lim_{n\to\infty} \frac{(4n-1)^2}{5n^2}$ by using a calculator and by considering the leading coefficients of the numerator and denominator.

15. Could you use the cylinder method from this lesson to determine the volume of a cone? What about the volume of a regular tetrahedron? Explain.

LESSON 37-3 PRACTICE

16. Suppose the hemisphere from this lesson was split into n shapes of the same width, but cut *perpendicular* to the base.

a. Explain why only half of the hemisphere would need to be used.

b. Describe the shapes that are cut. What volume formula could you use to represent each piece?

17. Determine the value of each limit by making a table of values that get closer to the value that the variable is approaching.

a. $\lim_{n\to\infty} \frac{n-3}{4n^2}$

b. $\lim_{n\to 2} \frac{n-2}{2-n}$

18. **Construct viable arguments.** Consider your results from Item 17. Do you think an expression or function must be defined at the value a limit approaches in order for the limit to exist?

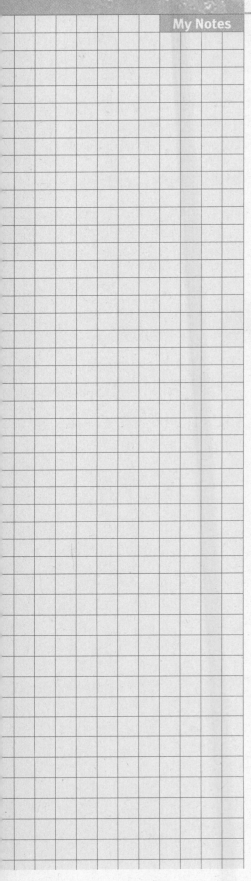

ACTIVITY 37 PRACTICE

Write your answers on notebook paper. Show your work.

Lesson 37-1

1. The cat scratch post shown is formed using 110 square pieces of cardboard. The pieces can be turned to form different shapes.

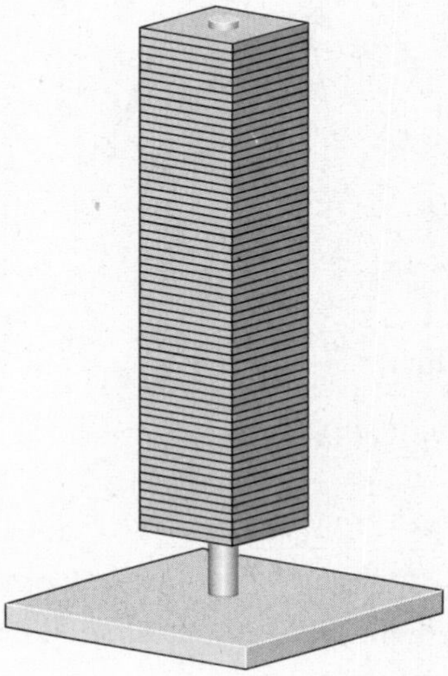

   a. What simple solid figure can be formed by arranging each cardboard piece on top of the next?
   b. Each piece of cardboard is 4 inches on a side and $\frac{1}{4}$ inch thick. Use Cavalieri's Principle to find the volume of the cardboard in the scratch post.
   c. Do you think an oblique square prism can be formed with the scratch post? Explain your reasoning.

2. A cube and an oblique cylinder have the same height and equal cross-sectional areas.
   a. If the volume of the cube is 512 cubic meters, what is the radius of the oblique cylinder?
   b. What is the volume of the cylinder?

3. The triangular prism has a 30°-60°-90° triangle for a base, and hypotenuse x. The cylinder has a radius r and the same height as the prism. Assume that Cavalieri's Principle applies to the figures. Write an equation that relates x and r. Justify.

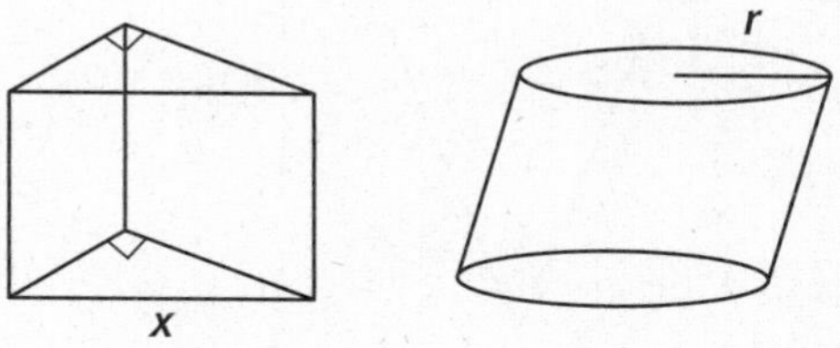

4. Three rectangular prisms all have the same volume. If Cavalieri's Principle were to apply to any two of the prisms, what must be true about the dimensions of the prisms? Explain your reasoning.

Lesson 37-2

5. A candy company creates a spherical chocolate ball. At the center of the ball is a spherical pool of liquid chocolate.
   a. If the radius of the pool is 1 cm and the radius of the ball is 2 cm, what is the volume of solid chocolate?
   b. If you slice through the chocolate at a random position, what is the likelihood that the liquid chocolate will ooze out of the ball? Explain your reasoning.

6. A right cone fits snugly inside a hemisphere. The base of the hemisphere is the base of the cone. Write an expression that gives the volume of the hemisphere that lies outside of the cone.

7. A spherical scoop of vanilla ice cream is plopped on top of the cone shown.

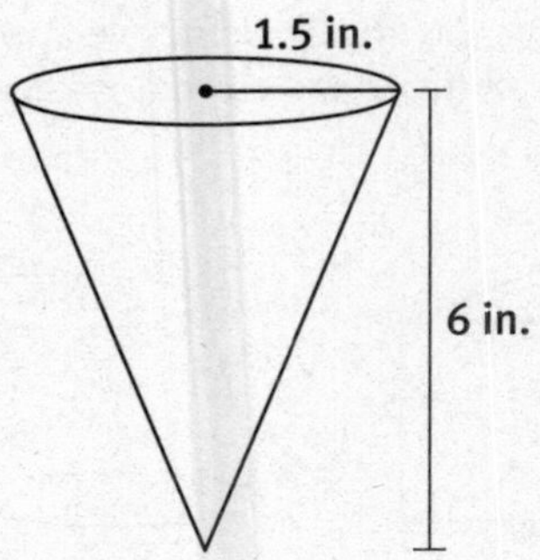

a. If the scoop of ice cream has a radius of 1.5 inches, how does the volume of the scoop compare with the volume of the cone? Explain.

b. Suppose the scoop of ice cream has a radius of 1.2 inches. If the scoop completely melts, how high will be level of melted ice cream be inside the cone? Justify.

Lesson 37-3

8. Dennis draws the figure below. He wants to derive the formula for the volume of a tetrahedron. The solid cross section has lateral faces perpendicular to the base of the tetrahedron.

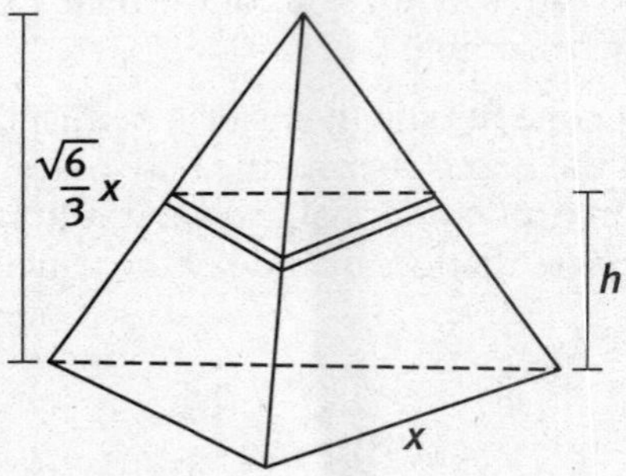

Describe the general approach Dennis can take to derive the formula for the volume of the tetrahedron.

9. Francine divides the square pyramid shown into n rectangular prisms. She derives an expression to find the volume of the pyramid. Which could be that expression?

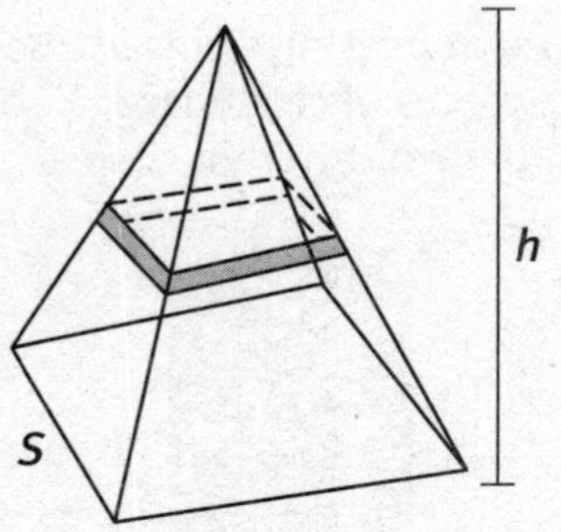

A. $\lim\limits_{n \to \infty} \dfrac{hS^2}{n}\left(\dfrac{(2n-1)(n-1)}{6n}\right)$

B. $hS^2 \lim\limits_{n \to \infty}\left(\dfrac{(2n-1)(n-1)}{6n}\right)$

C. $\lim\limits_{n \to \infty} \dfrac{hS^2}{n}\left(\dfrac{(4n-1)(n-1)}{6n}\right)$

D. $\lim\limits_{n \to \infty} \dfrac{hS^2}{3}\left(\dfrac{(2n-1)(n-1)}{6n^2}\right)$

10. Complete the table of values. Then make a conjecture about $\lim\limits_{x \to 0} \dfrac{\sin x}{x}$.

x	$\dfrac{\sin x}{x}$
0.5	
0.05	
0.0005	
0.00005	

MATHEMATICAL PRACTICES
Look For and Express Regularity in Repeated Reasoning

11. Describe how the idea of a limit applies to previous topics you have studied, such as sequences and asymptotes of functions, as well as the topics in this activity.

You work as a mathematician at a company that makes ornaments and figurines. A new snowman design will involve 3 spherical steel balls, which will be stacked and attached vertically to form the snowman. Your boss gives you the following information about the design:

- The height of the snowman will be 5 centimeters.
- Each ball will be $\frac{2}{3}$ as tall as the ball beneath it.

1. Write 3 equations that relate the radius of each ball. Use the information that your boss gave you.

2. Write a matrix equation to represent the equations from Item 1. Identify the coefficient matrix, the variable matrix, and the constant matrix.

3. The production department needs to know the radius of each ball to the nearest hundredth of a centimeter.

a. Solve the matrix equation.
b. Write each radius to the specifications required for production.

4. To control costs, your boss says that he does not want the snowman to require more than 70 cubic centimeters of steel.

a. Use the values you found in Item 3b to demonstrate if the snowman meets his requirements.

b. To impress your boss, you decide to decrease the height of the snowman by as little as possible, and still meet the volume requirement. You will also maintain the $\frac{2}{3}$ ratio of the height of the balls. Write a plan describing how you can do this.

c. Find the new radii of the balls to the nearest hundredth of a centimeter. By how much did the height of the snowman decrease?

Scoring Guide	Exemplary	Proficient	Emerging	Incomplete
	The solution demonstrates these characteristics:			
Mathematics Knowledge and Thinking (Item 2)	• Clear and accurate understanding of how to write a matrix equation and solve it	• A functional understanding of using matrices to solve systems	• Partial understanding of matrices and using them to solve systems	• Little or no understanding of matrices
Problem Solving (Items 3, 4a, 4c)	• An appropriate and efficient strategy that results in a correct answer	• A strategy that may include unnecessary steps but results in a correct answer	• A strategy that results in some incorrect answers	• No clear strategy when solving problems
Mathematical Modeling / Representations (Items 1, 4a)	• Clear and accurate understanding of modeling systems using equations • Clear and accurate understanding of how to get data from a matrix and relate it to a problem	• A functional understanding of modeling systems using equations • Mostly accurate understanding of how to get data from a matrix and relate it to a problem	• Partial understanding of modeling systems using equations • Partial understanding of how to get data from a matrix and relate it to a problem	• Little or no understanding of systems of equations • Inaccurate or incomplete understanding of how to get data from a matrix and relate it to a problem
Reasoning and Communication (Item 4b)	• Precise use of appropriate math terms and language to describe a plan to satisfy the problem using formulae and matrices	• Correct characterization of the data from the matrix with an appropriate attempt to satisfy the scenario	• Misleading or confusing characterization of how the data from the matrix can be used to satisfy the scenario	• Incomplete or inaccurate characterization of data from the matrix and how to use it

Symbols

$f(x)$	function
$f^{-1}(x)$	inverse function
a_n	the *n*th term of *a* sequence
$\|a\|$	absolute value
$\sqrt[n]{}$	*n*th root
(x, y)	ordered pair
(x, y, z)	ordered triple
$\begin{bmatrix} a & b \\ c & d \end{bmatrix}$	2 • 2 matrix
$\begin{vmatrix} a & b \\ c & d \end{vmatrix} = ad - bc$	
or	determinant of a matrix
$\det\begin{vmatrix} a & b \\ c & d \end{vmatrix} = ad - bc$	
$a + bi$	complex number
$\sqrt{-1} = i$	imaginary number
!	factorial

Resources

Formulas

Linear Equations	
Slope	$m = \frac{y_2 - y_1}{x_2 - x_1}$
Slope-intercept form	$y = mx + b$
Point-slope form	$y - y_1 = m(x - x_1)$
Standard form	$Ax + By = C$

Quadratic Equations	
Standard form	$ax^2 + bx + c = 0$
Quadratic formula	$x = \frac{-b \pm \sqrt{b^2 - 4ac}}{2a}$

Coordinate Geometry	
Distance	$d = \sqrt{(x_2 - x_1)^2 + (y_2 - y_1)^2}$
Midpoint	$m = \left(\frac{x_1 + x_2}{2}, \frac{y_1 + y_2}{2}\right)$

Sequences and Series	
***n*th term of an arithmetic sequence**	$a_n = a_1 + (n - 1)d$
Sum of an arithmetic sequence	$S_n = \frac{n}{2}(a_1 + a_n)$ $S_n = \frac{n}{2}(2a_1 + (n-1)d)$
***n*th term of a geometric sequence**	$a_n = a_1 r^{n-1}$
Sum of a geometric sequence	$S_n = \frac{a_1(1 - r^n)}{1 - r}$ $S_n = \frac{a_1 - ra_n}{1 - r}$

Other Formulas

Pythagorean Theorem	$a^2 + b^2 = c^2$, where c is the hypotenuse of a right triangle
Direct variation	$y = kx$
Inverse variation	$y = \frac{k}{x}$

Probability and Statistics

Permutations	${}_nP_r = \frac{n!}{(n-r)!}$
Combinations	${}_nC_r = \frac{n!}{r!(n-r)!}$
Standard Deviation	$\sigma = \sqrt{\frac{(x_1 - \overline{x})^2 + (x_2 - \overline{x})^2 + \ldots + (x_n - \overline{x})^2}{n}}$

Trigonometry

For an acute angle A in a right triangle:

$$\sin A = \frac{\text{opposite}}{\text{hypotenuse}}$$

$$\cos A = \frac{\text{adjacent}}{\text{hypotenuse}}$$

$$\tan A = \frac{\text{opposite}}{\text{adjacent}}$$

Law of Sines	$\frac{\sin A}{a} = \frac{\sin B}{b} = \frac{\sin C}{c}$
Law of Cosines	$a^2 = b^2 + c^2 - 2bc \cos A$
Area of Triangles (Heron's Formula):	Area $= \sqrt{s(s-a)(s-b)(s-c)}$, where s is the semiperimeter

Trigonometric Identities

Reciprocal identities

$$\csc\theta = \frac{1}{\cos\theta},\ \sec\theta = \frac{1}{\cos\theta},\ \cot\theta = \frac{1}{\tan\theta}$$

Quotient identities

$$\tan\theta = \frac{\sin\theta}{\cos\theta},\ \cot\theta = \frac{\cos\theta}{\sin\theta}$$

Pythagorean identities

$$\sin^2\theta + \cos^2\theta = 1$$

$$\tan^2\theta + 1 = \sec^2\theta$$

$$\cot^2\theta + 1 = \csc^2\theta$$

Cofunction identities

$$\sin\left(\frac{\pi}{2} - x\right) = \cos x \quad \cos\left(\frac{\pi}{2} - x\right) = \sin x$$

$$\sec\left(\frac{\pi}{2} - x\right) = \csc x \quad \csc\left(\frac{\pi}{2} - x\right) = \sec x$$

$$\tan\left(\frac{\pi}{2} - x\right) = \cot x \quad \cot\left(\frac{\pi}{2} - x\right) = \tan x$$

Sum and difference identities

$$\sin(A \pm B) = \sin A \cos B \pm \cos A \sin B$$

$$\cos(A \pm B) = \cos A \cos B \mp \sin A \sin B$$

$$\tan(A \pm B) = \frac{\tan A \pm \tan B}{1 \mp \tan A \tan B}$$

Double-angle and half-angle identities

$$\sin(2A) = 2\sin A \cos A$$

$$\cos(2A) = \cos^2 A - \sin^2 A \quad \text{or} \quad 1 - 2\sin^2 A \quad \text{or} \quad 2\cos^2 A - 1$$

$$\tan(2A) = \frac{2\tan A}{1 - \tan^2 A}$$

$$\sin\frac{u}{2} = \pm\sqrt{\frac{1-\cos u}{2}} \quad \cos\frac{u}{2} = \pm\sqrt{\frac{1+\cos u}{2}} \quad \tan\frac{u}{2} = \frac{\sin u}{1+\cos u}$$

Odd and even identities

$$\sin(-x) = -\sin x$$

$$\cos(-x) = \cos x \tan(-x) = -\tan x$$

Properties of Exponents

For any numbers a and b and all integers m and n,

$a^m \cdot a^n = a^{m+n}$

$(a^m)^n = a^{mn}$

$(ab)^m = a^m b^m$

$\frac{a^m}{a^n} = a^{m-n}, a \neq 0$

$\left(\frac{a}{b}\right)^m = \frac{a^m}{a^m}, b \neq 0$

$a^{-n} = \frac{1}{a^n}, a \neq 0 \ \frac{1}{a^{-n}} = a^n, a \neq 0$

$a^0 = 1, a \neq 0$

Properties of Radicals

In the expression $\sqrt[n]{a}$,

a is the radicand, $\sqrt{\ }$ is the radical symbol and n is the root index.

$\sqrt[n]{a} = b$, if $b^n = a$ b is the nth root of a.

$a\sqrt{b} \pm c\sqrt{b} = (a \pm c)\sqrt{b}$, where $b \geq 0$.

$(a\sqrt{b})(c\sqrt{d}) = ac\sqrt{bd}$, where $b \geq 0, d \geq 0$.

$\frac{a\sqrt{b}}{c\sqrt{d}} = \frac{a}{c}\sqrt{\frac{b}{d}}$, where $b \geq 0, d > 0$.

Properties of Logarithms

For all positive x, y, a, and b and $a \neq 1$.

$\log_a b = c$ means that $a^c = b$

$\log_a a^x = x$ and $a^{\log_a x} = x$

$\log_a(xy) = \log_a x + \log_a y$

$\log_a\left(\frac{x}{y}\right) = \log_a x - \log_a y$

$\log_a (x^p) = p \log_a x$

$\log_a x = \frac{\log_b x}{\log_b a}, b \neq 1$

SpringBoard Learning Strategies

READING STRATEGIES

STRATEGY	DEFINITION	PURPOSE
Activating Prior Knowledge	Recalling what is known about a concept and using that information to make a connection to a new concept	Helps students establish connections between what they already know and how that knowledge is related to new learning
Chunking the Activity	Grouping a set of items/questions for specific purposes	Provides an opportunity to relate concepts and assess student understanding before moving on to a new concept or grouping
Close Reading	Reading text word for word, sentence by sentence, and line by line to make a detailed analysis of meaning	Assists in developing a comprehensive understanding of the text
Graphic Organizer	Arranging information into maps and charts	Builds comprehension and facilitates discussion by representing information in visual form
Interactive Word Wall	Visually displaying vocabulary words to serve as a classroom reference of words and groups of words as they are introduced, used, and mastered over the course of a year	Provides a visual reference for new concepts, aids understanding for reading and writing, and builds word knowledge and awareness
KWL Chart (Know, Want to Know, Learn)	Activating prior knowledge by identifying what students know, determining what they want to learn, and having them reflect on what they learned	Assists in organizing information and reflecting on learning to build content knowledge and increase comprehension
Marking the Text	Highlighting, underlining, and/or annotating text to focus on key information to help understand the text or solve the problem	Helps the reader identify important information in the text and make notes about the interpretation of tasks required and concepts to apply to reach a solution
Predict and Confirm	Making conjectures about what results will develop in an activity; confirming or modifying the conjectures based on outcomes	Stimulates thinking by making, checking, and correcting predictions based on evidence from the outcome
Levels of Questions	Developing literal, interpretive, and universal questions about the text while reading the text	Focuses reading, helps in gaining insight into the text by seeking answers, and prepares one for group and class discussions
Paraphrasing	Restating in your own words the essential information in a text or problem description	Assists with comprehension, recall of information, and problem solving
Role Play	Assuming the role of a character in a scenario	Helps interpret and visualize information in a problem
Shared Reading	Reading the text aloud (usually by the teacher) as students follow along silently, or reading a text aloud by the teacher and students	Helps auditory learners do decode, interpret, and analyze challenging text
Summarizing	Giving a brief statement of the main points in a text	Assists with comprehension and provides practice with identifying and restating key information
Think Aloud	Talking through a difficult text or problem by describing what the text means	Helps in comprehending the text, understanding the components of a problem, and thinking about possible paths to a solution
Visualization	Picturing (mentally and/or literally) what is read in the text	Increases reading comprehension and promotes active engagement with the text
Vocabulary Organizer	Using a graphic organizer to keep an ongoing record of vocabulary words with definitions, pictures, notes, and connections between words	Supports a systematic process of learning vocabulary

SpringBoard Learning Strategies

COLLABORATIVE STRATEGIES

STRATEGY	DEFINITION	PURPOSE
Critique Reasoning	Through collaborative discussion, respond to the arguments of others; question the use of mathematical terminology, assumptions, and conjectures to improve understanding and to justify and communicate conclusions	Helps students learn from each other as they make connections between mathematical concepts and learn to verbalize their understanding and support their arguments with reasoning and data that make sense to peers
Debriefing	Discussing the understanding of a concept to lead to consensus on its meaning	Helps clarify misconceptions and deepen understanding of content
Discussion Groups	Working within groups to discuss content, to create problem solutions, and to explain and justify a solution	Aids understanding through the sharing of ideas, interpretation of concepts, and analysis of problem scenarios
Group Presentation	Presenting information as a collaborative group	Allows opportunities to present collaborative solutions and to share responsibility for delivering information to an audience
Jigsaw	Reading different texts or passages, students become "experts" and then move to a new group to share their information; after sharing, students go back to the original group to share new knowledge	Provides opportunities to summarize and present information to others in a way that facilitates understanding of a text or passage (or multiple texts or passages) without having each student read all texts
Sharing and Responding	Communicating with another person or a small group of peers who respond to a piece of writing or proposed problem solution	Gives students the opportunity to discuss their work with peers, to make suggestions for improvement to the work of others, and/or to receive appropriate and relevant feedback on their own work
Think-Pair-Share	Thinking through a problem alone, pairing with a partner to share ideas, and concluding by sharing results with the class	Enables the development of initial ideas that are then tested with a partner in preparation for revising ideas and sharing them with a larger group

WRITING STRATEGIES

Drafting	Writing a text in an initial form	Assists in getting first thoughts in written form and ready for revising and refining
Note Taking	Creating a record of information while reading a text or listening to a speaker	Helps in organizing ideas and processing information
Prewriting	Brainstorming, either alone or in groups, and refining thoughts and organizing ideas prior to writing	Provides a tool for beginning the writing process and determining the focus of the writing
Quickwrite	Writing for a short, specific amount of time about a designated topic	Helps generate ideas in a short time
RAFT (Role of Writer, Audience, Format, and Topic)	Writing a text by consciously choosing a viewpoint (role of the writer), identifying an audience, choosing a format for the writing, and choosing a topic	Provides a framework for communicating in writing and helps focus the writer's ideas for specific points of communication
Self Revision / Peer Revision	Working alone or with a partner to examine a piece of writing for accuracy and clarity	Provides an opportunity to review work and to edit it for clarity of the ideas presented as well as accuracy of grammar, punctuation, and spelling

SpringBoard Learning Strategies

PROBLEM-SOLVING STRATEGIES

Construct an Argument	Use mathematical reasoning to present assumptions about mathematical situations, support conjectures with mathematically relevant and accurate data, and provide a logical progression of ideas leading to a conclusion that makes sense	Helps develop the process of evaluating mathematical information, developing reasoning skills, and enhancing communication skills in supporting conjectures and conclusions
Create a Plan	Analyzing the tasks in a problem and creating a process for completing the tasks by finding information needed for the tasks, interpreting data, choosing how to solve a problem, communicating the results, and verifying accuracy	Assists in breaking tasks into smaller parts and identifying the steps needed to complete the entire task
Create Representations	Creating pictures, tables, graphs, lists, equations, models, and/or verbal expressions to interpret text or data	Helps organize information using multiple ways to present data and to answer a question or show a problem solution
Guess and Check	Guessing the solution to a problem, and then checking that the guess fits the information in the problem and is an accurate solution	Allows exploration of different ways to solve a problem; guess and check may be used when other strategies for solving are not obvious
Identify a Subtask	Breaking a problem into smaller pieces whose outcomes lead to a solution	Helps to organize the pieces of a complex problem and reach a complete solution
Look for a Pattern	Observing information or creating visual representations to find a trend	Helps to identify patterns that may be used to make predictions
Simplify the Problem	Using "friendlier" numbers to solve a problem	Provides insight into the problem or the strategies needed to solve the problem
Work Backward	Tracing a possible answer back through the solution process to the starting point	Provides another way to check possible answers for accuracy
Use Manipulatives	Using objects to examine relationships between the information given	Provides a visual representation of data that supports comprehension of information in a problem

Glossary
Glosario

A

absolute value of a complex number (p. 455) The distance from the origin to z on the complex plane, written as $|a + bi|$ or $|z|$. Also called modulus.
valor absoluto de un número complejo (pág. 455) Distancia del origen a z sobre el plano complejo, que se escribe $|a + bi|$ o $|z|$.

altitude (p. 324) The perpendicular line drawn from the base of a triangle to the opposite vertex.
altitud (pág. 324) La recta perpendicular trazada entre la base de un triángulo y el vértice opuesto.

ambiguous case [SSA] (p. 337) The situation in which two sides and an opposite angle of a triangle are given and it is possible to have zero, one, or two distinct triangles.
caso ambiguo [SSA] (pág. 337) Situación en la que dos lados y un ángulo opuesto de un triángulo están dados y es posible tener cero, uno o dos triángulos distintos.

amplitude (p. 206) Half the difference of the maximum and minimum values of a periodic function.
amplitud (pág. 206) Mitad de la diferencia entre los valores máximo y mínimo de una función periódica.

angle in standard position (p. 187) An angle whose vertex is at the origin and whose initial side is on the positive x-axis.
ángulo en posición estándar (pág. 187) Ángulo cuyo vértice está en el origen y cuyo lado inicial está sobre el eje de las x positivo.

angle of declination (p. 247) The angle from the horizontal to a point below the horizontal.
ángulo de depresión (pág. 247) Ángulo desde la horizontal hasta un punto bajo la horizontal.

angle of elevation (p. 251) The angle from the horizontal to a point above the horizontal.
ángulo de elevación (pág. 251) Ángulo desde la horizontal hasta un punto sobre la horizontal.

angular velocity (p. 425) The rate at which an object rotates, defined as $\frac{\Delta\theta}{\Delta t}$ where $\Delta\theta$ measures the change of the angle of rotation and Δt measures the change of time.
velocidad angular (pág. 425) Tasa a la que rota un objeto, definida como $\frac{\Delta\theta}{\Delta t}$, donde $\Delta\theta$ mide el cambio en el ángulo de rotación y Δt mide el cambio de tiempo.

annulus (p. 536) A ring shape.
corona circular (pág. 536) Una figura con forma de aro.

argument of a complex number (p. 456) An angle formed by the positive real axis and the line segment connecting the origin to z on the complex plane.
argumento de un número complejo (pág. 456) Ángulo formado por el eje real positivo y el segmento de recta que conecta el origen con z sobre el plano complejo.

arithmetic sequence (p. 11) A sequence with a constant difference between consecutive terms.
progresión aritmética (pág. 11) Sucesión que tiene una diferencia constante entre términos consecutivos.

arithmetic series (p. 12) The sum of all the terms of an arithmetic sequence.
serie aritmética (pág. 12) Suma de los términos de una progresión aritmética.

B

base of a logarithm (p. 61) The factor which is raised to a power to yield a product. If b and x are positive real numbers with $b \neq 1$, then the logarithm of x base b is written as $\log_b x$ and is defined as: $\log_b x = y$ if and only if $b^y = x$.
base de un logaritmo (pág. 61) Factor que se eleva a una potencia para producir un producto. Si b y x son números reales positivos con $b \neq 1$, entonces el logaritmo de x en base b se escribe $\log_b x$ y se define como: $\log_b x = y$ si y sólo si $b^y = x$.

bounded function (p. 161) A function f is bounded on an interval if there is some constant M such that $|f(x)| < M$ for all x in that interval.
función acotada (pág. 161) Una función f es acotada en un intervalo si existe una constante M tal que $|f(x)| < M$ para todo x en ese intervalo.

C

cardioid (p. 404) The graph of a polar equation in the form $r = a \pm b \sin\theta$ or $r = a \pm b \cos\theta$, where $a = b$.
cardioide (pág. 404) Gráfica de una ecuación polar de la forma $r = a \pm b\text{sen}\theta$ o $r = a \pm b\cos\theta$, donde $a = b$.

Cavalieri's Principle (p. 532) If every plane parallel to these two planes intersects both figures with equal cross sections, then the two figures have equal volumes.
el principio de Cavalieri (pág. 532) Si cada plano paralelo a estos dos planos intersecta ambas figuras con secciones transversales iguales, entonces las dos figuras poseen volúmenes iguales.

change of base formula (p. 65) A formula that allows you to express any logarithm as the quotient of two logarithms that both have the same base. See Properties of Logarithms.
fórmula de cambio de base (pág. 65) Fórmula que permite expresar cualquier logaritmo como cociente de dos logaritmos que tienen ambos la misma base. Ver Propiedades de los logaritmos.

circle (p. 36) The set of all points in a plane that are equidistant from a fixed point called the center.
círculo (pág. 36) Conjunto de todos los puntos de un plano que son equidistantes de un punto fijo llamado centro.

coefficient matrix (p. 517) The matrix consisting of the coefficients of the variable terms in a system of linear equations in standard form.
matriz de coeficientes (pág. 517) La matriz que contiene los coeficientes de los términos variables en un sistema de ecuaciones lineales en forma estándar.

cofunction identity (p. 295) A trigonometric identity in which one trigonometric function is written as another trigonometric function. The sine and cosine functions are cofunctions. The secant and secant functions are cofunctions. The tangent and cotangent functions are cofunctions.

cofunción trigonométrica (pág. 295) Una identidad trigonométrica en la cual una función trigonométrica se escribe en términos de otra función trigonométrica. Las funciones seno y coseno son cofunciones. La secante y cosecante son cofunciones. La tangente y cotangente son cofunciones.

column matrix (p. 499) A matrix that has dimension $m \times 1$.

matriz columna (pág. 499) Una matriz con las dimensiones $m \times 1$.

common logarithm (p. 61) The exponent when the positive real number x is written as a power of 10. It can be written as $\log_{10} x$ and is also written as $\log x$. $\log x = y$ means $10^y = x$.

logaritmo común (pág. 61) El exponente, cuando el número real positivo x se escribe como potencia de 10. Puede escribirse $\log_{10} x$ y también puede escribirse $\log x$. $\log x = y$ significa que $10^y = x$.

common ratio (p. 20) The ratio of a term to its preceding term in a geometric sequence. The common ratio is a constant usually denoted by r.

razón común (pág. 20) La razón entre un término y el término precedente en una secuencia geométrica. La razón común es una constante normalmente denotada por r.

Complex Conjugate Theorem (p. 144) For a polynomial equation with real coefficients, if $a + bi$ is a root and a and b are real numbers, then the complex conjugate of $a + bi$, $a - bi$, is also a root of the polynomial equation.

Teorema de los complejos conjugados (pág. 144) Para una ecuación polinómica con coeficientes reales, si $a + bi$ es una raíz y a y b son números reales, entonces el complejo conjugado de $a + bi$, $a - bi$, también es una raíz de la ecuación polinómica.

complex number (p. 454) A number in the form $a + bi$, where a and b are real numbers and $i = \sqrt{-1}$.

número complejo (pág. 454) Un número con la forma $a + bi$, donde a y b son números reales y donde $i = \sqrt{-1}$.

composition of functions (p. 103) An operation that combines functions in such a way that the output of one function is used as the input for the other.

composición de las funciones (pág. 103) Operación que combina funciones de manera tal que la salida de una función se usa como entrada para la otra.

concentric circles (p. 470) Circles that share the same center.

círculos concéntricos (pág. 470) Dos o más círculos que tienen el mismo centro.

conic section (p. 348) A conic section is formed by the intersection of a plane and a double-napped cone.

sección cónica (pág. 348) Una sección cónica se forma por la intersección de un plano y un cono doble.

conjugate axis of a hyperbola (p. 368) The segment perpendicular to the transverse axis passing through the center of the hyperbola. It is the line of symmetry between the branches.

eje conjugado de una hipérbola (pág. 368) Segmento de recta perpendicular al eje transversal, que pasa por el centro de una hipérbola. Está sobre el eje de simetría y entre las ramas.

constant matrix (p. 517) The matrix consisting of the constant terms in a system of linear equations in standard form.

matriz de constantes (pág. 517) La matriz que contiene los términos constantes en un sistema de ecuaciones lineales en forma estándar.

continuous at a point A function $f(x)$ where $x = c$ is continuous if these conditions are met: $f(c)$ exists; $\lim_{x \to c} f(x)$ exists; and $f(c) = \lim_{x \to c} f(x)$.

continua en un punto Una función $f(x)$, donde $x = c$, es continua si se cumplen estas condiciones: $f(c)$ existe; $\lim_{x \to c} f(x)$ existe; y $f(c) = \lim_{x \to c} f(x)$.

continuous on an interval A function $f(x)$ is continuous on an interval if it is continuous at each value of x in the interval.

continua en un intervalo Una función $f(x)$ es continua en un intervalo si es continua para cada valor de x en el intervalo.

converge (p. 27) An infinite sequence converges if it approaches some number L as n increases without bound.

converger (pág. 27) Una sucesión infinita converge si se aproxima a cierto número L a medida que n aumenta sin límite.

converse (p. 534) The converse of the statement "if p then q" is "if q then p."

conversa (pág. 534) La conversa lógica de la proposición "si p entonces q" es "si q entonces p".

correlation coefficient (p. 92) A unit-less number between -1 and 1, inclusive, that indicates the strength of the linear relationship existing between two numerical variables.

coeficiente de correlación (pág. 92) Número sin unidades entre -1 y 1, inclusive, que indica la fortaleza de la relación lineal existente entre dos variables numéricas.

cosecant (p. 219) The cosecant function is defined as follows: $\csc\theta = \frac{r}{y}$, where $x^2 + y^2 = r^2$. This is the reciprocal function of the sine function.

cosecante (pág. 219) La función cosecante se define de la manera siguiente: $\csc\theta = \frac{r}{y}$, donde $x^2 + y^2 = r^2$. La cosecante es la función recíproca de la función seno.

cosine (p. 215) The cosine function is defined as follows: $\cos\theta = \frac{x}{r}$, where $x^2 + y^2 = r^2$.

coseno (pág. 215) La función coseno se define de la manera siguiente: $\cos\theta = \frac{x}{r}$, donde $x^2 + y^2 = r^2$.

cotangent (p. 219) The cotangent function is defined as follows: $\cot\theta = \frac{x}{y}$, where $x^2 + y^2 = r^2$. This is the reciprocal function of the tangent function.

cotangente (pág. 219) La función cotangente se define de la siguiente manera: $\cot\theta = \frac{x}{y}$, donde $x^2 + y^2 = r^2$. La función cotangente es la función recíproca de la función tangente.

coterminal angles (p. 188) Angles formed by different rotations that have the same initial and terminal sides.

ángulos coterminales (pág. 188) Ángulos que se forman por diferentes rotaciones que tienen los mismos lados inicial y terminal.

cross product An operation on two vectors that results in a vector with special properties.

producto cruzado Operación con dos vectores, que resulta en un vector con propiedades especiales.

D

DeMoivre's Theorem The formula $[r(\cos(\theta) + i\sin(\theta)]^n = r^n[(\cos(n\theta) + i\sin(n\theta))]$.

Teorema de De Moivre La fórmula $[r(\cos(\theta) + i\,\text{sen}(\theta)]^n = r^n[(\cos(n\theta) + i\,\text{sen}(n\theta))]$.

depreciation (p. 56) The reduction in the value of an asset over time.

depreciación (pág. 56) Reducción en el valor de un activo en el tiempo.

Descartes' Rule of Signs (p. 138) A rule that gives information about the number of positive and negative real roots of a polynomial. It states that if $f(x)$ is a polynomial function in standard form with real coefficients and a nonzero constant term, then the number of positive real zeros of $f(x)$ equals the number of variations in sign of the terms of $f(x)$, or is less than this number by an even integer; and the number of negative real zeros of $f(x)$ equals the number of variations in sign of the terms of $f(-x)$, or is less than this number by an even integer.

Regla de los signos de Descartes (pág. 138) Regla que da información acerca del número de raíces reales positivas y negativas de un polinomio. Establece que si $f(x)$ es una función polinómica en forma estándar con coeficientes reales y un término constante distinto de cero, entonces el número de ceros reales positivos de $f(x)$ es igual al número de variaciones en el signo de los términos de $f(x)$ o es menor que este número en un entero par; y el número de ceros reales negativos de $f(x)$ es igual al número de variaciones en el signo de los términos de $f(-x)$ o es menor que este número en un entero par.

determinant (p. 494) A real number calculated from the values of a square matrix.

determinante (pág. 494) Un número real calculado a partir de los valores de una matriz cuadrada.

direction angle The angle a vector would make with the positive x-axis when the tail (initial point of the ray) is located at the origin.

ángulo de dirección Ángulo que un vector formaría con el eje de las x positivo si la cola (punto inicial del rayo) estuviera ubicada en el origen.

directrix (p. 348) The fixed line which, along with a fixed point called a focus, helps define a parabola.

directriz (pág. 348) Recta fija, que conjuntamente con un punto fijo llamado foco, ayuda a definir una parábola.

dilation (p. 507) A transformation of a figure in the coordinate plane that results in a similar image.

dilatación (pág. 507) La transformación de una figura en el plano cartesiano que resulta en una imagen semejante.

dimension (p. 485) The number of rows and columns of a matrix, usually written as m (rows) $\times$ n (columns). Also, called the order of a matrix.

dimensión (pág. 485) El número de filas y columnas de una matriz, normalmente escrito como m (filas) $\times$ n (columnas). También se le conoce como el orden de la matriz.

discontinuity (p. 174) Any x-value for which a rational function is undefined. If a value of x makes the numerator and denominator 0, then a hole in the graph occurs. If a value of x only makes the denominator 0, then a vertical asymptote occurs in the graph.

discontinuidad (pág. 174) Cualquier valor de x para el cual una función racional no está definida. Si un valor de x hace que el numerador y denominador sean 0, entonces una asíntota vertical ocurre en la representación gráfica.

discontinuous function (p. 174) A function that is not continuous. Discontinuities can be either removable or non-removable. The graph of a discontinuous function contains breaks, holes, or jumps.

función discontinua (pág. 174) Función que no es continua. Las discontinuidades pueden ser reparables o no reparables. La gráfica de una función discontinua contiene quiebres, hoyos o saltos.

diverge (p. 27) An infinite sequence diverges if it does not converge.

divergir (pág. 27) Una sucesión infinita diverge si no converge.

double root (p. 126) Two roots of a polynomial equation with the same value.

raíz doble (pág. 126) Dos raíces de una ecuación polinómica con el mismo valor.

double-napped cone (p. 348) A solid made from two cones with the same axis and vertex that open in opposite directions.

doble cono (pág. 348) Cuerpo geométrico formado por dos conos que comparten el eje y el vértice y que se abren en ambas direcciones.

E

elements (p. 485) The numbers or variables in a matrix. Also, called the entries of a matrix.

elementos (pág. 485) Los números o las variables en una matriz, también conocidas como las entradas de una matriz.

ellipse (p. 360) The set of all points (x, y) in a plane such that the sum of the distances from the point (x, y) to each of two fixed points is constant. Each of the fixed points is called a focus of the ellipse.

elipse (pág. 360) Conjunto de todos los puntos (x, y) de un plano, tal que la suma de las distancias desde el punto (x, y) a cada uno de dos puntos fijos es constante. Cada uno de los puntos fijos se llama foco de la elipse.

end behavior (p. 124) What happens to the graph of a function on the extreme left and right ends of the x-axis; that is, what happens to y as x approaches $-\infty$ and ∞.

comportamiento final (pág. 124) Lo que ocurre con la gráfica de una función en los extremos izquierdo y derecho del eje de las x; es decir, lo que ocurre con y a medida que x se aproxima a $-\infty$ y ∞.

entries (p. 485) The elements of a matrix.

entradas (pág. 485) Los elementos de una matriz.

equal vectors (p. 444) Vectors that have equal magnitude and point in the same direction.

vectores equivalentes (pág. 444) Vectores que tienen igual magnitud y apuntan en la misma dirección.

even function (p. 81) A function whose graph is symmetric with respect to the y-axis. A function f is even if and only if for each x of the domain of f, $f(-x) = f(x)$.

función par (pág. 81) Función cuya gráfica es simétrica con respecto al eje de las y. Una función f es par si y sólo si para cada x en el dominio de f, $f(-x) = f(x)$.

explicit form (p. 39) The form of a recursive sequence that is defined in terms of n and not previous terms of the sequence.

forma explícita (pág. 39) La forma de una secuencia recursiva que se define en términos de n y no en términos anteriores de la secuencia.

exponential decay factor (p. 49) The constant multiplier or scale factor of an exponential function $f(x) = ab^x$ where $0 < b < 1$. It causes the value of the function to decrease as the independent variable x increases.

factor de disminución exponencial (pág. 49) Multiplicador constante o factor de escala de una función exponencial $f(x) = ab^x$, donde $0 < b < 1$. Hace que el valor de la función disminuya a medida que aumenta la variable independiente x.

exponential function (p. 47) A function of the form $f(x) = ab^x$, where a is a nonzero constant, and b is a positive constant, $b \neq 1$.

función exponencial (pág. 47) Función de la forma $f(x) = ab^x$, donde a es una constante distinta de cero y b es una constante positiva, con $b \neq 1$.

exponential growth factor (p. 49) The constant multiplier or scale factor of an exponential function $f(x) = ab^x$, where $b > 1$. It causes the values of the function to increase as the values of the independent variable increase.

factor de crecimiento exponencial (pág. 49) Multiplicador constante o factor de escala de una función exponencial $f(x) = ab^x$, donde $b > 1$. Hace que el valor de la función aumente a medida que aumenta el valor de la variable independiente x.

extraneous solution (p. 71) A root of a transformed equation that is not a root of the original equation because it was excluded from the domain of the original equation.

solución extraña (pág. 71) Raíz de una ecuación transformada que no es raíz de la ecuación original, ya que fue excluida del dominio de la ecuación original.

extrapolation Making a prediction beyond the range of a data set.

extrapolación Hacer una predicción más allá del rango de un conjunto de datos.

Extreme Value Theorem If a function f is continuous on a closed interval $[a, b]$, then there are numbers c and d in $[a, b]$, for which $f(c)$ and $f(d)$ are the maximum and the minimum values for $f(x)$ in $[a, b]$.

Teorema de los valores extremos Si una función f es continua en un intervalo cerrado $[a, b]$, entonces existen números c y d en $[a, b]$, para los cuales $f(c)$ y $f(d)$ son los valores máximo y mínimo, respectivamente, para $f(x)$ en $[a, b]$.

F

Factor Theorem (p. 135) States that a polynomial $f(x)$ has a factor $(x - k)$ if and only if $f(k) = 0$.

Teorema del factor (pág. 135) Establece que un polinomio $f(x)$ tiene un factor $(x - k)$ si y sólo si $f(k) = 0$.

focus of an ellipse (p. 360) One of the two fixed points used to define an ellipse. Plural: foci.

foco de una elipse (pág. 360) Uno de los dos puntos fijos que se usan para definir una elipse.

focus of a parabola (p. 348) A fixed point which, along with a fixed line called a directrix, defines a parabola

foco de una parábola (pág. 348) Punto fijo que conjuntamente con una recta fija llamada directriz define una parábola.

Fundamental Theorem of Algebra (p. 133) States that if $p(x)$ is a non-constant polynomial of degree n with complex coefficients, then $p(x)$ has a least one complex root.

Teorema fundamental del álgebra (pág. 133) Establece que si $p(x)$ es un polinomio no constante de grado n con coeficientes complejos, entonces $p(x)$ tiene al menos una raíz compleja.

G

geometric sequence (p. 20) A sequence with a constant ratio, r, between consecutive terms.

progresión geométrica (pág. 20) Sucesión con una razón constante, r, entre los términos consecutivos.

geometric series (p. 26) The sum of the terms of a geometric sequence.

serie geométrica (pág. 26) Suma de los términos de una progresión geométrica.

growth factor (p. 49) The annual growth factor for any interest rate, r, is $1 + r$.

factor de crecimiento (pág. 49) El factor de crecimiento anual para cualquier tasa de interés, r, es $1 + r$.

H

half-angle identities (p. 311) Trigonometric identities for half angles.

identidades de ángulo medio (pág. 311) Identidades trigonométricas para ángulos medios.

half-life (p. 56) The time required for an exponentially decaying quantity to be reduced by a factor of one-half.

vida media (pág. 56) Tiempo que se requiere para que una cantidad que se decae exponencialmente decreciente se reduzca a la mitad.

hole (p. 174) An example of a discontinuity that can be removed by redefining the function at the point of discontinuity to make the function continuous.

agujero (pág. 174) Un ejemplo de una discontinuidad que se puede eliminar al redefinir la función en el punto de discontinuidad para que la función sea continua.

hole in the graph (p. 174) A discontinuity at a single point in the graph of a rational function at an x-value that is not an asymptote.

hoyo en la gráfica (pág. 174) Discontinuidad en un único punto de la gráfica de una función racional en un valor de x que no es una asíntota.

horizontal asymptote (p. 162) The line $y = a$ when the end behavior of a function approaches some constant a.

asíntota horizontal (pág. 162) Recta $y = a$ cuando el comportamiento final de una función se aproxima a cierta constante a.

hyperbola (p. 365) The set of points (x, y) in the plane such that the difference of the distances from (x, y) to each of the two fixed points, called foci, is a constant.

hipérbola (pág. 365) Conjunto de todos los puntos (x, y) del plano, tal que la diferencia entre las distancias desde (x, y) a cada uno de dos puntos fijos, llamados focos, es constante.

I

identity (p. 279) A relationship of equality that is true for all values of the variables for which each side of the equation is defined.

identidad (pág. 279) Relación de igualdad que es verdadera para todos los valores de las variables para los cuales está definido cada lado de la ecuación.

image (p. 507) The resultant figure after a transformation.

imagen (pág. 507) La figura resultante de una transformación.

infinite form A fraction in the form $\frac{non - zero\#}{0}$, obtained when evaluating a rational function that indicates the existence of a non-removable discontinuity, producing a vertical asymptote in the graph.

forma infinita Fracción de la forma $\frac{non - zero\#}{0}$, que se obtiene cuando se evalúa una función racional, que indica la existencia de una discotinuidad no reparable, produciendo una asíntota vertical en la gráfica.

infinite sequence (p. 29) A sequence with infinitely many terms.
sucesión infinita (pág. 29) Sucesión con infinita cantidad de términos.

infinite series (p. 29) The sum of the terms of an infinite sequence.
serie infinita (pág. 29) Suma de los términos de una sucesión infinita.

initial ray (p. 378) The ray from pole O along the positive x-axis.
rayo inicial (pág. 378) Rayo desde un polo O a lo largo del eje de las x positivo.

initial side (p. 187) The fixed ray from which an angle is rotated to the terminal side of the angle.
lado inicial (pág. 187) El rayo fijo a partir del cual se rota un ángulo hasta el lado terminal del ángulo.

iteration (p. 35) A repetitive application of the same rule.
iteración (pág. 35) Una aplicación repetitiva de la misma regla.

interest rate (p. 49) The percentage paid either for money deposited in an account or charged for borrowing money.
tasa de interés (pág. 49) El porcentaje pagado por el dinero prestado o el porcentaje ganado por el dinero depositado en una cuenta.

Intermediate Value Theorem States that if a function f is continuous on a closed interval $[a, b]$ and y is any number between $f(a)$ and $f(b)$, then there is at least one number $x = c$ between a and b for which $f(c) = y$.
Teorema de los valores intermedios Establece que si una función f es continua en un intervalo cerrado $[a, b]$ e y es cualquier número entre $f(a)$ y $f(b)$, entonces existe al menos un número $x = c$ entre a y b tal que $f(c) = y$.

interpolation Estimating an outcome within the range of a data set.
interpolación Estimar un resultado dentro del rango de un conjunto de datos.

inverse function (p. 108) If $f(x) = y$, then the function f^{-1} is the inverse function of f if $f^{-1}(y) = x$. The domain of f is the range of f^{-1}, and the range of f is the domain of f^{-1}.
función inversa (recíproca) (pág. 108) Si $f(x) = y$ entonces la función f^{-1} es la función inversa de f si $f^{-1}(y) = x$. El dominio de f es el rango de f^{-1}, y el rango de f es el dominio de f^{-1}.

inverse trigonometric function (p. 250) The inverse function of a trigonometric function, with a suitably restricted domain.
función trigonométrica inversa (pág. 250) La función inversa de una función trigonométrica con un dominio debidamente restringido.

L

Law of Cosines (p. 326) A formula that shows the relationship between the sides and angles of any triangle. Depending on the given information, it may be written $c^2 = a^2 + b^2 - 2ab \cos C$; $b^2 = a^2 + c^2 - 2ac \cos B$; or $a^2 = b^2 + c^2 - 2bc \cos A$.
Ley del coseno (pág. 326) Fórmula que muestra la relación entre los lados y los ángulos de cualquier triángulo. Dependiendo de la información dada, puede escribirse como $c^2 = a^2 + b^2 - 2ab \cos C$; $b^2 = a^2 + c^2 - 2ac \cos B$; o $a^2 = b^2 + c^2 - 2bc \cos A$.

Law of Sines (p. 332) A formula that shows the relationship between the sides and angles of any triangle: $\frac{a}{\sin A} = \frac{b}{\sin B} = \frac{c}{\sin C}$.
Ley del seno (pág. 332) Fórmula que muestra la relación entre los lados y los ángulos de cualquier triángulo: $\frac{a}{\sin A} = \frac{b}{\sin B} = \frac{c}{\sin C}$.

least squares regression line A linear model for data that minimizes the sum of the squared residuals.
regresión lineal por mínimos cuadrados Modelo lineal de datos que minimiza la suma de los cuadrados de los residuos.

limaçon (p. 404) The graph of a polar equation in the form $r = a \pm b \sin\theta$ or $r = a \pm b \cos\theta$ when $a \neq b$.
caracol (pág. 404) Gráfica de una ecuación polar de la forma $r = a \pm b \operatorname{sen}\theta$ o $r = a \pm b \cos\theta$ cuando $a \neq b$.

limit from the left The limit value as x approaches c from x-values less than c. It is written as $\lim\limits_{x \to c-} f(x)$.
límite por la izquierda Valor del límite a medida que x se aproxima a c desde valores de x menores que c. Se escribe $\lim\limits_{x \to c-} f(x)$.
limit from the right The limit value as x approaches c from x-values greater than c. It is written as $\lim\limits_{x \to c+} f(x)$.
límite por la derecha Valor del límite a medida que x se aproxima a c desde valores de x mayores que c. Se escribe $\lim\limits_{x \to c+} f(x)$
limit of a function (p. 541) The one number L that $f(x)$ becomes arbitrarily close to as x approaches, but does not equal, a number c. In other words, when a function has a limit, as x approaches a value c, the y value of the function $f(x)$ approaches the limit value, L.
límite de una función (pág. 541) Número único L al que $f(x)$ se acerca arbitrariamente a medida que x se aproxima, aunque no se iguala, a un número c. En otras palabras, cuando una función tiene un límite, a medida que x se aproxima a un valor c, el valor y de la función $f(x)$ se aproxima al valor límite L.

limit of a sequence (p. 28) The real number L to which a sequence converges. It is denoted $\lim\limits_{n \to \infty} an = L$. If a sequence diverges, the limit does not exist.
límite de una sucesión (pág. 28) Número real L al cual converge una sucesión. Se denota $\lim\limits_{n \to \infty} an = L$. Si una sucesión diverge, el límite no existe.

linear combination The sum or difference of terms where each term is composed of a constant multiplied by a product of mathematical elements that may be composed of variable(s), vector(s), or scalar(s).
combinación lineal Suma o diferencia de términos donde cada término está compuesto por una constante multiplicada por un producto de elementos matemáticos
que pueden estar compuestos por variable(s), vector(es) o escalar(es).

Linear Factorization Theorem (p. 133) States that a polynomial function $p(x)$ of degree n with real coefficients has precisely n linear factors.

Teorema de factorización lineal (pág. 133) Establece que una función polinómica $p(x)$ de grado n con coeficientes reales tiene exactamente n factores lineales.

linear velocity (p. 426) The linear distance that an object moves divided by the time required to cover that distance. It is defined as $\frac{\Delta s}{\Delta t}$, where Δs measures the change of distance and Δt measures the change of time.

velocidad lineal (pág. 426) Distancia lineal que se desplaza un objeto, dividida por el tiempo requerido para cubrir esa distancia. Se define comos $\frac{\Delta s}{\Delta t}$, donde Δs mide el cambio en la distancia y Δt mide el cambio de tiempo.

logarithm (p. 61) The power to which a base is raised. If b and x are positive real numbers with $b \neq 1$, then the logarithm of x base b is written as $\log_b x$ and is defined as: $\log_b x = y$ if and only if $b^y = x$.

logaritmo (pág. 61) Potencia a la que una base b se eleva. Si b y x son números reales positivos con $b \neq 1$, entonces el logaritmo de x en base b se escribe $\log_b x$ y se define como: $\log_b x = y$ si y sólo si $b^y = x$.

M

magnitude of a vector (p. 443) The length of a vector without regard to direction.

magnitud de un vector (pág. 443) Longitud de un vector sin importar su dirección.

major axis of an ellipse (p. 360) The segment with its endpoints on the ellipse that passes through the foci of the ellipse.

eje mayor de una elipse (pág. 360) El segmento con extremos en una elipse y que pasa a través de los focos de la elipse.

mathematical induction (p. 13) A two-step method that is used to prove a property or algebraic rule.

inducción matemática (pág. 13) Un método de dos pasos que se emplea para demostrar una propiedad o una regla algebraica.

matrix (p. 485) A rectangular arrangement of numbers written inside brackets. (plural: matrices)

matriz (pág. 485) Un arreglo rectangular de números escrito entre corchetes. (plural: matrices)

matrix equation (p. 517) An equation of the form $AX = B$, which represents a system of linear equations in standard form. A is the coefficient matrix, X is the variable matrix, and B is the constant matrix.

ecuación matricial (pág. 517) Una ecuación de la forma $AX = B$, y que representa un sistema de ecuaciones lineales en forma estándar. A es la matriz de coeficientes, X es la matriz de variables y B es la matriz de constantes.

matrix multiplication (p. 494) The process of multiplying two or more matrices. Matrix multiplication uses the arithmetic operations of both multiplication and addition.

multiplicación de matrices (pág. 494) La operación de multiplicar dos o más matrices. En la multiplicación de matrices se emplean las operaciones aritméticas de multiplicación y adición.

minor axis of an ellipse (p. 360) The segment with its endpoints on the ellipse perpendicular to the major axis and containing the center of the ellipse.

eje menor de una elipse (pág. 360) Segmento con sus extremos en la elipse perpendicular al eje mayor y que contiene el centro de la elipse.

multiple root (p. 126) Occurs when a polynomial equation has a root with multiplicity of two or greater.

raíz múltiple (pág. 126) Ocurre cuando una ecuación polinómica tiene una raíz de multiplicidad 2 o más.

multiplicative inverse (p. 494) The multiplicative inverse of a non-zero real number a is a number of the form $\frac{1}{a}$. The multiplicative inverse of a matrix A with a non-zero determinant is the matrix A^{-1} such that the AA^{-1} is equal to the identity matrix. Every square matrix A has a multiplicative inverse A^{-1}, except when $\det A = 0$. For the matrix $A = \begin{bmatrix} a & b \\ c & d \end{bmatrix}$, if $\det A \neq 0$, then $A^{-1} = \frac{1}{\det A}\begin{bmatrix} d & -b \\ -c & a \end{bmatrix} = \frac{1}{ad - bc}\begin{bmatrix} d & -b \\ -c & a \end{bmatrix}$.

inverso multiplicativo (pág. 494) El inverso multiplicativo de un número real a que no sea 0, es un número con la forma $\frac{1}{a}$. El inverso multiplicativo de una matriz A con un determinante que no sea 0, es la matriz A^{-1}, de manera que AA^{-1} es igual a la matriz identidad. Cada matriz cuadrada A tiene un inverso multiplicativo A^{-1}, excepto cuando $\det A = 0$. Para la matriz $A = \begin{bmatrix} a & b \\ c & d \end{bmatrix}$, si $\det A \neq 0$, entonces $A^{-1} = \frac{1}{\det A}\begin{bmatrix} d & -b \\ -c & a \end{bmatrix} = \frac{1}{ad - bc}\begin{bmatrix} d & -b \\ -c & a \end{bmatrix}$.

multiplicity (p. 126) The number of times a given polynomial equation has a root at a given point.

multiplicidad (pág. 126) Número de veces que una ecuación polinómica dada tiene una raíz en un punto dado.

N

natural logarithm (p. 62) The logarithm with a base of e. It is written as $\log_e x$ and is often written as $\ln x$. $\ln x = y$ is equivalent to $e^y = x$.

logaritmo natural (pág. 62) Logaritmo en base e. Se escribe $\log_e x$, y con frecuencia se escribe $\ln x$. $\ln x = y$ es equivalente a $e^y = x$.

non-removable discontinuity A discontinuity that cannot be eliminated by redefining the function at the point of discontinuity to make the function continuous. A vertical asymptote is an example of a non-removable discontinuity.

discontinuidad no reparable Discontinuidad que no puede eliminarse al redefinir la función en el punto de discontinuidad para hacer la función continua. Una asíntota vertical es un ejemplo de discontinuidad no reparable.

n^{th} partial sum (p. 24) The sum of the first n terms of a sequence.

suma parcial enésima (pág. 24) Suma de los n primeros términos de una sucesión.

O

oblique asymptote (p. 176) An asymptote that is not parallel to the *x*- or *y*-axis. It is also called a slant asymptote. A graph approaches the oblique asymptote as the absolute value of *x* becomes very large.

asíntota oblicua (pág. 176) Asíntota que no es paralela al eje de las *x* ni al de las *y*. También se llama asíntota inclinada. Una gráfica se aproxima a la asíntota oblicua a medida que el valor absoluto de *x* se hace muy grande.

oblique angle (p. 533) An angle that is not a right angle.

ángulo oblicuo (pág. 533) Ángulo que no es ángulo rectángulo.

oblique triangle (p. 327) A non-right triangle.

triángulo oblicuángulo (pág. 327) Un triángulo sin ángulo interior recto.

odd function (p. 81) A function whose graph is symmetric with respect to the origin. A function f is odd if and only if for each x in the domain of f, $f(-x) = -f(x)$.

función impar (pág. 81) Función cuya gráfica es simétrica con respecto al origen. La función f es impar si y sólo si para cada x en el dominio de f, $f(-x) = -f(x)$.

one-sided limit The limit of $f(x)$as x approaches a number c from one direction.

límite unilateral Límite de $f(x)$ a medida que x se aproxima a un número c desde una dirección.

one-to-one function (p. 250) A function where each element of the range corresponds to exactly one element of the domain.

función uno a uno (pág. 250) Función donde cada elemento del rango corresponde exactamente a un elemento del dominio.

order (p. 485) The dimension of a matrix.

orden (pág. 485) La dimensión de una matriz.

orthogonal Forming right angles or perpendicular lines.

ortogonal Que forma ángulos rectos o rectas perpendiculares.

outliers Points that do not fit the overall pattern in a data set.

valores atípicos Puntos que no calzan en el patrón general de un conjunto de datos.

P

parabola (p. 348) The set of points in a plane that are equidistant from a fixed point and a fixed line. The fixed point is called the focus, and the fixed line is called the directrix.

parábola (pág. 348) Conjunto de todos los puntos de un plano que equidistan de un punto fijo y una recta fija. El punto fijo se llama foco y la recta fija se llama directriz.

parameter A constant in an equation that varies in other equations of the same general form. For example, in the quadratic equation $y = ax^2 + bx + c$, a, b, and c are parameters.

parámetro Constante en una ecuación, que varía en otras ecuaciones de la misma forma general. Por ejemplo, en la ecuación cuadrática $y = ax^2 + bx + c$, a, b y c son parámetros.

parametric equations (p. 415) A set of equations that relate two or more dependent variables to the same independent variable.

ecuaciones paramétricas (pág. 415) Conjunto de ecuaciones que relacionan dos o más variables dependientes con la misma variable independiente.

parent function (p. 77) The most basic function of a particular type, such as $f(x) = x$ (linear); $f(x) = x^2$ (quadratic); $f(x) = |x|$ (absolute value); $f(x) = b^x$ (exponential), $f(x) = \frac{1}{x}$ (rational), $f(x) = \sqrt{x}$ (square root), and $f(x) = \sin x$ (sine).

función básica (pág. 77) La función más básica de un tipo en particular, como $f(x) = x$ (lineal); $f(x) = x^2$ (cuadrática); $f(x) = |x|$ (valor absoluto), $f(x) = b^x$ (exponencial) , $f(x) = \frac{1}{x}$ (racional), $f(x) = \sqrt{x}$ (raíz cuadrada) y $f(x) = \sin x$ (seno).

partial sum (p. 24) The sum of the terms in a sequence. The *n*th partial sum is the sum of the first n terms of a sequence.

suma parcial (pág. 24) La suma de los términos en una secuencia. La enésima suma parcial es la suma de los primeros términos n de una secuencia.

periodic function (p. 206) A function that repeats at regular intervals. For all periodic functions, there is a positive number p such that $f(x) = f(x + p)$ for all x in the domain of f. The period of the function is p.

función periódica (pág. 206) Función que se repite a interalos regulares. Para toda función periódica existe un número positivo p tal que $f(x) = f(x + p)$ para todo x en el dominio de f. El período de la función es p.

perpendicular (p. 503) A line segment that is perpendicular to a given line segment.

perpendicular (pág. 503) Un segmento de recta que es perpendicular a otro determinado segmento de recta.

phase shift (p. 206) A horizontal translation from the vertical axis of a periodic function.

cambio de fase (pág. 206) Traslación horizontal de una función periódica desde el eje vertical.

planar motion (p. 476) Motion in a coordinate plane.

movimiento planar (pág. 476) Movimiento en un plano de coordenadas.

polar axis (p. 378) A fixed ray from which angles are measured on a polar grid. The polar axis is usually the ray from pole O along the positive x-axis.

eje polar (pág. 378) Un rayo fijo a partir del cual se miden los ángulos en una cuadrícula polar. Normalmente el eje polar es el rayo que parte de O y coincide con el eje de las x.

polar coordinate (p. 378) The polar coordinates for a point on the polar grid are given as (r, θ), where r gives the distance from the pole O and θ gives the angle from the polar axis.

coordenada polar (pág. 378) Las coordenadas polares para un punto de la cuadrícula polar son dados como (r, θ), donde r da la distancia desde el polo O y θ da el ángulo desde el eje polar.

polar equation (p. 393) An equation that defines a curve in terms of radius and angle.

ecuación polar (pág. 393) Ecuación que define una curva en términos de radio y ángulo.

polar form of a complex number (p. 463) The polar form of a complex number z is $r \cos \theta + (r \sin \theta)i$, where r is the absolute value of z and θ is the argument of z.

forma polar de un número complejo (pág. 463) La forma polar de un número complejo z es $r \cos \theta + (r \operatorname{sen} \theta)i$, donde r es el valor absoluto de z y θ es el argumento de z.

polar grid (p. 377) A grid made up of concentric circles and rays from a common center. These circles are used for graphing points in polar form.

cuadrícula polar (pág. 377) Cuadrícula formada por círculos concéntricos y rayos desde un centro común. Estos círculos se usan para graficar puntos en forma polar.

pole (p. 377) The center of the concentric circles on a polar grid.

polo (pág. 377) Centro de los círculos concéntricos de una cuadrícula polar.

polynomial function (p. 124) A function that can be written in the form $f(x) = a_n x^n + a_{n-1}x^{n-1} + \ldots + a_1 x + a_0$, where n is a nonnegative integer and the coefficients $a_0, a_1, \ldots a_n$ are real numbers with leading coefficient $a_n \neq 0$.

función polinómica (pág. 124) Función que puede escribirse de la forma $f(x) = a_n x^n + a_{n-1}x^{n-1} + \ldots + a_1 x + a_0$, donde n es un entero no negativo y los coeficientes $a_0, a_1, \ldots a_n$ son números reales con coeficiente líder $a_n \neq 0$.

position vector (p. 476) Indicates the distance and direction of a vector from the origin or another fixed point.

vector de posición (pág. 476) Indica la distancia y la dirección de un vector partiendo del origen u otro punto fijo.

power function (p. 95) A function of the form $f(x) = ax^b$, where a and b are nonzero real numbers.

función potencia (pág. 95) Una función de la forma $f(x) = ax^b$, en que a y b son números reales que no son 0.

principal (p. 49) The initial amount of money borrowed or deposited.

capital (pág. 49) La cantidad inicial de dinero que se deposita o se presta.

Pythagorean identity (p. 282) The trigonometric identity $\cos^2\theta + \sin^2\theta = 1$.

identidad pitagórica (pág. 282) La identidad trigonométrica $\cos^2\theta + \sin^2\theta = 1$.

R

radian (p. 191) A unit of angle measure based on arc length. If the vertex of an angle is at the center of a circle and the sides of the angle are radii of that circle, the measure of the angle in radians is the length of the minor arc bounded by the radii divided by the length of the radius.

radián (pág. 191) Unidad de medida de ángulos, basada en la longitud del arco. Si el vértice de un ángulo está en el centro de un círculo y los lados del ángulo son radios de ese círculo, la medida del ángulo en radianes es la logitud del arco menor limitado por los radios, dividida entre la longitud del radio.

rational function (p. 162) A function that can be expressed as the ratio of two polynomials.

función racional (pág. 162) Función que puede expresarse como razón de dos polinomios.

Rational Root Theorem (p. 135) States that if a polynomial $f(x) = a_n x^n + a_{n-1}x^{n-1} + \ldots + a_1 x + a_0$, $a_n \neq 0$, has integer coefficients, then every rational zero of f has the form $\frac{p}{q}$, where p is a factor of a_0, and q is a factor of a_n. The Rational Root Theorem determines the possible rational roots of the polynomial.

Teorema de las raíces racionales (pág. 135) Establece que si un polinomio $f(x) = a_n x^n + a_{n-1}x^{n-1} + \ldots + a_1 x + a_0$, $a_n \neq 0$, tiene coeficientes enteros, entonces todo cero racional de f tiene la forma $\frac{p}{q}$, donde p es un factor de a_0 y q es un factor de a_n. El teorema de las raíces racionales determina las raíces racionales posibles del polinomio.

reciprocal functions (p. 219) The reciprocals of the sine, cosine, and tangent functions: cosecant, secant, and cotangent functions, respectively.

funciones recíprocas (pág. 219) Las recíprocas de las funciones de seno, coseno y tangente son cosecante, secante y cotangente respectivamente.

rectilinear motion (p. 471) Motion along a line.

movimiento rectilíneo (pág. 471) Movimiento a lo largo de una recta.

recursive sequence (p. 39) A sequence in which each term is generated from an expression the uses the preceding term(s).

sucesión recursiva (pág. 39) Sucesión en que cada término es generado a partir de una expresión que usa uno o más términos precedentes.

reference angle (p. 270) An acute angle α formed by the horizontal axis and the terminal side of angle θ when angle θ is in standard position.

ángulo de referencia (pág. 270) Ángulo agudo α formado por el eje horizontal y el lado terminal del ángulo θ cuando el ángulo θ está en posición estándar.

reference triangle (p. 194) A triangle formed by drawing a perpendicular segment from a point on the terminal side of an angle in standard position to the x-axis.

triángulo de referencia (pág. 194) Triángulo que se forma al dibujar un segmento perpendicular desde un punto del lado terminal de un ángulo en posición estándar hacia el eje de las x.

relative maximum (p. 121) A function value $f(a)$ is relative maximum of f if there is an interval around a where for any x in that interval, $f(a) \geq f(x)$.

máximo relativo (pág. 121) Un valor $f(a)$ de una función es un máximo relativo de f si existe algún intervalo alrededor de a donde para cualquier x de ese intervalo, $f(a) \geq f(x)$.

relative minimum (p. 121) A function value $f(a)$ is relative minimum of f if there is an interval around a where for any x in that interval, $f(a) \leq f(x)$.

mínimo relativo (pág. 121) Un valor $f(a)$ de una función es un mínimo relativo de f si existe algún intervalo alrededor de a donde para cualquier x de ese intervalo, $f(a) \leq f(x)$.

Remainder Theorem (p. 136) States that if a polynomial $f(x)$ is divided by $x - k$, the remainder r is $f(k)$.
Teorema de los residuos (pág. 136) Establece que si un polinomio $f(x)$ se divide entre $x - k$, el residuo r es $f(k)$.

residual The difference between an actual value and a predicted value of a dependent variable.
residuo Diferencia entre un valor real y un valor predicho de una variable dependiente.

residual plot A plot with the independent variable of a data set on the horizontal axis and residuals on the vertical axis.
gráfica de los residuos Gráfica con la variable independiente de un conjunto de datos en el eje horizontal y los residuos en el eje vertical.

resultant vector (p. 446) The sum of two or more vectors.
vector resultante (pág. 446) Suma de dos o más vectores.

rose curve (p. 403) The graph of a polar equation of the form $r = a\cos(n\theta)$ or $r = a\sin(n\theta)$.
rosa polar (pág. 403) Gráfica de una ecuación polar de la forma $r = a\cos(n\theta)$ o $r = a\text{sen}(n\theta)$.

row matrix (p. 499) A matrix that has dimension $1 \times n$.
matriz de fila (pág. 499) Una matriz de dimensión $1 \times n$.

S

scalar (p. 487) A quantity that can be represented by a single real number.
escalar (pág. 487) Cantidad que puede representarse por un único número real.

scalar multiplication (p. 487) The process of multiplying a scalar with each element of a matrix.
multiplicación escalar (pág. 487) El proceso de multiplicar un escalar por cada elemento de una matriz.

scalar product (p. 487) The product of a real number and a matrix.
producto escalar (pág. 487) El producto de un número real y una matriz.

secant (p. 219) The secant function is defined as follows: $\sec\theta = \frac{r}{x}$, where $x^2 + y^2 = r^2$. This is the reciprocal function of the cosine function.
secante (pág. 219) La función secante se define de la siguiente manera: $\sec\theta = \frac{r}{x}$, donde $x^2 + y^2 = r^2$. Esta es la función recíproca de la función coseno.

sequence (p. 3) A list of items or numbers.
sucesión (pág. 3) Lista de elementos o números.

sequence of partial sums (p. 12) A sequence where the nth term is the nth partial sum of another sequence.
sucesión de sumas parciales (pág. 12) Sucesión donde el enésimo término es la enésima suma parcial de otra sucesión.

series (p. 24) The sum of the terms of a finite or infinite sequence.
serie (pág. 24) Suma de los términos de una sucesión finita o infinita.

sigma notation (p. 8) Notation that uses the Greek letter sigma to indicate summation. $\sum_{j=1}^{n} P_j$ means $P_1 + P_2 + P_3 + \ldots + P_{n-1} + P_n$.
notación sigma (pág. 8) Notación que se expresa con la letra griega sigma para denotar la operación de sumar. $\sum_{j=1}^{n} P_j$ significa $P_1 + P_2 + P_3 + \ldots + P_{n-1} + P_n$.

sine (p. 210) The sine function is defined as follows: $\sin\theta = \frac{y}{r}$, where $x^2 + y^2 = r^2$.
seno (pág. 210) La función seno se define de la siguiente manera: $\sin\theta = \frac{y}{r}$, donde $x^2 + y^2 = r^2$.

speed The magnitude of a velocity vector.
velocidad Magnitud de un vector velocidad.

sphere (p. 535) A set of points in space that are equidistant from a given point, called the center of the sphere.
esfera (pág. 535) Un conjunto de puntos en el espacio que equidistan de un determinado punto, llamado el centro de la esfera.

standard position (p. 187) When the vertex of an angle is at the origin and the initial side is on the positive x-axis.
posición estándar (pág. 187) Cuando el vértice de un ángulo coincide con el origen y el lado inicial coincide con el eje de las x.

strictly monotonic function (p. 62) A function that either increases or decreases over its entire domain.
función estrictamente monotónica (pág. 62) Función que aumenta o bien disminuye en todo su dominio.

subscript notation (p. 3) Can be used to describe a term in a sequence. B_n is the nth term in a sequence. For example, B_9 is the 9th term.
notación subíndice (pág. 3) Se puede emplear esta notación para describir un término en una secuencia. B_n es el enésimo término en una secuencia. Por ejemplo, B_9 es el noveno término.

subtend (p. 189) To pass through the endpoints of an arc by the sides of angle.
subtender (pág. 189) Partir de un punto y pasar por los extremos de un arco de manera que se forma un ángulo.

sum and difference identities (p. 307) Trigonometric identities for the sum and difference of angles.
identidades de suma y diferencia (pág. 307) Identidades para la suma y la diferencia de ángulos.

T

tangent (p. 215) The tangent function is defined as follows: $\tan\theta = \frac{y}{x}$, where $x^2 + y^2 = r^2$.
tangente (pág. 215) La función tangente se define de la siguiente manera: $\tan\theta = \frac{y}{x}$, donde $x^2 + y^2 = r^2$.

terminal ray (p. 378) The ray of an angle on a polar grid from pole O that passes through a point of interest.
rayo terminal (pág. 378) En una cuadrícula polar, el rayo de un ángulo que parte del polo O y que pasa por un punto de interés.

terminal side (p. 187) The side of an angle that can rotate to change the measure of an angle.

lado terminal (pág. 187) Lado de un ángulo que puede rotar para cambiar la medida del ángulo.

three-dimensional coordinate system A coordinate system that uses three perpendicular axes for locating points in space with ordered triples of the form (x, y, z).

sistema tridimensional de coordenadas Sistema de coordenadas que usa tres ejes perpendiculares para ubicar puntos en el espacio con tríos ordenados de la forma (x, y, z).

transverse axis of a hyperbola (p. 368) The segment joining the vertices of a hyperbola.

eje transversal de una hipérbola (pág. 368) Segmento que une los vértices de una hipérbola.

trigonometric functions (p. 210) Functions that relate the angles of a triangle to the lengths of the sides of the triangle.

funciones trigonométricas (pág. 210) Funciones que relacionan los ángulos de un triángulo con las longitudes de los lados del triángulo.

trigonometric identity (p. 279) An identity that involves one or more trigonometric functions.

identidad trigonométrica (pág. 279) Identidad que involucra una o más funciones trigonométricas.

turning points (p. 121) The relative maxima and relative minima of a function.

extremos de una función (pág. 121) La máxima y mínima relativas de una función.

U

unit circle (p. 214) A circle of radius 1 centered at the origin.

círculo unitario (pág. 214) Círculo de radio 1 centrado en el origen.

unit vector A vector with a magnitude of 1.

vector unitario Vector de magnitud 1.

V

variable matrix (p. 517) The matrix consisting of the variables in a system of linear equations.

matriz de variables (pág. 517) La matriz que consiste en los variables de un sistema de ecuaciones lineales.

vector (p. 443) A mathematical quantity that has a magnitude and a direction. A vector is represented by a directed line segment.

vector (pág. 443) Cantidad matemática que tiene magnitud y dirección. Un vector se representa gráficamente con un segmento de recta dirigido.

vector notation (p. 443) A way to express a position vector with the coordinates of its terminal point.

notación de un vector (pág. 443) Manera de expresar un vector de posición con las coordenadas de su punto terminal.

vector projection The creation of a third vector that shares an initial point with two other vectors and has a terminal point where a perpendicular line dropped from one vector intersects the second vector.

projección de un vector Creación de un tercer vector que comparte un punto inicial con otros dos vectores y tiene su punto terminal donde una recta perpendicular que se baja desde un vector interseca el segundo vector.

velocity The rate and direction that an object travels.

velocidad Tasa y dirección en que viaja un objeto.

vertical asymptote (p. 161) The line $x = b$ if the absolute value of function f increases without bound as x approaches some number b.

asíntota vertical (pág. 161) Recta $x = b$ si el valor absoluto de la función f aumenta sin límite a medida que x se aproxima al número b.

volume (p. 531) The number of cubic units in a solid figure.

volumen (pág. 531) El número de unidades cúbicas en una figura sólida.

X

***x*-intercept** (p. 132) The value where a graph intercepts the x-axis.

intercepto en *x* (pág. 132) Valor en que una gráfica interseca el eje de las x.

Y

***y*-intercept** (p. 132) The value where a graph intercepts the y-axis.

intercepto en *y* (pág. 132) Valor en que una gráfica interseca el eje de las y.

Z

zero of a function (p. 132) For a function $f(x)$, any value of x such that $f(x) = 0$.

cero de una función (pág. 132) Para una función $f(x)$, cualquier valor de x tal que $f(x) = 0$.

Verbal & Visual Word Association

Definition in Your Own Words	Important Elements
Visual Representation	**Personal Association**

Academic Vocabulary Word

Word Map

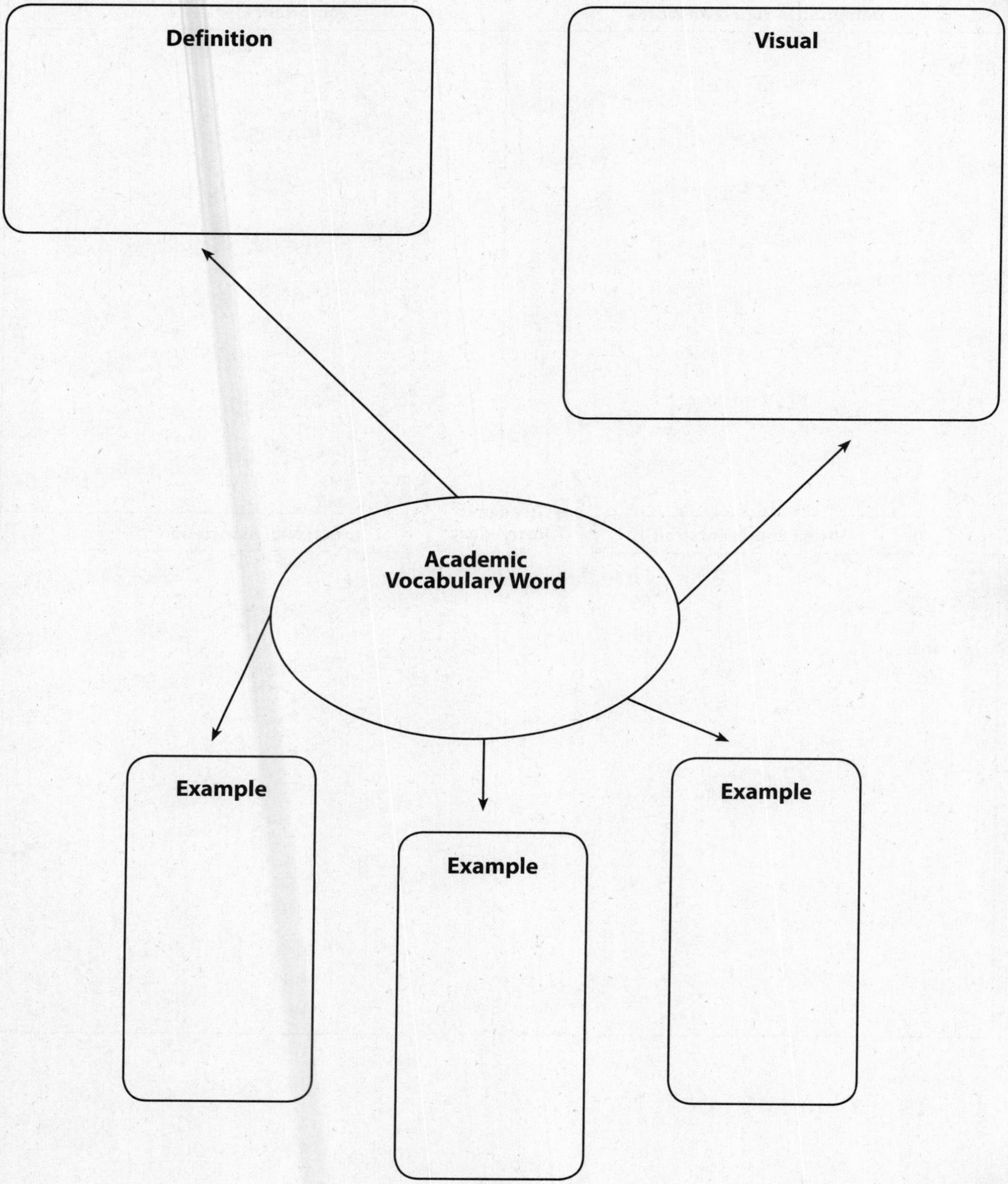
Definition
Visual
Academic
Vocabulary Word
Example
Example
Example

Eight Circle Spider

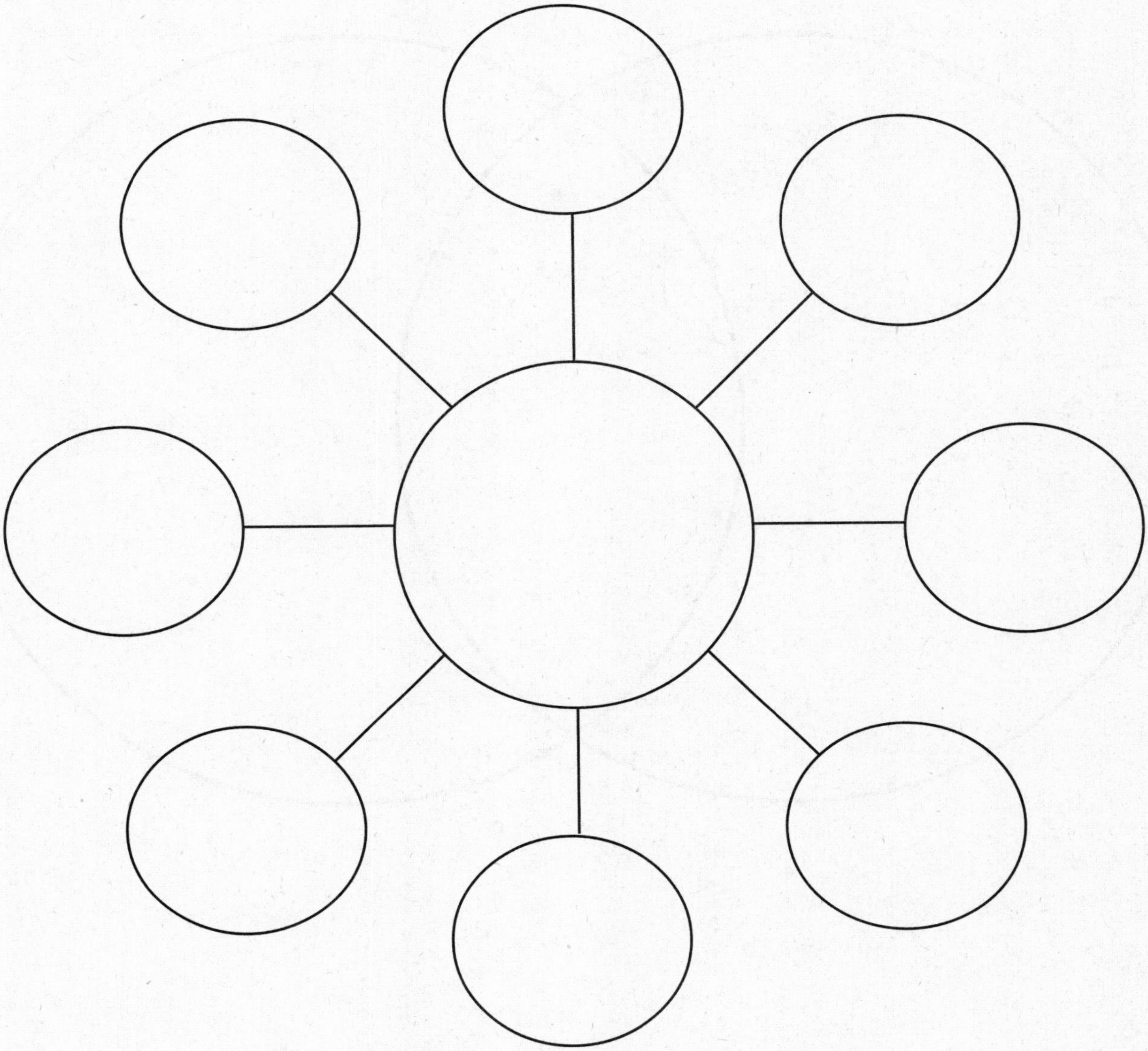

Venn Diagram

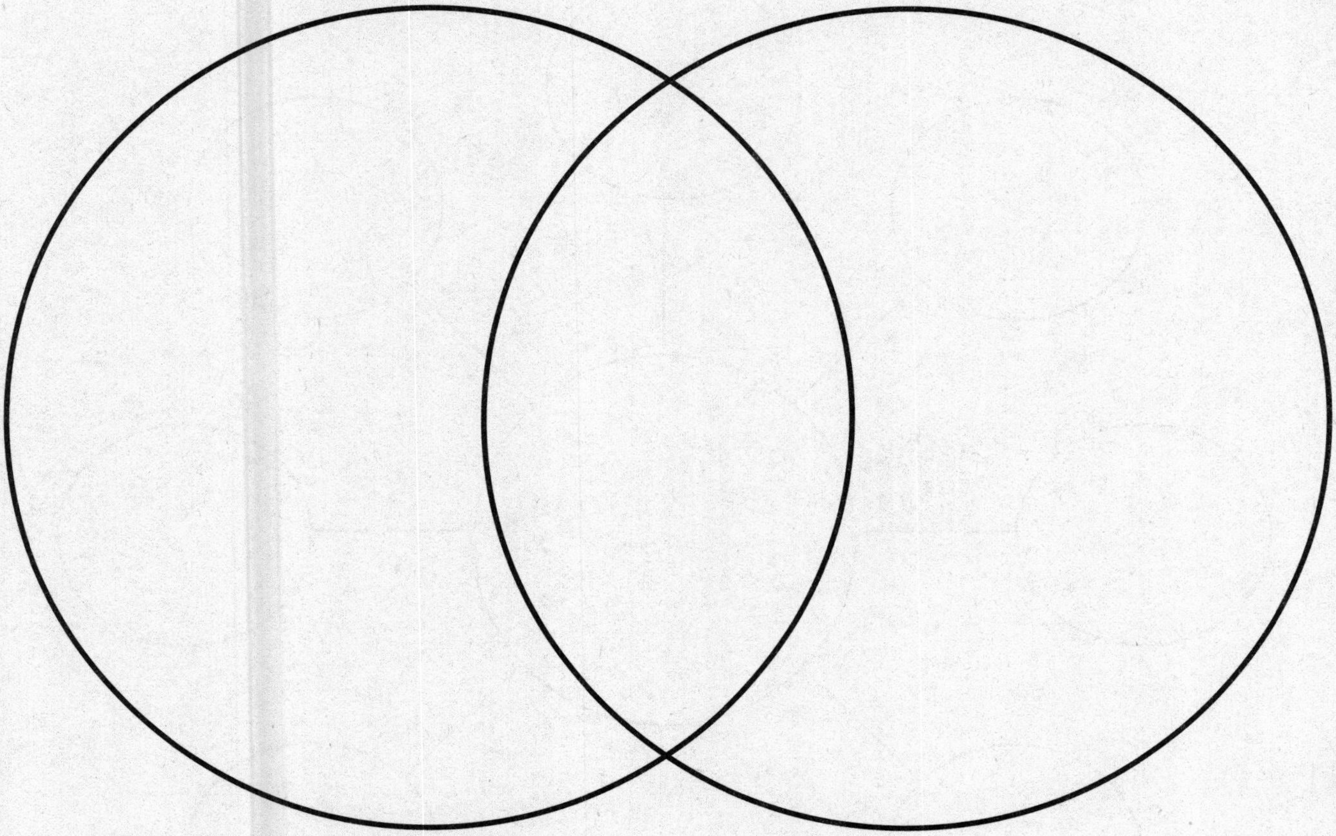

5 by 5 Coordinate Grids

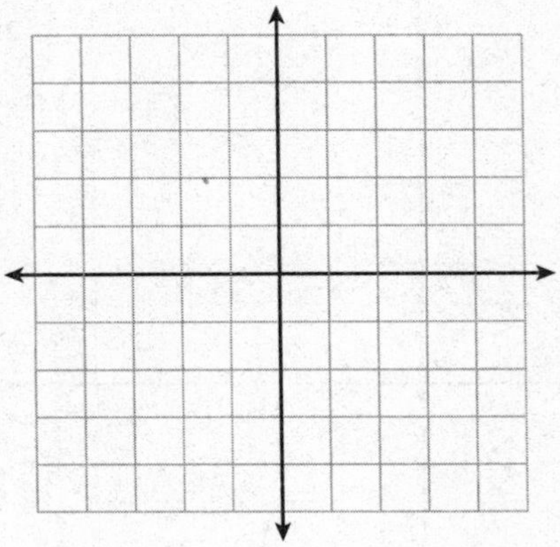

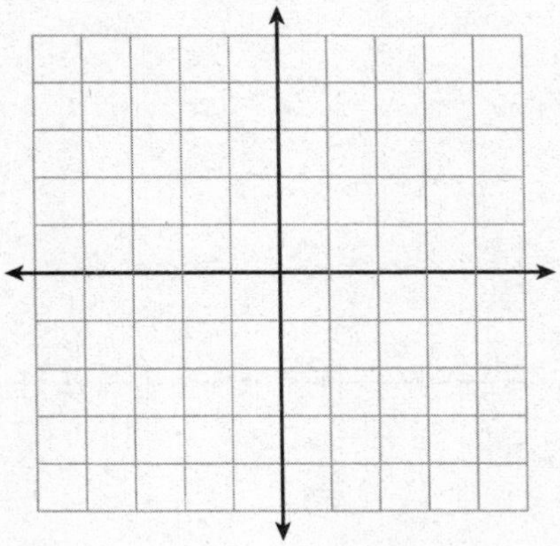

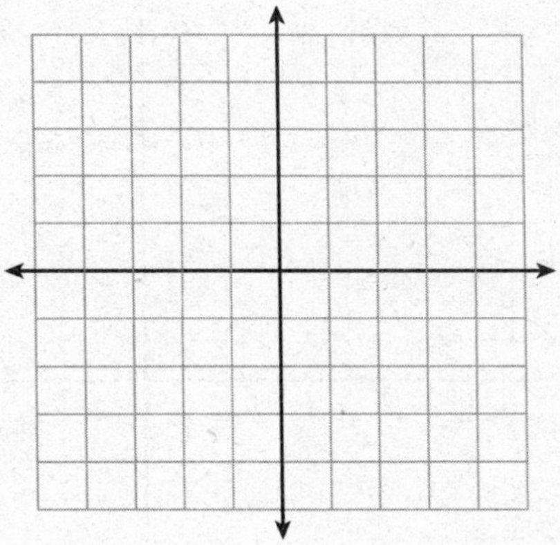

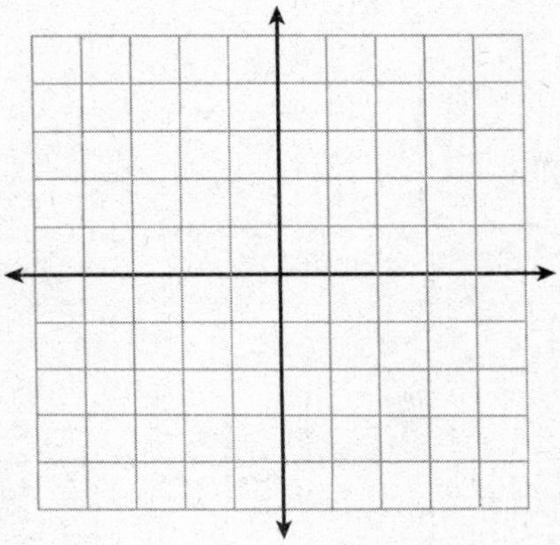

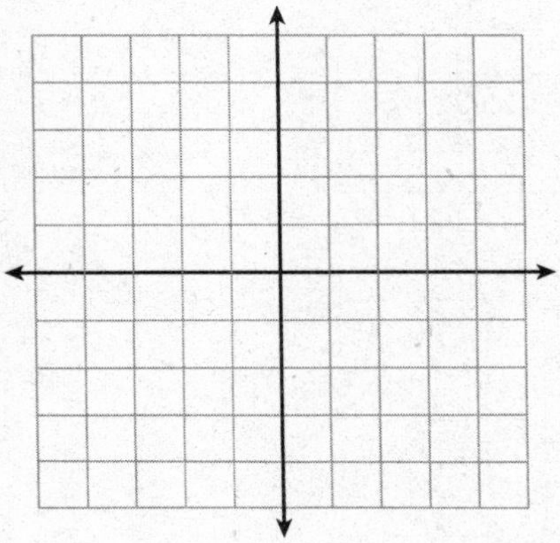

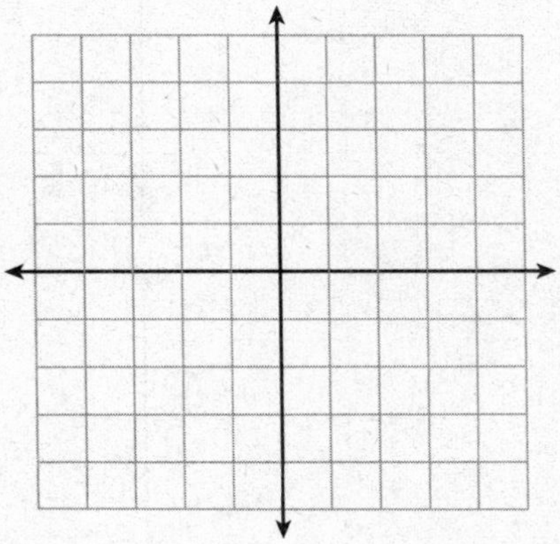

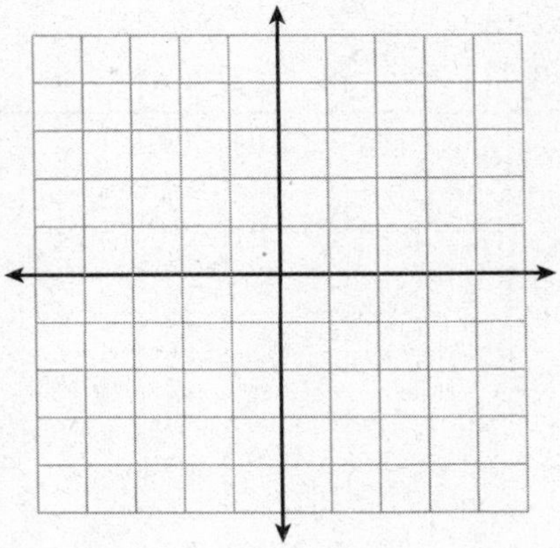

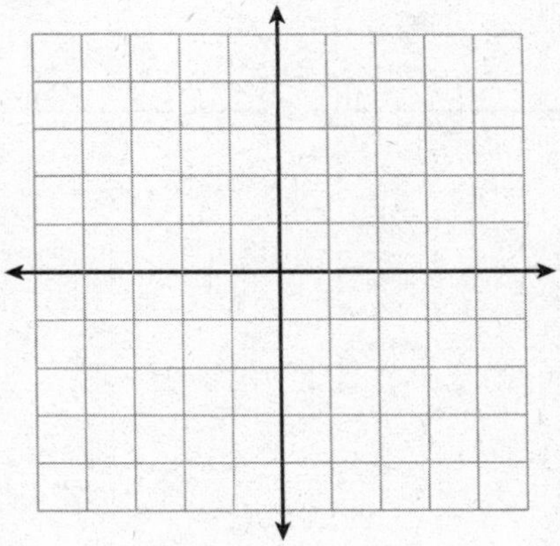

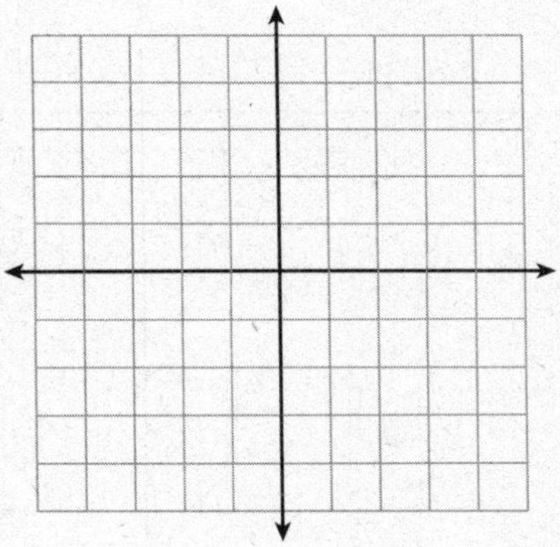

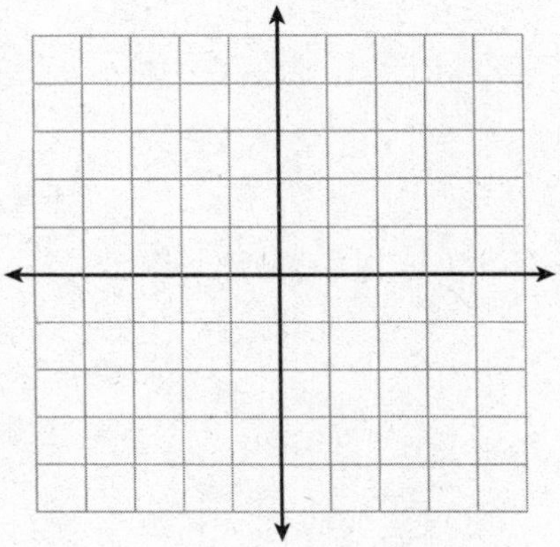

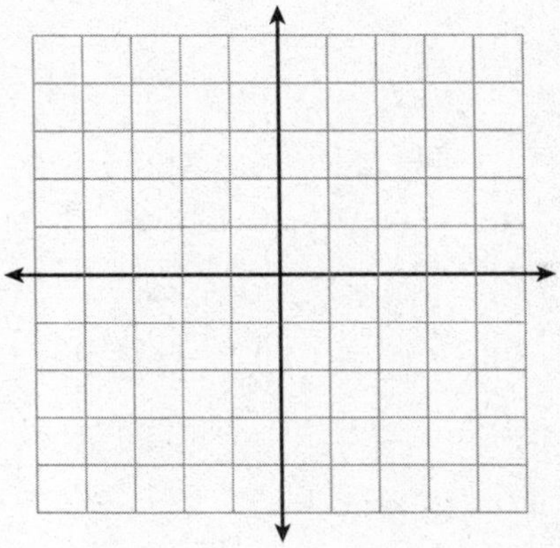

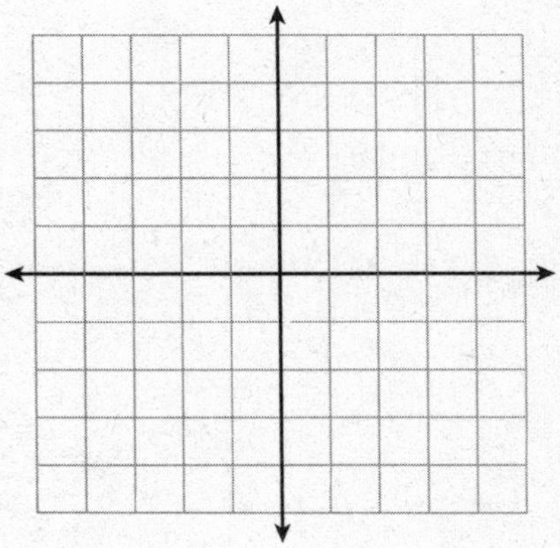

20 × 20 Grids

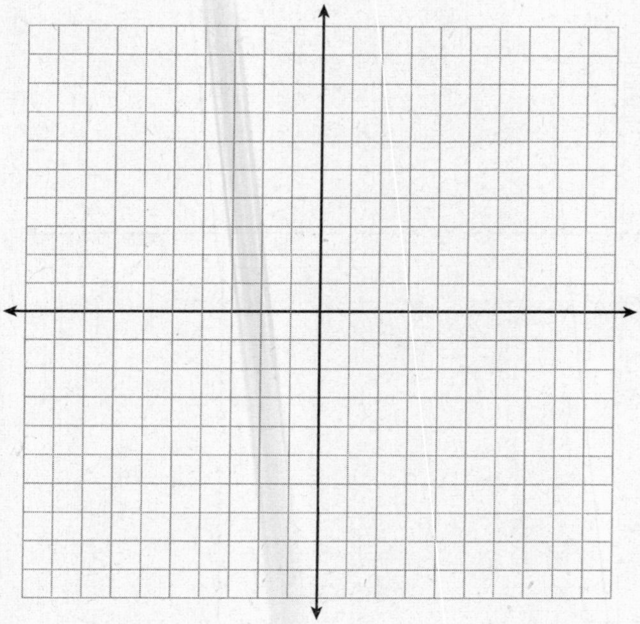

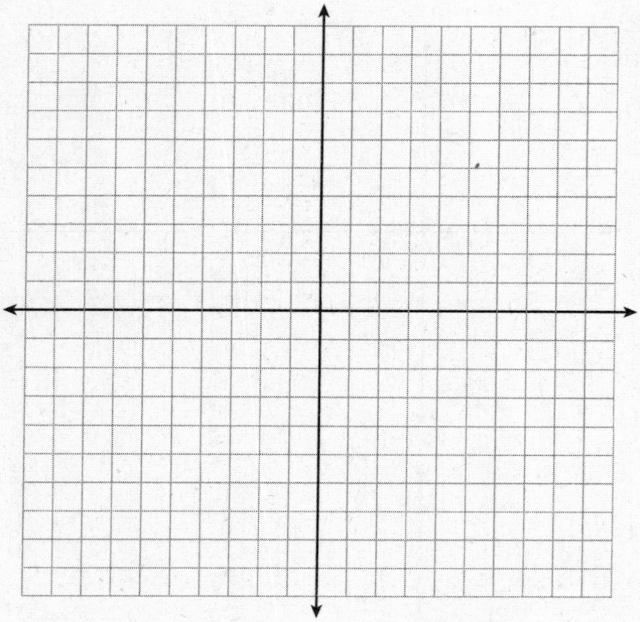

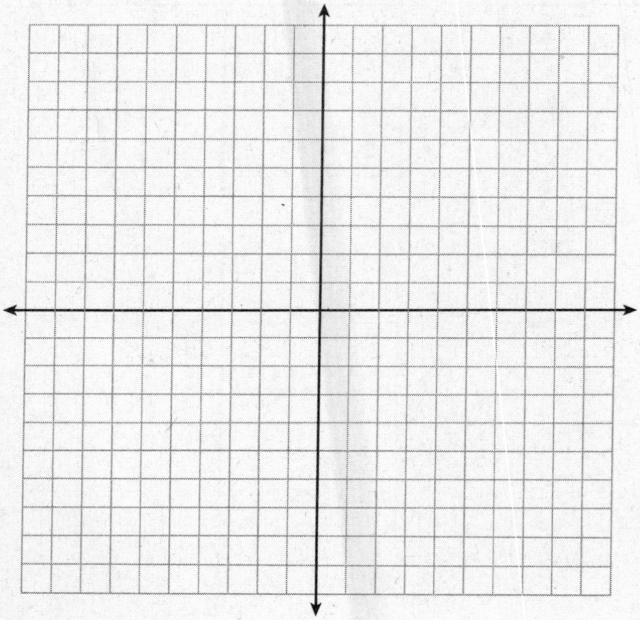

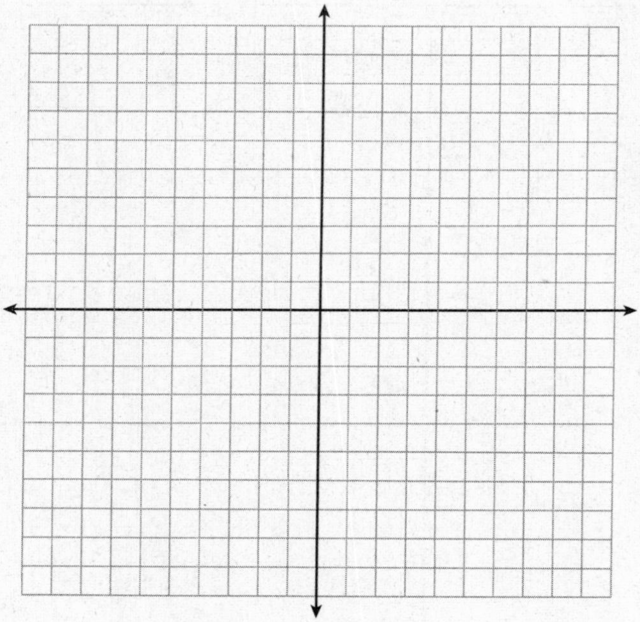

Unit Circle Template

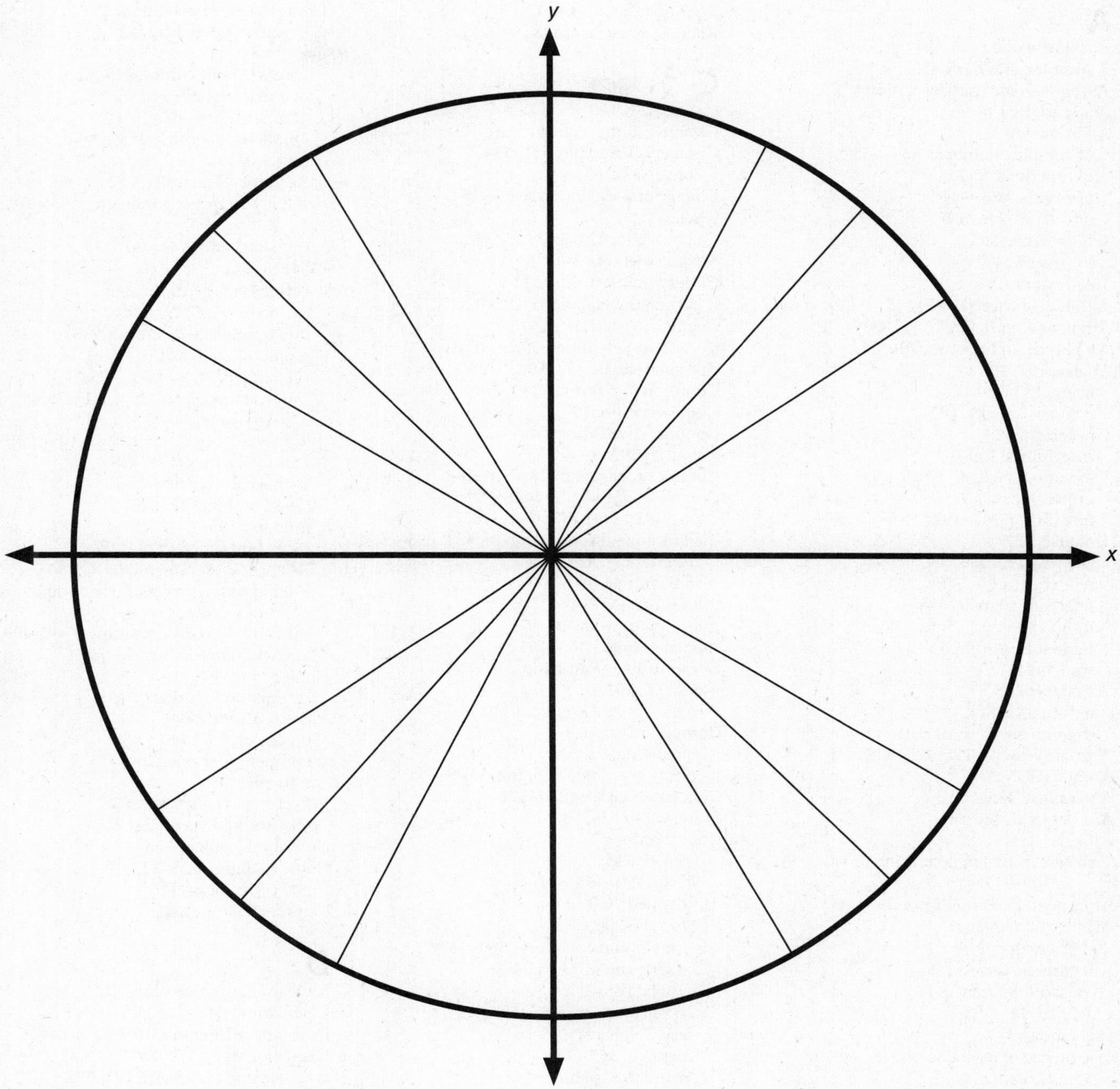

Index

A

B

C

D

E

F

G

H

I

J

L

M

N

O

P

Q

R

S

T

U

V

W

X

Y

Z

Photo Credits

Unit 5: London Eye (p. 425) Morguefile